CHEMISTRY RESEARCH AND APPLICATIONS

MICELLES

STRUCTURAL BIOCHEMISTRY, FORMATION AND FUNCTIONS AND USAGE

CHEMISTRY RESEARCH AND APPLICATIONS

Additional books in this series can be found on Nova's website
under the Series tab.

Additional e-books in this series can be found on Nova's website
under the e-book tab.

BIOCHEMISTRY RESEARCH TRENDS

Additional books in this series can be found on Nova's website
under the Series tab.

Additional e-books in this series can be found on Nova's website
under the e-book tab.

CHEMISTRY RESEARCH AND APPLICATIONS

MICELLES

STRUCTURAL BIOCHEMISTRY, FORMATION AND FUNCTIONS AND USAGE

DANIELLE BRADBURN

AND

TOM BITTINGER

EDITORS

publishers

New York

NOTICE TO THE READER

The Publisher has taken reasonable care in the preparation of this book, but makes no expressed or implied warranty of any kind and assumes no responsibility for any errors or omissions. No liability is assumed for incidental or consequential damages in connection with or arising out of information contained in this book. The Publisher shall not be liable for any special, consequential, or exemplary damages resulting, in whole or in part, from the readers' use of, or reliance upon, this material. Any parts of this book based on government reports are so indicated and copyright is claimed for those parts to the extent applicable to compilations of such works.

Independent verification should be sought for any data, advice or recommendations contained in this book. In addition, no responsibility is assumed by the publisher for any injury and/or damage to persons or property arising from any methods, products, instructions, ideas or otherwise contained in this publication.

This publication is designed to provide accurate and authoritative information with regard to the subject matter covered herein. It is sold with the clear understanding that the Publisher is not engaged in rendering legal or any other professional services. If legal or any other expert assistance is required, the services of a competent person should be sought. FROM A DECLARATION OF PARTICIPANTS JOINTLY ADOPTED BY A COMMITTEE OF THE AMERICAN BAR ASSOCIATION AND A COMMITTEE OF PUBLISHERS.

Additional color graphics may be available in the e-book version of this book.

Library of Congress Cataloging-in-Publication Data

Micelles : structural biochemistry, formation and functions & usage / [edited by] Danielle Bradburn and Tom Bittinger.
      pages cm
  Includes index.
  ISBN 978-1-62948-444-0 (hardcover)
 1. Micelles. 2. Colloids. 3. Colloids in medicine. I. Bradburn, Danielle, editor of compilation.
II. Bittinger, Tom, editor of compilation.
  QD549M643 2013
  572'.33--dc23
                        2013039486

Published by Nova Science Publishers, Inc. † *New York*

CONTENTS

PREFACE

In this book, the authors present current research in the study of the structural biochemistry, formation and function, and usage of micelles. Topics discussed in this compilation include acid-base equilibrium in aqueous micellar solutions of surfactants; computational methods as tools for the study of RM structure and dynamics; thermodynamic aspects of micelles; micellization of gemini surfactants in aqueous solutions; micelles from lipoamino acids; construction of block copolymer micelles and single-chain nanoparticles in non-selective solvents; block polyelectrolyte micelles/protein mixed nanostructures in aqueous media; and a treatment strategy for the gastrointestinal development of extremely premature infants by administration of micelles derived from pulmonary surfactants and the vernix caseosa in pregnant rabbits.

Chapter 1 – This chapter is aimed to gain insight into the acid-base equilibrium of various types of compounds embedded in micellar aqueous solutions of colloidal surfactants. The indices of the so-called apparent ionization constants, pK_a^{app}, of acids (mainly acid-base indicators) have been considered and the experimental methods of their determination have been analyzed. The approaches to estimate the partition of equilibrium acid-base species between bulk water and the pseudophase as well as the procedure of extrapolation to complete binding were elucidated. The two main accepted models of protolytic equilibrium, the electrostatic and the pseudophase ion exchange ones, were compared. The specificity of the versatile influence the micellar pseudophase on the acidic strength of acids was discussed. It was rationalized in terms of the strong differentiating action of the pseudophase, i.e., non-uniform changes of pK_a on going from water to the given system, and its possible causes were discussed. The peculiarities of the micelle properties were clarified using the solvatochromic scale and other data. The differentiating phenomenon was found to be the main reason for limitation of the common electrostatic model of acid-base interactions, and the principal hindrance to exact evaluations of the interfacial electrical potentials of ionic micelles by means of acid-base indicators. Salt effects, i.e., the influence of supporting electrolytes on the apparent ionization constants of acid-base indicators in the Stern region of ionic micelles, can be conventionally divided into two kinds. While the first type, general, or normal, adds up to screening of the surface charge, the second one, special, or specific, is a consequence of micellar transitions caused by hydrophobic counter-ions.

Chapter 2 – Reverse micelles (RM) or water-in-oil microemulsions, are thermodynamically stable, isotropic water nanodroplets surrounded by a surfactant monolayer and dispersed in apolar solvents. They are formed by a ternary system containing a large amount of organic solvent (> 80 % wt), a surfactant (< 10 % wt) and water (0 - 10 % wt). The size of the RM water pool, in the range of $0 - 10$ nm, can be experimentally controlled by varying the water-to-surfactant molar ratio: W_0. Since RM can solubilize a large variety of solutes within their water pool (amino-acids, peptides/proteins, nucleic acids, ligands, etc.) and because structural and dynamical properties of the confined water differ significantly from bulk water by a number of physicochemical properties, these systems have attracted considerable attention of investigators in various research and application domains. In particular, RM have been used as models of membranes, for the study of water properties in confined microenvironments, as well as to explore the hydration impact on macromolecular dynamics or folding/unfolding mechanisms. In addition, they can also serve as nanoreactors for nanoparticle synthesis and as a reaction medium for protein engineering and chemical reactions.

During the last few years, computational methods (such as molecular dynamics or Mesoscopic simulations) have been extensively used to gain insights into the many aspects of RM systems. By using different computational approaches or by changing the RM atomic representation level, simulations have provided additional data complementing experiments and have thus helped to better characterize the RM structural and thermodynamic properties.

In this chapter, the authors will discuss recent computational results obtained for reverse micelles with two surfactants: one ionic, dioctyl sodium sulfosuccinate (AOT) and a nonionic one: polyoxyethylene alkylether (C_iE_j) and compare them with literature and available simulation data. The authors will particularly focus on the micellar structure and the water pool properties in presence and in absence of confined proteins.

Chapter 3 – In this Chapter, thermodynamic aspects of micelles are discussed with particular emphasis on electric interaction (ionic micelles) and two-component mixed micelles. In the first section, the dual nature of micelles, a collection of small systems or a pseudophase is discussed followed by a brief history of the concept of surfactant micelles. In Section II, the free energy of micelle formation is described which is the basis of the micelle stability and related to the critical micelle concentration (*cmc*). Various contributions other than the electric interaction are discussed. The electrostatic free energy is described in Section III together with the electric potential in the solutions evaluated by the Poisson-Boltzmann equation where no further advanced approach is introduced. Stability of micelles mainly depends on the length of the nonpolar chain and the kind of polar head groups. the topic is discussed in Section IV. The integral and the differential chemical potentials are discussed. In Section V, effects of salt concentration, temperature and pressure on the stability of micelles are discussed. The size (the aggregation number) and the shape of micelles are important and they are determined by the condition of the free energy minimum but geometrical considerations are able to provide us with a simple but useful approach to the problem. The pioneering idea of Tanford was developed into 'the packing parameter' by Israelachvili-Mitchell-Ninham as described in Section VI, followed by a brief description on the light scattering and osmometry which are used for the determination of the aggregation numer of micelles. Rod-like or worm-like micelles are discussed also in Section VI. Mixed micelles are discussed extensively throughout Section VII though limited to the two-component mixed micelles, in particular, to ionic/nonionic mixed micelles. The micellar Gibbs-Duhem relation and several phenomenological approaches to analyze the *cmc* data are described. A 'phase diagram' is presented to describe the mixing behavior. As a special example of ionic/nonionic mixed micelles, the hydrogen ion titration of micelles is discussed in Section VIII.

Chapter 4 – Over the past few years, intensive studies have been performed on the synthesis and solution behavior of surfactants with more than one tail. Among these surfactants, the most widely studied are the gemini surfactants, which consist of two (or more) amphiphilic moieties connected at or close to the head group and separated by a spacer group. Gemini surfactants can be orders of magnitude more active than their single tail analogues.

All surfactants self-organize in solutions into different structures with interesting morphologies. Above a certain concentration, known as the critical micelle concentration (CMC), the molecules spontaneously associate to form larger aggregates of colloidal dimensions – micelles.

A considerable amount of research on gemini surfactants is currently being conducted in both academic institutions and in chemical companies because of an insufficient understanding of their fundamental properties and in view of their actual or envisaged applications. Over the past 25 years, many different types of gemini surfactants have been synthesized. At first, studies on the catalysis of chemical reactions in micellar solutions of cationic dimeric surfactants and the use of such solutions as antimicrobial agents were reported. Later, unique properties concerning not only the surface properties but also the molecular aggregation were demonstrated. Currently, the relationships between the structure and the properties have been widely investigated for cationic, anionic, zwitterionic and nonionic gemini surfactants.

This chapter describes the issues related to the aggregation behavior of new members of the gemini family of surfactants in solutions based on the latest research.

The structures of newly synthesized gemini surfactants are reported. The properties of the micelles of the gemini surfactants (ionic and nonionic) and their micellar solutions are reviewed. The following properties are discussed: the micelle shape, dispersity and size, micelle ionization degree, microstructure in solution and kinetics/dynamics of gemini surfactant micelles. In addition, the influence of additives, especially organic and inorganic salts, on the surface-active properties and aggregation behavior of surfactants are reviewed.

The current state of progress in solubilization studies of the hydrophobic compounds in micellar gemini surfactant solutions is also presented.

The experimental methods used in the determination of micellar properties are discussed. Examples of the determination of CMC values with the use of surface tension, light scattering, and fluorescence and UV spectroscopies are presented. The use of static light scattering, small angle neutron scattering and fluorescence methods for determining the aggregation number of self-assembled gemini structures is reported. The information derived from cryo-transmission electron microscopy, which provides a direct visualization of micelles and the highly organized structures of gemini surfactants, is presented.

The application of aggregated structures of gemini surfactants and their potential future in technology are also described.

Chapter 5 – Surfactants are used in a large scale in the petrochemical, agrochemical, food, cosmetic, pharmaceutical, textile, paint and coating industries due to their detergent, emulsifying, solubilising, wetting and foaming properties. The demand for more efficient and environmentally friendly surfactants leads to the growing need for new surfactants with improved performances and lower toxicity. Lipoamino acids (LAA), i.e. amino acids bearing a long hydrocarbon chain, are an important class of bio-based, eco-friendly surfactants that can be produced either by chemical synthesis or biotechnological procedures.

Our group is interested in the development of new biocompatible and biodegradable surfactants with improved performances for technological and biomedical applications. In that sense LAA become very attractive regarding their multifunctionality, low toxicity and renewable sources of raw materials and their potential use as antimicrobial, drug delivery and transfection agents.

LAA, with the exception of glycine derivatives, are chiral compounds, and stereochemistry variation may account for changes in surface active properties and self-assembly behaviour. Although the aggregation process of LAA in aqueous solution is analogous to conventional surfactants, their optical properties and the ability for hydrogen bond formation, especially in the case of the amide derivatives, confers them peculiar characteristics. LAA may form not only micelles but also other supramolecular aggregates in aqueous media, such as helical or cylindrical fibres, bilayers, vesicles and lyotropic liquid crystalline phases.

This review summarizes research on synthetic LAA obtained from the common proteinogenic amino acids, with an emphasis on micelle formation. LAA production is briefly addressed, and their surface active and biological properties, namely antimicrobial activity, are described. Self-assembly behaviour of their aqueous solutions is analysed in terms of LAA architecture, including the length of the hydrophobic chain, nature of the amino acid residue and type of counter-ion, and external conditions such as ionic strength of the solution, pH and temperature are also considered. Structure-property relationships offer valuable information for modulation of the LAA properties in order to meet specific applications.

Technological and biomedical applications of LAA will be briefly summarized that account for the emergence of LAA as a promising and reliable alternative to speciality surfactants aiming at production of biocompatible compounds with low environmental impact from renewable natural sources.

Chapter 6 – Block copolymer micelles and single-chain nanoparticles are artificial soft nano-objects of small size which have gained prominence in nanoscience and nanotechnology due to their exceptional and sometimes unique properties. Micelles and single-chain nanoparticles are very useful nano-objects for many applications such as cosmetics, drug delivery, electronics, pollution control, heterogeneous catalysis or separation technologies. This chapter focuses on the current state of the investigations in synthetic techniques for highly-efficient block copolymer micelle and single-chain nanoparticle construction in non-selective, good solvents. A comprehensive description of several approaches employed for micelle formation (hydrogen bonding, quaternization / complexation, salt-induced hidrophobicity change, metalation, radical coupling, etc.) in non-selective solvents is reviewed. Significant emphasis is placed on efficient techniques available for reversible, multi-responsive (pH, temperature, oxidant/reductant, etc.) micelle preparation in non-selective solvents. Additionally, the recent and complementary topic of single-chain nanoparticle construction in good solvents through covalent and non-covalent interactions is reviewed. Recent progress achieved for the use of these complex nano-objects in some promising fields, such as nanomedicine and catalysis, is highlighted.

Chapter 7 – The interactions between a globular protein, hen egg white lysozyme (HEWL), and star-like block polyelectrolyte micelles formed by the self-assembly of a poly(tert-butylstyrene)-b-poly(sodium(sulfamate-carboxylate)isoprene) (PtBS-SCPI) amphiphilic diblock copolymer were studied in aqueous solutions. Due to the opposite charges present in HEWL (positive charges) and on the SCPI polyelectrolyte coronas of the block copolymer micelles (negative charges), nanostructured hierarchical complexes are formed at neutral pH and low ionic strength. Structure and properties of the complexes were investigated by means of dynamic, static and electrophoretic light scattering, as well as atomic force microscopy.

The solution behaviour, structure and effective charge of the formed nanoscale complexes proved to be dependent on the ratio of the two components. Presumably block polyelectrolyte micelles with a PtBS core and a SCPI corona decorated with HEWL molecules are initially formed. Moreover, the degree of charge neutralization caused by complexation determines the conformation and solubility of the complexes. Complexation of the macromolecular components at higher solution ionic strengths led to complexes of lower mass and nearly constant size. Such behavior may be correlated to the polyelectrolyte nature of the components. The structural investigation of the complexed protein by fluorescence and infrared spectroscopy revealed no signs of HEWL denaturation upon complexation.

Chapter 8 – Introduction: Micelle particles have been derived from pulmonary surfactants in human amniotic fluid at term. Further, human pulmonary surfactant micelles are known to induce detachment of the vernix caseosa under *in vitro* conditions. Additionally, micellization is an important step in postnatal lipid absorption, with micelles being present in the amniotic fluid swallowed by the fetus and in human breast milk. Our study aimed to establish a treatment strategy to ensure the gastrointestinal development of extremely premature infants, by focusing on the presence of micelles in the environment of fetuses and neonates.

Methods: All procedures were performed in accordance with the University of Fukui Institutional Animal Care and Use Committee policy. The Institutional Review Board of the University of Fukui approved the study protocol. Because the direct assessment of the kinetics of human pulmonary surfactant and the vernix caseosa in amniotic fluid is difficult, the authors first prepared two types of fluorescently labeled liposomes with morphology similar to that of pulmonary surfactant and vernix caseosa complexes using the fluorescent membrane dye PKH26 and BODIPY®-labeled palmitic acid, and then continuously infused these liposomes into the amniotic fluid of pregnant rabbits. Fetal small intestines and livers were removed and examined histologically as stained frozen sections. In addition, the authors prepared bovine pulmonary surfactant (surfactant TA) and vernix caseosa complexes and introduced them into the amniotic fluid of pregnant rabbits. Fetal small intestines were removed and subjected to histologic and ultrastructural studies using light and transmission electron microscopy, respectively. The villous height was measured from the tip to the crypt-villous junction; at least 18 villi were measured in each hematoxylin and eosin sample. Ultrastructural examinations focused on the reduction in the number and length of the intestinal epithelial microvilli. Cesarean section was also performed for non-surgical interventional pregnant rabbits on gestational day 29 to confirm normal fetal intestinal morphology. Comparisons between groups were performed by using the paired Student t-test for continuous variables.

Results: (1) The intra-amniotically infused, fluorescently labeled liposomes were absorbed into the fetal intestinal epithelium, but were not transported to the livers of fetal rabbits. (2) The fetal intestinal villous heights were greater in the group receiving surfactant TA–vernix caseosa infusion than in the normal saline infusion group ($P < 0.05$). Moreover, ultrastructural examinations revealed reductions in the number and length of the intestinal microvilli on the epithelial surface in the control group. The non-surgical fetal villous heights of the intestines were significantly greater than those of the study and control group ($P <$ 0.05).

Discussion: The continuous administration of micelles derived from pulmonary surfactants and the vernix caseosa influenced the intestinal morphology of the rabbit fetus, thus protecting the enterocytes from damage due to surgical intervention. The authors subsequently focused on a necrotizing enterocolitis (NEC) newborn rat model induced by loading enteral special formula feeding and exposure to hypoxia after cold stress and hyperoxygenation, which provide some common features with surgical intervention stresses. In our preliminary study, surfactant TA–vernix caseosa complexes reduced the severity of NEC by intervening in the apoptotic pathway. Amniotic fluid intake *in utero* is believed to prepare the gut for the dramatic shift from a highly controlled *in utero* environment to the heavily burdened environment encountered immediately after birth. The human gut is constantly exposed to micelles during the perinatal period. Although further studies are needed to confirm our findings, our results shed light on the physiological interactions among pulmonary, dermal-epidermal, and gastrointestinal developmental processes, and raise the intriguing possibility for the improved nutritional care of preterm infants immediately after birth.

In: Micelles
Editors: Danielle Bradburn and Tom Bittinger

ISBN: 978-1-62948-444-0
© 2014 Nova Science Publishers, Inc.

Chapter 1

ACID-BASE EQUILIBRIUM IN AQUEOUS MICELLAR SOLUTIONS OF SURFACTANTS

Nikolay O. Mchedlov-Petrossyan[*], Natalya A. Vodolazkaya and Nika N. Kamneva

Department of Physical Chemistry, V. N. Karazin National University, Kharkov, Ukraine

ABSTRACT

This chapter is aimed to gain insight into the acid-base equilibrium of various types of compounds embedded in micellar aqueous solutions of colloidal surfactants. The indices of the so-called apparent ionization constants, pK_a^{app}, of acids (mainly acid-base indicators) have been considered and the experimental methods of their determination have been analyzed. The approaches to estimate the partition of equilibrium acid-base species between bulk water and the pseudophase as well as the procedure of extrapolation to complete binding were elucidated. The two main accepted models of protolytic equilibrium, the electrostatic and the pseudophase ion exchange ones, were compared. The specificity of the versatile influence the micellar pseudophase on the acidic strength of acids was discussed. It was rationalized in terms of the strong differentiating action of the pseudophase, i.e., non-uniform changes of pK_a on going from water to the given system, and its possible causes were discussed. The peculiarities of the micelle properties were clarified using the solvatochromic scale and other data. The differentiating phenomenon was found to be the main reason for limitation of the common electrostatic model of acid-base interactions, and the principal hindrance to exact evaluations of the interfacial electrical potentials of ionic micelles by means of acid-base indicators. Salt effects, i.e., the influence of supporting electrolytes on the apparent ionization constants of acid-base indicators in the Stern region of ionic micelles, can be conventionally divided into two kinds. While the first type, general, or normal, adds up to screening of the surface charge, the second one, special, or specific, is a consequence of micellar transitions caused by hydrophobic counter-ions.

---

[*] Corresponding author: E-mail: mchedlov@univer.kharkov.ua.

1. SURFACTANT MICELLES IN WATER

The formation of micelles in aqueous solutions of some *surf*ace *act*ive react*ants*, or surfactants, was established once and for all 100 years ago. The detailed study published by Reichler [1] and the brief report made by McBain during the discussion devoted to colloids and their viscosity [2] gave convincing proof that diphilic electrolytes with long hydrocarbon chains are able to associate thus giving highly charged colloidal species.

Nowadays, versatile micellar solutions of anionic, cationic, non-ionic, zwitterionic and other surfactants are explored probably just as most popular organic solvents and water–organic mixtures.

Thermodynamically stable (reversible) transparent micellar solutions of colloidal surfactants, i.e., surfactants that are able to form aggregates (associates, clusters) of colloidal size, as well as their "derivatives", such as microemulsions, belong to solvent systems extensively applied in various fields of modern science and technology. They are widely used for equilibrium shifts and acceleration of a variety of reactions [3-18], as useful media for analytical processes [3,6,7,12,19-27] including chromatography [28-35], for solubilization of various substances including drugs [36-39], in photophysical studies [40-42], in synthesis of nanoparticles [43], etc. Phospholipid vesicles, surfactant mono-, bi-, and multilayers on various interfaces, mixed micelles, and other self-assembled systems are also intensively utilized in academic research and applied chemistry.

The structures of spherical micelles of an ionic and a non-ionic surfactant are schematically depicted in Chart 1. The hydrophobic core is shielded from water by hydrophilic palisade, by either dense ionic layer or ethylene oxide chains.

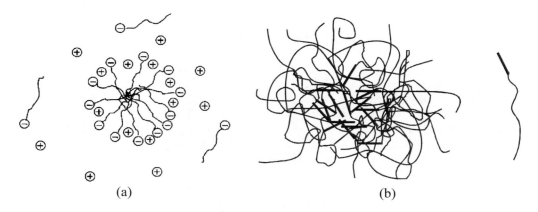

(a)   (b)

Chart 1. A schematic sketch of the section of anionic (a) and non-ionic (b) surfactant micelles.

The aggregation number of such micelles is of the order of magnitude of 10^2, the radius is normally within the range of ≈ 2 to ≈ 4 nm. The increase in surfactant concentration and addition of electrolytes usually results in size increase and polymorphic conversions, i.e., "sphere to ellipsoid", "sphere to rod", etc., transitions of micelles, first of all of ionic ones [44-47]. The number of publications devoted to detailed description of micellar size, shape, and other properties, is huge and permanently increasing. As an example, the recent study of cetyltrimethylammonium bromide aqueous solutions by means of dynamic light scattering should be cited [48].

The driving force of micelle formation in water is the hydrophobic interaction [49,50]. As a rule, micelles appearing in aqueous media when the surfactant concentration reaches the critical micelle concentration, *cmc*, are small and sphere-shaped. According to the generally recognized viewpoint, such micelles are highly porous strongly hydrated disordered clusters, being in the state of dynamic equilibrium with monomers in bulk phase [4,12,19,44-56]. For some surfactants, the formation of dimers at concentrations below *cmc* is well documented [57].

Most common surfactants are: cetyltrimethylammonium bromide, $C_{16}H_{33}N(CH_3)_3^+$ Br^- (CTAB); cetylpyridinium chloride, $C_{16}H_{33}NC_5H_5^+$ Cl^- (CPC); sodium dodecylsulfate $Na^+C_{12}H_{25}OSO_3^-$ (SDS); brij 35, $C_{12}H_{25}O(CH_2CH_2O)_{23}H$; Triton X – 100, $C_8H_{17}C_6H_4O(CH_2CH_2O)_{9.5}H$; and many others. The solution properties of zwitterionic and ampholytic surfactants, such as $C_nH_{2n+1}N(CH_3)_2^+-CH_2-CH_2-CH_2-SO_3^-$ and $C_nH_{2n+1}N(CH_3)_2 \rightarrow O$, respectively, are also well documented during past decades.

A relatively new class of ionic surfactants, the so-called gemini (duplicate, doubled) surfactants, was intensively studied in recent decades [58-65]. Colloidal properties of aqueous solutions of cationic surfactants with phosphonium head group [66,67] and novel dimeric diphilic surfactant of pyrimidinophane type, with two hydrocarbon chains [66,68] are described. Long-chain imidazolium ionic liquids also form micelles in water [69]. Very recently, interesting properties of amphiphilic derivatives of boronic acid were reported [70-72]. Another novel kind of cationic surfactant composed of an isosteviol moiety and different counter-ions allows creating biomimetic systems [73].

The two main approaches to description of micellization equilibria, the quasi-chemical model and the model of pseudophase, are probably of equal worth [44,45]. In the case of ionic surfactants, the double electrical layer appears on the micelle/water interface.

Rusanov [45,74] and other authors [5; 75-83] considered in detail the thermodynamics of micelle formation for different types of surfactants, including perfluorinated ones [82] and sodium desoxycholate [83]. For ionic surfactants, the nature of counter-ion plays a significant role in the micellization process [64,65,84,85].

In the last decade, the term "nanothermodynamics" was legitimated [86,87]. Taking into account the size of surfactants micelles, it is quite natural that their properties and fate should be predicted in terms of thermodynamics of small systems [87-89]. Treating micelle formation by small system thermodynamics, Gilányi suggested a diffuse monolayer structure instead of the idealized Goüy–Chapman model [75].

A set of papers is devoted to the molecular dynamics simulation of surfactant micelles [90-95].

In the dense interfacial portion of ionic micelles (Stern layer, or "Stern region" [53]), the charged head groups are partly neutralized by counter-ions. The rest of the last-named are distributed within the diffuse part of the double electrical layer. Together with co-ions they form the ionic atmosphere around the multi-charged particle. The degree of dissociation of ionic surfactant in the micelle, α, as estimated for various surfactants and by different methods [96, 97], varies within the range of 0.5 to 0.1. Another widely used parameter, the degree of neutralization of head groups in the Stern layer, β, equals $(1 - \alpha)$. More often, β is called as degree of counter-ion binding [4,5,13,14,98]. Note, that quantum-chemical calculations for common surface-active ions in vacuo reveal some distribution of the head group charge to the rest of the diphilic ion, first of all to the neighboring methylene group

[99]. In dodecylsulfate anion, the effective charge is found to be -1.13, whereas at the first CH_2 group and the hydrocarbon chain: $+0.18$ and -0.05. For dodecyltrimethylammonium cation, the effective charges are $+0.73$, $+0.16$, and $+0.11$, respectively [99]. If this is also true for aqueous medium, it may influence to some degree the micellar structure. Indeed, it may weaken the cohesion of polymethylene chains and enhance the hydration of the region of the first methylene groups.

The equilibrium concentration of the counter-ion in the bulk phase can be calculated using the values of surfactant concentration, c_{surf}, and cmc and α values under given conditions [4,5,100-107]. For example, for a cationic surfactant, in the presence of a foreign electrolyte with the same anion:

$$[X_W^-] = c_{X^-} + cmc + \alpha(c_{surf} - cmc). \tag{1}$$

Here is the initial concentration in the salt (or buffer) solution. The cmc values are small enough, e.g., 0.0009 M for CTAB and 0.0083 M for SDS in pure water, as reported by many authors. These values decrease on adding electrolytes. The concentration of surfactants in the micellar pseudophase is within the range of ca. 3–7 M (hereafter, 1 M $\equiv$ 1 mole dm^{-3}). The structural models of ionic micelles presume the entry of hydrocarbon chains, at least the first methylene group, into the Stern layer [4,53,54,108]. Therefore, the Stern region is actually a unique mixture of water, hydrocarbon, and electrolyte. Probably, just this is the reason for difficulties in modeling the influence of the Stern region on the equilibria state of embedded substances through comparing with effects of common water-organic mixtures [97].

The value of the electrostatic potential of the Stern region, Ψ, is of significance for interpretation of equilibrium data in ionic micelles. There are four main approaches for Ψ estimation: (1) electrokinetic studies; (2) theoretical calculations based on the double electrical layer theory; (3) application of solvatochromic or solvatofluoric indicators [109,110]; (4) using of pH-indicators (this approach will be considered later in detail).

Direct electrokinetic measurements allow only to determine the so-called zeta-potential, ζ, which is by absolute value knowingly lower than Ψ.

The theoretical Ψ calculations for nano-sized charged particles can be made using versatile formulae, according to the shape of the interface. In the case of small spherical micelles, the curvature of surface is too large to use the equations of the flat double electrical layer [111-115] for exact calculations. Here, the most appropriate is probably the formula obtained by Ohshima, Healy, and White for spherical colloidal particles with radius r, obtained by solving of non-linear Poisson – Boltzman equation [116,117]. It can be presented in the following form:

$$\frac{\alpha}{s_i} - \frac{2\varepsilon\varepsilon_o kRT}{F}\sinh(Y/2)\left(1 + \frac{2}{kr\cosh^2(Y/4)} + \frac{8\ln[\cosh(Y/4)]}{(kr)^2\sinh^2(Y/2)}\right)^{\frac{1}{2}} = 0. \tag{2}$$

Here, s_i is the area of charged head group, $Y = \Psi F/RT$, F is the Faraday constant, k^{-1} is the Debye length, $\varepsilon_o = 8.854 \times 10^{-12}$ F m^{-1}, $\varepsilon = 78.5$ at $T = 298.15$ K. Actually, α/s_i is the surface charge density.

The calculations demonstrate that the uncertainty of Ψ values obtained by eq. (2) is caused first of all by uncertainty of α values [97]. It is well known, that the latter, obtained by using various experimental values, differ markedly from each other [116,118-122]. So, for SDS micelles the mobility measurements lead to $\alpha = 0.3$–0.4 [118], or even higher, while pNa determination and analysis of salt effects upon *cmc* values result in 0.20–0.26 [121,122].

Even more so, such calculations are hindered for numerous colloidal systems, which are not so well defined as SDS or CTAB micelles are, because the complete set of parameters (r, α, and s_i) is as a rule unknown for them. Besides, we use the ε value for pure water, and such assumption may also be inexact. However, even in case if the possibility of exact calculations is doubtful, eq. (2) allows to obtain plausible estimates of Ψ values. Other approaches to estimate the Ψ values for colloidal particles are also known [123,124-127].

Increase in surfactant concentration or/and addition of substantial amounts of electrolytes makes the calculations uncertain, because under such conditions the micellar shape in general case is known to deviate from spherical. In this case, the formula for cylindrical particles is to be used [125].

In the case of non-ionic surfactant micelles, reliable evidences for the existence of interfacial electrostatic potential are absent.

More detailed information on the structure and properties of surfactant micellar solutions is available [128-135]. Though the main properties of the systems under discussion are of common knowledge and are even extensively used in undergraduate laboratory experiments [136-139], some unexpected findings are reported from time to time, such as intriguing information concerning the optical activity of surfactant micellar solutions that appeared in 2010 [140,141].

2. ACID-BASE EQUILIBRIUM AND APPARENT IONIZATION CONSTANTS

2.1. Ionization of Acids within the Pseudophase

Many problems of solution chemistry, biochemistry and biophysics are centered on the acid-base equilibrium. Therefore, it is significant to rationalize the influence of the micellar media on acid-base and other protolytic reactions. The present review is devoted to protolytic equilibria in dispersions with aqueous bulk (continuous) phase. The ionization of an acid with charge z in solution can be described by the below equation:

$$\mathrm{H_i B^z} \ \rightleftharpoons \ \mathrm{H_{i-1} B^{z-1}} + \mathrm{H^+}, \quad K_{a(1-z)} \,. \tag{3}$$

This style of numeration means that the constants K_{a0}, K_{a1}, and K_{a2} refer to the ionization of a cationic, neutral, and anionic acids, respectively. We use preferably the term "ionization constants" with understanding that ionic association of some species with surfactant ions or counter-ions in the dispersed phase cannot be excluded. In the case of organic solvents such complicated constants, determined vis-spectroscopically, may be considered as "observed" ones [142].

The concept of pseudophase [4,5,8,14,15,97] allows introduction of the ionization constant of an acid, K_a^m, in micelles, analogous to such quantities in other liquid media:

$$pK_a^m \equiv -\log K_a^m = -\log(a_{H^+}^m a_B^m / a_{HB}^m) \qquad (4)$$

Here $a_{H^+}^m$, a_B^m, and a_{HB}^m are activities of the corresponding species; in this paper we use the molar scale of activities and concentrations. Thus, micellar pseudophase can be considered as a kind of organic solvent or water-organic mixture, where the state of acid-base and tautomeric equilibria of dissolved substances differs from that in water. Thus, in general case the pK_a^m value may not coincide with the thermodynamic value in water, pK_a^w. The influence of organic solvents on the protolytic equilibria is discussed in a number of monographs [15,49,97,143-145].

However, the approach to the description of acid-base equilibrium in colloidal systems possesses some peculiarities. The principal specificity is caused by the impossibility of direct instrumental determining the pH value inside the highly dispersed pseudophase, pH_m ($pH_m \equiv -\log a_{H^+}^m$). Only the pH value of the continuous aqueous phase, pH_w, is available. But it is just this parameter, which is controlling the state of equilibrium (3) within the nanoscopic pseudophase. On the other hand, most appropriate (though not only one) kind of the $H_i B^z$/ $H_{i-1} B^{z-1}$ acid-base couple for examining in colloidal solutions are the indicator dyes, because the ratio of the equilibrium concentrations within the pseudophase, $[H_i B^z]/[H_{i-1} B^{z-1}]$, can be detected via spectral methods.

2.2. Indicator Acids in the Pseudophase: Spectrophotometric Study

Acid-base [6,14,146-153] and solvatochromic [44,152-158] indicators, including fluorescent dyes and stable free radical probes [40-42,152,159-167], are known to be a touchstone for examining micelles, microdroplets and related nanosized particles, including biomolecules [109,110,152,168]. Indicator dyes serve as useful tools for estimating the solubilizing ability [44, 169], microviscosity and interfacial polarity [108,154-158], for monitoring local acidity and electrical potentials [40,109-111,149-151,153-158,168,170-173], etc. Colored and fluorescent dyes embedded in organized solutions are widely used in sensor devices [174-182]. Fluorescing molecular probes are of particular significance for medical studies [164]. Hydrophobic species can be absorbed within the micellar core [36,44, 169,183]; in some papers, the (adsorption absorption) equilibrium is discussed [36,109, 169,184].

A set of new reviews also reflects the utilization of organic dyes for examination of colloidal, biocolloidal, and supramolecular systems [97,185-189].

Acid-base indicators are generally believed to be located in the Stern region of ionic micelles [4,100-106,149,151,190]. As a rule, molar absorptivities of such dyes are of the order of magnitude of 10^5 mole^{-1} dm^3 cm^{-1}, hence the working concentrations can be 10^{-5} M or even lower. Sulfonephthaleins and other triphenylmetanes, xanthenes, azo- and azine compounds, and many other dyes were already utilized for examining micelles. As example, the indicator bromophenol blue is given below:

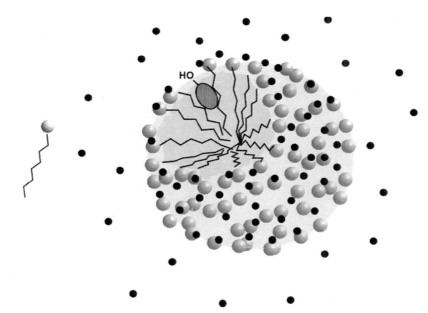

HR$^-$, yellow   R^{2-}, blue

Typically, only a single indicator molecule (or ion) is situated in a micelle. Diagrammatic picture of an indicator molecule located in the micellar palisade is shown in Chart 2.

Chart 2. The ionic micelle with an acid-base indicator molecule; grey and black circles depict the head groups and counter-ions, respectively.

Since the experimental determination of pH$_m$ is impossible, and hence determination of pK$_a^m$ is hindered, it appeared more practical to discuss and analyze the so-called "apparent" value, pK$_a^{app}$, which is the key characteristic of an indicator embedded in the micellar pseudophase.

$$pK_a^{app} = pH_w + \log\frac{[HB^z]_t}{[B^{z-1}]_t}. \tag{5}$$

The subscript t (*total*) denotes that the concentration is expressed in moles per dm^3 of the whole solution. The pH$_w$ value characterizes the bulk phase; it may be maintained via buffer solutions and is determined as a rule using a glass electrode in a cell with liquid junction. Some complications caused by the presence of a surfactant in the buffer system are considered in supplementary electronic material to an earlier publication [191]; see also ref. [192]. The ratio of equilibrium concentrations of indicator species can be obtained by means of UV-vis spectroscopy at extremely low indicator concentrations.

Hence, pK_a^{app} is an "instrumental" parameter that can be observed as a constant of two-phase equilibrium. In general, some fractions of B^{z-1} and HB^z species can stay in the bulk phase (the problem of incomplete binding will be considered in section 2.7). To ensure complete binding, ionic indicators with charge opposite to that of micellar surface can be used [100-102,107,112,149,190,193-202]. Alternatively, hydrophobic indicators, ordinarily with long hydrocarbon tails can be applied [116,118-120,151, 191,203-208]; such probes can be fixed in micelles despite the like charges of dye species and that of the interface. Finally, the indicator dye may be covalently bound, e.g., as fluorescein isothiocyanate to proteins and other biomolecules with NH$_2$ groups. The pK_a^{app} value under conditions of *complete* binding of B^{z-1} and HB^z we designate as $pK_a^{app,c}$.

Occupying even 0.1 to 1 % of the total volume of the aqueous solution, surfactant micelles can exert strong influence on acid-base equilibria. For instance, the old-established "protein error" of indicators [209,210] reflects the modification of acid-base properties by the giant biomolecule, which acts as a pseudophase. Hartley explained the "protein" and "colloidal" errors of indicators [146] and put forward rules, which allowed micellar effects upon acid-base equilibria [146,148,211,212] to be predicted. Specifically, cationic surfactants influence mainly anionic indicator dyes, decreasing their pK_a^{app} value as compared with pK_a^w, while anionic surfactants first of all shift acid-base equilibria of cationic indicators, increasing their pK_a^{app}. Actually, these rules reflect both the phenomenon of dye binding to micelles caused by opposite charges attraction and acid-base equilibria shift of the bound dyes, also of electrostatic origin.

Starting from the Boltzmann distribution law, the concentration of H$^+$ ions nearby the positively charged interface must be lower as compared with the bulk, while that of HO$^-$ ions must be higher. In the case of negatively charged surface, the situation is opposite. If one assumes as a very rough approximation that K_a^m is equal to K_a^w, then decrease (increase) in H$^+$ concentration must just result in $\{[B^{z-1}]/[HB^z]\}$ increase (decrease). In many cases, this simplistic approach explains qualitatively the changes of indicator ratio in cationic and anionic micelles, respectively. However, little by little it became clear that micelles display some influence besides the electrostatic one [149]. Indeed, in non-ionic micelles, the $pK_a^{app,c}$ values of indicators often differ from their pK_a^ws distinctly.

2.3. Utilization of Dye Emission

Sometimes, the absorption bands of the acid-base equilibrium species are poorly resolved, while the dependence of light emission on pH is more pronounced and may be used to determine the indicator ratio. This is the case with the standard lipophilic molecular probes undecyl- and heptadecyl hydroxycoumarin (HHC) [151,207]:

and N,N'-di-n-octadecylrhodamine [191,213]:

The fluorescence spectra were also used to examine the ionization of two dicarboxylic Zn-containing porphyrins in the presence of liposomes [214]. In such cases, the researcher should be convinced of the attribution of thus obtained pK_a^{app} values to the ground state of the dye.

2.4. Electron Spin Resonance Measurements

Besides spectrophotometric determination of the acid/base ratio, the ESR method may also be successfully utilized [215-221]. In these studies, the pH-responsible imidazole and imidazolidin derivatives of nitroxides were used: the isotropic nitrogen hyperfine-coupling constant of ESR spectra in various media changes along with the variation of the bulk pH (or pH_w). Attaching the paramagnetic portions to phospholipid moiety allows ensuring the position of the molecular probes within the phospholipid bilayers and surfactant micelles [220,221].

Moreover, this approach appeared to be useful also on studying solid inorganic porous materials [217,218] and thiol-protected gold nanoparticles [219].

For examining biomembranes, a number of versatile indicator dyes, including fluorescent probes have been proposed [222-225]. A set of oxazoles and oxadiazoles with gradually increasing hydrophobicity allows monitoring the polarity at different depth [226].

2.5. Potentiometric Estimation of the Apparent Ionization Constant

Whereas in the above-mentioned methods the bulk acidity is created using foreign buffer mixtures (or diluted HCl, NaOH, etc.), the pH_w values during the potentiometric determination of pK_a^{app} result from the titration of the studied compound itself [227]. Therefore, the concentrations of the last-named should be higher as compared with the working concentrations used in spectroscopic methods. Naturally, the pH-metric titration is utilized first of all if the absorption/emission spectra cannot be used. In a number of papers, the potentiometric determination of the pK_a^{app} values of carboxylic acids $CH_3(CH_2)_nCOOH$ in water in the presence of different surfactants is reported [228-233]. The pH-titrations with alkali solution in water in the presence of micelles were carried out for alendronic, pamidronic, olpadronic [234,235], and aminopropylidenebisphosphonic [236] acids. Water-insoluble long-tailed amines were titrated with HCl solution in SDS micellar solution [228]. The pK_a^{app} value of tetradecanoic acid in micelles of sugar-derived surfactants was obtained using the dependence of the ^{13}C NMR shifts vs pH [192]. Da Silva et al. [229] and Söderman et al. [230] used pH-titration and calorimetry to study the ionization of dodecanoic acid in micelles of cationic, anionic, and non-ionic surfactants. Morrow et al. [237] used the molecular dynamics method to predict the pK_a^{app} value of the same acid in micelles of the same three types. Maeda proposed a detailed thermodynamic analysis of acid-base titrations in micellar systems [238-240].

There are two aspects that one should keep in mind on starting such studies.

Firstly, if the titrated acid or base is not the isolated molecule embedded in the micelle, but it is the micelle-forming surfactant itself, then the data should be processed as in the case of titration of a polyelectrolyte. Indeed, the electrostatic repulsion and possible hydrogen bond formation between the ionized and neutral groups may display additional influence on the average pK_a^{app} value.

This is true for micelles of long-tailed alkylammonium chlorides and sodium alkylcarboxylates [241], for bilayers of such compounds [242] and their monolayers on water/air interface [241,243], for micelles of ampholytic surfactants such as dimethyldodecylamine oxide [244,245], a double-chain amine oxide [246] and N-dodecyl-β-iminodipropionic acid [247], and for more complicated systems, such as alkyldimethylamine oxide – sodium oleate mixtures [248], pH sensitive mixed surfactant micelles [249], polyelectrolyte multilayers [250], carboxyl-terminated dendrimers [251], etc.

Secondly, one should be aware of complete binding of the molecule under study to the micellar pseudophase. Pallavicini and co-authors [233] examined 11 carboxylic acids (conc. 5 $\times 10^{-4}$ M) in micellar solutions of Triton X – 100 (0.01 M) and revealed that acids from acetic to valeric were not included in the micelles, judging by their pK_a^{app} s. Moreover, pelargonic and even undecanoic acids penetrate the micelles practically completely only on increase in the surfactant concentration. These data agree in outline with the results obtained with propanoic, butanoic, pentanoic, and hexanoic acids in brij 35 and SDS solutions [232] and undecanoic, tetradecanoic, and hexadecanoic acids in micellar solutions of CTAB, SDS, brij 35, and cetyldimethylammonium propanesulfonate [231].

2.6. The Micellar Effect, ΔpK_a^{app}, and the Differentiating Influence of Micelles

Medium effects, i.e., the quantity $\Delta pK_a^{app} = pK_a^{app} - pK_a^{w}$, can in some cases exceed 4 units by absolute value at low ionic strength of the bulk phase [15,103-106,252-254], while introduction of electrolytes into the micellar solution can change these values to the extent of 3 units in opposite direction [15,97,119,200-202]. In the review published by El Seoud in 1989, about 400 pK_a^{app} values were collected [253]. Since then, the number of published data has increased substantially. For instance, in this Laboratory alone, over 1500 pK_a^{app} values have been determined. One of the interesting properties of surfactant micelles and similar aggregates is their strong and versatile *differentiating influence* on the strength of the acids located in the dispersed pseudophase [97].

The phenomenon of differentiating influence is now well known for organic solvents and is determined by the chemical nature of the last-named. *Differentiating* can be understood as non-uniform changes of the strength of different acids on going from a standard solvent (normally from water) to the given solvent [15,97,143,255-260].

Basing on the Born electrostatic theory for ion energy in a dielectric continuum, Brönsted has explained the dependence of the values ($\Delta pK_a^{solvent} = pK_a^{solvent} - pK_a^{w}$) on the charge of the acid, z [49,144,145]. The concept of charge type of the acid/base couple utilized by Kolthoff appeared to be very useful [209]. We use the designations HB^+/B^0, HB^0/B^-, HB^-/B^{2-}, and so on, for cationic, neutral, anionic, etc. acids.

Shortly after the pioneering works of Brönsted, it appeared that not only the charge type, but also the "chemical type" is of significance [255]. The dependences ($pK_a^{solvent}$ vs. pK_a^{w}) appeared to be different not only for cationic and neutral acids, but also for carboxylic acids and phenols, etc. This phenomenon was examined in detail by Izmailov [143,256,259,260], who explained it in terms of different solvation of molecular and ionic species in water and in organic solvents. Namely, the acids of different ionizing group or charge type of acid-base couple give different plots of $pK_a^{solvent}$ vs. pK_a^{w} [143,144,259].

The differentiating influence of micellar pseudophase upon the acid-base properties of indicator couples of various charge types and chemical types, i.e., the disparity in their $\Delta pK_a^{app,c}$ values, manifests itself distinctly, depending on the nature of the surfactant. This effect is caused, on the one hand, by the miscellaneous character of any micellar surface, and on the other hand by the dissimilarity among hydrophilic portions of cationic, anionic, nonionic (with oxyethylene chains), and zwitterionic surfactants, as well as of the Stern region of ionic micelles containing counter-ions of different hydrophobicity.

For instance, in SDS micelles at bulk ionic strength $I = 0.05$ M (NaCl + buffer), $\Delta pK_a^{app,c} = -1.60, +1.56$, and $+3.1$ for pinacyanol, methyl yellow, and bromothymol blue, respectively.

In CPC micellar solutions, at the same salt background, $\Delta pK_a^{app,c} = -0.37, -0.76$, and -2.16 for thymol blue, N,N'-di-n-octadecylrhodamine, and bromophenol blue, respectively.

Thus, relatively small $\Delta pK_a^{app,c}$ values, as compared with the $\Delta pK_a^{solvent}$ on going from water to entire organic solvents, exhibit impressing specificity.

In addition to this "*true*" differentiating influence, "*trivial*" differentiating, originating from incomplete binding of some dye species, can take place. Such kind of differentiating manifests itself in the differences in $pK_a^{app,c}$, not $\Delta pK_a^{app,c}$. Therefore, we shall first of all consider the problem of incomplete binding and estimation of $pK_a^{app,c}$, if it is unavailable for direct determination. Then the approaches meant to explain the values $\Delta pK_a^{app,c} = pK_a^{app,c} - pK_a^{w}$ of different types of acids will be analyzed.

2.7. Incomplete Binding of the Acid-Base Couple to the Micelles

In general case, the binding of different molecules and ions by the pseudophase can be incomplete. Hence, it is necessary to evaluate the degree of binding under different conditions and (if possible) to extrapolate the pK_a^{app} values to $pK_a^{app,c}$. For such purposes, the so-called binding constants, $K_{b,i}$, are appropriate. These constants refer to the quasichemical equilibrium {(substrate i in bulk water) + (surfactant head group situated in micelle) (substrate in bound state)}. In micellar solutions, if the inequality $[i_m]_t << (c_{surf} - cmc)$ is valid, the $K_{b,i}$ value can be calculated using eq. (6):

$$K_{b,i} = \frac{[i_m]_t}{[i_w]_t} \times \frac{1}{c_{surf} - cmc}. \qquad (6)$$

Indeed, such constants can be used if the precise values of the micellar size, pseudophase volume, etc., are unknown. To estimate the degree of binding of various molecules and ions by surfactant micelles, a number of methods are developed, for example, spectroscopic, chromatographic, diffusion ones, etc. For acid-base equilibrium, the analysis of the pK_a^{app} plots vs. surfactant concentration in the region above cmc [3,8,14,261-277] is most helpful and universal method for estimation of $K_{b,i}$.

The relation between the pK_a^{app} value of the acid ($HB^z \rightleftharpoons B^{z-1} + H^+$) in micellar solutions at fixed ionic strength and the indices of ionization constant in water, pK_a^{w*}, determined at the same ionic strength, is as follows:

$$pK_a^{app} = pK_a^{w*} + \log\frac{1+K_{b,HB}\,(c_{surf}-cmc)}{1+K_{b,B}(c_{surf}-cmc)}. \qquad (7)$$

Evidently, if the binding constants of the HB^z and B^{z-1} species, $K_{b,HB}$ and $K_{b,B}$, are large enough, the pK_a^{app} completely coincides with $pK_a^{app,c}$. On the contrary, if the both binding constants are so small that $K_{b,i}(c_{surf}-cmc) \ll 1$, then pK_a^{app} is equal to pK_a^{w*}, and the pseudophase does not influence the acid-base equilibrium state at all. At last, in case if either both species or one of them are bound incompletely, eq. (7) can be used for $K_{b,i}$ determination using the increasing or decreasing sigmoid (pK_a^{app} vs. c_{surf}) curve, exemplified in Figure 1 [15,261-277]. The equation can be linearized, but the non-linear fitting is also possible [278].

Such processing of data appeared to be proper for micellar solutions of colloidal surfactants [263,264,267-275], phospholipid liposomes [278], and microemulsions [266,276,279].

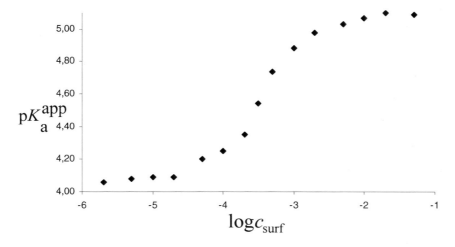

Figure 1. The increase in the $pK_{a,2}^{app}$ of bromophenol blue along with rise in brij 35 concentration; ionic strength $I = 0.01$ M.

Finally, having the $K_{b,i}$ values, it is possible to calculate the $pK_a^{app,c}$ value [15,97,275]:

$$pK_a^{app,c} = + \log\frac{K_{b,B}^{-1}+c_{surf}-cmc}{K_{b,HB}^{-1}+c_{surf}-cmc}. \qquad (8)$$

It should be noted, however, that if the $K_{b,i}$ value of one of the equilibrium species, HB^z or B^{z-1}, is too small to be estimated, the $pK_a^{app,c}$ value is unavailable. Some typical data for the dye bromophenol blue are presented in Table 1.

Dutta and his colleagues developed somewhat another procedure [270,271,280].

Naturally, it is advisable to have available some independent methods for estimating the degree of binding [281]. Though alteration of electronic absorption spectra along with binding is sometimes not distinct enough, the spectrophotometry is nevertheless a useful tool [44,282-284]. In some cases, fluorescence provides valuable information [282-286]. For instance, emission spectra of curcumin in the presence of surfactant micelles differ markedly in comparison with that in water [287]. Chromatography [28,29,288] and kinetic data [155,289] also are often used for such purposes. It should be noted that using the kinetic data, the binding parameters of substrates in the terms of Piszkiewicz theory [290] may be evaluated in some appropriate cases.

Diverse degree of binding of indicators or other substrates, as well as of equilibrium species of one and the same reagent can evidently result in the "trivial" differentiating influence of the pseudophase (see above). At the same time, this phenomenon may serve as a model of selective solvation, so typical for mixed solvents.

In the case of ionic surfactants, there are three main problems while determining the values of $K_{b,i}$ and $pK_a^{app,c}$. They are briefly considered below as **(A)**, **(B)**, and **(C)**.

(A) Other things being equal, *the same sign of the charge* of the substrate and micelle surface hinders binding of indicators [148,149], metal complexes [214], alkyl carboxylates with medium length of hydrocarbon chains [232], etc. The data for thymol blue and bromothymol blue in SDS solutions [291] may be explained in terms of incomplete binding of these anionic dyes; the effect is less expressed for the more hydrophobic sulfonephthalein, bromothymol blue. The pK_a^{app} s for a set of sulfonephthaleins in SDS micellar solutions [277,292] are also determined under conditions of incomplete binding. The same is probably true for methyl orange ($HB^\pm/B^-$) in SDS micellar solutions [293]. The reported pK_a^{app} value for loratadine in CTAB micelles [294] is seemingly influenced by incomplete binding of the HB^+ species. Maybe, the early results obtained with membranes and surfactant micelles of different types using umbelliferone [295,296] lead to the suggestion to use its hydrophobic analogue HHC (see above) in order to ensure binding to any pseudophase.

A universal way to facilitate the binding in such cases is the shielding of the surface charge of micelles by an indifferent electrolyte, including the particular case of sulfonephthaleins in SDS solutions [267,275].

In some cases, the shielding of the micellar charge may substantially weaken the binding of an ion even by oppositely charged surfaces. For example, whereas the HB^- and B^{2-} anions of the most hydrophobic sulfonephthalein, bromothymol blue, are practically completely bound to SDS micelles in the presence of 0.2 M NaCl and $c_{surf} = 0.1$ M [275], the relatively hydrophilic unsubstituted sulfonephthalein phenol red is incompletely bound even to cationic micelles, if the concentration of bromides or nitrates in the system is high enough to reduce partly the interfacial electrical potential. (On the other hand, phenol red was considered as completely bound by micelles of *n*-dodecyltrimethylammonium bromide at 4 M NaBr [195].)

Interestingly, in chloride-containing CTAB solutions, up to 4 M of KCl, this sulfonephthalein is practically completely fixed at the micelles [15].

Table 1. The values of binding constants/M^{-1} of mono- and dianions of bromophenol blue and the calculated $pK_{a}^{app,c}$ values in solutions of non-ionic surfactants [15,97]

Surfactant	c_{surf}, M	$10^{-3} K_{b,HB^-}$	$10^{-3} K_{b,B^{2-}}$	$pK_{a,2}^{app,c}$
Brij 35[a]	$1 \times 10^{-4} - 0.01$	12	1.2	5.10 ± 0.03
Triton X – 100[a]	$5 \times 10^{-4} - 0.005$	11	1.7	5.00 ± 0.02
Triton X – 305[a]	$1.3 \times 10^{-3} - 0.005$	2.4	0.13	4.88 ± 0.03
Nonyl phenol 12[b]	$2 \times 10^{-4} - 0.004$	20	2.7	4.80 ± 0.03
Tween 80[b]	$1.5 \times 10^{-4} - 0.05$	13	0.90	5.09 ± 0.03

[a] Ionic strength $I = 0.01$ M; [b] $I = 0.05$ M.

By contrast, in the case of hydrophobic rose Bengal B with different anionic surfactants [297] and of eryochrome Black-T with sodium dodecyl benzene sulfonate [298] the interaction of dye anions with anionic surfactants is rather expressed.

It should be also taken into account, that the anions are known to be bound by phospholipid liposomes better than cations of the same hydrophobicity; for example, for $B(C_6H_5)_4^-$ and $As(C_6H_5)_4^+$ the difference amounts to 19 kJ mol^{-1} [299]; see also ref. [300]. This is in qualitative agreement with the $K_{b,i}$ values of cationic and anionic dyes, notwithstanding the negative interfacial charge of the mixed phosphatidylcholine and diphosphatidylglycerol liposomes used in one of our studies [278].

(B) The second problem consists in premicellar ionic association of the ions of the substrate (e.g., dye) with *oppositely charged* free surfactant ions. If the concentration of ionic surfactant is below its *cmc* value, such an interaction could result in formation of neutral water-insoluble dye-surfactant associates and mixed micelles [301-306]. The dye ions can be then regarded as large counter-ions [15,97].

As early as 1955, Mukerjee and Mysels attracted attention to this problem [302]. Basing on the literature data and their own experiments with pinacyanol and bromophenol blue in solutions of anionic and cationic surfactants, respectively, they revealed the dye–surfactant complexes below the *cmc* value of homomicelles (= entire surfactant micelles). Hence, the *cmc* values obtained via the indicator method may sometimes be in error. Of course, in some cases the premicellar association between ions and non-ionic surfactant monomers or neutral molecules and ionic surface-active ions also cannot be excluded.

The abovementioned effects manifest themselves both in absorption and emission spectra. This is the case with anions of aminoindophenol dye [307] and sulfonephthaleins [308] with cationic surfactants. In the last-cited paper, it is demonstrated via surface tension measurements that the dye–surfactant ionic pairs form a monolayer on the water/air interface.

A recent fluorescence study of the behavior of dianions B^{2-} of fluorescein, eosin, erythrosin, rose bengal B in the presence of CTAB, SDS, and a non-ionic pluronic surfactant revealed strong interaction with CTAB well below the *cmc* [309]. The obtained binding constants are in line with the hydrophobicity of the dyes [309]. Such phenomenon is typical and well documented in the literature [15]. Figure 2 reflects some experiments from this Laboratory.

Analogous effects were observed for the cationic dye acridine orange [310] and crystal violet [311] in solutions of anionic surfactants. Micheau, Zakharova, and Chibisov studied the system cationic dye rhodamine 6G – SDS in detail, including the kinetic aspect [305]. Later it was shown that a similar cationic dye, rhodamine 123, interacts in the case of non-ionic and cationic surfactants only with micelles, though in the last case the counter-ions may quench the fluorescence of the dye [312]. In the case of anionic surfactants, the dye exists in form of ion pairs with anions, then in premicellar aggregates, and finally is involved in the surfactant homomicelles.

Probably, similar processes take place in the case of more complicated anionic dye in CTAB solutions [313] and in a recent study of tautomerism in the presence of anionic surfactants below cmc [314].

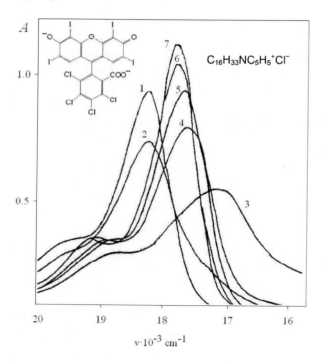

Figure 2. Absorption spectra of rose bengal B (2×10^{-6} M, optical path 5 cm) in aqueous solutions of CPC: $1-0$; $2-1 \times 10^{-5}$; $3-2 \times 10^{-5}$; $4-6 \times 10^{-5}$; $5-1 \times 10^{-4}$; $6-2 \times 10^{-4}$; $7-2 \times 10^{-3}$ M CPC; pH 6.9, 0.01% polyvinyl alcohol [15]. (Obtained by one of us, N. M.-P., in collaboration with V. N. Kleshchevnikova).

A special case is the behavior of the dye methyl orange. The main absorption band of the anionic form, B^-, displays a pronounced blue shift in the presence of a cationic surfactant. At small excess of the surfactant and $c_{surf} \ll cmc$, the so-called H-aggregates of the dye appear [315]. Along with the increase in c_{surf}, mixed dye–surfactant micelles and then homomicelles with adsorbed isolated dye anions are observed [15].

Finally, some authors prefer not to use the concept of apparent ionization constant at all, and study the stepwise acid–base equilibrium of melamine with participation of a definite number of surfactant ions or molecules [316].

(C) In the case of ionic surfactants, the curves pK_a^{app} vs. c_{surf} sometimes possess a *turning point* [8,261-264,267,282-284,291,317,318]. The most probable reason for appearance of a minimum in the case of cationic surfactants and a maximum in the case of anionic ones is the inconstancy of the counter-ion concentration. Indeed, along with increase in c_{surf}, the counter-ion concentration in the bulk phase increases due to dissociation of the colloidal electrolyte (see eq. (1)). This "negative adsorption" [149] leads to screening of the interfacial charge and to corresponding alterations of $pK_a^{app,c}$. Adding of an excess of supporting electrolyte eliminates the turning point [15,107]; in addition, the *cmc* decreases, and micelles appear at lower concentrations.

Figure 3 demonstrates the discussed effect by the example of quinaldine red ($HB^{2+} B^+ + H^+$) in SDS solutions. The extremum is registered only at low ionic strength (diluted HCl). In the presence of 0.2 M NaCl, the pK_a^{app} s, or, in fact, $pK_a^{app,c}$ values are quite stable. Probably, this effect is the reason of decrease in $pK_a^{app,c}$ of the cationic acids of acridine, neutral red, and Reichardt's dye at too high SDS concentrations [196,328] and increase in the $pK_a^{app,c}$ of the cation of Reichardt's dye at too high *n*-dodecyltrimethylammonium bromide concentrations [328] without substantial additions of foreign electrolytes.

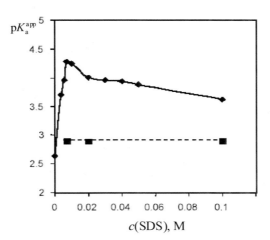

Figure 3. The dependence of pK_a^{app} of quinaldine red ($HB^{2+} B^+ + H^+$) on SDS concentration at low ionic strength (upper curve) and in the presence of 0.2 M (bottom points) [15]. (Obtained by one of us, N. M.-P., in collaboration with A. S. Shumakher).

Alternatively, such shapes of the curves can be explained in terms of the pseudophase exchange model [8,103-106,317,319] (see below).

Hence, the binding partition model seems to be capable. However, there are some aspects to be considered. First of all, the obtained values of binding parameters are often dependent on the working concentration range [15,268,275,276,279]. Therefore, the data precision is low; the accuracy can reach 30%, and in the case of microemulsions can be even worse. Note that alterations of $pK_a^{app,c}$ values along with variations in surfactant concentration are reported even for completely bound indicators [120]. The evident reasons are changes in micellar size and shape.

3. QUANTITATIVE DESCRIPTION OF ACID-BASE EQUILIBRIUM IN MICELLES

3.1. The Locus of the Acid-Base Couple in the Micelle

Hereafter, we consider the $pK_a^{app,c}$ values, i.e., the pK_a^{app} s of acid-base couples being practically completely associated with the micelles. For further discussion, some details concerning the locus of the H_iB^z and $H_{i-1}B^{z-1}$ species within the pseudophase should be clarified.

If the number of these species in solution is lower or around the number of micelles (the latter may be evaluated from the molar concentration of the surfactant knowing the aggregate number), the acid molecule could be considered as isolated from other ones. More detailed information may be obtained using the Poisson distribution [130].

Another important issue is the position of the substrate, first of all of its ionizing group, within the pseudophase. According to the ^{1}H NMR data, the COOH group of the 4-octadecyloxy-1-naphthoic acid is primarily located in the head group region of both CTAB and SDS micelles, and around the first ether linkage away from the hydrocarbon center of the non-ionic $C_{12}H_{25}O(CH_2CH_2O)_8H$ [320]. Drummond and Grieser deduced similar state for HHC from the visible absorption band [204]. Using the ^{1}H NMR data Minch et al. revealed that the aromatic carbanions interact tightly with the cationic head group of CTAB [252]. Bachofer et al. used the same method for the micellar solution of tetradecyltrimethylammonium bromide and demonstrated that the COO$^-$ groups of several naphthoates and benzoates are located near the $N(CH_3)_3^+$ groups of the surfactant, while the aromatic moieties of the anions are surrounded by the hydrocarbon chains [321,322]. Bunton and Minch expected similar position for benzoic acids [323]. In this connection, the recent study of phenol in CTAB micelles by means of ^{1}H NMR and NOESY techniques is of special interest [324]. The locus of the phenolate ion is similar to the above-mentioned for napthtoates and benzoates [321,322]. But the OH group of the neutral phenol molecule is exposed to more extent to the aqueous phase, while the phenyl portion is just between the cationic head groups [324].

The ^{1}H NMR method is helpful for investigation of intramicellar situation of different hydrophobic species: water-insoluble tetraphenylporphyrins [325], benzene [326], hydrophobic N-diazeniumdiolates [327], etc. The standard solvatochromic Reichardt dye is oriented with the phenolate (and phenolic in protonated form) group toward the interfacial region [156,328].

Also, the total size of the molecular probe (e.g., indicator) is of significance. Naturally, too large molecule may disturb the normal micellar structure [329,330].

3.2. The Electrostatic Approach

The electrostatic model is mostly used for the description of protolytic equilibria in micellar media and related systems. It is based on the concept of pseudophase and on taking into account (i) the electrostatic potential of the interface and (ii) solvation effects [97,100-102,107,112,116,118-120,149-151,183,190-192,194-208,215-221,229,230,278,320,331-336] The detailed consideration can be found in a set of reviews [5,8,97,153,227,317,337].

Within the framework of the electrostatic model, key relations can be derived, assuming that the partition of any ion or molecule, including the species HB^Z and B^{Z-1}, between the bulk aqueous phase and the pseudophase can be described by eq. (9):

$$P_i = = = \frac{1}{^w\gamma_i^m} \exp\frac{-z_i\Psi F}{RT}. \tag{9}$$

Here P_i is partition constant of i-species with charge z_i; a_i^m and a_i^w are activities in micellar and aqueous phases, respectively; $^w\gamma_i^m$ is the activity coefficient of transfer from water to the pseudophase. The quantity $P_i^o = (^w\gamma_i^m)^{-1}$ reflects the ability of the species to go from water to pseudophase, apart from electrostatic attraction or repulsion. Eq. (9) follows from the equality of the electrochemical potentials of the i-species in the two phases under equilibrium conditions. Actually, the Stern layer (or Stern region) is considered as a pseudophase. For Gibbs energy of transfer from water to pseudophase, eq. (10) is valid:

$$\Delta G_i^{tr}(w \rightarrow m) = = + z_i\Psi F. \tag{10}$$

In particular, applying eq. (9) to the proton (hydronium ion), the expression for interfacial pH, pH_m, can be obtained:

$$pH_m = + + \frac{\Psi F}{2.30 RT}. \tag{11}$$

Hence, the difference between pH_m and pH_w is caused both by the electrical charge of the interface and by its solvation properties. The deviations of pK_a^m and $pK_a^{app,c}$ from the pK_a^w value can be represented using the partition constants:

$$\Delta pK_a^m = - = - - \log P_{H^+}, \tag{12}$$

$$\Delta pK_a^{app,c} = - = - \log P_B. \tag{13}$$

The last equation is of particular interest, because it is just the $pK_a^{app,c}$ value, which is available experimentally. The agreed notation of the first two items in the expression for $pK_a^{app,c}$ is pK_a^i:

$$pK_a^{app,c} = pK_a^w + \log \frac{^w\gamma_B^m}{^w\gamma_{HB}^m} - \frac{\Psi F}{2.30RT} = pK_a^m - \log{^w\gamma_{H^+}^m} - \frac{\Psi F}{2.30RT} = pK_a^i - \frac{\Psi F}{2.30RT}, \quad (14)$$

Here K_a^i is called "intrinsic" constant. The spectroscopic method gives the ratio of equilibrium concentrations of HB^z and B^{z-1} species, not activities. However, because the Stern region is actually a concentrated electrolyte solution, the f_B^m / f_{HB}^m ratio of concentration activity coefficients is expected to be close to unity, and the corresponding logarithmic term is as a rule supposed to be negligible [328], taking into account the character of the dependence of ionization constants of indicators and other acids in aqueous media on ionic strength [328,338-340]. Moreover, since the Stern region can be also considered as a kind of ionic liquid or a solution of water and hydrocarbon in fused salt, the standardization "to infinite diluted indicator solution" still means the ionic environment. Therefore, it is more practical to suppose that the interaction energy of dye species with surrounding ions in Stern region is included in the $^w\gamma_i^m$ values.

Hartley and Roe used such an approach to describe apparent ionization constants as early as 1940; they utilized the zeta-potential and pK_a^w instead of Ψ and pK_a^i, respectively [147]. Mukerjee and Banerjee [149], Fromherz and co-workers [111,151,341], and Funasaki [107,150,332] developed the electrostatic model. Therefore, we find it justified calling eq. (14) the "HMFF equation" according to the names of Hartley, Mukerjee, Fromherz, and Funasaki. Later on, Gaboriaud and associates [100-102,190] and then Drummond, Grieser, Healy et al. [153,194-197,203-205,320,328,334,337,342-346] developed the electrostatic model. Similar equations were applied for polyelectrolytes [347-349] and monolayers [111,113-115,341]. The HMFF equation can be transformed for Ψ/mV estimation:

$$\Psi = 59.16\,(pK_a^i - pK_a^{app,c}); \; 25°C. \quad (15)$$

The pK_a^i value in ionic micelles is often equated to the $pK_a^{app,c}$ value of the same indicator bound by micelles of non-ionic surfactants [112,116,119,153,204,335]. In case if the surfactant is an ampholyte, e.g., dimethyl dodecylamine oxide, then the Ψ value changes along with pH_w [332].

In the classical version of the electrostatic model, the constancy of (i) the pK_a^i value of the given acid or acid-base indicator in any micellar system on the one hand, and of (ii) the value of electrostatic potential of the Stern layer of the given micellar surface as obtained by using any indicator, on the other hand is assumed. Consequently, the change in $pK_a^{app,c}$ on going from one kind of micelles to another must be equal for wide variety of acids.

This common electrostatic model, based on the HMFF equation, is justified in general way. However, the two aforementioned assumptions are holding true only roughly, and sometimes are invalid. In the cited papers, sulfonephthaleins, phenols, azo dyes, coumarines, hydroxyxanthenes, antraquinones, imidazoles, azines, triarylcarbinols, and some other dyes were studied. The more indicator dyes are involved into the determination of Ψ via eq. (15), the stronger discrepancy becomes evident [15, 97,120].

This can reflect the peculiar of dye location within the pseudophase. Indeed, some relatively large-sized dye molecules (ions) cannot completely come into the Stern region. On the other hand, some extremely hydrophobic dyes can penetrate even into the micellar or microdroplet core [183,331]. In the context of the approach under discussion, all these peculiarities are included in the $^{w}\gamma_{i}^{m}$ values. The existence of local charges and complicated potential profiles in the interfacial regions (micelles of zwitterionic surfactants, phospholipid vesicles, etc.) also results in different medium effects ($\Delta pK_{a}^{app,c}$) for various indicator dyes and other acids [97]. (The vesicles formed in water by cationic or anionic surfactants with two long tails influence the equilibria of indicators like the micelles of single-tailed amphiphiles, whereas in the case of the phospholipid bilayers, the picture is even more complicated [204,278,350].)

A distinct illustration of the limited validity of the simple electrostatic model can be obtained by comparing the indices of apparent ionization constants of a two-step indicator *n*-decylfluorescein:

$$H_2B^+ \qquad\qquad HB \qquad\qquad B^-$$

The neutral molecule, HB, participates in the both equilibria. The presence of a long hydrocarbon tail allows one to expect identical or at least similar character of location of cation and anion within micelles, with ionizing groups situated in the Stern region. Assuming that the Ψ value is the same for the both ionization steps, the difference between $pK_{a1}^{app,c}$ and $pK_{a0}^{app,c}$ can be expressed in a following way:

$$pK_{a1}^{app,c} - pK_{a0}^{app,c} = pK_{a1}^{i} - pK_{a0}^{i} = pK_{a1}^{w} - pK_{a0}^{w} + \log\frac{^{w}\gamma_{H_2B^+}^{m}\ ^{w}\gamma_{B^-}^{m}}{\left(^{w}\gamma_{HB}^{m}\right)^2}. \qquad (16)$$

Therefore, it can be anticipated that the difference $pK_{a1}^{app,c} - pK_{a0}^{app,c}$ will stay constant in versatile ultramicroheterogeneous systems. Unfortunately, the data obtained in this Laboratory [15,97,120,279] demonstrate that it is not the case. The above-mentioned dye was examined in 31 colloidal solutions of cationic, anionic, non-ionic, oxyethylated anionic, zwitterionic and mixed surfactants, microemulsions, and phospholipid suspensions. The substantial increase and decrease in $pK_a^{app,c}$ values on going from water to anionic and cationic surfactant systems, respectively, was observed at low bulk ionic strength. (Instead of experimentally unavailable pK_a^ws of n-decylfluorescein, the corresponding values for its water-soluble analogues can be used: $pK_{a1}^w = 6.28\text{--}6.31$ and $pK_{a0}^w = 2.94\text{--}3.10$ [15,120].)

However, the difference $pK_{a1}^{app,c} - pK_{a0}^{app,c}$ varies from 3.49 to 5.37 [97]. Thus, the imperfection of the simplified model manifests itself quite essentially. Even for non-ionic surfactants with oligomeric oxyethylene hydrophilic portion the value of ($pK_{a1}^{app,c} - pK_{a0}^{app,c}$) varies within 0.3 units. Generally speaking, such scatter of $pK_a^{app,c}$ values along with variations of the structure of ethylene oxide-based surfactants is quite typical [15,97,120].

In the paper by da Silva et al. [229], the following comment to the equation $pK_a^{app,c} = pK_a^i - \Psi F / 2.30 RT$ (in our designations) was given: "The apparent simplicity of this equation hides several fundamental problems". The latter are denoted as (i) a correct measurement of pK_a^i, (ii) the location of the probe, and (iii) the importance of non-electrostatic interactions [229].

It should be noted, however, that the rigorous determination of pK_a^i is impossible, because whereas $pK_a^{app,c}$ is experimentally available, the Ψ quantity is in fact a kind of Galvani potential. Hence, the desirable *intrinsic acidity constant cannot be estimated without some extrathermodynamic assumptions.*

If one tries to evaluate the electrostatic potential of the Stern layer, the proper indicator probe should be selected, and its "true" pK_a^i value should be searched out. Then some plausible Ψ value may be obtained. Strictly speaking, it should be ascribed to the probe-disturbed Stern layer. But even if the ionizing group of the probe is to certain extent displaced from the Stern layer, estimates of pK_a^i are advisable.

A popular procedure of pK_a^i estimation, irrespective of the dye location, consists in modeling of the pseudophase by water–organic mixtures [107,150,151,194-197,328, 334,335]. Fernandez and Fromherz [151] for HHC, Drummond, Grieser, Healy and their co-workers for a variety of indicator dyes (see above), Saha, Tiwari, and Dogra [335] for benzimidazoles, and recently Xi and Guo for puerarin [351] used water – 1,4-dioxane mixtures to mimic the non-electrostatic effects of the micellar pseudophase. On the other hand, Funasaki used the data for water – ethanol mixtures [107], and Voinov et al. compared their apparent constants with those in water – 2-propanol system [220].

The idea consists in determination of definite water–organic mixture being isodielectric with the pseudophase. As a rule, the choice of the latter is usually made using a solvatochromic probe, such as Reichardt's betaine dye, or some other pyridinium compounds, or HHC, which indicates the same polarity (relative permittivity) as registered in micellar pseudophase. Then the intrinsic acidity may be calculated as $= -\log{}^{w}\gamma_{H^+}^{m}$. In this case, the pK_a^m and ${}^{w}\gamma_{H^+}^{m}$ values are equated to corresponding pK_a and ${}^{w}\gamma_{H^+}^{solv}$ values of the indicator in a water–organic mixture [107,150,151,194-197,328,334,335]. Some variations of the approach are also possible [335].

However, the pK_a^i estimation by using water–organic mixtures for mimicking micellar interfacial regions has also some disadvantages. Indeed, the relative permittivity may be not the sole factor influencing the absorption spectra. Also, even if one knows the pseudophase relative permittivity, it must be taken into account that the pK_a values of an acid in various isodielectric water–organic mixtures can differ markedly. Finally, the ${}^{w}\gamma_{H^+}^{solv}$ quantity belongs to the extrathermodynamic ones. We have demonstrated [15,120] that the satisfactory fitting of the data, reported by several research groups, is reached by using the old-fashioned ${}^{w}\gamma_{H^+}^{solv}$ values, while the use of the ${}^{w}\gamma_{H^+}^{solv}$ values, obtained by means of the most recognized tetraphenylborate assumption [352], leads to essentially different pK_a^i values. The calculated Ψ values can differ up to ca. 100 mV, depending on the chosen ${}^{w}\gamma_{H^+}^{solv}$ values [120].

It was also reported that strong and peculiar differentiating influence of micellar pseudophase on protolytic equilibria of dissolved substances hinders modeling its properties with any water – organic mixture [15,97,120].

But in spite of all the criticism, the HMFF equation is a platform for developing the electrochemical model of acid-base equilibria in colloidal systems.

3.3. Application and Expansion of the Theory

Equations (11), (14), and (15) as well as their modifications are often used to describe the solid surfaces, such as water/silica or water/alumina, either "bare" or coated by surfactant layers [218,320,353-355], including CTAB-coated SiO_2 nanoparticles [356,357]. The electrostatic approach was applied for second harmonic generation (SHG) study of ionization of COOH groups at the aqueous interface of polymer nanoparticles [358] and spectrophotometric examining of cationic spherical polyelectrolyte brushes [359].

Recently we have demonstrated that aggregates formed by water-soluble cationic dendrimers [360,361] and calixarenes [361-363] influence the protolytic equilibria of dissolved dyes like cationic surfactant micelles. The data have been explained in terms of HMFF eq. (14).

The relationships under discussion are applicable to acid-base equilibrium in Langmuir – Blodgett films, both pH-insensitive [213,364] and pH-sensitive [365,366], and also to protolytic behavior of dyes embedded in gelatin films [367].

The electrostatic approach was used to describe ionizable monolayers on the water/air interface, though the term $\log{}^{w}\gamma_{H^+}^{m}$ in eq. (11) was usually neglected [368-371]. Caspers et al. used the electrostatic model for estimating the Ψ values for different pH-sensitive monolayers and compared them with the values of the Volta potential [113].

Of course, in the monolayers consisting of acidic or basic ionizing molecules the neighboring groups will influence each other [241,243] (see also section 2.5). By contrast, if a dye, for instance, the HHC, is penetrated in charged monolayers, the standard procedure may be used [111,341,372]. Just in such a manner Fromherz and Kotulla estimated the Ψ value in soap lamella [373]. The group of Tahara applied the heterodyne-detected electronic sum frequency generation technique to examine the acid-base equilibrium of an indicator dye embedded in the CTAB monolayer on the water/air interface [374]. These authors did not use the equation with the Ψ value and reported the difference between the bulk and interfacial pH. In fact, this difference is governed by the $^{w}\gamma_{H^{+}}^{m}$ and Ψ values, eq. (11).

Since 1987, Eisenthal and co-workers published a series of papers devoted to application of the SHG technique to the acid-base processes on water surface [375-381]. The results by Shen and associates [382,383] are also of significance. As a rule, entire indicator monolayers of nitro and alkyl phenols, long-tailed anilines, amines, and hemicyanines were examined. In some cases, the theoretical calculations of Ψ by the Goüy formula were helpful.

Normally, $\Delta pK_{a}^{app} > 0$ for acids of HB/B^{-} type, whereas $\Delta pK_{a}^{app} < 0$ for HB^{+}/B couples [375-383]. The same regularity for neutral and anionic acid is registered with 2,7-dinitro-4,5-dibromofluorescein, a dye exhibiting a rather low interfacial excess concentration [384]. This dye is able to two-step ionization. Another dye, a hydrophobic pyridine derivative, may successively add two protons; its behavior in monolayers on water/air interface was a matter of detailed studies [382,383,385,386]:

The first stage of protonation of this hemicyanine dye was studied quantitatively by SHG method in order to evaluate the interfacial $pK_{a,0}^{surf}$ and pH$_{surf}$ values of the acid-base couple HB^{+}/B^{0} [382]. The protonation was studied in monolayers of completely ionized stearic acid, where the Ψ value was calculated using the Goüy formula, at a fixed NaCl concentration in the subphase. Thus obtained $pK_{a,0}^{surf} = 3.5$ value was substantially lower than $pK_{a,0}^{w} = 6.7$ [382]. Then the $pK_{a,0}^{surf}$ value was used to estimate the pH$_{surf}$ s at various pH$_{w}$. It should be noted, however, that the $^{w}\gamma_{H^{+}}^{surf}$ was put equal to unity on default, and the dense counter-ion layer (Stern layer) near the ionized COO^{-} groups was omitted from consideration.

Qualitatively similar results have been obtained with the same dye by using fluorescence [385]. In order to avoid the aggregation typical for this dye [386], its mixed monolayers with arachidic acid have been used [385]. The values $pK_{a,0}^{w} = 6.7$ and $pK_{a,(-1)}^{w} = 3.2$ were determined for the analogous dye without long tail. The second equilibrium (H_2B^{2+}/HB^+) of the hydrophobic dye is also strongly shifted toward the acidic region in the monolayer. The monocation HB^+ predominates at bulk pH_w between 1.5 and 9 [385].

The procedure of determination of the interfacial $pK_{a.}^{surf}$ and pH_{surf} by using the Goüy formula was further developed by Shen and co-workers [383]. However, for highly charged surfaces such approach may be considered only as the first approximation. If the solvation properties of the water/air surface, caused by dielectric environment and hydrogen bonding, may result in the deviation of $pK_{a.}^{surf}$ from pK_a^w, then the term analogous to $\log\ {}^w\gamma_{H^+}^m$ in eq. (11) should be taken into account. (See also section 3.4.)

For surfactant systems, at least for well-defined systems such as SDS or CTAB micelles, the idea of pK_a^i estimation of the given indicator using theoretically calculated Ψ quantities via eq. (2) looks out more soundly [116, 194-197].

Now let us return to surfactant micelles in water. Pal and Jana underlined that if the dye probe has no large hydrophobic group, the possibility of different locations of various dyes may take place [183]. For instance, these authors concluded that the data for acid-base couples of different isomers of hydroxyanthraquinones result in different Ψ values in the same micelles [183].

Da Silva et al. [229] and Söderman et al. [230] used Monte Carlo simulations and thermodynamic modeling to interpret the results of titration of dodecanoic acid in micelles of cationic, anionic, and non-ionic surfactants. The dissociation reaction of this acid becomes endothermic when it occurs in micelles [230]. The upward pK_a in micellar solutions of dodecyltrimethylammonium chloride and bromide da Silva et al. qualified as "surprisingly enough" [229]. In the both papers, the $pK_a^{app,c}$ values are higher in the case of bromide counter-ions. This agrees with the results of Drummond, Grieser, and Healy group and with our data [97].

Cuccovia and colleagues synthesized a set of salicylic acid derivatives for pH probing in micellar solutions of SDS [128]. These indicators bear alkyldimethylammonium cationic groups in *para* position to the OH group of the salicylic moiety (two compounds are shown below):

The conformations of probes were analyzed theoretically, and the experimental determinations of acidity constants of both OH and COOH groups were made at different bulk concentrations of Na^+ counter-ions. The SDS micelles are taken as non-interacting. The ionic product of water and the intrinsic ionization constants of the alkyldimethylammonium substituted probes were considered to be independent on local medium electrostatic potential. As a result, the pK_a^{app} s were rationalized simply by taking into account the H^+ distribution using a Poisson – Boltzmann model [128].

Bissell et al. created earlier an even more complicated construction [222]. These authors synthesized a number of fluorescent photoinduced electron transfer sensors with targeting/anchoring modules, which they called "molecular versions of submarine periscopes" for mapping membrane-bounded protons. The pK_a^{app} values in micellar solutions of cetyltrimethylammonium chloride, SDS, and Triton X – 100 were determined as well; the complete binding is observed at proper hydrophobicity of the anchoring tail group [222].

Goldsipe and Blankschtein developed a theoretical model of pH-titration in mixed micelles of pH-sensitive and pH-insensitive surfactants, based in the pseudophase approximation and regular solution theory [249]. Their approach allows simultaneously determining the acidity constant of surfactant monomers, the *cmc* values of neutral and deprotonated surfactant, the composition of the mixed micelles, and the parameters characterizing the pairwise interactions in the mixed micelles. At the same time, the possible deviations caused by extensive concentration-dependent growth of cylindrical micelles were mentioned [249].

As an example of theoretical treatment of a biological pH-dependent system, the work of Mihajlovic and Lazaridis may be noted [387]. Basing on a thermodynamic cycle, the authors considered the binding of proteins to membranes. The components of binding free energies were obtained from molecular dynamics trajectories on an implicit membrane [387].

Morrow et al. [237] made an overview of the above theoretical approaches and used the molecular dynamics method. Before making their attack on the problem, they stated that the micellar structures are not available, and an effective relative permittivity for describing the micellar environment is not known [237]. After simulations based on generalized Born implicit-solvent and hybrid-solvent models, the authors estimated the pK_a shifts of dodecanoic acid in micelles of anionic, cationic, and non-ionic surfactants. The hybrid-solvent data gave a more realistic description of the conformational environment of the acid-base probe. These data, however, revealed that the positively charged head groups of dodecyltrimethylammonium only show a slight preference for the ionized form of the lauric acid head group [237]. Like da Silva et al. [229] (see above), the authors note that the predicted positive pK_a shift (or $\Delta pK_a^{app,c}$ in our designations) in cationic micelles that cannot be explained by chemical intuition and other theoretical models.

Meanwhile, such positive $\Delta pK_a^{app,c}$ values were reported for dodecanoic and tetradecanoic acids in micelles of cationic surfactants [230, 231]. The value $\Delta pK_a^{app,c} = 0.1$ was reported for 4-octadecyloxy-1-naphthoic acid in 0.05 M CTAB solution, whereas the values in 0.05 M SDS solution and in non-ionic micelles were 4.0 and 2.5, respectively [194, 203, 320]. The reason of such effects is the substantial increase in the pK_a^i values: sharp drop in the acidic strength on going from water to non-aqueous environment is typical for the COOH group (see sections 2.6 and 4.3). Indeed, taking some reasonable Ψ value and using eq. (14) and (15), one may obtain a high pK_a^i value for the carboxylic group in this case. In addition, the concentration of cationic surfactants in the above-mentioned papers was about 0.1 M or even higher [229-231]; the bulk ionic strength, in accord with eq. (1), might screen the interfacial charge and decrease the Ψ value to some extent.

    Therefore, the theoretical modeling [237] is quite correct for cationic surfactants as well. The majority of published $pK_a^{app,c}$ data refer to indicator dyes either of HB/B$^-$ type with phenolic groups, or of HB$^+$/B^0 type, and thus the regularity $\Delta pK_a^{app,c} < 0$ at low bulk ionic strength seems to be natural. The data for neutral carboxylic acids are very few in number, and the value $\Delta pK_a^{app,c} > 0$ seems to be out-of-order, though it is quite correct.

    In their next paper, Morrow and co-workers studied the pH-dependent self-assemble of dodecanoic acid in water [242].

3.4. Phantom Micellar Effect for pH-Indicators: Water/Air Interface as a Pseudophase

    Very recently, Tahara and associates used the SHG technique in concert with the above-mentioned procedure of modeling the polarity of micellar surface and the pK_a^{surf} value of the indicator by corresponding parameters of water–organic mixtures for solving the problem of the acidity of water/air interface [388]. They revealed that the $pK_a^{app,c}$ value of the surface-active HHC indicator spread in form of a monolayer appeared to be 3 units higher as compared with the pK_a^w value of the water-soluble hydroxycoumarin in the bulk. Analogously to their own work with an indicator located in a surfactant monolayer [374], they estimated the difference between pK_a^{surf} and $pK_a^{app,c}$ and equated it to the (pH$_{surf}$ − pH$_w$) value, thus stating that the water interface is ca. 1.7 units more acidic than the bulk water is. In fact, Tahara's group used a procedure, previously developed for micellar interfaces, to describe the water interface as a kind of a pseudophase.

    These interesting data give rise to further discussion. First, the $pK_a^{app,c}$ value was extrapolated by the authors from substantially filled HHC monolayer to an interfacial concentration of about 1 molecule per 10 nm^2 [388]. This step is reasonable taking into account the mutual influence of the neighboring ionizing groups in a dense monolayer [243]. However, the orientation of the ionizing OH group is probably gradually changing along with interfacial dilution.

    Second, the length of $C_{17}H_{35}$ chains is 2.3 nm, and in their flat orientation even at such relatively low concentration they may significantly alter the properties of the water/air interface.

    Third, within the framework of the approach used by Tahara and colleagues, such difference between $pK_a^{app,c}$ and pK_a^w inevitably means that Ψ is negative. Indeed, according to eq. (11), either at $\log {}^{\mathrm{w}}\gamma_i^{\mathrm{m}} > 0$ (Fromherz – Drummond – Grieser – Healy) or at somewhat negative $\log {}^{\mathrm{w}}\gamma_i^{\mathrm{m}}$ values in the same water – 1,4-dioxane model solvent [352], Ψ falls within the range from ≈ -120 to ≈ -60 mV. So long as, contrary to anionic micelles, there are no negatively charged groups in the interfacial layer (except the O^- groups of HHC itself), the reason of the negative electrostatic potential may be the orientation of water dipoles with the negative ends toward the air. Thus, the water/air interface may be negative and therefore somewhat acidified as compared with the bulk. For similar explanation of experimental data, but without using the ${}^{\mathrm{w}}\gamma_i^{\mathrm{m}}$ values, see ref. [368,369,382,383]

Fourthly, it should be mentioned, that Eisenthal and co-workers have found that the polarity of the water/air interface is close to that of hydrocarbons; they used the standard Reichardt's dye (see section 4.1) and estimated the value $E_{\mathrm{T}}^{\mathrm{N}}$ (water/air) = 0.01 ± 0.02 [389]. In n-hexane, $E_{\mathrm{T}}^{\mathrm{N}} = 0.009$ [49], whereas for the n-hexane/water interface, this parameter equals to 0.51–0.52 [389]. Hence, judging from the $E_{\mathrm{T}}^{\mathrm{N}}$ values, the water/air interface is absolutely apolar, contrary to the determination with hydroxycoumarin, where the relative dielectric permittivity of the interface was estimated by Tahara's group as $\varepsilon_{\mathrm{m}} = 39$ [388]. (Seemingly, such estimates strongly depend on the tool used; fluorescence studies of 6-dodecyl-2-naphthol in monolayers at the water/air interface allowed concluding that in the region of the OH group the *upper* limit of the apparent relative permittivity is 60 [390].

In the fifth place, a much simpler explanation of the enhancement of the $pK_{\mathrm{a}}^{\mathrm{app,c}}$ in comparison with $pK_{\mathrm{a}}^{\mathrm{w}}$ is the stabilization of the non-polar molecules and destabilization (poor solvation) of ions on the water surface. If the interfacial pH_{surf} is really lower than pH_{w}, then the dissociation of cationic acids of HB^+/B^0 type may be expected to be lower as well. But according to the numerous results of Eisenthal, this is not the case and the picture is reverse [375-381]. For example, for the 4-cetylanilinium cation, $pK_{\mathrm{a}}^{\mathrm{app}}$ in the monolayer is 3.5, while $pK_{\mathrm{a}}^{\mathrm{w}} = 5.3$ at bulk ionic strength of 1 M (KCl) [377]. Utilization of a hydrophobic long-tailed hemicyanine as acid-base indicator resulted in much higher pH_{surf} values as compared with the bulk pH_{w} [382] (see above).

Meanwhile, in micelles of anionic surfactants, the $pK_{\mathrm{a}}^{\mathrm{app,c}}$ values of indicator couples both of HB/B^- and HB^+/B^0 charge type as a rule increase as compared with those in non-ionic micelles, despite some specificity of medium effects. This is the notable difference between water/air interface and the surface of anionic micelles in water.

So, the conclusion about the acidity of the water/air interface made basing on application of indicator dyes depend on the charge type of the latter and may be diametrically opposite.

At this place, some remarks should be made concerning the problem of the acidity/basicity and charge of water surface. According to the predominating viewpoint, the molecules H_2O are oriented with the oxygen atom toward the air [391,392]. This may not be, however, the case if the OH group is not involved into hydrogen bonds [393]. Though the so-called χ-potential is actually a Galvani potential and cannot be determined directly, its value for water/air interface is with high probability within the range from +0.1 to +0.2 V

[391,392,394]: the positive poles of water molecules are on average directed into the bulk. It should be mentioned, however, that some experimental methods and theoretical modeling result also in negative χ values [393]. For the majority of organic solvents, the χ value is of opposite sign, sometimes up to $\chi = -0.5$ V, because the CH_3 groups are turned to the gas phase [392].

At the same time, quantum-chemical calculations, molecular dynamics modeling, and spectral data made it possible to conclude that the concentration of hydrogen cations in the water/air interface is higher than in the bulk water, contrary to that of HO^- [393,395,396]. So, for pure water the interfacial pH value is 4.8 or even lower; this finding may be of significance for the environmental chemistry, corrosion, etc. [393,395,396]. The theoretical consideration predicts the preferred adsorption of the Br^- and I^- ions on the water interface [393], in agreement with the well-known experimental data [391].

For the hydroxide ion, however, these theoretical and some spectroscopic results [395,396] disagree with the results of electrophoresis, pH determinations, and electroacoustic measurements. It was firmly stated, that the interface of air bubbles and hydrocarbon droplets in water are charged negatively; this was explained by the adsorption of HO^- ions [397,398].

Such contradiction became a subject of heated debates [398-404].

However, even if one assumes a relatively small surface excess of the ions H_3O^+ (or $H_5O_2^+$, ... $H_{13}O_6^+$) located directly in the monomolecular layer [395,396], the χ potential will be still caused mainly by the orientation of the H_2O dipoles. (Indeed, if pH_m equals even 4, and the thickness of the layer is 0.3 nm, the interfacial concentration will be as low as one hydrogen ion per 5.5×10^4 nm^2.) This, in turn, may cause the condensation of the HO^- ions, which will be collected in a high concentration along the plate formed by positive poles of H_2O, oriented toward the bulk. The hydrogen cations will be distributed within the extensive diffuse region. Such a picture is suitable to explain the negative sign of the ζ-potential.

3.5. The Partition Constants

Strictly speaking, the partition constant, P_i, defined by eq. (9), is more obvious characteristic of the distribution of species in micellar solutions, as compared with the binding constant, $K_{b,i}$, introduced via eq. (6), even if $[i_m]_t \ll (c_{surf} - cmc)$. If the volume fraction of the pseudophase is known, and the concentration activity coefficient of the i species in the aqueous phase, f_i^w, can be estimated, the $K_{b,i}$ values can be converted into P_i:

$$P_i = = = K_{b,i}\, s / f_i^w \ . \tag{17}$$

Here V_w and V_m are volumes of the bulk and micellar phases, respectively, s is the surfactant concentration in the pseudophase [15,97]. A vast number of $K_{b,i}$ and P_i values are accumulated in the literature for various substances, from noble gases to dyes and metal complexes [38,155,263,282-284,319, 405-419]. The $K_{b,i}$ values can be used as criteria of hydrophobicity of compounds; correlations are known between logarithms of water/micelle and water/octanol-1 partition coefficients [263,420,421]. As an example of solubility enhancement via solubilization, a report on micelle/water partitioning of polychlorinated biphenyls in micellar solutions may be cited [421].

In some cases, both the analysis of pK_a^{app} dependences on c_{surf} and spectral data allow to obtain directly the P_i^o and $^w\gamma_i^m$ values for ionic species. In the case of transfer from one bulk phase to another, these quantities are unavailable without extrathermodynamic assumptions. In the systems under consideration, the introduction of the pseudophase concept may be considered as such an assumption.

Now let us consider other models, besides the electrostatic approach, which are used for quantitative description of acid–base equilibria in micellar solutions of colloidal surfactants.

3.6. Using the Binding or Partition Constants for Interpretation of $\Delta pK_a^{app,c}$ Values

Though the surface of micelles formed by ionic surfactants is charged, the micellar effects can be described without using the Ψ values in an explicit form [184,193,252,422-426]. Some authors used only the equilibrium constants of partition between the aqueous and micellar phases, or of binding of the indicators or other reactants by the micelles, or of reactants' association with surfactants [252,261,262,427,428]. Here, eqs. (7), (8), and (13) may be applied.

In general case, such binding (association) constants can be re-calculated to the P_i constants (eq. 17) and thus (in the case of ionic surfactants) implicitly include the Ψ values. Similar approaches can be used for processing the micellar liquid chromatography data [28,29,32-35].

The constants of HB^z and B^{z-1} binding by micelles (or droplets of microemulsions) can be obtained using the dependences of pK_a^{app} on surfactant concentrations (or volume fraction of dispersed phase) [261-277]; see section 2.7. However, this is impossible in the case of very hydrophobic, water-insoluble indicators, which are practically completely bound by micelles, though eq. (13) is still valid. Also, if the protolytic species and surface-active ions are charged oppositely, interactions may take place well below the *cmc* value of homomicelles (see section 2.7).

3.7. Pseudophase Ion Exchange Model

Alternatively, Berezin, Bunton, Romsted, and some other authors developed another model for equilibria in solutions of ionic surfactants. This model is based on the concept of pseudophase ion exchange, or PIE [4, 51,103-106, 319,429]. Namely, it is supposed that the increase in pH_w leads to the decrease in H_m^+ concentration and to the increase in that of HO_m^- in the Stern layer, as a sequent of ion exchange. In case of pH_w decrease, the result is opposite. The aforementioned β parameter of ionic micelles ($\beta = 1 - \alpha$) is assumed to be constant; more detailed consideration and perfection of the PIE model is available in literature [5,8,317,430-440].

The principal equations of PIE model are based on a special concentration scale [4,5,13,103-106,430-440]. For each molecule or ion fixed at the micellar surface, the micellar concentration is expressed as a dimensionless quantity: $m_i^s = [i_m]_t / (c_{surf} - cmc)$. The acidity constant is also dimensionless:

$$K_A == K_a^m / s. \tag{18}$$

Here s is the surfactant concentration in the pseudophase; it varies within the range of 3–7 M as estimated for various micelles by different authors [103-105,107,200,275]. Assuming that the β value stays constant during the ion exchange $+ +$ or $+ +$ Cl_m^-, one may use these values instead of and in anionic and cationic micelles, respectively:

$$\beta = + m_{Na^+}^s, \tag{19}$$

$$\beta = + m_{Br^-}^s, \tag{20}$$

Turning to the molar concentration scale, the relations between the $pK_a^{app,c}$ and pK_a^m values can be re-written for micelles of cationic [107] and anionic surfactants, respectively, in the following manner:

$$pK_a^{app,c} = + + \log[X_w^-], \tag{21}$$

$$pK_a^{app,c} = pK_a^m + \log(\beta s / K_{H^+}^{M^+}) - \log[M_w^+]. \tag{22}$$

Here, $K_{HO^-}^{X^-}$ is a constant of HO^- ion exchange for X^- ions ($X^- = Cl^-$, Br^-, NO_3^-, etc.) in the Stern layer of cationic surfactant micelle, $K_{H^+}^{M^+}$ is the constant of H^+ (hydronium) ions exchange for M^+ ions ($M^+ = Li^+$, Na^+, $N(CH_3)_4^+$, etc.) in the Stern layer of anionic surfactant micelle, $[X_w^-]$ and $[M_w^+]$ are equilibrium ionic concentrations in the bulk phase, K_W^w and K_W^m are ionic products of water in aqueous and interfacial phases, respectively. In a vast series of publications, the PIE model is used for processing equilibrium and kinetic data.

The ion exchange constants for cetyltrimethylammonium-based pseudophase typical for all the cationic surfactant systems; they are as follows: = 10 [107]; 12 [103,104]; 15 [438]; = 4.17; = 15 [103]; = 0.50; = 0.098; $K_{Br^-}^{HPO_4^{2-}} = 0.15$ [434]. In SDS micellar solutions, the constant is around unity.

The papers, where this model was confronted with the electrostatic one [5,8,107,317], are of special interest. In particular, the unification of electrostatic and PIE models leads to the following expressions for activity coefficients of hydrated proton transfer from water to micellar pseudophase of cationic and anionic surfactants, respectively:

$$^w\gamma_{H^+}^m = \beta s K_W^w \{K_{HO^-}^{X^-}[X_w^-]K_W^m\}^{-1}\exp(-\Psi F/RT),\tag{23}$$

$$^w\gamma_{H^+}^m = K_{H^+}^{M^+}[M_w^+](\beta s)^{-1}\exp(-\Psi F/RT).\tag{24}$$

Combining the Ψ values for SDS micelles in aqueous NaCl solutions, determined by Hartland, Grieser, and White by using 4-heptadecyl-7-hydroxycoumarin [116], with the PIE parameters for (SDS + NaCl) system reported by Romsted and Zanette [105], we obtained the estimate $\log{^w\gamma_{H^+}^m} = -0.2\pm0.1$ for SDS system [120]. Besides, the value of $\log{^w\gamma_{HO^-}^m} = -\log P_{0,HO^-} = 0.76$ was reported for CTAB micelles [107]. The estimation of $\log{^w\gamma_{H^+}^m}$ values in micelles of cationic surfactants is hindered by uncertainty of the pK_W^m values. For example, Funasaki [107] used the value of 15.65, which lead to $\log{^w\gamma_{H^+}^m} = 1.0\pm0.1$. On the contrary, Romsted [103,104] and Pal and Jana [183] supposed that $K_W^m \approx K_W^w$; in this case, eq. (23) gives the value $\log{^w\gamma_{H^+}^m} \approx -0.6$.

Concluding, the PIE model is useful and has a clear physical sense. But its application requires the knowledge of a set of parameters, some of which are indefinite, especially in the case of cationic micelles.

3.8. Other Approaches

In general case, the coexistence of oppositely charged ions within the Stern layer is favorable for inter-ionic interactions. Basing upon spectral data, the association between dye ions and oppositely charged surfactant head groups is supposed by numerous researchers [193,252, 261,262,270,422,423]. In such terms the protolytic reactions of the dye species in ionic micelles can be regarded as competition with ion association, e.g., $HB_m + surf_m^+$ $(B^- surf^+)_m + H_w^+$. Then the apparent $pK_a^{app,c}$ contains an additional contribution [120], e.g.:

$$pK_a^{app,c} = pK_a^{app,c}(\text{"}true\text{"}) - \log(1 + K_{ass}[surf_m^+])\tag{25}$$

Here K_{ass} is a constant of ion association in the pseudophase. The "true" apparent $pK_a^{app,c}$ value describes the equilibria without ion association. On the other hand, there is good reason to believe that the possible association of the sulfonate or carboxylate groups of sulfonephthalein and fluorescein dyes with cationic surfactant head groups cannot be regarded as a neutralization of their negative charge [201]. In other words, even if such ion pairs exist, they can be regarded as rather solvent-separated than intimate ones. Similar conclusion may be deduced from the results of theoretical modeling of the state of dodecanoate anion in dodecyltrimethylammonium-based micelles [237].

Besides, if the dye ion is located within the Stern region, having the same charge as the head group, the ion association with the counter-ion cannot be excluded. For instance, the B^- ion can interact with the Na^+ cation in anionic micelles, while the HB^+ ion with Cl^- anions in cationic micelles. Formation of ionic triplets, e.g. $(surf^- HB^+ surf^-)_m$, $(Na^+ B^- Na^+)_m$, or $(surf^+ B^- surf^+)_m$, $(Cl^- HB^+ Cl^-)_m$, etc., also cannot be excluded.

On the whole, taking into account the peculiarities of the discussed systems, it is worthwhile just to include all these effects into $^w\gamma_i^m$.

Some authors [441,442] apply the principle of Donnan equilibrium to surfactant micelles, considering both the pseudophase (or the Stern region) and the bulk phase as two aqueous solutions. However, such an approach seems to be unobvious, taking into account the essentially non-aqueous properties of micellar interfaces, or, more precise, the absence of structurally "normal" water [443-445] even within the Stern region. In such a case, the processing of data becomes complicated.

4. THE PECULIARITIES OF ACID-BASE EQUILIBRIUM IN VARIOUS SURFACTANT MICELLAR SYSTEMS

4.1. Polarity of Micelles as Estimated via the Standard Reichardt's Solvatochromic Dye

Solvatochromic parameters, such as $E_T(30)$, E_T^N, π^*, etc., are useful for characterization of the polarity of micellar interfaces [49].

The values of relative dielectric permittivity of micellar interfaces, ε_m, as estimated using versatile experimental approaches, are markedly higher than those of low polarity solvents. Comparison of absorption spectra of different probes, from alkylpyridinium iodide to metal ion complexes, in micelles and in water-organic mixtures [154-158,281,328], leads to strong scatter of ε_m values [51, 97].

On the average, the ε_m values of interfaces of micelles of cationic tetraalkylammonium surfactants are within the range of 30 to 40, while those of anionic sulfate or sulfonate surfactants are somewhat higher. In the case of phospholipid bilayers organized in vesicles and biomembranes, the situation becomes even more complicated. This can reflect both the multiplicity of location sites of probes within the pseudophase, from hydrophobic interior to hydrophilic exterior regions, and selective solvation of the probes.

Among the family of pyridinium N-phenolate zwitterionic indicators, there are several compounds that exhibit the largest range of solvatochromism among up-to-now known organic dyes [49]. In order to compare the polarity of different micelles, we used the standard Reichardt's dye, 2,6-diphenyl-4-(2,4,6-triphenylpyridinium-1) phenolate:

The normalized polarity parameter, E_T^N, can be calculated from the absorption maximum value of the intramolecular charge transfer band, λ_{max} /nm, using the formula $E_T^N = [(28591/\lambda_{max}) - 30.7]/32.4$, where λ_{max} /nm is the absorption maximum of the charge transfer band of the dye. For water and tetramethylsilane, $E_T^N \equiv 1.00$ and 0.00, respectively.

The betaine dyes, and first of all the above standard one, are very useful probes for studying micelles and related associates [15,49,97,112,120,155-157,328,446-448]. Maitra et al. investigated quantitatively the solubility of the Reichardt's dye and other solvatochromic probes in micellar media [449], whereas Novaki and El Seoud considered the possible positions of various zwitterionic dyes in the interfacial region of cationic micelles [450,451]. Drummond, Grieser, and Healy proposed to use this dye as a single solvatochromic and acid-base probe for micelles [328]: the colored zwitterion becomes colorless after protonation of the phenolate group ($B^\pm + H^+$ HB^+).

Summarizing up our experimental data [97,112,120,331], the following conclusions can be made. The E_T^N value in SDS is 0.828, and in 16 micellar systems of various anionic surfactants, including microemulsions and SDS micelles with hydrophobic counter-ions, $0.779 \leq E_T^N \leq 0.835$. For mixed SDS – non-ionic and sulfonated ethylene oxide surfactant systems, E_T^N is 0.724 to 0.749. For 7 non-ionic oxyethylated surfactant systems and microemulsions, $0.645 \leq E_T^N \leq 0.702$. whereas for 9 cationic surfactant-based systems and the zwitterionic $C_{16}H_{33}N(CH_3)_2^+-CH_2-CH_2-CH_2-SO_3^-$, $0.623 \leq E_T^N \leq 0.708$. For CTAB micelles, $E_T^N = 0.687$. Hence, the locus of this solvatochromic dye is less polar in the case of cationic and non-ionic micelles and most polar in the case of anionic micelles. On the whole, the interfacial regions of micelles are strongly hydrated. So, the E_T^N values of least polar microenvironments correspond approximately to that of ethanol ($E_T^N = 0.654$), and thus markedly outnumber the values for acetonitrile, DMSO, and acetone ($E_T^N = 0.460, 0.444$, and 0.355, respectively [49]) and of 3.2 M aqueous solution of tetra-n-butylammonium bromide ($E_T^N = 0.48$ [452]).

The orientation of the Reichardt's dye in anionic and cationic micelles is likely of opposite character; at least, this was revealed using the ^{1}H NMR method for a dye without phenyls in 2,6-positions of the phenolate moiety [453,454]. The shift of tautomeric equilibrium of both lipoid fluorescein [205] and rose bengal B molecules [297] toward the colorless lactone is less expressed in SDS micelles than in cationic and non-ionic ones, the fluorescence lifetime of rose bengal B, depending on microviscosity, is in CTAB micelles ca.

twice that of SDS micelles [108]. Some other probes also give evidence for a more hydrated surface in the case of SDS micelles [109,155,161].

Strictly speaking, the molecular probes give information not on the "pure" homomicelle, but rather on the micellar microenvironment disturbed by the dye itself. Even more so, it refers to the large-sized dipole the Reichardt's dye: according to Fromherz, the results can be considered as investigation of physical chemistry of the chromophore rather than studying a true probe of the interface [329]. However, according to Healy [330], the Ψ values and polarity obtained with the betaine dye and with less "bulky" probes, such as coumarins, coincide for micelles of cationic surfactants. Studying nitrophenols [120,428,455] leads to similar conclusions.

The recent thermochromic and NMR study and molecular dynamic simulations of the standard Reichardt's dye and some other betaines in solutions of block-copolymers of "pluronic" type, performed by Rezende and co-workers [456,457], are of special interest. The micelle formation of these polyethyleneoxy – polypropyleneoxy copolymers is temperature-dependent, and the sensitive solvatochromic probe readily sense the appearance of colloidal particles at elevated temperatures [456]. In the next paper, the authors state that "conclusions based on the response of a single probe about the "polarity" of a micellar system are … too simplistic" [457]. They recommend using a set of analogous solvatochromic probes of variable lipophilicity. Such studies have been already performed in this Laboratory [97,331].

Our data for a block-copolymer of ethylene oxide and propylene oxide without hydrocarbon tail, $E_xP_{30}E_y$ (x + y = 27), are also indicative. In a 0.05 M aqueous solution of this sample, at I = 0.05 M (NaCl) and 25°C, the value $\Delta pK_{a,2}^{app,c}$ = 0.82 was registered for bromothymol blue, and the E_T^N = 0.85 was unusually high for non-ionic micelles. However, at 40 °C $\Delta pK_{a,2}^{app,c}$ rises up to 2.06 and E_T^N drops to 0.687, which is typical for common non-ionic surfactants [15, 458].

Also, the shift of the tautomeric equilibrium of the neutral form H$_2$B of fluorescein from the zwitterion and quinonoid tautomers toward the colorless lactone results in $\approx$ 40-fold decrease in molar absorptivity on going from water to non-ionic micelles.

But in the case of the above block-copolymer, this effect was observed only by heating [458].

Besides the polarity, another significant characteristic of micellar pseudophase is microviscosity. On the whole, it is much higher than that of surrounding aqueous phase [108]. However, the estimates made using photophysical data are rather contradictory [97].

Now let us consider the picture of acid-base equilibrium in various micellar solutions.

4.2. Non-Ionic Surfactants

Normally, the $\Delta pK_{a,1}^{app,c}$ values are positive, whereas the $\Delta pK_{a,0}^{app,c}$ ones are negative in the case of non-ionic micelles. Some typical data are presented in Table 2. In the case of non-ionic surfactants, the variations of ionic strength cause but small effects on the $pK_a^{app,c}$ s, except the case of high I values.

For pK_a in water–organic mixed solvents, the increasing and U-shaped curves are typical for the acid-base couples HB^0/B^- and HB^+/B^0, respectively [15,26,49,97,120,144, 150,151,194-197,203,209,233,335,351]. First additives of organic co-solvents result in pK_a decrease for cationic acids [15,97,120,144,151,194,196,197,335,351], but for zwitterionic acids of $HB^+/B^\pm$, the pK_a values increase as compared with pK_a^w, though as a rule not so sharp as for the HB^0/B^- type [15,328,334,459].

The influence of non-ionic micelles with polyoxyethylene hydrophilic portion resembles that of water–organic mixtures. As a rule, the strength of carboxylic functions decreases more obvious as compared with hydroxylic groups; the $\Delta pK_a^{app,c}$ values are positive for neutral and anionic acids and distinctly negative for cationic ones [112,120,150,151,183,194-197, 204,206,253,263,274,281,320,328,427,428]. The $\Delta pK_a^{app,c}$ values of 2.50 and 1.56 for 4-octadecyloxy-1-naphthoic and tetradecanoic acids, respectively, and the values from –0.89 to –2.13 for four cations, and other data given in Table 2 are rather typical.

Assuming $\Psi \approx 0$, one can conclude that in the both cases, HB^0/B^- and HB^+/B^0, the reason of such micellar effects is the better solvation of neutral species than ions within the pseudophase. Note, that this statement is self-evident, contrary to the case of water–organic mixtures, where the extrathermodynamic $^w\gamma_{H^+}^{solv}$ values for the given water–organic mixtures must be known.

In addition to the information collected in section 3.1, it should be noted that the depth of penetration of indicator species into the voluminous oxyethylene mantle (Chart 1b) is of significance [97,150,460,461]. Bulky substituents provide more "non-aqueous" microenvironment in the hydrophilic oxyethylene portion of non-ionic micelles.

Despite the similarity of non-ionic surfactants, the $pK_a^{app,c}$ values of a fixed indicator in different non-ionic systems as a rule do not coincide [15,97,120]. For example, the ionization of bromothymol blue in micellar solutions of 16 non-ionic surfactants, including block-copolymers of ethylene oxide and propylene oxide with hydrocarbon tails, was studied at $I = 0.05$ M (NaCl) and 25 °C [15,97,120]. At $c_{surf} = 0.05$ M, the $pK_{a,2}^{app,c}$ values (± 0.03) equals 9.06 (nonyl phenol 12); 9.13 (Triton X – 100); 9.19 (brij 35); 9.43 (Tween 80). For bromophenol blue, see Table 1. Such variability was also observed for different indicators by others [206].

Though these values differ markedly from that determined in water under the same conditions ($pK_{a,2}^{w*} = 7.21$), such spread of $pK_{a,2}^{app,c}$ values in different non-ionic surfactant solutions must be taken into account by using one of such micellar systems as a reference media with $\Psi = 0$. It should be noted that the commercial samples of non-ionic surfactants are as a rule mixtures of molecules with different oxyethylation degree. Finally, rise in surfactant concentration in the region $c_{surf} \gg cmc$ can also influence the $pK_a^{app,c}$ values, which reflects the structural transitions of micelles. Therefore, the data compiled in Table 2 for non-ionic micelles demonstrates only the most general features of these colloidal systems.

In oil-in-water microemulsions, based on non-ionic surfactants, the picture is similar. For example, the acid-base equilibrium of the above dye, bromothymol blue, has been studied in 17 microemulsions. The dispersions of n-hexane, n-heptane, n-octane, n-dodecane, cyclohexane, benzene, and toluene, stabilized by brij 35, Tween 80, Triton X – 100, and Triton X – 305 have been examined at volume fraction of the organic pseudophase $\varphi = 1.3$ %, $I = 0.05$ M (NaCl) and 25 °C using butanol-1, pentanol-1, and cyclohexanol as co-surfactants. The $pK_a^{app,c}$ values (± 0.01 to 0.03) varied within the range from 9.05 to 9.61 [15,97,276, 462].

Table 2. The indices of the apparent ionization constants in brij 35 micellar solution, 25°C or room temperature [a]

Indicator dye	Charge type	$pK_a^{app,c}$	$\Delta pK_a^{app,c}$
Bromophenol blue, $pK_{a,2}$	HB^-/B^{2-}	5.10	0.90
Bromothymol blue, $pK_{a,2}$	HB^-/B^{2-}	9.19	1.89
Phenol red, $pK_{a,2}$	HB^-/B^{2-}	8.73	0.73
2-Nitro-4-n-nonylphenol, $pK_{a,1}$ [b]	HB^0/B^-	8.52	1.05
4-Octadecyloxy-1-naphthoic acid, $pK_{a,1}$ [c]	HB^0/B^-	6.60	2.50
Tetradecanoic acid, $pK_{a,1}$ [d]	HB^0/B^-	6.36	1.56
Rhodamine B, $pK_{a,0}$	$HB^+/B^{\pm}$	4.08	0.86
N,N'-Di-n-octadecylrhodamine, $pK_{a,0}$	$HB^+/B^{\pm}$	4.12	0.88
Acridinium, $pK_{a,0}$ [e]	HB^+/B^0	3.69	−1.39
Neutral red cation, $pK_{a,0}$ [e]	HB^+/B^0	5.64	−0.86
Hexamethoxy red, $pK_{a,0}$	B^+/BOH^0	2.10	−1.00
Methyl yellow cation, $pK_{a,0}$	HB^+/B^0	1.12	−2.13

[a] From ref. [15,97] and papers cited therein, if not otherwise specified.
[b] From ref. [428], 30 °C.
[c] From ref. [320].
[d] From ref. [231].
[e] From ref. [196].

In micelles of n-dodecyl β-D-maltoside, n-nonyl β-D-glucopyranoside, and other sugar-derived surfactants, the $pK_a^{app,c}$ values of tetradecanoic [192] and 4-octadecyloxy-1-naphthoic acids [203] and of HHC [203,204] are 0.4 to 0.75 units lower than in micelles of an oxyethylated non-ionic surfactant $C_{12}H_{25}O(C_2H_4O)_8H$. On the other hand, the $\Delta pK_a^{app,c}$ values for cations of azine indicators are less negative in micelles of n-octyl β-D-glucoside, as compared with those in brij 35 solutions [196]. Hence, the sugar head groups are somewhat more hydrated as compared with ethylene oxide chains.

4.3. Cationic Surfactants

The $pK_a^{app,c}$ values in micelles of cationic surfactants were reported by many authors [4,6,103,104,107,112,120,149-151,153,183,191-201,203-206,208,211,229,230,252-254,261, 262, 267-270,272,320,328,332-334,342-346,422,423,426,428,455,463,464]. In a previous review, we considered the role of the hydrocarbon tail length, head group, counter-ion, etc. [97]. The strong differentiating influence of micellar pseudophase in respect to the strength of the indicator acids is practically independent of the hydrocarbon tail length, of the structure of the cationic head group, counter-ion nature (Cl⁻, Br⁻, and NO₃⁻) and, in first approximation, of the bulk ionic strength [97]. Here, we will discuss only a set of results for CTAB. In Table 3, the data are gathered at low Br⁻ concentrations. The latter are estimated by eq. (1).

The differentiating influence of cationic micelles is similar to that of mixtures of water with non-hydrogen bond donor solvents, such as acetone, CH_3CN, DMSO [15,97,120]. In particular, sulfonephthaleins (Table 3) are arranged in the same sequence according to their $\Delta pK_{a,2}^{app,c}$ values in cetylpyridinium chloride [97,464] and other cationic micelles [465] and to their ($pK_{a,2}^{solvent} - pK_{a,2}^{w}$) values in acetonitrile, water-acetone, and water-DMSO mixtures [15,120,198,199]. The similarity of cationic micellar interfaces and mixtures of water with non-hydrogen bond donor solvents follows also from the analysis of $\pi*$ values and other Kamlet – Taft parameters [155].

The $\Delta pK_a^{app,c}$ values corresponding to COOH groups are as a rule higher as compared with those of phenolic ones [151,191,198,199,201,229,230,320,428,455,465-470]. Note, that for 4-octadecyloxy-1-naphthoic and tetradecanoic acids, $\Delta pK_{a,1}^{app,c} > 0$ (Table 3). Naturally, at high bulk ionic strength the $\Delta pK_{a,1}^{app,c}$ values are larger [231].

But even at low ionic strength, for such complicated indicators as bromopyrogallole red, chromazurole, eriochrome black, gallein, and other trihydroxyfluorones, the $pK_a^{app,c}$ values corresponding to formation of polycharged anions (z = –2, –3, etc.) in cationic micelles are higher than pK_a^ws [466-469], *despite the Hartley's rules* [146,211,212]. The explanation may be as follows. On going from water to water-organic mixtures, the increase in pK_a values for anionic acids may be higher than for neutral ones, in the case of dianionic acids they are even greater, etc., in agreement with the classical Brönsted theory. By analogy, for cationic micelles the increase in pK_a^i overcomes the item $-\Psi F / 2.30RT$ in eq. (14).

The shift of the state of tautomeric equilibria of conjugated species can also contribute to the $\Delta pK_a^{app,c}$ values. For example, it takes place for hydroxyxanthenes in micellar solutions [198,199,201,470]. The $\Delta pK_{a,1}^{app,c}$ of fluorescein is higher than $\Delta pk_{a,1}^{COOH}$, because the shift of the tautomeric equilibrium of the molecule H_2B toward the lactone in CTAB micelles additionally decreases the apparent acidic strength.

The results presented in Table 3 have been determined at somewhat different Br⁻ bulk concentrations. The $pK_a^{app,c}$s may be re-calculated from one ionic strength to another using the slopes $\mathrm{d}(\mathrm{p}K_{\mathrm{a}}^{\mathrm{app,c}})/\mathrm{d}\log[\mathrm{Br}_{w}^{-}]$ (see section 5.1), which are close to the β values. Table 4 presents an example of the $\mathrm{p}K_{\mathrm{a}}^{\mathrm{app,c}}$ at constant I value [213,279,331].

Table 3. The indices of the apparent ionization constants in CTAB micellar solution, at low bulk Br⁻ concentrations; 20–25 °C

Indicator dye	Charge type	Br⁻	$pK_{\mathrm{a}}^{\mathrm{app,c}}$	$\Delta pK_{\mathrm{a}}^{\mathrm{app,c}}$
Bromophenol blue, $pK_{\mathrm{a,2}}$ [a]	HB^-/B^{2-}	0.011	2.26	−1.94
Bromocresol green, $pK_{\mathrm{a,2}}$ [a]	HB^-/B^{2-}	0.011	3.47	−1.43
Bromothymol blue, $pK_{\mathrm{a,2}}$ [a]	HB^-/B^{2-}	0.011	6.59	−0.71
Thymol blue, $pK_{\mathrm{a,2}}$ [a]	HB^-/B^{2-}	0.011	8.90	−0.30
Fluorescein, $pK_{\mathrm{a,2}}$ [b]	HB^-/B^{2-}	0.030	5.81	−0.99
HHC, $pK_{\mathrm{a,1}}$ [c]	HB^0/B^-	0.014	6.48	−1.49
2-Nitro-4-n-nonylphenol, $pK_{\mathrm{a,1}}$ [d]	HB^0/B^-	< 0.01	5.86	−1.61
Di-(4-nitrophenyl)cyanomethane, $pK_{\mathrm{a,1}}$ [e]	HB^0/B^-	< 0.01	5.75	−4.60
Fluorescein, $pK_{\mathrm{a,1}}$ [b]	H_2B^0/HB^-	0.030	4.48	+0.03
Fluorescein, $pk_{\mathrm{a,1}}^{\mathrm{COOH}}$ [b,f]	H_2B^0/HB^-	0.030	3.10	−0.39
4-Octadecyloxy-1-naphthoic acid, $pK_{\mathrm{a,1}}$ [g]	HB^0/B^-	0.014	4.20	+0.10
Tetradecanoic acid, $pK_{\mathrm{a,1}}$ [h]	HB^0/B^-	< 0.01	5.34	+0.54
N,N'-Di-n-octadecylrhodamine, $pK_{\mathrm{a,0}}$ [i]	$HB^+/B^{\pm}$	0.019	2.24	−1.00
Standard Reichardt dye, $pK_{\mathrm{a,0}}$ [j]	$HB^+/B^{\pm}$	0.014	7.22	−1.41
1-Hexadecyl-6-hydroxyquinoline, $pK_{\mathrm{a,0}}$ [k]	$HB^+/B^{\pm}$	0.014	6.32	−0.83
N-n-Dodecylanilinium, $pK_{\mathrm{a,0}}$ [l]	HB^+/B^0	< 0.01	1.65	−3.1

[a] From ref. [200].

[b] From ref. [360].

[c] From ref. [204]; the values 7.05 and 6.35 have been reported for HHC [320] and undecylhydroxycoumarin [151], respectively; the pK_{a}^{w} for water-soluble 4-methyl analogue is reported as 7.75 [151] and 7.97 [204].

[d] From ref. [428], 30 °C.

[e] From ref. [252].

[f] $k_{\mathrm{a,1}}^{\mathrm{COOH}}$ is a microscopic ionization constant of the carboxylic group singled out from the experimentally determined $K_{\mathrm{a,1}}$ value.

[g] From ref. [320].

[h] From ref. [231].

[i] From ref. [191].

[j] From ref. [328].

[k] From ref. [334].

[l] From ref. [206].

Table 4. The indices of the apparent ionization constants in the direct microemulsion benzene – 1-pentanol – CPC – water, vol. fraction of the organic phase $\varphi = 1.3\%$, $I = 0.05$ M (buffer + NaCl), 25 °C

Indicator dye	Charge type	$pK_a^{app,c}$	pK_a^w	$\Delta pK_a^{app,c}$
Bromophenol blue, $pK_{a,2}$	HB^-/B^{2-}	2.40 ± 0.05	4.20	−1.80
Bromocresol green, $pK_{a,2}$	HB^-/B^{2-}	3.23 ± 0.06	4.90	−1.67
Bromocresol purple, $pK_{a,2}$	HB^-/B^{2-}	4.89 ± 0.01	6.40	−1.51
Bromothymol blue, $pK_{a,2}$	HB^-/B^{2-}	6.67 ± 0.01	7.30	−0.63
Phenol red, $pK_{a,2}$	HB^-/B^{2-}	7.05 ± 0.03	8.00	−0.95
o-Cresol red, $pK_{a,2}$	HB^-/B^{2-}	7.84 ± 0.05	8.46	−0.62
m-Cresol purple, $pK_{a,2}$	HB^-/B^{2-}	7.89 ± 0.02	8.70	−0.81
Thymol blue, $pK_{a,2}$	HB^-/B^{2-}	8.81 ± 0.03	9.20	−0.83
Sulfonefluorescein, $pK_{a,2}$	HB^-/B^{2-}	5.65 ± 0.05	6.76	−1.11
6-Hydroxy-9-phenylfluorone, $pK_{a,1}$	HB^0/B^-	5.04 ± 0.08	6.28	−1.24
Ethylfluorescein, $pK_{a,1}$	HB^0/B^-	5.15 ± 0.18	6.31	−1.16
n-Decylfluorescein, $pK_{a,1}$	HB^0/B^-	5.28 ± 0.20	6.30[a]	−1.02
Ethyleosin, $pK_{a,1}$	HB^0/B^-	0.61 ± 0.14	1.9	−1.3
n-Decyleosin, $pK_{a,1}$	HB^0/B^-	0.70 ± 0.15	1.9[a]	−1.2
Standard Reichardt dye, $pK_{a,0}$	$HB^+/B^{\pm}$	7.8 ± 0.3 [b]	8.64[c]	−0.8
N,N'-Dioctadecylrhodamine, $pK_{a,0}$	$HB^+/B^{\pm}$	2.53 ± 0.07	3.24	−0.71
n-Decylfluorescein, $pK_{a,0}$	HB^+/B^0	0.94 ± 0.02	3.02[a]	−2.08

[a] pK_a^w of less hydrophobic water-soluble analogues.
[b] The microemulsion contains n-hexane instead of benzene.
[c] From ref. [97,328,471].

In Table 4, all the $\Delta pK_a^{app,c}$ s except the next to last, refer to the hydroxy groups. The expressed differentiating influence is evident. The last value also refers to the charge type of the acid-base couple HB^+/B^0, and the $\Delta pK_a^{app,c}$ is the most negative. The same is the case with the N-n-dodecylanilinium ion in Table 3. These results give evidence for the substantially negative value of $\log({}^w\gamma_B^m / {}^w\gamma_{HB^+}^m)$, which agrees with the decrease in the $pK_{a,0}^{solvent}$ on going from water to water-organic mixed solvents (see above).

4.4. Anionic Surfactants

Despite the well-hydrated state of SDS micellar interface (see section 4.1), the latter displays expressed differentiating influence on ionization of embedded acids. In Table 5, some data obtained at SDS concentration mainly within 0.01 to 0.05 M are collected. In addition to earlier described indicator systems, the $pK_a^{app,c}$ values of two newly reported compounds, the photoinduced electron charge transfer (CS1) and internal charge transfer (CS2) indicators [472], are given.

CS1   CS2

In the publications cited in Table 5, the precise value of ionic strength was often unavailable. However, the buffer concentrations were low, and indifferent salts were not added. As an example of stabilized ionic strength, our data for SDS-based microemulsions are presented in Table 6 [279].

The medium effects for different types of indicators are as a rule increasing in the sequence: $(HB^-/B^{2-}) > (HB^0/B^-) > (HB^+/B^0)$. This is typical for $\Delta pK_a^{solvent}$ on going from water to water-organic mixtures [49,143,194-197,209,473-475]. Despite the Hartley's rules, some $\Delta pK_{a(-1)}^{app,c}$ values are even negative: see Table 6, section 2.6, and Table 4 in ref. [97]. In other words, deprotonation of dications is revealed. This effect is hardly being explained in terms of ion pair formation, because DS^- associates with HB^{2+} cations would be more stable than those with B^+. It is more probable that the contribution of the item pK_a^i overcomes that of the quantity $-\Psi F / 2.30RT$.

4.5. Zwitterionic Surfactants

The data obtained with fifteen indicator dyes in cetyldimethylammonium propanesulfonate (CDAPS) micellar solutions allow revealing the strong differentiating influence of such kind of micelles [97]. The micellar effects vary from $\Delta pK_a^{app,c} = +1.28$ (thymol blue, HB^-/B^{2-}) to $\Delta pK_a^{app,c} = -1.45$ (methyl yellow, HB^+/B^0) [97].

In addition to the results collected in Table 4 of ref. [97], the $pK_a^{app,c}$ values of stepwise ionization of a set of fluorescein dyes were obtained in CDAPS solutions [477]. In the both cases, the sequence of indicator dyes according to their $\Delta pK_a^{app,c}$ values in CDAPS micelles is rather similar to that in cationic surfactant ones.

Table 5. The indices of the apparent ionization constants in SDS micellar solution, 25 °C or room temperature

Indicator dye	Charge type	$pK_a^{app,c}$	$\Delta pK_a^{app,c}$
HHC[a]	HB^0/B^-	11.48	3.51
2-Nitro-4-*n*-nonylphenol [b]	HB^0/B^-	10.05	2.58
4-Octadecyloxy-1-naphthoic acid[c]	HB^0/B^-	8.10	4.0
Tetradecanoic acid[d]	HB^0/B^-	8.45	3.65
Rhodamine B, $I = 0.015$ M[e]	$HB^+/B^\pm$	5.70	2.48
N,N'-Di-*n*-octadecylrhodamine, $I = 0.02$ M[f]	$HB^+/B^\pm$	5.52	2.28
Standard Reichardt dye[g]	$HB^+/B^\pm$	10.72	2.09
1-Hexadecyl-6-hydroxyquinoline[h]	$HB^+/B^\pm$	9.84	2.69
Acridinium[i]	HB^+/B^0	7.01	1.75
Neutral red cation[i]	HB^+/B^0	9.17	2.67
N-n-Dodecylanilinium [j]	HB^+/B^0	7.35	2.6
1-Methyl-2-phenylbenzimidazolium [k]	HB^+/B^0	7.8	2.4
CS1 [l,m]	$HB^+/B^{0\ m}$	10.10	1.58
CS2 [l]	HB^+/B^0	8.17	2.09
4-Hecadecyl-7-dimethylaminocoumarin cation [n]	HB^+/B^0	3.55	1.2
Hexamethoxy red, $I = 0.01$ M	B^+/BOH^0	5.89	2.79
Methyl yellow cation, $I = 0.01$ M	HB^+/B^0	5.28	2.03

[a] From ref. [204]; the $pK_a^{app,c}$ value 10.80 was reported by Lovelock et al. [320], for undecylhydroxycoumarin $pK_a^{app,c} = 11.15$ [151].

[b] From ref. [428], 30 °C.

[c] From ref. [320].

[d] From ref. [231].

[e] From ref. [476].

[f] From ref. [191].

[g] From ref. [328].

[h] From ref. [334].

[i] From ref. [196].

[j] From ref. [206].

[k] From ref. [335].

[l] From ref. [472].

[m] the isolated dimethylaminogroup is probably also protonated at the working pH; then the charge type is H_2B^{2+}/HB^+.

[n] From ref. [151].

During past five years, Nome, Bunton, and their colleagues published the results of a series of kinetic and related colloidal studies with such zwitterionic surfactants [478-483]. Some of their data concerning salt effects in such colloidal systems will be compared with ours in section 5.

Table 6. The indices of the apparent ionization constants in the direct microemulsion benzene – 1-pentanol – SDS – water, vol. fraction of the organic phase 1.3%, $I = 0.05$ M (buffer + NaCl), 25 °C

Indicator dye	Charge type	$pK_a^{app,c}$	pK_a^w	$\Delta pK_a^{app,c}$
Bromothymol blue, $pK_{a,2}$	HB^-/B^{2-}	9.24 ± 0.10	7.30	1.94
n-Decylfluorescein, $pK_{a,1}$	HB^0/B^-	8.52 ± 0.04	6.30 [a]	2.22
n-Decyeosin, $pK_{a,1}$	HB^0/B^-	4.05 ± 0.07	1.9 [a]	2.15
Standard Reichardt dye, $pK_{a,0}$	$HB^+/B^{\pm}$	10.35 ± 0.11	8.64	1.71
N,N$'$-Di-n-octadecylrhodamine, $pK_{a,0}$	$HB^+/B^{\pm}$	5.00 ± 0.02	3.24	1.76
Neutral red, $pK_{a,0}$	HB^+/B^0	8.90 ± 0.03	6.5	2.4
Methyl yellow, $pK_{a,0}$	HB^+/B^0	4.36 ± 0.10	3.25	1.11
Hexamethoxy red, $pK_{a,0}$	B^+/BOH^0	4.89 ± 0.10	3.1	1.8
n-Decylfluorescein, $pK_{a,0}$	HB^+/B^0	4.69 ± 0.11	3.02 [a]	1.67
Quinaldine red, $pK_{a,(-1)}$	HB^{2+}/B^+	3.02 ± 0.09	2.63	0.39
Pinacyanol, $pK_{a,(-1)}$	HB^{2+}/B^+	3.33 ± 0.03	4.00	−0.67

[a] As pK_a^w, the value for water-soluble ethyl analogue is used.

4.6. Additional Features of Differentiating Influence of the Pseudophase

The above analysis of $pK_a^{app,c}$ data reveals strong differentiating influence of micellar media. The most ample evidence is essential non-uniformity of the $\Delta pK_a^{app,c}$ values of different indicator dyes in the same media. However, there is a second sign of differentiating influence: the essential inconstancy of variations in $pK_a^{app,c}$ on going from one lyophilic nano-sized dispersion to another. Some representative data are given in Table 7.

Such disparity of $pK_a^{app,c}$ changes is also observed on going from SDS micelles to phospholipid liposomes, the $pK_{a,1}^{app,c}$ value of n-decylfluorescein decreases by 0.54 units, while the $pK_{a,0}^{app,c}$ value of hexamethoxy red by 3.14, and so on [97, 278].

According to the HMFF equation, such effects may be ascribed to the specificity of solvation of dye species in the two pseudophases, m' and m", i.e., to the difference of the $^{m'}\gamma_B^{m''}/^{m'}\gamma_{HB}^{m''}$ values or to the difference between the local electrostatic potentials. The peculiarities of the location of dye probes may contribute the both factors. In particular, in such a case the Ψ value in eq. (14) may not be the true potential of the Stern layer.

As the evaluation of the latter via eq. (15) is connected with using of $pK_a^{app,c}$ differences, one must be sure that the choice of the indicator is correct.

In any case, the differentiating influence of the micellar pseudophase is the main obstacle to exact evaluations of the Ψ values of ionic micelles by means of acid-base indicators [97].

Table 7. The differences between the $pK_{a,2}^{app,c}$ values on going from one micellar system to another

Indicator dye	CPC $\to$ SDS $I = 0.05$ M	Brij 35 $\to$ SDS $I = 0.01$ M
Bromothymol blue, $pK_{a,2}^{app,c}$	4.05	—
n-Decyleosin, $pK_{a,1}^{app,c}$	4.53	—
n-Decylfluorescein, $pK_{a,1}^{app,c}$	4.04	—
Reichardt's dye, $pK_{a,0}^{app,c}$	3.46	—
N,N'-Di-n-octadecylrhodamine, $pK_{a,0}^{app,c}$	2.73	—
n-Decylfluorescein, $pK_{a,0}^{app,c}$	4.38	—
Rhodamine B, $pK_{a,0}^{app,c}$	—	1.62
Hexamethoxy red, $pK_{a,0}^{app,c}$	—	3.79
Methyl yellow, $pK_{a,0}^{app,c}$	—	4.16

5. MODIFICATION OF THE PROPERTIES OF THE MICELLAR PSEUDOPHASE

5.1. Salt Effects: Screening of the Interfacial Micellar Charge and Ion Exchange

Addition of indifferent salts such as NaCl (supporting electrolytes, following the biophysical terminology) displays but small influence on the $pK_a^{app,c}$ values in non-ionic surfactant solutions, whereas in the case of cationic and anionic surfactants this normally leads respectively to the increase and decrease in $pK_a^{app,c}$ of acids located in the pseudophase.

In the terms of electrostatic theory, the salt effects can be explained by surface charge screening and thus by decrease in $|\Psi|$ (eq. 14). The dependences of $pK_a^{app,c}$ vs. logarithm of counter-ion activity or concentration can be successfully fitted by eq. (26) and (27) for cationic and anionic micelles, respectively [97]:

$$pK_a^{app,c} = + = + b' \log a_{X_w^-} , \qquad (26)$$

$$pK_a^{app,c} = - = - . \qquad (27)$$

As a rule, the plots are linear (with $r \approx 0.99$) up to salt concentrations of several moles per dm^3. Such dependences can be considered as *general,* or *normal salt effects.* The values b and b' are close to the parameter β (see sections 1 and 3.7).

Utilization of ionic activities is sometimes hindered by the lack of information on activity coefficients. The (micelle + indicator) complex can be considered as a nanodevice with response to counter-ion bulk concentration [484].

It should be noted, however, that the slopes of the above equations in a fixed colloidal system are somewhat different as obtained with different indicators. For example, in CTAB + KBr system, utilization of a set of sulfonephthalein dyes at $0.005 \leq [Br_w^-] \leq 1.0$ M and 20 °C resulted in b values from 0.77 to 0.88 and b' values from 0.83 to 0.96 [200]. Some data for anionic surfactant micelles are exemplified in Table 8.

The β value of SDS micelles as determined with DS$^-$-selective electrode by Loginova et al. [119,485] is equal to 0.74 ± 0.04. Some examples of detailed consideration of ionic equilibria in micellar solutions are available in literature [122,486-495]. In these publications, the approaches to β estimation are refined, as well as methods of calculation of true ionic strength of the bulk, etc.

The items B in eq. (26) and (27) also depend on counter-ions nature. Strictly speaking, such a specificity likely caused by different pK_a^i values already reflects the peculiarities of counter-ions. But until the counter-ions are similar and the differences are moderate, for example, on going from Br$^-$ to Cl$^-$ in CTA$^+$-based systems [200], the salt effects can be still regarded as normal ones.

Table 8. The slope of the $pK_a^{app,c}$ vs. $\log[Na_w^+]$ in SDS micelles[a]

Indicator dye	b
n-Decyleosin, HB^0/B$^-$	0.73 ± 0.04
HHC [b]	0.77 ± 0.05
Rhodamine B, HB$^+$/B$^\pm$	0.83 ± 0.09
N,N'-Di-*n*-octadecyl rhodamine, HB$^+$/B$^\pm$	0.89 ± 0.05
Hexamethoxy red, B$^+$/BOH^0	0.84 ± 0.04
Methyl yellow, HB$^+$/B^0	0.91 ± 0.03
Quinaldine red, HB^{2+}/B$^+$	0.92 ± 0.07

[a] At $[Na_w^+]$ up to 0.4–1.0 M; 25 °C [112,119,191,202,476].

[b] The data published by Hartland et al. [116] are used in calculations.

If the difference between the $pK_a^{app,c}$ and pK_a^w values is ascribed to association of ionic dye species with oppositely charged surfactant head groups, the salt effects can be considered in terms of decomposition of such associates by electrolytes added [193,261,262,423, 496]. Finally, the PIE model describes the salt effects by eqs. (21) and (22).

5.2. Mixed Supporting Electrolytes

In practice, salt backgrounds are often of mixed character. Within the framework of PIE model, the inequality of effects displayed by different counter-ions, including organic ones, are described by the $K_{HO^-}^{X^-}$ and $K_{H^+}^{M^+}$ values in cationic and anionic micelles, respectively. The differences of β values for different counter-ions can be also taken into account in a refined model [8,317].

Gaboriaud and co-workers proposed a combination of electrostatic and ion-exchange models [100-102,190]. Using the dependence of *cmc* on the concentration and nature of counter-ions, they obtained the following expression for the $pK_a^{app,c}$ value of an indicator in micelles of anionic surfactants in the presence of a mixture of counter-ions $M_{i,w}^{z+}$:

$$pK_a^{app,c} = const - \log \sum_i S_i [M_{i,w}^{z+}]^{b_i} . \tag{28}$$

Here S_i are selectivity parameters. For the standard counter-ion, S_i is equated to unity: $S_{Na^+} \equiv 1$. The S_i values are close to ion exchange constants [200], while b_i parameters to the β values used in PIE model. For mixed salt background in micellar solutions of cationic surfactants, analogous equation can be used [200]:

$$pK_a^{app,c} = B + \log \sum_i S_i [X_{i,w}^{z-}]^{b_i} = B' + \log \sum_i S_i (a_{i,w}^{z-})^{b_i} . \tag{29}$$

The S_i and b_i values for the CTAB-based system were published earlier [97]. Thus-estimated parameters allow fitting the variation in $pK_a^{app,c}$ values in mixed salt backgrounds. The deviations of calculated $pK_a^{app,c}$ s from experimental ones do not exceed 0.2 units. Note, that the b_i values for double-charged counter-ions are ca. two times lower as compared with those of single-charged ones.

5.3. Special (or Specific) Salt Effects: Counter-Ions Cause Micellar Transitions

Very often, the influence caused by organic counter-ions is much larger than that of inorganic ones. This phenomenon was called as *special* (or *specific*) *salt effect* [97]. For instance, the $pK_{a,0}^{app,c}$ value of methyl yellow in 0.02 M SDS solutions equals 4.81 in diluted acetate buffers at $[Na_w^+] = 0.05$ M. However, in the presence of 0.05 M $N(n\text{-}C_4H_9)_4^+$ in diluted HCl solutions $pK_{a,0}^{app,c} = 1.61$. For bromophenol blue in CTAB micellar solutions, at

$[Cl_w^-] = 0.1$ M, the $pK_{a,2}^{app,c}$ value is 2.68, whereas at the same concentration of tosylate instead of chloride, $pK_{a,2}^{app,c} = 4.33$.

Equations presented in previous sections are derived with understanding that the parameters β, b, b', S_i, B, pK_a^i, and pK_a^m stay unchanged in the given (indicator + micelle + salt) system. However, the rearrangement of micelles, dehydration of their surface, and decrease in α values along with increase in surfactant and salt concentrations is well documented. Under such conditions, not only surface charge screening, but also pK_a^i alteration can be expected [201]. The CTAB micelles in the presence of NaBr and SDS micelles on NaCl addition can lengthen up to ca. 50 and 70 nm, respectively [497]. However, effects of variation of Cl^-, Br^-, and NO_3^- concentrations in CTA^+-based systems and that of Na^+ in SDS solutions were satisfactorily explained using the PIE model [4,103-107]. The $K_{Br^-}^{X^-}$ and S_i values for several inorganic anions in micellar solutions of CTAB and other cationic surfactants are available in literature.

One can expect that organic counter-ions display principal changes in micellar structure. For example, it is proved using ESR and NMR spectroscopy, SANS, cryo-TEM, and rheological methods, that the entry of aromatic and some other anions into cationic micelles [321,322,463,497-507] and involving ammonium and alkylammonium cations in DS^--based micelles [202,508-519] results in serious transformation of micellar structure and micelle/water interface. Jansson and Stilbs demonstrated using the ^1H NMR self-diffusion measurements that the degree of counter-ion binding in decylammonium alkylcarboxylaytes depends on the hydrophobicity of the last-named anions [520].

The rearrangement of the Stern layer may lead to reduction of surface charge density and thus to $|\Psi|$ decrease. Degeneration of the pseudophase can readily reflect itself in the intrinsic acidity of acid-base indicators (pK_a^i values). In our pervious review, these effects have been illustrated and discussed in detail [97].

For inorganic anions in cationic surfactant micelles, the above lyotropic series are in line with the corresponding *cmc* values [6,521,522]. This is natural, because eq. (26)-(29) are derived from equations describing dependences of *cmc* values on counter-ions' nature.

For organic anions, however, the S_i values obtained using acid-base indicators are much higher than those calculated using the *cmc* data. For example, the S_i values for n-$C_6H_{13}SO_3^-$, $C_7H_7SO_3^-$, and hydrosalicylate in CTA^+-based micelles are 14 ± 2, 23 ± 5, and ≈ 60, respectively [15,463,523], whereas the *cmc* values of a set of several cetyltrimethylammonium benzoates are only 5 times lower as compared with that of CTAB [463]. The same is true for the ion-exchange constants obtained without using acid-base indicators [524].

Application of the Gaboriaud equation to the $pK_a^{app,c}$ values of methyl yellow (HB^+/B^0) and hexamethoxy red (B^+/BOH^0) in DS^--based systems resulted in following S_i values against Na^+ as a reference cation [202]:

Cation	$N(CH_3)_4^+$	$N(C_2H_5)_3H^+$	$N(C_2H_5)_4^+$	$N(n\text{-}C_4H_9)_4^+$
S_i	5 ± 1	15 ± 2	22 ± 3	125 ± 5

Again, the estimates of ion exchange constants as obtained by processing *cmc* data [508-511] are sometimes lower by an order of magnitude. This gives evidence for changes of the pK_a^i values of indicators along with micellar transitions. The value $S_i = 110$ for tetraethylammonium reported by Gaboriaud et al. [100-102,190] is much higher than our value and that obtained by fluorescence technique [515], $S_i = 6$–6.5. In turn, the last-named procedure [515] leads to an unlikely high value of 180 for triethylammonium [515].

Interestingly, the aforementioned effect of deprotonation of indicator dications in SDS micelles (section 4.4) is less expressed in tetraalkylammonium-modified DS^- aggregates [15]. Moreover, the $pK_a^{app,c}$s of some dyes, e.g., rhodamines ($HB^+/B\pm$), are not so strong affected by such kind of counter-ions [476].

The high affinity of organic cations to the adsorbent phase is also typical for ion-exchange resins [473,525-531]. In the last-named systems, the equilibrium constants of replacing inorganic ions by organic ones often depend on the ionic concentrations.

Indeed, our data demonstrate that the S_i values of counter-ions often essentially depend on the concentration range used in calculations. For example, the S_{M^+} value of tetra-*n*-propylammonium, obtained in 0.001 M SDS solutions at $[Na_w^+] = 0.031$ M, using the $pK_a^{app,c}$ value of hexamethoxy red, decreases from 66 to 36 on going from $[M_w^+] = 0.019$ M to $[M_w^+] = 0.199$ M, etc. This appeared to be a general trend: increase in working concentration of organic counter-ion results in decrease in the S_i estimate.

The $pK_{a,0}^{app,c}$ values of hexamethoxy red ($B^+ \rightleftharpoons BOH + H^+$) in 0.01 M SDS solution, determined with uncertainty of $\pm (0.01$–0.03), are given in Table 9. The data have been either presented in ref. [532] or obtained in some earlier experiments. They reflect the extreme influence first of all of small additives of organic counter-ions.

The $pK_{a,0}^{app,c}$ value, as obtained in acetate buffers at $[Na_w^+] = 0.016$ M, equals 5.93, while adding of only 0.003 M of C_6H_5–CH_2–$N(C_2H_5)_3^+$, n-C_4H_9–$NC_5H_5^+$, or n-C_nH_{2n+1}–$N(C_2H_5)_3^+$, n = 5, 6, 9, 10, and 11, decreases $pK_{a,0}^{app,c}$ up to 5.24–5.02 [532]. The $\delta\Delta pK_{a,0}^{app,c}$ in Table 9 values reflect the deviations from the above $pK_{a,0}^{app,c} = 5.93$ value.

Introduction of small concentrations of $C_nH_{2n+1}SO_3^-$ ions, n = 5, 6, 7, 8, and 10, to the CTAB micellar solutions displays marked effects on the $pK_{a,2}^{app,c}$ values of bromophenol blue with various alkyl sulfonate additives at 25 °C. The $pK_{a,2}^{app,c}$ (± 0.02) values were determined in 0.01 M CTAB solution at HBr concentrations of 4×10^{-4}, 6.3×10^{-3}, and 0.01 M. Without the alkylsulfonate counter-ions, $pK_{a,2}^{app,c} = 2.11$, 2.21, and 2.32 at the chosen HBr concentrations. At 0.001 M of $C_nH_{2n+1}SO_3^-$, the increase in $pK_{a,2}^{app,c}$ is 0.11 to 0.13, practically irrespective of HBr concentration and the tail length of the alkylsulfonate. The same is true for 0.003 M $C_nH_{2n+1}SO_3^-$, but here $pK_{a,2}^{app,c}$ increases by 0.24 to 0.28 units.

If one supposes that the penetration of bulky counter-ions into the Stern layer decreases the interfacial electrical charge and in some extreme cases even neutralizes the surface charge, then the decrease in $pK_a^{app,c}$ in anionic micelles and increase in cationic ones becomes clear. For an indicator with the charge type BH^-/B^{2-} of the acid-base couple, the $pK_{a,2}^i$ value is expected to additionally increase as a result of hydrophobization of the Stern layer. It should also be taken into account that according to quantum-chemical calculations, the negative charge in alkylsulfonates is distributed between the sulfonate group and the first methylene group [99]. For hexamethoxy red, the indicator with the charge type B^+/BOH of the acid-base couple, the $pK_{a,0}^i$ value may also be influenced by the introduction of bulky alkylammonium counter-ions.

The enlarging of the head group of the cationic surfactants also leads to the $pK_{a,2}^{app,c}$ increase of bromophenol blue. The surfactants with different cationic head groups can be arranged in a sequence according to the $pK_{a,2}^{app,c}$ values at fixed bulk ionic strength: $-NH_3^+ <$ $-NC_5H_5^+ < -N(CH_3)_3^+ \approx -N(C_2H_5)_3^+$. At bulk Cl^- concentration of 0.1 M, the $pK_{a,2}^{app,c}$ value changes from 1.8 to 2.68 on going from ammonium to trimethylammonium head group.

Judging by the data published by Warr and his colleagues [207], the $pK_{a,1}^{app,c}$ of HHC in cetyl- or tetradecyl-alkylammonium surfactants increases by 0.83 units on going from tetramethylammonium to tetrabutylammonium head group. This was explained by the decrease in surface charge density and hence in Ψ [207].

The excess adsorption of organic counter-ions in the Stern region is also probable; the possibility of re-charging of cationic micelles is open to question [208,501]. Decrease in $|\Psi|$ value due to both decrease in surface charge density and excess adsorption leads to $pK_a^{app,c}$ increase in micelles of cationic surfactants, while in DS^--based micelles the effect is opposite.

Concluding, one can stress that the S_i and b values as obtained with indicators can be somewhat noisy in case of hydrophobic counter-ions.

Transformation of cationic surfactant micelles into rod-like, worm-like ones, etc., under addition of hydrosalicylate, tosylate, and other organic anions is proved by examining the viscosity and using electron microscopy and other methods [208,321,322,497,499-507,533-536]. In (CTAB + hydrosalicylate) system, the micelles can lengthen up to 137 nm [497].

Introduction of tosylate, hydrosalicylate, benzoate, and some other organic anions leads to micellar transitions of cationic surfactants; the micelles become anisometric, sometimes even "worm-like". For Reichardt's dyes, these results in changes of $pK_{a,0}^{app,c}$ and in expressed spectral effects [463,498]. In the case of counter-ions with long hydrocarbon tail, e.g., n-$C_7H_{15}SO_3^-$, n-$C_8H_{17}SO_3^-$, n-$C_{10}H_{21}SO_3^-$, and especially of "pseudospherical" hydrophobic anions $B(C_6H_5)_4^-$ and ClO_4^-, micellar solutions of cationic surfactants transform into lyophobic unstable suspensions [15]. (Recently, the thermodynamics of $CTA^+ClO_4^-$ and $CP^+ClO_4^-$ solubility in water and organic solvents was studied in full [537].) In SDS solutions, the cation $N(n$-$C_7H_{15})_4^+$ displays similar precipitating influence.

Table 9. The $pK_{a,0}^{app,c}$ values of hexamethoxy red in various micellar systems at 25 °C [a,b]

Cation added to the SDS + buffer system	Ct^+, M	$pK_{a,0}^{app,c}$	$-\delta\Delta pK_{a,0}^{app,c}$
— [c]	0	5.93±0.01	0
Na^+ [d]	0.130	5.09	0.84
Na^+ [d]	0.200	4.98	0.95
$N(n\text{-}C_4H_9)_4^+$	0.001	5.83±0.01	0.10
$N(n-C_5H_{11})_4^+$	0.001	5.80	0.13
$n-C_{11}H_{23}N(C_2H_5)_3^+$	0.001	5.52±0.05	0.41
$N(C_2H_5)_4^+$	0.003	5.66±0.03	0.27
$N(n-C_3H_7)_4^+$	0.003	5.09±0.06	0.84
$N(n\text{-}C_4H_9)_4^+$	0.003	5.54±0.09	0.39
$C_6H_5-CH_2-N(C_2H_5)_3^+$	0.003	5.24±0.01	0.69
$n-C_4H_9-NC_5H_5^+$	0.003	5.38±0.01	0.55
$n-C_5H_{11}N(C_2H_5)_3^+$	0.003	5.21±0.05	0.72
$n-C_6H_{13}N(C_2H_5)_3^+$	0.003	5.02±0.01	0.91
$n-C_9H_{19}N(C_2H_5)_3^+$	0.003	5.05±0.02	0.88
$n-C_{10}H_{21}N(C_2H_5)_3^+$	0.003	5.08±0.04	0.85
$n-C_{11}H_{23}N(C_2H_5)_3^+$	0.003	5.09±0.01	0.84
1-(4-Amino-4-oxo-3,3-diphenylbutyl)-1-methylpiperidinium	0.003	4.99±0.03	0.94
(5α, 6α)-7,8-Didehydro-4,5-epoxy-17-methylmorphinan-3,6-diol [e]	0.003	5.40±0.10	0.53
(5α, 6α)-7,8-Didehydro-4,5-epoxy-3-methoxy-17-methylmorphinan-6-ol [e]	0.003	5.26±0.02	0.67
$N(C_2H_5)_4^+$ [f]	0.020	3.77±0.02	2.16
$n-C_5H_{11}N(C_2H_5)_3^+$ [f]	0.020	3.72±0.01	2.21
$N(n-C_3H_7)_4^+$ [f]	0.020	3.73±0.04	2.20
$N(n\text{-}C_4H_9)_4^+$ [f]	0.020	3.6±0.1	2.33
$N(n-C_3H_7)_4^+$ [f]	0.200	3.27±0.02	2.66

[a] 0.01 M SDS + Ct^+; acetate buffer solutions with $I = 0.01$ M.

[b] On adding of 0.001 M $N(n-C_7H_{15})_4^+$ and $n-C_{16}H_{33}N(CH_3)_3^+$ or 0.003 M $N(n-C_5H_{11})_4^+$ to the 0.01 M SDS solutions, turbidity was observed by naked eye.

[c] The buffer solution contains 0.01 M Na^+, and the total $[Na_w^+]$ value is 0.016 M.

[d] 0.02 M SDS.

[e] In protonated form.

[f] 0.001 M SDS, the total $[Na_w^+]$ value is 0.03 M.

In the case of the zwitterionic surfactant CDAPS, only hydrophobic anions, not cations, display marked effects on the $pK_a^{app,c}$s of acid-base indicators [120,532]. It is reasonable to expect the adsorption of such anions in the region of quaternary nitrogen atom. Nome, Bunton, et al. proved the adsorption of hydrophobic anions at the interface of zwitter-ionic micelles using, in particular, electrokinetic data [538-540]; see also ref. [478-483].

The $pK_a^{app,c}$ values of two indicator dyes, bromothymol blue (HB^-/B^{2-}) and neutral red (HB^+/B^0), determined in this Laboratory [15,97,120,532] are collected in Table 10 and 11 together with the wavelengths of absorption maxima of dye species.

Whereas the effects caused by NaCl addition are somewhat uncertain, the increase in $pK_a^{app,c}$ of the acid-base probes of both charge types on introducing of relatively hydrophobic anions manifests itself distinctly. According to their influence on the $pK_{a,2}^{app,c}$ value of bromothymol blue, the anions may be ranged in the following row:

$$Br^- < SCN^- < I^- < BF_4^- < Tos^- < HSal^- < ClO_4^-.$$

Another notable feature: the variation of ClO_4^- concentration from 2.5×10^{-3} to 0.1 M does not influence on the $pK_{a,2}^{app,c}$ value of bromothymol blue in CDAPS micelles.

Table 10. The $pK_{a,2}^{app,c}$ values and λ_{max} of bromothymol blue in CDAPS micelles, 25°C

CDAPS, $c \times 10^4$/M	Added salt (conc./M)	$pK_{a,2}^{app,c}$	λ_{max} (B^{2-})/ nm
$0, I \to 0$	–	7.30 [a]	617
4.0	–	8.16±0.01	625
15.0	NaCl (0.05)	8.22±0.02	624
4.0	NaCl (0.2)	8.15±0.05	624
4.0	NaCl (0.5)	8.05±0.01	625
15.0	Na_2SO_4 (0.2)	8.24±0.03	626
15.0	KBr (0.2)	8.54±0.02	626
4.0	NaSCN (0.01)	8.40±0.01	624
4.0	KI (0.01)	8.58±0.01	625
4.0	$NaBF_4$ (0.01)	8.66±0.01	624
4.0	$NaClO_4$ (0.01)	8.88±0.05	621
15.0	Potassium benzoate (0.01)	8.40±0.02	626
4.0	Sodium tosylate (0.01)	8.74±0.01	619
15.0	Sodium hydrosalicylate (0.01)	8.78±0.06	626.5

[a] $pK_{a,2}^w$.

In the case of another dye, neutral red, with charge type HB^+/B^0 also the modification of CDAPS micelles by various anions results in the increase of the $pK_{a,0}^{app,c}$ values and this influence on $pK_{a,0}^{app,c}$ is following:

$$SO_4^{2-} < Br^- < SCN^- < HSal^- < ClO_4^-.$$

Hence, the data for both cationic and anionic dyes demonstrate that modification of CDAPS micelles by relatively hydrophobic anions makes the properties of these micelles similar to those of anionic surfactants.

Table 11. The $pK_{a,0}^{app,c}$ values and λ_{max} values of neutral red in CDAPS micelles, 1.5×10^{-3} M, 25°C

Added salt (conc./M)	$pK_{a,0}^{app,c}$	λ_{max}/nm	
		B	HB$^+$
$0, I \to 0$	6.5 [a]	453	534
NaCl (0.05)	5.82±0.01	457	537
Na$_2$SO$_4$ (0.2)	5.99±0.12	458	529
KBr (0.2)	6.08±0.02	459	540
NaSCN (0.01)	6.19±0.26	460	540
NaClO$_4$ (0.01)	6.72±0.09	460	540
Potassium benzoate (0.01)	5.72±0.22	458	539
Sodium hydrosalicylate (0.01)	6.24±0.18	459	539

[a] $pK_{a,0}^w$.

5.4. Non-Ionic Additives

First, let us consider non-colloidal additives. Mostly used non-ionic additives, which modify the structure of ionic micelles, are 1-butanol, 1-pentanol, and some other substances, which are limitedly soluble in water. They are located in the Stern region [116,343,541-543], and this results in α increase [544,545]. Crown ethers and cryptands can be used for peculiar modification of anionic micelles and vesicles [119,476,546-549], because they are able to form complexes with Li$^+$, Na$^+$, and other cations. The counter-ions thus enlarged become more hydrophobic.

In the case of cationic and anionic micelles, the addition of non-ionic species leads to increase and decrease in $pK_a^{app,c}$, respectively [15,112,119,470]. These effects are evidently caused by drop in interfacial charge density and thus in $|\Psi|$ of micelles. However, such "dilution" of the surface charge can be (partly) compensated by the increase in the α values. Alterations of the pK_a^i values are also probable.

In the case of colloidal non-ionic additives, i.e., non-ionic colloidal surfactants, the influence on the apparent ionization of indicators embedded in ionic micelles is more expressed. In systems containing two hydrocarbon-tailed surfactants, ionic and non-ionic ones, mixed micelles appear. The $pK_a^{app,c}$ gradually change from the value in ionic surfactant micelle to that in non-ionic one. For more detailed consideration, the reader is addressed to our previous review [97].

Salt effects in mixed (ionic + non-ionic) micelles are of special interest. The dependences (26) and (27) are still valid, but the slope b decreases as much as the fraction of non-ionic component increases [97,112]. This general regularity has been observed both for non-colloidal (1-pentanol, etc.) and colloidal additives. As an example, for methyl yellow and hexamethoxy red in micelles with SDS : brij 35 ratio 1 : 9, the b value for the $pK_{a,0}^{app,c}$ vs. NaCl concentration equals 0.38, whereas in entire SDS micelles $b = 0.84$ to 0.91 [97]. The $pK_{a,2}^{app,c}$ values of bromophenol blue in (CTAB + brij 35 + Br$^-$) system demonstrated gradual decrease in b from 0.84 in pure CTAB to 0.36 at CTAB : brij 35 ratio of 5 : 95 [97]. It seems unlikely that the effect may be attributed to substantial extent to the (possible) variations of pK_a^i values.

As the b values are close to $\beta = 1 - \alpha$, these findings confirm the increase in α values for mixed (ionic + non-ionic) surfactant micelles, earlier obtained by conductivity, electrophoresis, potentiometry, and other methods [44,89,550-558].

To the best of our knowledge, this is the sole evidence for strengthening of counter-ion dissociation from the mixed micelles obtained by acid-base probes.

CONCLUSION

The concept of apparent ionization constant allows explaining the acid-base equilibrium in micellar solutions in outline. The main reasons that cause deviations from the classical Hartley's rules are the specificity of location of the acid and its conjugated base within the pseudophase and the peculiar of solvation. The latter is substantially governed by the charge type of the acid-base couple.

The differentiating influence upon the acid-base properties of embedded compounds is a characteristic feature of the micellar pseudophase. The non-uniform change of the $pK_a^{app,c}$ values manifests itself distinctly, depending of various charge types and nature of the ionizing groups. For instance, other things being equal, the $\Delta pK_a^{app,c}$ values of COOH groups are relatively high, and those of cationic acids are low, irrespective the nature of the micelle-forming surfactant.

This property of the micellar pseudophase is the main obstacle to exact evaluations of the interfacial electrical potentials of ionic micelles by means of acid-base indicators. The miscellaneous character of the surface of ionic micelles likely causes their specific action. Indeed, the Stern region is a unique mixture of electrolyte, water, and hydrocarbon.

Recently, some advanced methods of molecular dynamics simulations have been proposed, which allow verging towards the experimentally determined $pK_a^{app,c}$ values.

Attempts to diagnose the acidity of the water/air interface via indicators are of potential interest. However, using the procedure developed for micellar pseudophase may lead to obvious contradictions.

The ion-exchange model satisfactorily describes salt effects on acid-base equilibrium in micellar solutions of ionic surfactants. This kind of effects may be called as either general or normal one. However, the micellar structure may undergo serious disturbance if the counterions are more hydrophobic as compared with Cl^-, Br^-, Na^+ and the like, or if they are of expressed diphilic nature. Such salt effects overstep the limits of the common ion-exchange model. This case is worth to consider as the special or specific salt effect.

The salt effects in the case of zwitter-ionic reveal the specific adsorption of relatively hydrophobic anions.

REFERENCES

[1] Reychler, A. *Z. Chem. Ind. Koll.*, 1913, 12, 277–283.

[2] McBain, JW. *Trans. Faraday Soc.*, 1913, 9, 99–101.

[3] Pelizzetti, E; Pramauro, E. *Anal. Chim. Acta*, 1985, 169, 1–29.

[4] Bunton, CA; Savelli, G. In: *Adv. in Phys. Org. Chem.*, 1986, 22, 213–309.

[5] Hall, DG. *J. Phys. Chem.*, 1987, 91, 4287–4297.

[6] Savvin, SB.; Chernova, RK; Shtykov, SN. *Surfactants*, Nauka: Moscow, 1991.

[7] *Organized Solutions. Surfactants in Science and Technology*, eds. S.E. Friberg, B. Lindman, Marcel Dekker, Inc.: N. Y., 1992.

[8] Minero, C; Pelizzetti, E. *Adv. Coll. Int. Sci.*, 1992, 37, 319–334.

[9] Engberts, JBFN. *Pure Appl. Chem.*, 1992, 64, 1653–1660.

[10] Ruasse, MF; Blagoeva, IB; Ciri, R; Garcia-Rio, L; Leis, JR; Marques, A; Mejuto, J; Monnier, E. *Pure Appl. Chem.*, 1997, 69, 1923–1932.

[11] Tonellato, U. *Pure Appl. Chem.*, 1998, 70, 1961–1968.

[12] Shtykov, SN. *Zh. Anal. Khim.*, 2000, 55, 679–686.

[13] Bunton, CA; Yatsimirsky, AK. *Langmuir*, 2000, 16, 5921–5931.

[14] Romsted, LS; Zhang, J; Cuccovia, IM; Politi, MJ; Chaimovich, H. *Langmuir*, 2003, 19, 9179–9190.

[15] Mchedlov-Petrossyan, NO. *Differentiation of the Strength of Organic Acids in True and Organized Solutions*, Kharkov National University Press: Kharkov, 2004.

[16] Holmberg, K. *Eur. J. Org. Chem.*, 2007, 731–742.

[17] Khan, MN. *Micellar Catalysis*. CRC Press: Boca Raton, 2007.

[18] Onel, L; Buurma, NJ. *Annu. Rep. Prog. Chem.*, Sect. B., 2009, 105, 363–379.

[19] Antonovich, VP; Novoselova, MM; Nazarenko, VA. *Zh. Anal. Khim.*, 1984, 39, 1157–1176.

[20] Chernova, RK; Shtykov, SN. *Frezenius Z. Anal. Chem.*, 1989, 335, 111–116.

[21] Pramauro, E; Bianco Prevot, A. *Pure Appl. Chem.*, 1995, 67, 551–559.

[22] Loginova, LP; Chernysheva, OS. *J. Mol. Liquids*, 2000, 85, 351–359.

[23] Shtykov, SN. *Zh. Anal. Khim.*, 2002, 57, 1018–1028.

[24] Diaz-Fernandez, Y; Perez-Gramatges, A; Rodriguez-Calvo, S; Mangano, C; Pallavicini, P. *Chem. Phys. Lett.*, 2004, 398, 245–249.

[25] Diaz-Fernandez, Y; Perez-Gramatges, A; Amendola, V; Foti, F; Mangano, C; Pallavicini, P; Patroni, S. *Chem. Comm.*, 2004, 1650–1651.

[26] Pallavicini, P; Diaz-Fernandez, YA; Foti, F; Mangano, C; Patroni, S. *Chem. Eur. J.*, 2007, 13, 178–187.

[27] Pallavicini, P; Diaz-Fernandez, YA; Pasotti, L. *Coord. Chem. Rev.*, 2009, 253, 2226–2240.

[28] Armstrong, DW; Stine, GY. *Anal. Chem.*, 1983, 55, 2317-2320.
[29] Rodgers, AH; Khaledi, MG. *Anal. Chem.*, 1994, 66, 327–334.
[30] Shtykov, SN; Sumina, EG; Smushkina, EV; Tyurina, NV. *J. Planar. Chromatogr.*, 1999, 12, 129–134.
[31] Berthod, A; Garcia-Alvarez-Coque, C. *Micellar Liquid Chromatography*. Marcel Dekker, Inc.: N.Y.–Basel, 2000.
[32] Samokhina, L; Loginova, L; Stepanko, D. *Tenside. Surfactants. Detergents*, 2006, 43, 6–11.
[33] Loginova, LP; Samokhina, LV; Boichenko, AP; Kulikov, AU. *J. Chromatogr. A*, 2006, 1104, 190–197.
[34] Boichenko, AP; Iwashchenko, AL; Loginova, LP; Kulikov, AU. *Anal. Chim. Acta.*, 2006, 576, 229–238.
[35] Boichenko, AP; Kulikov, AU; Loginova, LP; Iwashchenko, AL. *J. Chromatogr. A*, 2007, 1157, 252–259.
[36] Mukerjee, P. *Pure Appl. Chem.*, 1980, 52, 1317–1321.
[37] Treiner, C; Vaution, C; Miralles, E; Puisieux, F. *Colloids Surf.*, 1985, 14, 285–292.
[38] Valsaraj, KT; Thibodeaux, LJ. *Separation Sci. a. Technol.*, 1990, 25, 369–395.
[39] Corrigan, OI; Healy, AM. In: *Encyclopedia of Pharmaceutical Technology*, Marcel Dekker: N. Y., 2002, 2639–2653.
[40] Blatt, E. *J. Phys. Chem.*, 1986, 90, 874–877.
[41] Grand, D. *J. Phys. Chem.*, 1990, 94, 7585–7588.
[42] Goryacheva, I; Shtykov, S; Melnikov, G; Fedorenko, E. *Environ. Chem. Lett.*, 2003, no. 1, 82–85.
[43] Lisiecki, I; Billoudet, F; Pileni, MP. *J. Phys. Chem.*, 1996, 100, 4160–4166.
[44] Shinoda, K; Nakagawa, T; Tamamushi, B; Isemura, T. *Colloidal Surfactants*. Academic Press: N. Y. – London, 1963.
[45] Rusanov, AI. *Micellization in Surfactant Solutions*. Harwood Academic Publishes: Reading, 1997.
[46] Ikeda, S. *J. Phys. Chem.*, 1984, 88, 2144–2149.
[47] Warr, GG; Magid, LJ; Caponetti, E; Martin, CA. *Langmuir*, 1988, 4, 813–817.
[48] Movchan, TG; Soboleva, IV; Plotnikova, EV; Shchekin, AK; Rusanov, AI. *Colloid J.* 2012, 74, 239–247.
[49] Reichardt, C; Welton, T. *Solvents and Solvent Effects in Organic Chemistry*, 4rd updated and enlarged ed., Wiley-VCH: Weinheim, 2011.
[50] Kessler, Yu M; Zaitsev, AL. *Solvophobic Effects*, Khimiya: Leningrad, 1989.
[51] Berezin, IV; Martinek, K; Yatsimirsky, AK. *Usp. Khim. (Russ. Chem. Rev.)* 1973, 42, 1729–1756.
[52] Menger, FM. *Acc. Chem. Res.* 1979, 12, 111–117.
[53] Südholter, EJR; van de Langkruis, GB; Engberts, JBFN. *Rec. Trav. Chim. Pays-Bas.*, 1980, 99, 73–82.
[54] Fromherz, P. *Chem. Phys. Lett.*, 1981, 77, 460–465.
[55] Fromherz, P. *J. Phys. Chem.*, 1989, 93, 8383–8384.
[56] Wong, TC; Ikeda, K; Meguro, K; Söderman, O; Olsson, U; Lindman, BP. *J. Phys. Chem.*, 1989, 93, 8384–8385.
[57] Mukerjee, P; Mysels, KJ; Dulin, CJ. *J. Phys. Chem.* 1958, 62, 1390–1396.
[58] Menger, FM; Littau, CA. *J. Am. Chem. Soc.*, 1993, 115, 10083–10090.

[59] Menger, FM; Keiper, JS. *Angew. Chem. Int. Ed.*, 2000, 39, 1906–1920.
[60] Geng, Y; Romsted, LS; Menger, F. *J. Am. Chem. Soc.*, 2006, 128, 492–501.
[61] Zana, R; Xia, J. *Gemini surfactants*, Marcel Dekker, Inc.: N.Y., Basel, 2004.
[62] Luchetti, L. *Langmuir*, 2000, 16, 161–165.
[63] Bernheim-Groswasser, A; Zana, R; Talmon, Y. *J. Phys. Chem.*, 2000, 104, 4005–4009.
[64] Manet, S; Karpichev, Y; Bassani, D; Kiagus-Ahmad, R; Oda, R. *Langmuir* 2010, 26, 10645–10656.
[65] Manet, S; Karpichev, Y; Dedovets, D; Oda, R. *Langmuir* 2013, 29, 3518–3526.
[66] Zakharova, L Ya; Konovalov, AN. *Koll. Zh.* 2012, 74, 209–221.
[67] Gainanova, GA; Vagapova, GI; Syakaev, VV; Ibragimova, AR; Valeeva, FGE; Tudriy, V; Galkina, IV; Kataeva, ON; Zakharova, L Ya; Latypov, Sh K; Konovalov, AI. *J. Coll. Int. Sci.* 2012, 367, 327–336.
[68] Voronin, MA; Valeeva, FG; Zakharova, L Ya; Giniyatullin, R Kh; Semenov, VE; Reznik, VS. *Koll. Zh.*, 2010, 72, 314–322.
[69] Inoue, T; Ebina, H; Dong, B; Zheng, L. *J. Coll. Int. Sci.*, 2007, 314, 236–241.
[70] Savsunenko, O; Matondo, H; Karpichev, Y; Poinsot, V; Popov, A; Rico-Lattes, I; Lattes, A. *J. Surf. Deterg.* 2012, no.15, 345–350.
[71] Karpichev, Y; Matondo, H; Kapitanov, I; Savsunenko, O; Vendrenne, M; Poinsot, V; Rico-Lattes, I; Lattes, A. *Cent. Eur. J. Chem.*, 2012, 10, 1059–1065.
[72] Savsunenko, O; Matondo, H; Franceschi-Messant, S; Perez, E; Popov, AF; Rico-Lattes, I; Lattes, A; Karpichev, Y. *Langmuir*, 2013, 29, 3207–3213.
[73] Voronin, MA; Gabdrakhmanov, DR; Khaibullin, RN; Strobykina, I Yu; Kataev, VE; Idiyatullin, BZ; Faizullin, DA; Zuev, Yu F; Zakharova, L Ya; Konovalov, AI. *J. Coll. Int. Sci.*, 2013, 405, 125–133.
[74] Rusanov, AI. *Usp. Khim. (Russ. Chem. Rev.)*, 1989, 58, 169–196.
[75] Gilányi, T. *Colloids Surf. A*, 1995, 104, 119–126.
[76] Gilányi, T. *Colloids Surf. A*, 1995, 104, 111–118.
[77] Zana, R. *Langmuir*, 1995, 11, 2314–2315.
[78] Kallay, N; Glušac, T; Preočanin, T; Čop, A. *Colloids Surf. A*, 2009, 347, 76–80.
[79] Lebedeva, N; Zana, R; Bales, BL. *J. Phys. Chem. B*, 2006, 110, 9800–9801.
[80] Korotkikh, OP; Kochurova, NN; Hong, P -D. *Mendeleev Commun.*, 2008, 18, 347–349.
[81] Zdziennicka, A; Szymczuk, K; Krawczyk, J; Jańczuk, B. *Fluid Phase Equil.*, 2012, 322–323, 126–134.
[82] Tomašić, V; Chittofrati, A; Kallay, N. *Colloids Surf. A.*, 1995, 104, 95–99.
[83] Bogdanova, LR; Gnezdilov, OI; Idiyatullin, BZ; Kurbanov, R Kh; Zuev, Yu F; Usyarov, OG. *Koll. Zh.* 2012, 74, 3–9.
[84] Feitosa, E; Alves, FR. *Chem. Phys. Lipids*, 2008, 156, 13–16.
[85] Maiti, K; Mitra, D; Guha, S; Moulik, SP. *J. Mol. Liquids*, 2009, 146, 44–51.
[86] Hill, T. *Nano Lett.*, 2001, 1, 111–112.
[87] Rusanov, AI. *Russian Chem. J.*, 2006, 50, 145–151.
[88] Hill, TL. *Thermodynamics of Small Systems, Part 1,* W. A. Benjamin, Inc., Publishers: N. Y., Amsterdam, 1963.
[89] Hill, TL. *J. Chem. Phys.*, 1962, 15, 3182–3197.
[90] Watanabe, K; Ferrario, M; Klein, ML. *J. Phys. Chem.*, 1988, 92, 819–821.
[91] MacKerell, AD. *J. Phys. Chem.*, 1995, 99, 1846–1855.
[92] Wang, Y; Wallace, JA; Koenig, PH; Shen, JK. *J. Comput. Chem.* 2011, 32, 2348–2358.

[93]   Balasubramanian, S; Pal, S; Bagchi, B. *Current Sci.*, 2002, 82, 845–854.

[94]   Bruce, CD; Berkowitz, ML; Perera, L; Forbes, MDE. *J. Phys. Chem. B*, 2002, 106, 3788–3793.

[95]   Vries, AH; Mark, AE; Marrink, SJ. *J. Am. Chem. Soc.*, 2004, 126, 4488–4489.

[96]   Zana, R. *J. Coll. Int. Sci.*, 1980, 78, 330–337.

[97]   Mchedlov-Petrossyan, NO. *Pure Appl. Chem.*, 2008, 80, 1459–1510.

[98]   Chaimovich, H; Cuccovia, IM; Bunton, CA; Moffatt, JR. *J. Phys. Chem.*, 1983, 87, 3584–3586.

[99]   Huibers, PDT. *Langmuir*, 1999, 15, 7546–7550.

[100] Dorion F, Charbit G, Gaboriaud R. *J. Coll. Int. Sci.*, 1984, 101, 27–36.

[101] Charbit, G; Dorion, F; Gaboriaud, R. *J. Chim. Phys.*, 1984, 81, 187–196.

[102] Gaboriaud, R; Charbit, G; Dorion, F. In: *Surfactants in solution*, Vol. 2, ed. K. L. Mittal. Plenum Press, 1984, 1191–1206.

[103] Romsted, LS. *J. Phys. Chem.*, 1985, 89, 5107–5113.

[104] Romsted. LS. *J. Phys. Chem.*, 1985, 89, 5113–5118.

[105] Romsted, LS; Zanette, D. *J. Phys. Chem.*, 1988, 92, 4690–4698.

[106] He, Z-M; O'Connor, PJ; Romsted, LS; Zanette, D. *J. Phys. Chem.*, 1989, 93, 4219–4226.

[107] Funasaki, N. *J. Phys. Chem.* 1979, 83, 1998–2003.

[108] Reed, W; Politi, MJ; Fendler, JH. *J. Am. Chem. Soc.*, 1981, 103, 4591–4593.

[109] Ramachandran, C; Pyter, RA; Mukerjee, P. *J. Phys. Chem.*, 1982, 86, 3198–3205.

[110] Maiti, NC; Krishna, MMG; Britto, PJ; Periasamy, N. *J. Phys. Chem. B.*, 1997, 101, 11051–11060.

[111] Fromherz, P; Masters, B. *Biochem. Biophys. Acta.*, 1974, 356, 270–275.

[112] Mchedlov-Petrossyan, NO; Plichko, AV; Shumakher, AS. *Chem. Phys. Reports*, 1996, 15, 1661–1678.

[113] Caspers, J; Goormaghtigh, E; Ferreira, J; Brasseur, R; Vandenbranden, M; Ruysschaert J-M. *J. Coll. Int. Sci.*, 1983, 91, 546–551.

[114] Petrov, JG; Möbius, D. *Langmuir*, 1990, 6, 746–751.

[115] Noh, JS; Schwarz, JA. *J. Coll. Int. Sci.*, 1990, 139, 139–148.

[116] Hartland, GV; Grieser, F; White, LR. *J. Chem. Soc., Faraday Trans. 1*, 1987, 83, 591–613.

[117] Ohshima, H; Healy, TW; White, LR. *J. Coll. Int. Sci.*, 1982, 90, 17–26.

[118] Frahm, J; Diekmann, S; Haase, A. *Ber. Bunsenges. Phys. Chem.*, 1980, 84, 566–571.

[119] Loginova, LP; Samokhina, LV; Mchedlov-Petrossyan, NO; Alekseeva, VI; Savvina, L P. *Colloids Surf. A*, 2001, 193, 207–219.

[120] Mchedlov-Petrossyan, NO; Vodolazkaya, NA; Timiy, AV; Gluzman, EM; Alekseeva, VI; Savvina, LP. http://preprint.chemweb.com/physchem/0307002; *Chem. Abstr.*, 2003, 524451.

[121] Gunarsson, G; Jönsson, B; Wennerström, H. *J. Phys. Chem.*, 1980, 84, 3114–3121.

[122] Gilányi, T. *J. Coll. Int. Sci.*, 1988, 125, 641–648.

[123] Bulavin, LA; Garamus, VM; Karmazina, TV; Pivnenko, EN. *Colloids Surf. A*, 1998, 131, 137–144.

[124] Tanford, C. *Physical Chemistry of Macromolecules.* John Wiley and Sons, Inc.: N. Y., 1961.

[125] Guéron, M; Weisbuch, G. *J. Phys. Chem.* 1979, 83, 1991–1998.

[126] Corti, M; Degiorgio, V. *J. Phys. Chem.*, 1981, 85, 711–717.

[127] Gunaseelan, K; Ismail, K. *J. Coll. Int. Sci.*, 2003, 258, 110–115.

[128] Souza, TP; Zanette, D; Kawanami, AE; de Rezende, L; Ishiki, HM; do Amaral, AT; Chaimovich, H; Agostinho-Neto, A; Cuccovia, IM. *J. Coll. Int. Sci.*, 2006, 297, 292–302.

[129] Israelachvili, JN. *Intermolecular and Surface Forces*; Academic Press Ltd.: London, 1992.

[130] Moroi, Y. *Micelles. Theoretical and Applied Aspects*, Plenum Press: N. Y., 1992.

[131] Holmberg, K; Jonsson, B; Kronberg, B; Lindman, B. *Surfactants and Polymers in Aqueous Solution*, Second ed., Willey and Sons, Ltd., 2007.

[132] Rosen, MJ. *Surfactants and Interfacial Phenomena*, John Wiley &b Sons, Inc.: Hoboken, New Jersey, 2004.

[133] *Dynamics of Surfactant Self-assemblies. Micelles, Microemulsions, Vesicles, and Lyotropic Phases*, ed. R. Zana, CRC Press: Boca Raton, 2005.

[134] *Giant Micelles. Properties and Applications*, ed. R. Zana, E. W. Kaler, CRC Press: Boca Raton, 2007.

[135] *Handbook of Surface and Colloid Chemistry*, ed. K. S. Birdi, CRC Press: Boca Raton, 2009.

[136] Bachofer, S. J. *J. Chem. Educ.*, 1996, 73, 861–864.

[137] Coello, A; Meijide, F; Mougán, MA; Núñez, ER; Tato, JV. *J. Chem. Educ.*, 1995, 72, 73–75.

[138] Dominguez, A; Fernández, A; González, N; Iglesias, E; Montenegro, L. *J. Chem. Educ.*, 1997, 74, 1227–1231.

[139] Marcolongo, JP; Mirenda, M. *J. Chem. Educ.*, 2011, 88, 629–633.

[140] Rusanov, AI; Nekrasov, AG. *Langmuir*, 2010, 26, 13767–13769.

[141] Rusanov, AI; Nekrasov, AG. *Doklady Phys. Chem.*, 2010, 434, 166–168.

[142] Mchedlov-Petrossyan, NO; Salamanova, NV; Vodolazkaya, NA; Gurina, Yu A; Borodenko, VI. *J. Phys. Org. Chem.*, 2006, 19, 365–375.

[143] Shatenshtein, AI. *Isotopic Exchange and the Replacement of Hydrogen in Organic Compounds*. Authorized translation from the 1960 Russian edition. By C. N. Turton and T. L. Turton. Consultants Bureau: New York, 1962.

[144] Cox, BG. *Acids and Bases. Solvent Effects on Acid–Base Strength*, Oxford University Press: Oxford, 2013.

[145] Izutsu, K. *Electrochemistry in Nonaqueous Solutions*. Wiley–VCH Verlag & Co. KgaA: Weinheim, 2009.

[146] Hartley, GS. *Trans. Faraday Soc.*, 1934, 30, 444–450.

[147] Hartley, GS; Roe, JW. *Trans. Faraday Soc.*, 1940, 36, 101–109.

[148] Hartley, GS. *Quart. Rev.*, 1948, 2, 152–183.

[149] Mukerjee, P; Banerjee, K. *J. Phys. Chem.*, 1964, 68, 3567–3574.

[150] Funasaki, N. *Nippon Kagaku Kaishi.*, 1976, 5, 722–726.

[151] Fernandez, MS; Fromherz, P. *J. Phys. Chem.*, 1977, 81, 1755–1761.

[152] Mackay, A. *Adv. Coll. Int. Sci.*, 1981, 15, 131–156.

[153] Grieser, F; Drummond, CJ. *J. Phys. Chem.*, 1988, 92, 5580–5593.

[154] Mukerjee, P; Ray; A. *J. Phys. Chem.*, 1966, 70, 2144–2149.

[155] Vitha, MF; Carr, PW. *J. Phys. Chem. B.*, 1998, 102, 1888–1895.

[156] Zachariasse, K; Van Phuc, N; Kozankiewicz, B. *J. Phys. Chem.*, 1981, 85, 2676–2683.

[157] Reichardt, C. *Chem. Rev.*, 1994, 94, 2319–2358.

[158] Reichardt, C. *Pure Appl. Chem.*, 2004, 76, 1903–1919.

[159] Williamson, CE; Corwin, AH *J. Coll. Int. Sci.*, 1972, 38, 567–576.

[160] Waggoner, AS. *Ann. Rev. Biophys. Bioeng.*, 1979, 8, 47–68.

[161] Sarpal, RS; Belletête, M; Durocher, G. *Phys. Chem. Lett.*, 1994, 221, 1–6.

[162] Yan, Y; Myrick, ML. *Anal. Chim. Acta*, 2001, 441, 87–93.

[163] Tavenier, HL; Laine, F; Fayer, MD. *J. Phys. Chem. A.*, 2001, 105, 8944–8957.

[164] Haugland, RP. *Handbook of Fluorescent Probes and Research Products*, 9th ed. Molecular Probes, Inc.: Eugen, OR, 2002.

[165] Reungpatthanaphong, P; Dechsupa, S; Meesungnoen, J; Loetchutinat, C; Mankhetkorn, S. *J. Biochem. Biophys. Methods*, 2003, 57, 1–16.

[166] Fayed, TA. *Colloids Surf. A*, 2004, 236, 171–177.

[167] Pandey, S. *J. Dispersion Sci. Technol.*, 2005, 26, 381–387.

[168] Handa, T; Ichihashi, C; Yamamoto, I; Nakagaki, M. *Bull. Chem. Soc. Jpn.*, 1983, 56, 2548–2554.

[169] Mukerjee, P. In: *Solution Chemistry of Surfactants*. Vol. *1*. Ed. K.L. Mittal. Plenum Publ. Corp.: N.Y., 1979, 153–174.

[170] Gross, E; Bedlack, RS; Loew, LM. *Biophys. J.*, 1994, 67, 208–216.

[171] Clarke, R. *J. Biochim. Biophys. Acta*, 1997, 1327, 269–278.

[172] Sjoback, R; Nygren, J; Kubista, M. *Biopolymers*, 1998, *46*, 445–453.

[173] Klonis, N; Sawyer. WH. *Photochem. Photobiol.*, 2003, *77*, 502–509.

[174] Saari, A; Seitz, WR. *Anal. Chem.*, 1982, 54, 821–823.

[175] Janata, J. *Anal. Chem.*, 1987, 59, 1351–1356.

[176] Janata, J. *Anal. Chem.*, 1992, 64, 921A–927A.

[177] Lobnik, A; Oehme, I; Murkovic, I; Wolfbeis, O. *Anal. Chim. Acta*, 1998, 367, 159–165.

[178] Weidgans, BM; Krause, C; Klimant, I; Wolfbeis, O. S. *Analyst*, 2004, 129, 645–650.

[179] Schröder, CR; Weidgans, BM; Klimant, I. *Analyst*, 2005, 130, 907–916.

[180] Choi, F; Hawkins, PJ. *Chem. Soc., Faraday Trans.*, 1995, 91, 881–885.

[181] Choi, F; Hawkins, P. *Anal. Chem.*, 1995, 67, 3897–3902.

[182] Choi, M. M. F. *J. Photochem. Photobiol. A. Chemistry.*, 1998, 114, 235–239.

[183] Pal, T; Jana, N. R. *Langmuir*, 1996, 13, 3114–3121.

[184] James, AD; Robinson, BH; White, NC. *J. Coll. Int. Sci.*, 1977, 59, 328–336.

[185] Han, J; Burgess, K. *Chem. Rev.*, 2010, 110, 2709–2728.

[186] Dsousa, RN; Pischel, U; Nau, WM. *Chem. Rev.*, 2011, 111, 7941–7980.

[187] Correa, NM; Sibler, JJ; Riter, RE; Levinger, NE. *Chem. Rev.* 2012, 112, 4569–4602.

[188] Hu, J; Xu, T; Cheng, Y. *Chem. Rev.*, 2012, 112, 3856–3891.

[189] Sameiro, M; Gonçalves, T. *Chem. Rev.*, 2009, 109, 190–212.

[190] Dorion, F; Gaboriaud, R. *J. Chim. Phys. Phys. Chim. Biol.*, 1981, 78, 555–561.

[191] Mchedlov-Petrossyan, NO; Vodolazkaya, NA; Yakubovskaya, AG; Grigorovich, AV; Alekseeva, VI; Savvina, LP. *J. Phys. Org. Chem.*, 2007, 20, 332–344.

[192] Whiddon, CR; Bunton, CA; Söderman, O. *J. Phys. Chem. B*, 2003, 107, 1001–1005.

[193] Rosendorfová, J; Čermáková, L. *Talanta*, 1980, 27, 705–708.

[194] Drummond, CJ; Grieser, F; Healy, TW. *J. Chem. Soc., Faraday Trans. 1*, 1989, 85, 521–535.

[195] Drummond, CJ; Grieser, F; Healy, TW. *J. Chem. Soc., Faraday Trans. 1*, 1989, 85, 537–550.

[196] Drummond, CJ; Grieser, F; Healy, TW. *J. Chem. Soc., Faraday Trans.* 1, 1989, 85, 551–560.

[197] Drummond, CJ; Grieser, F; Healy, TW. *J. Chem. Soc., Faraday Trans.* 1, 1989, *85*, 561–578.

[198] Mchedlov-Petrossyan, NO; Kleshchevnikova, VN. *Dokl. AN SSSR*, 1990, 312, 397–402.

[199] Mchedlov-Petrossyan, NO; Kleshchevnikova, VN. *Zh. Obsh. Khim.*, 1990, 60, 900–911.

[200] Mchedlov-Petrossyan, NO; Loginova, LP; Kleshchevnikova, VN. *Zh. Fiz. Khim.*, 1993, 67, 1649–1653.

[201] Mchedlov-Petrossyan, NO; Kleshchevnikova, VN. *J. Chem. Soc., Faraday Trans.*, 1994, 90, 629–640.

[202] Mchedlov-Petrossyan, NO; Pulyaeva, AS. *Functional Materials*, 1995, 2, 530–531.

[203] Drummond, CJ; Warr, GG; Grieser, F; Ninham, BW; Evans, DF. *J. Phys. Chem.*, 1985, 89, 2103–2109.

[204] Drummond, CJ; Grieser, F. *J. Photochem. Photobiol.*, 1987, 45, 19–34.

[205] Kibblewhite, J; Drummond, CJ; Grieser, F; Thistlethwaite, PJ. *J. Phys. Chem.*, 1989, 93, 7464–7473.

[206] Khaula, EV; Zaitsev, NK; Galashin, AE; Goldfeld, MG; Alfimov, MV. *Zh. Fiz. Khim.*, 1990, 64, 2485–2492.

[207] Buckingham, SA; Garvey, CJ; Warr, GG. *J. Phys. Chem.*, 1993, 97, 10236–10244.

[208] Cassidy, MA; Warr, G. *J. Phys. Chem.*, 1996, 100, 3237–3240.

[209] Bates, RG. *Determination of pH*. John Wiley & Sons Inc.: N. Y. – London – Sydney, 1964.

[210] Clark, WM; Lubs, HA. *J. Bacteriol.*, 1917, 2, 1–34.

[211] Fendler, EJ; Fendler, JH. *Adv. Phys. Org. Chem.*, 1970, 8, 271–397.

[212] Duxbury, DF. *Chem. Rev.*, 1993, 93, 381–433.

[213] Mchedlov-Petrossyan, NO; Vodolazkaya, NA; Bezkrovnaya, ON; Yakubovskaya, AG; Tolmachev, AV; Grigorovich, AV. *Spectrochim. Acta. A*, 2008, 69, 1125–1129.

[214] Kępcziński, M; Ehrenberg, B. *Photochem. Photobiol.*, 2002, 76, 486–492.

[215] Khramtsov, VV; Marsh, D; Weiner, L; Reznikov, VA. *Biochim. Biophys. Acta*, 1992, 1104, 317–324.

[216] Smirnov, AI; Ruuge, A; Reznikov, VA; Voinov, MA; Grigor'ev, IA. *J. Am. Chem. Soc.*, 2004, 126, 8872–8873.

[217] Molochnikov, LS; Kovaleva, EG; Golovkina, EL; Kirilyuk, IA; Grigor'ev, IA. *Koll. Zh.*, 2007, 69, 1–8.

[218] Golovkina, EL; Kovaleva, EG; Molochnikov, LS; Hartmann, M; Govindasamy, Ch; Grigor'ev, IA; Kirilyuk, IA. *Sorption Chromatogr. Processes*, 2008, 8, 971–985.

[219] Khlestkin, VK; Polienko, JF; Voinov, MA; Smirnov, AI; Chechik, V. *Langmuir*, 2008, 24, 609–612.

[220] Voinov, MA; Kirilyuk, IA; Smirnov, AI. *J. Phys. Chem. B.*, 2009, 113, 3453–3460.

[221] Voinov, MA; Rivera-Rivera, I; Smirnov, AI. *Biophys. J.*, 2013, 104, 106–116.

[222] Bissell, RA; Bryan, AJ; de Silva, AP; McCoy, CP. *J. Chem. Soc. Chem. Commun.*, 1994, 405–407.

[223] Compton, RG; Winkler, J; Riley, DJ; Beaarpark, SD. *J. Phys. Chem.*, 1994, 98, 6818–6826.

[224] Vasylevska, AS; Karasyov, AA; Borisov, S; Krause, C. *Anal. Bioanal. Chem.*, 2007, 387, 2131–2141.

[225] Demchenko, AP; Yesylevskyy, SO. *Chem. Phys. Lipids*, 2009, 160, 63–84.

[226] Posokhov, YA. *Kharkov Univ. Bull.* 2011, no. 976, *Chem. Ser.*, issue *20* (43), 92–99.

[227] Tokiwa, F. *Adv. Coll. Int. Sci.*, 1972, 3, 389–424.

[228] Underwood, AL. *Anal. Chim. Acta.*, 1977, 93, 267–273.

[229] Da Silva, FLB; Bogren, D; Söderman, O; Åkesson, T; Jönsson, B. *J. Phys. Chem. B.*, 2002, 106, 3515–3522.

[230] Söderman, O; Jönsson, B; Olofsson, G. *J. Phys. Chem. B.*, 2006, 110, 3288–3293.

[231] Eltsov, SV; Barsova, ZV. *Kharkov Univ. Bull.*, 2008, no 820, *Chem. Ser.*, issue 16 (39), 292–298.

[232] Boichenko, AP; Le Thi Kim Dung; Loginova, LP. *J. Solut. Chem.*, 2011, 40, 968–979.

[233] Chirico, G; Collini, M; D'Alfonso, L; Denat, F; Diaz-Fernandez, YA; Pasotti, L; Rousselin, Y; Sok, N; Pallavicini, P. *ChemPhysChem.*, 2008, 9, 1729–1737.

[234] Boichenko, AP; Markov, VV; Cong, HL; Matveeva, AG; Loginova, LP. *Cent. Eur. J. Chem.*, 2009, 7, 8–13.

[235] Kamneva, NM; Boichenko, AP; Ivanov, VV; Markov, VV; Loginova, LP. *Ukr. Khim. Zh.*, 2012, 78, 74 –78.

[236] Cong, HL; Boichenko, AP; Levin, IV; Matveeva, AG; Loginova, LP. *J. Mol. Liquids.*, 2010, 154, 76–81.

[237] Morrow, BH; Wang, Y; Wallace, JA; Koenig, PH; Shen, JK. *J. Phys. Chem. B.*, 2011, 115, 14980–14990.

[238] Terada, Y; Maeda, H; Odagaki, T. *J. Phys. Chem. B*, 1997, 101, 5784–5788.

[239] Maeda, H. *J. Coll. Int. Sci.*, 2003, 263, 277–287.

[240] Maeda, H. *Adv. Coll. Int. Sci.*, 2010, 156, 70–82.

[241] Seim, J; Sillén, LG; Ulfvarson, U. *Acta Chem. Scand.*, 1956, 10, 683–686.

[242] Morrow, BH; Koenig, PH; Shen, JK. *J. Chem. Phys.*, 2012, 137, 194902-1–7.

[243] Kanicky, JR; Poniatowski, AF; Mehta, NR; Shah, DO. *Langmuir*, 2000, 16, 172–177.

[244] Tokiwa, F; Ohki, K. *J. Phys. Chem.*, 1966, 70, 3437–3441.

[245] Mille, M. *J. Coll. Int. Sci.*, 1981, 81, 169–179.

[246] Yamashita, Y; Hoffmann, H; Maeda, H; Li, L; Ballauff, M. *Langmuir*, 2007, 23, 1073–1080.

[247] Tokiwa, F; Ohki; K. *J. Phys. Chem.*, 1967, 71, 1824–1829.

[248] Tanaka, S; Kawasaki, H; Maeda, H. *Coll. Polym. Sci.*, 2004, 282, 468–475.

[249] Goldsipe, A; Blankschtein, D. *Langmuir*, 2006, 22, 9894–9904.

[250] Rmaile, HH; Schlenoff, JB. *Langmuir*, 2002, 18, 8263–8266.

[251] Huang, QR; Dubin, PL; Moorefield, CN; Newkome, GR. *J. Phys. Chem. B.*, 2000, 104, 898–904.

[252] Minch, MJ; Giaccio, M; Wolff, R. *J. Am. Chem. Soc.*, 1975, 97, 3766–3772.

[253] El Seoud, OA. *Adv. Coll. Int. Sci.*, 1989, 30, 1–30.

[254] Jana, NR., Pal, T. *J. Surface Sci. Technol.*, 2001, 17, 191-212.

[255] Verhoek, FH. *J. Am. Chem. Soc.* 1936, 58, 2577–2584.

[256] Izmailov, NA. *Zh. Fiz. Khim.* 1950, 24, 321–336.

[257] Davis, MM. *Acid-Base Behavior in Aprotic Organic Solvents*. NBS Monograph No. 105: Washington, 1968.

[258] Kolthoff, IM. *Anal. Chem.*, 1974, 46, 1992–2003.

[259] Kabachnik, MI; Mastryukova, TA. *Zh. Obshch. Khim.*, 1985, 55, 713–720.

[260] Fialkov, Yu. Ya. *Solvent as an Agent of Chemical Process Control,* Khimiya: Leningrad, 1990.

[261] Havel, J; Burešova-Jančářová, I; Kubán, V. *Collect. Czech. Chem. Commun.*, 1983, 48, 1290–1304.

[262] Kubán, V; Hedbávný, J; Jančářová, I; Vrchlabský, M. *Collect. Czech. Chem. Commun.*, 1989, 54, 622–632.

[263] Tong, LKJ; Glesmann, MC. *J. Am. Chem. Soc.* 1957, 79, 4305–4310.

[264] Herries, DG; Bishop, W; Richards, FM. *J. Phys. Chem.*, 1964, 68, 1842–1852.

[265] Pramauro, E; Pelizzetti, E. *Analyt. Chim. Acta.*, 1981, 126, 253–257.

[266] Berthod, A; Georges, J; Breant, M. *Anal. Chem.*, 1981, 53, 1579–1582.

[267] Berthod, A; Georges, J. *Nouv. J. Chimie.*, 1985, 9, 101–108.

[268] Pilipenko, AT; Savranskiy, LI; Kulichenko, SA. *Zh. Anal. Khim.*, 1987, 42, 1493–1501.

[269] Zakharova, LYa; Fedorov, SB; Kudryavtseva, LA; Belskiy, BE; Ivanov, BE. *Izv. AN SSSR. Ser. Khim.*, 1990, no. 5, 991–994.

[270] Dutta, RK; Bhat, SN. *Canad. J. Chem.*, 1993, 71, 1785–1791.

[271] Dutta, RK; Chowdhury, R; Bhat, SN. *J. Chem.Soc., Faraday Trans.*, 1995, 91, 681–686.

[272] Gohain, B; Saikia, PM; Sarma, S; Bhat, SN; Dutta, RK. *Phys. Chem. Chem. Phys.*, 2002, 4, 2617–2620.

[273] Sarma, S; Bora, N; Dutta, RK. *Colloids Surf. A.*, 2005, 256, 105–110.

[274] Saikia, M; Bora, N; Dutta, RK. *Colloids Surf. A.*, 2005, 285, 382–387.

[275] Mchedlov-Petrossyan, NO; Timiy, AV; Vodolazkaya, NA. *J. Mol. Liquids.*, 2000, 87, 75–84.

[276] Mchedlov-Petrossyan, NO; Isaenko, YuV; Tychina, ON. *Zh. Obsh. Khim.*, 2000, 70, 1963–1971.

[277] Kulichenko, SA; Fesenko. SA. *Ukr. Khim. Zh.*, 2002, 68, 100–104.

[278] Gorbenko, GP; Mchedlov-Petrossyan, NO; Chernaya, TA. *J. Chem. Soc., Faraday Trans.*, 1998, 94, 2117–2125.

[279] Mchedlov-Petrossyan, NO; Isaenko, YuV; Salamanova, NV; Alekseeva, VI; Savvina, LP. *J. Anal. Chem.*, 2003, 58, 1018–1030.

[280] Boruah, B; Saikia, PM; Gohain, B; Dutta, RK. *J. Mol. Liquids*, 2010, 151, 81–85.

[281] Sarpal, RS; Belletête, M; Durocher, G. *J. Phys. Chem.*, 1993, 97, 5007–5013.

[282] Sarpal, RS; Dogra, SK. *Indian J. Chem.*, 1993, 32A, 754–761.

[283] Sarpal, RS; Dogra, SK. *J. Photochem. Photobiol.*, 1993, 69, 329–335.

[284] Nigam, SN; Sarpal, RS; Dogra, SK. *J. Coll. Int. Sci.*, 1994, 163, 152–157.

[285] Kapoor, R. C; *J. Ind. Chem. Soc.*, 1986, 63, 541–546.

[286] Bordello, J; Novo, M; Al-Soufi, W. *J. Colloid Int. Sci.*, 2010, 345, 369–376.

[287] Priyadarsini, KI. *J. Photochem. Photobiol. C: Photochem. Rev.*, 2009, 10, 81–95.

[288] Shtykov, SN; Sumina, EG; Tyurina, NV. *Zh. Anal. Khim.*, 2002, 57, 383–387.

[289] Ferrit, M; del Valle, C; Martinez, F. *Coll. Surf. A*, 2009, 345, 26–30.

[290] Piszkiewicz, D. *J. Am. Chem. Soc.*, 1977, 99, 1550–1557.

[291] Yuanqin, Z; Fan, L; Xiaoyan, L; Jing, L. *Talanta*, 2002, 56, 705–710.

[292] Zarei, K; Atabati, M; Abdinasab, E. *Eurasian J. Anal. Chem.*, 2009, 4, 314–327.

[293] Dakiky, M; Khamis, M; Manasara, A; Takrouri. K. *Color. Technol.*, 2002, *118*, 191–197.

[294] Popović, G; Čakar, M; Agbaba, D. *J. Pharm. Biomed. Anal.*, 2009, 49, 42–47.

[295] Grünhagen, HH; Witt, HT. *Z. Naturforsch.*, 1970, 25b, 373–386.

[296] Montal, M; Gitler, C. *J. Bioenerg. Biomembr.*, 1973, 4, 383–382.

[297] Mchedlov-Petrossyan, NO; Rubtsov, MI; Lukatskaya, LL. *Russian J. Gen. Chem.*, 2000, 70, 1177–1183.

[298] Ghosh, S. *Chem. Phys. Letters.*, 2010, 500, 295–301.

[299] Flewelling, RF; Hubbell, WL. *Biophys. J.*, 1986, 49, 531–540.

[300] Schamberger, J; Clarke, R. *Biophys. J.*, 2002, 82, 3081–3088.

[301] Hiskey, CF; Downey, TA. *J. Phys. Chem.*,1954, 58, 835–840.

[302] Mukerjee, P; Mysels, KJ. *J. Am. Chem. Soc.*,1955, 77, 2937–2943.

[303] Bilski, P; Dabestani, R; Chignell, CF. *J. Phys. Chem.*, 1991, *95*, 5784–5791.

[304] Buwalda, RT; Engberts, JBFN. *Langmuir*, 2001, 17, 1054–1059.

[305] Micheau, JC; Zakharova, GV; Chibisov, AK. *PhysChemChemPhys.*, 2004, 6, 2420–2425.

[306] Pereira, RV; Ghelen, MH. *Spectrochim. Acta A*, 2005, 61, 2926–2932.

[307] Yang, J. *J. Coll. Int. Sci.*, 2004, 274, 237–243.

[308] Gohain, B; Dutta, RK. *J. Coll. Int. Sci.*, 2008, 323, 395–402.

[309] Pellosi, DS; Estevão, BM; Semensato, J; Severino, D; Baptista, MS; Politi, MJ; Hioka, N; Caetano, W. *J. Photochem. Photobiol. A.*, 2012, 247, 8–15.

[310] Dutta, A; Dutta, RK. *J. Mol. Liq.*, 2013, 178, 25–30.

[311] Ghosh, S; Mondal, S; Das, S; Biswas, R. *Fluid Phase Equil.*, 2012, 332, 1–6.

[312] Freire, S; Bordello, J; Granadero, D; Al-Soufi, W; Novo, M. *Photochem. Photobiol. Sci.*, 2010, 9, 687–696.

[313] Gao, H.-W; Xu, W.-Q. *Anal. Chim. Acta*, 2002, 458, 417–424.

[314] Maity, A; Ghosh, P; Das, T; Dash, J; Purkayastha, P. *J. Coll. Int. Sci.*, 2011, 369, 395–399.

[315] Reeves, RL; Harkaway, SA. In: *Micellization, Solubilization, and Microemulsions* (Russian transl.), ed. K. L. Mittal, Mir: Moscow, 1980.

[316] Salnikov, Yu. I; Boos, GA; Ryzhkina, IS; Fattakhov, SG. Memoirs of Kazan University, *Natural Sci.*, 2010, *152*, 65–71.

[317] Chaimovich, H; Aleixo, RMV; Cuccovia, IM; Zanette, D; Quina, F. In: *Solution Behaviour of Surfactants,* Plenum Press: N. Y., 1982, 949–973.

[318] Buresova, I; Kuban, V; Sommer, L. *Coll. Czech. Chem. Commun.*, 1981, 46, 1090–1106.

[319] Bunton, CA; Romsted, LS; Sepulveda, L. *J. Phys. Chem.*, 1980, 84, 2611–2618.

[320] Lovelock, B; Grieser, F; Healy, TW. *J. Phys. Chem.*, 1985, 89, 501–507.

[321] Bachofer, SJ; Turbitt, RM. *J. Coll. Int. Sci.*, 1990, 135, 325–334.

[322] Bachofer, SJ; Simonis, U; Nowicki, TA. *J. Phys. Chem.*, 1991, 95, 480–488.

[323] Bunton, CA; Minch, MJ. *J. Phys. Chem.*, 1974, 78, 1490–1498.

[324] Sabatino, P; Szczygiel, A; Sinnaeve, D; Hakimhashemi, M; Saveyn, H; Martins, JC; Van der Meeren, P. *Colloids Surf. A*, 2010, 370, 42–48.

[325] Vermathen, M; Louie, EA; Chodosh, AB; Ried, S; Simonis, U. *Langmuir.*, 2000, 16, 210–221.

[326] Cerichelli, G; Mancini, G. *Langmuir*, 2000, 16, 182–187.

[327] Mohr, PC; Mohr, A; Vila, TP; Korth, H-G. *Langmuir*, 2010, 26, 12785–12793.

[328] Drummond, CJ; Grieser, F; Healy, TW. *Faraday Discuss. Chem. Soc.*, 1986, 81, 95–106.

[329] Fromherz, P. *Faraday Discuss. Chem. Soc.*, 1986, 81, 139–140.

[330] Healy, TW. *Faraday Discuss. Chem. Soc.*, 1986, 81, 140.

[331] Mchedlov-Petrossyan, NO; Isaenko, YuV; Goga, ST. *Zh. Obsh. Khim.*, 2004, 74, 1741–1747.

[332] Funasaki, N. *J. Coll. Int. Sci.*, 1977, 60, 54–59.

[333] Fedorov, SB; Il'iina, OM; Kudryavtseva, LA; Belskiy, VE; Ivanov, BE. *Koll. Zh.*, 1981, 43, 1184–1186.

[334] Drummond, CJ; Grieser, F; Healy, TW. *J. Phys. Chem.*, 1988, 92, 2604–2613.

[335] Saha, SK; Tiwari, PK; Dogra, SK. *J. Phys. Chem.*, 1994, 98, 5953–5955.

[336] Williams KR., Tennant LH. *J. Chem. Educ.*, 2001, 78, 349-351.

[337] Healy, TW; Lovelock, B; Grieser, F. In: *Solid/Liquid Dispersions,* Academic Press: London, 1987, no. 12, 275–282.

[338] Komar' NP. *Zh. Anal. Khim.* 1975, 30, 421–442.

[339] *Indicators* (Russian transl.). Vol. *1,* ed. E. Bishop. Mir: Moscow, 1976.

[340] Meloun, M; Kotrly, S. *Coll. Czech. Chem. Commun.*, 1977, 42, 2115–2125.

[341] Fromherz, P. *Biochem. Biophys. Acta*, 1973, 323, 326–334.

[342] Drummond, CJ; Grieser, F; Healy, TW. *Chem. Phys. Lett.*, 1987, 140, 493–498.

[343] Kibblewhite, J; Drummond, CJ; Grieser, F; Healy, TW. *J. Phys. Chem.*, 1987, 91, 4658–4660.

[344] Fornasiero, D; Grieser, F; Sawyer, W. *J. Phys. Chem.*, 1988, 92, 2301–2305.

[345] Healy, TW; Drummond, CJ; Grieser, F; Murray, BS. *Langmuir*, 1990, 6, 506–508.

[346] Drummond, CJ; Murray, BS. *Progr. Coll. Polym. Sci.*, 1992, 88, 23–29.

[347] Tanford, C. *J. Phys. Chem.*, 1955, 59, 788–793.

[348] Moller, JV; Kragh-Hansen, U. *Biochem.*, 1975, 14, 2317–2322.

[349] Mille, M; Vanderkooi, G. *J. Coll. Int. Sci.*, 1977, 61, 455–474.

[350] Lukac, S. *J. Phys. Chem.*, 1983, 87, 5045–5050.

[351] Xi, J; Guo, R. *J. Solution Chem.*, 2008, 37, 107–118.

[352] Kalidas, C; Hefter, G; Marcus, Y. *Chem. Rev.*, 2000, 100, 819–852.

[353] Wang, H; Callahan, PM. *J. Chromatogr. A*, 1998, 828, 124–134.

[354] Monticone, V; Favoriti, P; Lemordant, D; Treiner, C. *Langmuir*, 2000, 16, 258–264.

[355] Sverjensky, DA. *Geochim. Cosmochim. Acta*, 2005, 69. 225–257.

[356] Bryleva, E. Yu; Vodolazkaya, NA; Mchedlov-Petrossyan, NO; Samokhina, LV; Matveevskaya, NA. *Funct. Mater.*, 2006, 13, 662–668.

[357] Bryleva, E Yu; Vodolazkaya, NA; Mchedlov-Petrossyan, NO; Samokhina, LV; Matveevskaya, NA; Tolmachev, AV. *J. Coll. Int. Sci.*, 2007, 316, 712–722.

[358] Subir, M; Liu, J; Eisenthal, KB. *J. Phys. Chem. C*, 2008, 112, 15809–15812.

[359] Vodolazkaya, NA; Mchedlov-Petrossyan, NO; Bryleva, EYu; Biletskaya, SV; Schrinner, M; Kutuzova, LV; Ballauff, M. *Funct. Mater.*, 2010, 17, 470–476.

[360] Mchedlov-Petrossyan, NO; Bryleva, EYu; Vodolazkaya, NA; Dissanayake, AA; Ford, WT. *Langmuir*, 2008, 24, 5689–5899.

[361] Vodolazkaya, NA; Mchedlov-Petrossyan, NO; Bogdanova, L. N; Rodik,V; Kalchenko, VI. *The Influence of Aggregates of Calixarenes and Dendrimers on Protolytic Equilibria of Dyes in Aqueous Solution.* In: *From Molecules to Functional Architecture.*

Supramolecular Interactions. Ed. V. I. Rybachenko, East Publisher House: Donetsk, 2012, 49–69.

[362] Mchedlov-Petrossyan, NO; Vodolazkaya, NA; Rodik, RV; Bogdanova, LN; Cheipesh, TA; Soboleva, O. Yu; Kryshtal, AP; Kutuzova, LV; Kalchenko, VI. *J. Phys. Chem. C*, 2012, 116, 10245–10259.

[363] Mchedlov-Petrossyan, NO; Vodolazkaya, NA; Vilkova, LN; Soboleva, Yu; Kutuzova, LV; Rodik, RV; Miroshnichenko, SI; Drapaylo, AB. *J. Mol. Liquids.*, 2009, *145*, 197–203.

[364] Murray, BS; Godfrey, JS; Grieser, F; Healy, TW; Lovelock, B; Scales, PJ. *Langmuir*, 1991, *7*, 3057–3064.

[365] Bezkrovnaya, ON; Mchedlov-Petrossyan, NO; Vodolazkaya, NA; Savvin, YuN; Tolmachev, AV. *J. Brazil. Chem. Soc.*, 2006, 17, 655–666.

[366] Bezkrovnaya, ON; Mchedlov-Petrosyan, NO; Vodolazkaya, NA; Alekseeva, VI; Savvina, LP; Yakubovskaya, AG. *Russ. J. Appl. Chem.*, 2008, 81, 696–703.

[367] Nikitina, NA; Reshetnyak, EA; Svetlova, NV; Mchedlov-Petrossyan NO. *J. Brazil. Chem. Soc.*, 2011, 22, 855–864.

[368] Davies, JT. *Adv. Catal.* 1954, 6, 1–65.

[369] Davies, JT; Rideal, EK. *Interfacial Phenomena.* Academic Press: N.Y. – London, 1961.

[370] Möbius, D; Bücher, H; Kuhn, H; Sondermann, J. *Ber. Bunsenges. Phys. Chem.*, 1969, 73, 845–850.

[371] Goddard, ED. *Adv. Coll. Int. Sci.*, 1974, 4, 45–78.

[372] Petrov, JP; Möbius, D. *Langmuir*, 1990, 6, 746–751.

[373] Fromherz, P; Kotulla, R. *Ber. Bunsenges. Phys. Chem.*, 1984, 88, 1106–1112.

[374] Yamaguchi, S; Bhattacharyya, K; Tahara, T. *J. Phys. Chem. C*, 2011, 115, 4168–4173.

[375] Bhattacharyya, K; Sitzmann, EV; Eisenthal, KB. *J. Chem. Phys.*, 1987, 87, 1442–1443.

[376] Bhattacharyya, K; Castro, A; Sitzmann, EV; Eisenthal, KB. *J. Chem. Phys.*, 1988, 89, 3376–3377.

[377] Zhao, X; Subrahmanyan, S; Eisenthal, KB. *Chem. Phys. Lett.*, 1990, 171, 558–562.

[378] Castro, A; Bhattacharyya, K; Eisenthal, KB. *J. Chem. Phys.*, 1991, 95, 1310–1315.

[379] Eisenthal, KB. *Chem. Rev.*, 1996, 96, 1343–1360.

[380] Wang, H; Zhao, X; Eisenthal, KB. *J. Phys. Chem. B*, 2000, 104, 8855–8861.

[381] Rao, Y; Subir, M; McArthur, EA; Turro, NJ; Eisenthal, KB. *Chem. Phys. Lett.*, 2009, 477, 241–244.

[382] Xiao, X-D; Vogel, V; Shen, YR. *Chem. Phys. Lett.*, 1989, 163, 555–559.

[383] Xiao, X-D; Vogel, V; Shen, YR; Marowsky, G. *J. Chem. Phys.*, 1991, 94, 2315–2323.

[384] Tamburello-Luca, AA; Hébert, Ph; Antoine, R; Brevet, PF; Girault, HH. *Langmuir*, 1997, 13, 4428–4434.

[385] Chi, LF; Dhathathreyan, A; Möbius, D. *Langmuir*, 1990, 6, 1360–1363.

[386] Song, Q; Evans, C. E; Bohn, P. W. *J. Phys. Chem.*, 1993, 97, 13736–13741.

[387] Mihajlovic, M; Lazaridis, T. *J. Phys. Chem. B*, 2006, 110, 3375–3384.

[388] Yamaguchi, S; Kundu, A; Sen, P; Tahara, T. *J. Chem. Phys.*, 2012, 137, 151101-1–151101-4, and references cited therein.

[389] Wang, H; Borguet, E; Eisenthal, KB. *J. Phys. Chem. B.*, 1998, 102, 4927–4932.

[390] Grieser, F; Thistlethwaite, P; Triandos, P. *J. Am. Chem. Soc.*, 1986, 108, 3844–3846.

[391] Frumkin, AN; Iofa, AN; Gerovich, MA. *Zh. Fiz. Khim.*, 1956, 30, 1455–1468.

[392] Parfenyuk, VI. *Koll. Zh.*, 2004, 66, 520–524.

[393] Jungwirth, P; Tobias, DJ. *Chem. Rev.*, 2006, 106, 1259–1281.

[394] Paluch, M. *Adv.Coll. Int. Sci.*, 2000, 84, 27–45.

[395] Petersen, MK; Iyengar, SS; Day, TF; Voth, GA. *J. Phys. Chem. B*, 2004, 108, 14804–14806.

[396] Buch, V; Milet, A; Vácha, R; Jungwirth, P; Devlin, JP. *Proc. Nat. Acad. Sci. USA*, 2007, 104, 7342–7347.

[397] Marinova, KG; Alargova, RG; Denkov, ND; Velev, OD; Petsev, DN; Ivanov, IB; Borwankarm, RP. *Langmuir*, 1996, 12, 2045–2051.

[398] Beattie, JK. *Lab Chip.*, 2006, 6, 1409–1411.

[399] Winter, B; Faubel, M; Vácha, R; Jungwirth, P. *Chem. Phys. Lett.*, 2009, 474, 241–247.

[400] Gray-Weale, A; Beattie, JK. *PhysChemChemPhys.*, 2009, 11, 10994–11005.

[401] Gray-Weale, A. *Chem. Phys. Lett.*, 2009, 481, 22–24.

[402] 141st Faraday Discussion. *Faraday Discuss.*, 2009, 141, 81–98.

[403] Liu, M; Beattie, J. K; Gray-Weale, A. *J. Phys. Chem. B*, 2012, 116, 8981–8988.

[404] Vácha, R; Marsalek, O; Willard, AP; Bonthuis, DJ; Netz, RR; Jungwirth, P. *J. Phys. Chem. Lett.*, 2012, 3, 107–111.

[405] Azaz, E; Donbrow, M. *J. Coll. Int. Sci.*, 1976, 57, 11–19.

[406] Saitoh, T; Hoshino, H; Yotsuyanagi, T. *J. Chem. Soc., Faraday Trans.*, 1994, 90, 479–486.

[407] Ownby, DW; Prapaitrakul, W; King, Jr. AD. *J. Coll. Int. Sci.*, 1988, 125, 526–533.

[408] King, Jr., AD. In: *Solubilization in Surfactant Aggregates*. Ed. S. D. Christian and J. F. Scamehorn. *Surfactant Science Series*. Dekker, New York, 1995, 55, 35–38.

[409] Milioto, S; Crisantino, R; De Lisi, R. *J. Coll. Int. Sci.*, 1994, 166, 356–362.

[410] Khan, MN. *J. Phys. Org. Chem.*, 1996, 9, 295–300.

[411] Biederman, W; Datyner, A. *J. Coll. Int. Sci.*, 1981, 82, 276–285.

[412] Pramauro, E; Minero, C; Saini, G; Graglia, R; Pelizzetti, E. *Analyt. Chim. Acta*, 1988, 212, 171–180.

[413] Suslov, DA; Solomonov, BN. *Zh. Fiz. Khim.*, 1993, 67, 757–760.

[414] Suslov, DA; Solomonov, *Zh. Fiz. Khim.*, 1993, 67, 1611–1614.

[415] Nowick, JS; Cao, T; Noronha, G. *J. Am. Chem. Soc.*, 1994, 116, 3285–3289.

[416] Hussam, A; Basu, SC; Hixon, M; Olumee, Z. *Anal. Chem.*, 1995, 67, 1459–1464.

[417] Quina, FH; Alonso, EO; Farah, JPS. *J. Phys. Chem.*, 1995, 99, 11708–11714.

[418] Vitha, MF; Dallas, AJ; Carr, PW. *J. Phys. Chem.*, 1996, 100, 5050–5062.

[419] Belskiy, S. *Izv. AN. Ser. Khim.*, 1999, № 5, 873–878.

[420] Abraham, MN; Chadha, HS; Dixon, JP; Rafols, C; Treiner, C. *J. Chem. Soc., Perkin Trans.*, 1997, 2, 19–24.

[421] Dulfer, WJ; Bakker, MWC; Govers, HAJ. *Environ. Sci. Technol.*, 1995, 29, 985–992.

[422] Yano, Y; Kawada, S; Tagaki, W. *Bull. Chem. Soc. Jpn.*, 1981, 54, 493–495.

[423] Diaz Garcia, M; Sanz-Medel, A. *Talanta*, 1986, 33, 255–264.

[424] Esteve Romero, JS; Ramis Ramos, G; Garcia Alvarez-Coque, MC. *J. Coll. Interface Sci.*, 1991, 141, 44–55.

[425] Esteve Romero, JS; Garcia Alvarez-Coque, MC; Ramis Ramos, G. *Talanta*, 1991, 38, 1285–1289.

[426] Shtykov, SN; Amelin, VG; Sorokin, NN; Chernova, RK. *Zh. Fiz. Khim.*, 1986, 60, 345–349.

[427] Guo, Z-j; Miyoshi, H; Komoyoji, T; Haga, T; Fujita, T. *Biochim. Biophys. Acta.*, 1991, 1059, 91–98.

[428] Seguchi, K. *Yukugaku* 1979, 28, 20–25.

[429] Bunton, CA; Ohmenzetter, K; Sepulveda, L. *J. Phys. Chem.* 1977, 81, 2000–, 2004.

[430] Quina, F; Chaimovich, H. *J. Phys. Chem.* 1979, 83, 1844–1850.

[431] Chaimovich, H; Bonliha, JBS; Politi, MJ; Quina, FH. *J. Phys. Chem.* 1979, 83, 1851–1854.

[432] Bonliha, JBS; Chaimovich, H; Toscano, VG; Quina, FH. *J. Phys. Chem.*, 1979, 83, 2463–2470.

[433] Quina, FH; Politi, MJ; Cuccovia, IM; Baumgarten, E; Martins-Franchetti, SM; Chaimovich, H. *J. Phys. Chem.*, 1980, 84, 361–365.

[434] Bartet, D; Gamboa, C; Sepúlveda, L. *J. Phys. Chem.*, 1980, 84, 272–275.

[435] Gamboa, C; Sepúlveda, L; Soto, R. *J. Phys. Chem.*, 1981, 85, 1429–1434.

[436] Romsted, LS. *Micellar Effects on Reaction Rates and Equilibria.* In: *Surfactants in Solutions*, Plenum Press: N. Y., 1984, Vol. 2, 1015–1068.

[437] Sepúlveda, L; Cortés, J. *J. Phys. Chem.*, 1985, 89, 5322–5324.

[438] Biresaw, G; Bunton, CA; Savelli, G. *J. Org. Chem.*, 1985, 50, 5374–5376.

[439] Bunton, CA; Moffatt, JR. *J. Phys. Chem.*, 1986, 90, 538–541.

[440] Iglesias, E; Montenegro, L. *J. Chem. Soc., Faraday Trans.*, 1996, 92, 1205–1212.

[441] Kaz, VA; Vericat, F. *Phys. Rev. E*, 1994, 50, 1672–1673.

[442] Pesavento, M. *J. Chem. Soc., Faraday Trans.*, 1992, 88, 2035–2040.

[443] Hojo, M. *Bunseki Kagaku*, 2004, 53, 1279–1293.

[444] Hojo, M. *Kharkov University Bulletin.* No. 626. *Chem. Ser.*, 2004, 47–64.

[445] Baruah, B; Roden, JM; Sedgwick, M; Correa, NM; Crans, DC; Levinger, NE. *J. Am. Chem. Soc.*, 2006, 128, 12758–12765.

[446] Lucetti L. *Coll. Surf. A.*, 2007, 297, 249–252.

[447] Reichardt, C. *Pure Appl. Chem.*, 2008, 80, 1415–1432.

[448] Aliaga, C; Briones, L; Rezende, MC; Tirapegui, CJ. Coll. Int. Sci., 2010, 349, 565–570.

[449] Maitra, A; Deb, N; Bagchi, S. *J. Mol. Liquids*, 2008, 139, 104–109.

[450] Novaki, LP; El Seoud, OA. *Phys. Chem. Chem. Phys.*, 1999, 1, 1957–1964.

[451] Novaki, LP; El Seoud, OA. *Langmuir.*, 2000, 16, 35–41.

[452] Herodes, K; Leito, I; Koppel, J; Reichardt, C; Koppel, IA. *J. Phys. Org. Chem.*, 2005, *18*, 1013–1017.

[453] Plieninger, P; Baumgärtel, H. *Ber. Bunsenges. Phys. Chem.*, 1986, 86, 161-167;

[454] Plieninger, P; Baumgärtel, H. *Justus Liebigs Ann. Chem.*, 1983, 860–875.

[455] Yakubovskaya, AG; Vodolazkaya, NA; Mchedlov-Petrossyan, NO. *Kharkov University Bulletin*, No. 731, *Chem. Ser.*, 2006, 217–229.

[456] Aliaga, C; Briones, L; Rezende, MC; Tirapegui, CJ. *Coll. Int. Sci.*, 2010, *349,* 565–570.

[457] Rezende, MC; Mascayano, C; Briones, L; Aliaga, C. *Dyes Pigm.*, 2011, *90*, 219–224.

[458] Volkov, YuM; Mchedlov-Petrossyan, NO; Rubtsov, MI; Lukatskaya, LL. *IX Conference Surfactants and Raw Materials for their Production,* Proceedings, Belgorod, Russia, 1996, 31–32.

[459] Drummond, CJ; Grieser, F; Albers, S. *Coll. Surf.*, 1991, 54, 197–208.

[460] Mchedlov-Petrossyan, NO; Rubtsov, MI; Lukatskaya, LL; Chernaya, TA; Pereversev, AYu. *Doklady AN SSSR*, 1988, 299, 921–925.

[461] Mchedlov-Petrossyan, NO; Rubtsov, MI; Lukatskaya, LL. *Ukr. Khim. Zh.*, 1990, 56, 69–75.

[462] Mchedlov-Petrossyan, NO; Isaenko, YuV. *Kharkov University Bull.* No. 532. *Chem. Ser.*, 2001, Issue 7 (30), 130–134.

[463] Mchedlov-Petrossyan, NO; Vodolazkaya, NA; Reichardt, C. *Colloids Surf. A*, 2002, 205, 215–229.

[464] Politi, MJ; Fendler, JH. *J. Am. Chem. Soc.*, 1984, 106, 265–273.

[465] Kulichenko, SA; Fesenko, SA; Fesenko, NI. *Zh. Anal. Khim.*, 2001, 56, 1144–1148.

[466] Evtimova, BE. *Compt. Rend. de l'Acad. Bulg. Sci.*, 1978, 31, 552–562.

[467] Nazarenko, VA; Novoselova, MM; Antonovich, VP. *Doklady AN Ukrainian SSR Ser. B*, 1980, 53–56.

[468] Kobylecka, J. *Chem. Analit.*, 1986, 31, 833–842.

[469] Jarosh, M. *Analyst*, 1987, 112, 1279–1284.

[470] Mchedlov-Petrossyan, NO; Timiy, AV; Vodolazkaya, NA. http://preprint.chemweb. com/physchem/0203011.

[471] Kessler, MA; Wolfbeis, OS. *Chem. Phys. Lipids*, 1989, 50, 51–56.

[472] Qian, J; Xu, Y; Qian, X; Wang, J; Zhang, S. *J. Photochem. Photobiol. A: Chem.*, 2008, 200, 402–409.

[473] Izmailov, NA. *Electrochemistry of Solutions*. Kharkov University Press: Kharkov, 1959.

[474] Bykova, LN; Petrov, SI. *Usp. Khim. (Russ. Chem. Rev.)*, 1970, 39, 1631–1660.

[475] Bates, R. *Electroanal. Chem. a. Interfacial Electrochem.*, 1971, 29, 1-19.

[476] Mchedlov-Petrossyan, NO; Vodolazkaya, NA., Doroshenko, AO. *J. Fluoresc.*, 2003, 13, 235–248.

[477] Vodolazkaya, NA; Shakhova, PV; Mchedlov-Petrossyan, NO. *Russ. J. Gen. Chem.*, 2009, 79, 1437–1445.

[478] Tondo, DW; Priebe, JM; Souza, BS; Priebe, JP; Bunton, CA; Nome, F. *J. Phys. Chem. B*, 2007, 111, 11867–11869.

[479] Farrukh, MA; Beber, RC; Priebe, JP; Satnami, ML; Micke, GA; Costa, ACO; Fiedler, HD; Bunton, CA; Nome, F. *Langmuir*, 2008, 24, 12995–13000.

[480] Priebe, JP; Satnami, ML; Tondo, DW; Souza, BS; Priebe, JM; Micke, GA; Costa, ACO; Fiedler, HD; Bunton, CA; Nome, F.*J. Phys. Chem. B*, 2008, 112, 14373–14378.

[481] Priebe, JP; Souza, BS; Micke, GA; Costa, ACO; Fiedler, HD; Bunton, CA; Nome, F. *Langmuir*, 2010, 26, 1008–1012.

[482] Priebe, JP; Souza, BS; Silva, M; Tondo, DW; Priebe, JM; Micke, GA; Costa, ACO; Bunton, CA; Quina, FH; Fiedler, HD; Nome, F. *Langmuir*, 2012, *28*, 1758–1746.

[483] Pedro, JA; Mora, JR; Silva, M; Fiedler, HD; Bunton, CA; Nome, F. *Langmuir*, 2012, 28, 17623–17631.

[484] Plichko, AV; Mchedlov-Petrossyan, NO; Chernaya, TA; Shapovalov, SA. *Kharkov University Bull*, 1997, *Chem. Ser.*, issue 1, 164–173.

[485] Loginova, LP; Masliy, OG; Reshetnyak, EA; Evsyukova, LV; Kotsyur, IN; Dementyeva, TA; Shumakher, AS; Mchedlov-Petrossyan, NO. *Kharkov University Bull.*, 1998, no. 420, *Chem. Ser.* 223–229; *Chem. Abstr.*, 2000, 132, 55942.

[486] Sharma, P; MacNeil, JA; Bowles, J; Leaist, DG. *PhysChemChemPhys*, 2011, 13, 21333–21343.

[487] Shah, SS; Saeed, A; Sharif, QM. *Colloids Surf. A*, 1999, 155, 405–412.

[488] Quina, FH; Nassar, PM; Bonilha, JBS; Bales, BL. *J. Phys. Chem.*, 1995, 99, 17028–17031.

[489] Ranganathan, R; Tran, L; Bales, BL. *J. Phys. Chem. B*, 2000, 104, 2260–2264.

[490] Bales, BL. *J. Phys. Chem. B*, 2001, 105, 6798–6804.

[491] Benrraou, M; Bales, BL; Zana, R. *J. Phys. Chem. B*, 2003, 107, 13432–13440.

[492] Paul, A; Griffiths, PC; Petttersson, E; Stilbs, P; Bales, BL; Zana, R; Heenan, RK. *J. Phys. Chem. B*, 2005, 109, 15775–15779.

[493] Tcacenco, CM., Zana, R, Bales, BL. *J. Phys. Chem. B*, 2005, 109, 15997-16004;

[494] Lebedeva, NV, Shahine, A, Bales, BL. *J. Phys. Chem. B*, 2005, 109, 19806-19816

[495] Jalšenjak, N. *J. Coll. Int. Sci.*, 2006, *293*, 230-239.

[496] Shtykov, SN; Sumina, EG; Chernova, RK; Semenenko, EV. *Zh.Anal. Khim.*, 1984, 39, 1029–1033.

[497] Magid, L. *J. Phys. Chem. B*, 1998, *102*, 4064–4074.

[498] Mchedlov-Petrossyan, NO; Vodolazkaya, NA; Kornienko, AA; Karyakina, EL; Reichardt, C. *Langmuir*, 2005, *21*, 7090–7096.

[499] Bellare, JR; Kaneko, T; Evans, DF. *Langmuir,* 1988, 4, 1066–1067.

[500] Magid, LJ; Han, Z; Li, Z; Butler, PD. *Langmuir*, 2000, *16*, 149–156.

[501] Imae, T; Kohsaka, T. *J. Phys. Chem.*, 1992, 96, 10030–10035.

[502] Bijma, K; Rank, E; Engberts, JBFN. *J. Coll. Int. Sci.*, 1998, 205, 245–256.

[503] Magid, LJ; Han, Z; Warr, GG; Cassidy, MA; Butler, PD; Hamilton,WA. *J. Phys. Chem. B*, 1997, *101*, 7919–7927.

[504] Geng, Y; Romsted, LS; Froehner, S; Zanette, D; Magid, LJ; Cuccovia, IM; Chaimovich, H. *Langmuir*, 2005, *21*, 562–568.

[505] Inoue, T; Inoue, Y; Watanabe, H. *Langmuir*, 2005, 21, 1201–1208.

[506] Joshi, JV; Aswal, VK; Goyal, PS. *Physica B*, 2007, 391, 65–71.

[507] Abdel-Rahem, R; Hoffmann, H. *J. Coll. Int. Sci.*, 2007, 312, 146–155.

[508] Goddard, ED; Harva, O; Jones, TG. *Trans. Faraday Soc.* 1953, 49, 980–984.

[509] Schick, MJ. *J. Phys. Chem.*, 1964, 68, 3585–3592.

[510] Mukerjee, P; Mysels, KJ; Kapauan, P. *J. Phys. Chem.*, 1967, 71, 4166–4175.

[511] Saito, S; Taniguchi, T; Kitamura, K. *J. Coll. Int. Sci.*, 1971, 37, 154–164.

[512] Mirgorod, YuA. *Zh. Fiz. Khim.*, 1985, 59, 1418.

[513] Mirgorod, YuA; Yarosh, NV. *Ukr. Khim. Zh.*, 1994, 60, 394–398.

[514] Zaev, EE; Zaitsev, NK; Kuzmin, MG. *Khim. Fiz.*, 1988, 7, 1147–1151.

[515] Bonilha, JBS; Zumstein Georgetto, RM; Abuin, E; Lissi, E; Quina, F. *J. Coll. Int. Sci.*, 1990, 135, 238–245.

[516] Szajdzinska-Pietek, E; Gebicki, JL. *J. Phys. Chem.*, 1995, 99, 13500–13504.

[517] Kumar, S; David, SL; Aswal, VK; Goyal, PS; Kabir-ud-Din. *Langmuir*, 1997, 13, 6461–6464.

[518] Aswal, VK. *J. Phys. Chem. B*, 2003, 107, 13323–13328.

[519] Bales, BL; Tiguida, K; Zana, R. *J. Phys. Chem. B*, 2004, 108, 14948–14955.

[520] Jansson, M; Stilbs, P. *J. Phys. Chem.*, 1987, 91, 112–116.

[521] *Surfactants (a Handbook)*. Ed. A. A. Abramson, G. M. Gaevoy. Khimiya: Leningrad, 1979.

[522] Balakina, TD. *Kolloidn. Zh.*, 1985, 67, 388–391.

[523] Mchedlov-Petrossyan, NO; Timiy, AV; Vodolazkaya, NA; Pinchukova, N. A. *Kharkov Unive. Bull*. No. 454. *Chem. Ser.*, 1999, 203–205.

[524] Bachofer, SJ; Simonis, U. *Langmuir*, 1996, 12, 1744–1754.

[525] Grissbach, R. *Theory and Practice of Ion Eschange* (Russian transl.), Izd. Inostr. Lit.: Moscow, 1963.

[526] Samuelson,O. *Ion-exchange Separations in Analytical Chemistry* (Russian transl.), Khimiya: Moscow – Leningrad, 1966.

[527] Tremiyon, B. *Separation by Ion Exchange Resins* (Russian transl.), Mir: Moscow, 1967.

[528] Marcholl, M. *Ion Exchangers in Analytical Chemistry* (Russian transl.), Mir: Moscow, 1985.

[529] Izmailov, NA; Mushinskaya, S. Kh. *Dokl. AN SSSR* 1955, 100, 101–104.

[530] Izmailov, NA; Mushinskaya, S. Kh. *Zh. Fiz. Khim.*, 1962, 36, 1210–1218.

[531] Petrishchev, KP; Davydov, AT. *Kharkov University Bull.* No. 46. *Chem. Ser.*, 1970, 43–46.

[532] Vodolazkaya, NA. Ph D Thesis, Kharkov, 2001.

[533] Barnes, HA; Eastwood, AR; Yates, B. *Reol. Acta*, 1975, 14, 53–60.

[534] Wolff, T; Emming, CS; Von Bunau, G; Zierold, K. *Coll. Polym. Sci.*, 1992, 270, 822–824.

[535] Hartmann, V; Cressely. R; *Colloids Surf. A.*, 1997, 121, 151–162.

[536] Abdel-Rahem, R. *Adv. Coll. Int. Sci.*, 2008, 141, 24–36.

[537] Goga, ST; Mchedlov-Petrossyan, NO; Glazkova, EN; Lebed, AV. *J. Mol. Liq.*, 2013, 177, 237–242.

[538] Frescura, VLA; Marconi, DMO; Zanette, D; Nome, F. *J. Phys. Chem.*, 1995, 99, 11494–11500.

[539] Profio, PDi; Germani, R; Savelli, G; Cerichelli, G; Chiarini, M; Mancini, G; Bunton, C. A; Gillitt, ND. *Langmuir*, 1998, 14, 2662–2669.

[540] Beber, RC; Bunton, C; Savelli, G; Nome, F. *Progr. Coll. Polym. Sci.*, 2004, 128, 249–254.

[541] Pletnev, M. Yu. *Cosmetic and Sanitary Detergents,* Khimiya: Moscow, 1990.

[542] Chaudhury, A; Loughlin, JA; Romsted, LS; Yao, J. *J. Am. Chem. Soc.*, 1993, 115, 8351–8361.

[543] Chaudhuri, A; Romsted, LS; Yao J. *J. Am. Chem Soc.*, 1993, 115, 8362–8367.

[544] Abu-Hamdiyyah, M; El-Danab, CM. *J. Phys. Chem.*, 1983, 87, 5443–5448.

[545] Abu-Hamdiyyah, M. *J. Phys. Chem.*, 1986, 90, 1345–1349.

[546] Miller, DD; Evans, DF; Warr, GG; Bellare, JR; Ninham, BW. *J. Coll. Int. Sci.*, 1987, 116, 598–601.

[547] Myassoedova, T; Grand, D; Hautecloque, S. *J. Photochem. Photobiol. A*, 1992, 64, 159–169.

[548] Baglioni, P; Bencini, A; Teixeira, J; Kevan, L. *J. Phys.: Condens. Matter*, 1994, 6, 369–373.

[549] Baglioni, P., Gambi, CMC, Giordano, R, Teixeira, J. *Colloids Surf. A*, 1997, 121, 47–52.

[550] Kuriyama, K; Inoue, H; Nakagawa, T. *Kolloid-Z. Z. Polym.*, 1962, 183, 68–71.

[551] Rathman, JF; Scamehorn, JF. *J. Phys. Chem*, 1984, 88, 5807–5816.

[552] Rathman, JF; Scamehorn, JF. *Langmuir*, 1987, 3, 372–377.

[553] Abuin, EB; Lissi, EA; Nuner, R; Olea, A. *Langmuir*, 1989, 5, 753–757.

[554] Dubin, PL; The, SS; McQuigg, DW; Chew, CH; Gan, LM. *Langmuir*, 1989, 5, 89–95.

As indicated above, in spite of the abundance of publications and of the large amount of experimental data available, several questions remain a subject of discussion and debate: what is the precise molar composition of a RM at a given W_o value? What is the RM exact size and shape, in particular when they host a small number of water molecules in their inner core? What is the structural and dynamical behavior of the encapsulated water within the micelle? What is the effect of protein encapsulation on the micellar shape and size fluctuations, on the hosted protein hydration, or the structure and protein dynamics?

During the last decade, computational studies of biomolecules and in particular surfactant solutions have become fairly common (see reviews [26–28]). By applying different computational techniques such as Molecular Dynamics (MD) or Mesoscopic simulation (such as Dissipative Particles Dynamics (DPD)) approaches at different atomic levels and timescales it is possible, nowadays, to obtain detailed information about surfactant solutions. Therefore, these tools can provide additional information about RM and help us to elucidate, at least in part, the above mentioned controversial questions.

2. MICROEMULSIONS

The three basic types of microemulsions are pictured in Figure 1:

1. The oil-continuous (water-in-oil; W/O) type microemulsion which consists of surface surfactant-coated droplets of water in an oil-continuous phase (or RM)
2. The water-continuous (oil-in-water; O/W) microemulsion which is the dispersions of surfactant-coated oil droplets in a water-continuous phase.
3. The droplet-type structure is typical of a system which is predominantly (>80% v/v) oil or water.

As seen in Figure 1, the three structures are quite different, but each is formed by a single surfactant monolayer separating the oil and water domains. The W/O and O/W structures are considered here as spheres, but they may be ellipsoidal, as function of the surfactant type used, the temperature, or the concentration of the mixture in oil. Bicontinuous microemulsions contain approximately equal volumes of water and oil and a correspondingly a large amount of surfactant; they differ from W/O and O/W systems by the fact that the oil, water and surfactant sub-phases are physically continuous throughout the sample.

The relation between the phase behavior of a mixture and its composition can be better understood with the help of a phase diagram. In the case of a simple microemulsion system composed of oil, water and surfactant, it displays a ternary phase diagram where each corner of the diagram represents 100 % of a particular component (see Figure 2 for the ternary AOT/Water/Isooctane system at 25°C [13], [29]). In general, the single phase microemulsions (i.e. O/W, W/O and bicontinuous) are in equilibrium with either the aqueous or organic phase or both (Winsor systems [30]) and thus the phase diagram can be divided into two or four regions. Winsor identified four general types of phase equilibrium (Winsor I-IV). The single-phase (isotropic) micellar solution formed upon addition of a sufficient quantity of amphiphile (and alcohol) is the Winsor IV phase; Winsor I system consists of an O/W microemulsion in equilibrium with an excess oil phase; the surfactant is only present as monomers at low concentration. In Winsor II, the microemulsion phase is in equilibrium with an aqueous phase in excess. Finally, in the Winsor III phase, the microemulsion phase is in equilibrium with both the aqueous and organic phases (three-phase system).

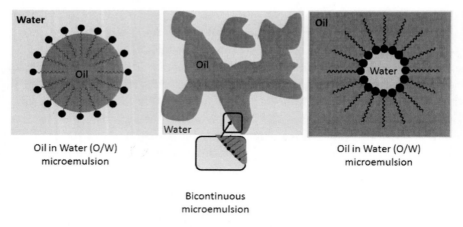

Figure 1. Schematic representation of the three types of microemulsions.

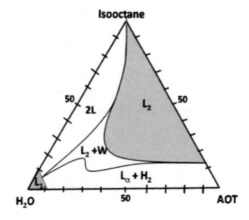

Figure 2. Simplified phase diagram of AOT (Aerosol OT)/water/isooctane system at 25 °C. L_4, Aqueous micellar solution, 2L emulsion, L_2 reversed micellar solution (in grey), LC liquid crystal the structure is divided into lamellar (D) and hexagonal (H_2) phases. $L_2 + W$ indicates that the phase region where the liquid crystal exists in equilibrium with the solution. Figure from [29] and redrawn from [293] with permission of the author.

The transitions between the different microemulsion phases can be modulated by manipulating experimental parameters such as the ionic strength, the temperature or the ionic and nonionic types of the surfactant respectively, also by the addition of co-surfactants, or by modifying the oil chemical nature, changing thus the energies of interaction between the amphiphile layer, the oil and water regions [30], [31]. During the last decades, large number of reviews [4], [13], [20], [32–34] and books [31], [35], [36] have described and discussed in details the physical chemical properties of microemulsions.

In this chapter, we will focus on the water-in-oil (W/O) microemulsions (L_2 region in the ternary phase diagram, in Figure 2) when oil is added in larger concentration (80 – 90 %) than water (0 - 10%) or surfactant (< 10 %). In particular, we will focus on the structural and dynamical properties of RM modeled with ionic and nonionic surfactants (i.e. mainly AOT and polyoxy ethylene alkyl ethers, hereafter C_iE_j) and the confined water. We will also examine the effect of protein encapsulation on the micelle itself and on confined water structural and dynamical properties, as well as on the hosted protein structure and hydration.

3. STRUCTURE OF REVERSE MICELLES

3.1. Overview of AOT-Based RM

The most used anionic surfactant to form RM is the dioctyl sodium sulfosuccinate or AOT (Figure 3) [37–40]. The AOT molecule has a conic shape with a small headgroup area, a_s of ~56 $Å^2$ [41], [42], a large molecular volume, v_s, of 650 – 670 $Å^3$ [29], [43] and a branched alkyl tail with a medium length, l_s of 12 Å [29], [44], given a packing parameter (or factor) $p = v_s/al_s \approx 1$). This surfactant forms preferentially lamellar and W/O structures. Moreover, AOT has 3 stereo-chemical centers (indicated by asterisks in Figure 3) and thus 8 possible conformations indicating that the two acyl chains are not equivalent. Their relative conformations are known to affect AOT molecular packing in the lamellar or in reversed micellar states, [45–48]. AOT can form RM in a wide range of apolar solvents including alkanes [39] and supercritical CO_2 [49] or a mixture of both [50]. The structural properties of RM (including size and shape, number of water and surfactant molecules) depend on several parameters such as the bulk solvent nature, temperature, surfactant molecular conformation or the presence of a cosurfactant.

For example, Maitra et al. [48], [51] indicates that RM in cyclohexane are formed at W_0 = 20, with less AOT molecule (257) and contain less water (5140) compared to an identical RM in isooctane (302 and ~6000, respectively). The authors explain this result by the fact that isooctane changes the internal rotation of the AOT molecule favoring a better packing factor and a larger water solubilization. To explore the structures and dynamics of RM, a wide range of experimental techniques have been used (e.g. time-resolved IR spectroscopy, neutron, X-ray or static and dynamic light scattering) [52] and references herein) as well as computational approaches have been used such as molecular dynamics (MD) or mesoscopic simulations, developed below.

Despite the large use of AOT RM during processes such as protein solubilization or extraction, the strong electrostatic interactions and slow phase separation can become difficult, hampering the recovery of proteins. To overcome these problems, phosphate-based surfactants (e.g. Dioleyl phosphoric acid (DOLPA) [53], sodium dioleylphosphate (SDOLP)) or with cationic headgroups, such as cetyl-trimethyl-ammonium bromide (CTAB) [54], [55], nonionic surfactants, such as Triton X-100 [56], C_iE_j [57–59] or Igepals [60], and zwitterionic surfactants [61], for example, phosphatidylcholine [62] were synthetized. The main goal of the mixed RM systems is to control the micro-environmental polarity surrounding the solubilized enzyme molecules; the extraction and the separation are thus enhanced compared to the use of single ionic RM.

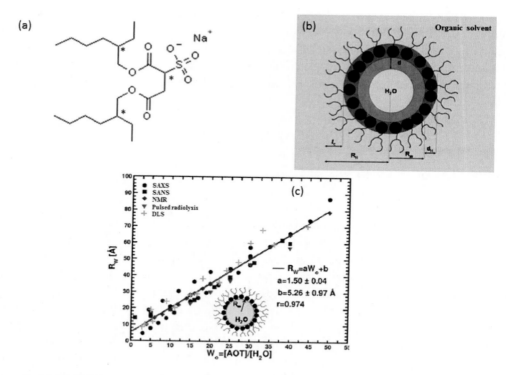

Figure 3. (a) The AOT (sodium bis(2-ethylhexyl) sulfosuccinate surfactant. The three chiral centers are marked by asterisks. (b) Schematic representation of a RM with the different regions and characteristic lengths. l_c: length of the surfactant tail, R_H and R_w are the hydrodynamic and water pool radii, respectively and d_H the surfactant headgroup thickness. (c) RM water pool size as function of W_o values. Figures from [29] with permission of the author. Experimental values in (c) are from [42], [51], [210], [212], [221], [294–297].

Besides, the strong electrostatic interaction is weakened by the second surfactant and the size of the mixed RM increases by the introduction of the companion surfactant molecules [63], [64]. The structure and solubilization properties of these microemulsions differ significantly from ionic ones [65].

3.2. Overview of Nonionic Reverse Micelles

To avoid the charges present on the polar headgroup of ionic RM, often responsible for the destabilization of protein structures, it is possible to form RM with nonionic surfactant instead of AOT. As nonionic surfactants, poly(ethyleneglycol)-based surfactants are often used for this goal. These surfactants have a headgroup formed by a repeated unit of O-CH$_2$-CH$_2$ linked to a hydrophobic tail with various structures (linear, cyclic and branched, etc.).

The behavior of this surfactant depends on the hydrophilic-lipophilic balance (HLB) [66], value computed from the relative proportions of hydrophobic and hydrophilic groups within the molecule [67]. Nonionic surfactants with a HLB value of 10, smaller than 10 and greater than 10, form bicontinuous and W/O and O/W microemulsions, respectively [68]. Nonionic surfactants form water–oil microemulsions (and emulsions) with high temperature sensitivity.

In particular, there is a specific phase inversion temperature (PIT) and the film curvature changes from positive to negative [69]:

- if T < PIT, an oil-in-water microemulsion form (Winsor I),
- if T > PIT, a water-in-oil microemulsion form (Winsor II),
- at T = PIT, a middle-phase microemulsion exists (Winsor III) with a spontaneous curvature equal to zero, and a HLB number approximately equal to 10

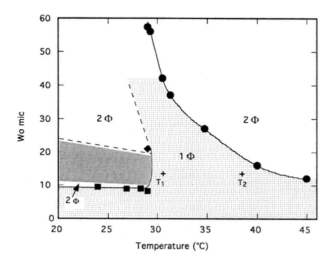

Figure 4. $C_{12}E_4$/water/n-dodecane phase diagram showing the single-phase microemulsion boundaries delineated by the maximum W_o water-surfactant ratio as a function of temperature. The darkest area represents the LC phase. The dotted area represents the isotropic phase. The dashed line indicates approximated boundaries. T1 and T2 are temperatures of the samples studied. Reprinted with permission from [70]. Copyright 1996, American Chemical Society.

HLB, PIT and packing parameter describe the same basic concept, and therefore are influenced by the surfactant geometry and the experimental conditions.

Nonionic-based RM offer to the investigator a number of advantages compared to AOT: (i) the high purity of the surfactants, (ii) the wide selection of length of polar and nonpolar chains available, (iii) the rich phase behavior of the ternary system C_iE_j-oil-water. In this system, the size, shape, polydispersity and interactions between the aggregates varies continuously with temperature and concentration. A two dimensional phase diagram giving the precise limits of the microemulsion phase as a function of both temperature and water-to-surfactant molar ratio is presented in Figure 4 for the surfactant tetraethylene glycol monododecyl ester ($C_{12}E_4$) in n-dodecane [70].

Structural data present a picture with a sharp transition at 29.2°C from a liquid crystal (LC) to the isotropic phase. In the latter they reveal, near the transition, a prolate shape and a hydrodynamic radius decreasing at higher temperatures. Near the two phase boundary (38.5°C) micelles exist as slightly solvated spherical droplets. Such a behavior exemplifies the differences between AOT and $C_{12}E_4$ RM where different structural types can be obtained by varying a single parameter: temperature (Figure 4).

4. SIMULATION APPROACHES OF SURFACTANT SOLUTIONS

In this section, we will review the computational methods used to model surfactant solutions. In particular, we will focus on molecular dynamics and mesoscopic simulations. The reader interested by detailed information on the simulation techniques may refer to excellent books [71–73] and reviews [27], [74], [75].

4.1. Choice of the Simulation Methods for Simulation of Surfactant Solutions

The choice of the computational approach used to study a molecular system depends on the system size and the simulation time scale. Figure 5 provides a rough estimate of the various time and length scales of the different phenomena observed in a solution of sodium dodecyl sulfate in water.

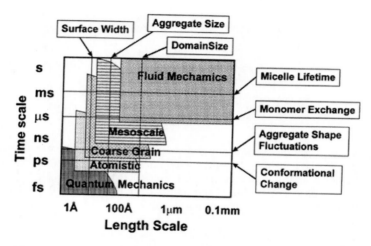

Figure 5. Time and length scales in surfactant solutions. Reprinted from [26]. Copyright 1996, with permission from Elsevier.

As shown in Figure 5, studies of surfactant solutions behavior employ different approaches and molecular representations as a function of length and time scales. The lower limits for each method are determined by the basic units that are simulated. The upper limits are dictated by the processing power of current computers and the manner in which each method is implemented. In practical applications the behavior of surfactants at many different levels of time and length can typically be done in separate studies.

4.2. Molecular Models in Simulations

4.2.1. Empirical Force Fields

In classical molecular simulations, the interactions between atoms of molecules are modeled explicitly or with particles that incorporate a group of atoms (for example, all hydrogens on an aliphatic carbon are united with carbons). Identical atoms can be also represented as a bead in the case of the coarse grained approach. The united-atom representation differs from the coarse grain approach by the degree of details of the molecular model (see below). The interactions between each atom are described with a potential energy function (also called a force field) which is parameterized based upon spectroscopic measurements of small molecules and quantum chemistry calculations [72]. Such simplified description of molecular interactions entails approximations, i.e. the Born–Oppenheimer approximation and the treatment of nuclei as classical particles. In the simulations of soft materials and biological systems, the potential energy functions have a typical form given in Eq. 1 and is divided into two groups: the bonded (bond, angle, torsion angle and optionally the improper angle) and the non-bonded (i.e. coulombic and van der Waals) interactions:

$$U(r) = \frac{K_b(b - b_0)^2 + K_\theta(\theta - \theta_0)^2 + K_\omega(\omega - \omega_0)^2 + K_t(1 + \cos(n(\varphi - \varphi_\theta))}{\frac{q_i q_j}{\epsilon r_{ij}} + \frac{A}{r_{ij}^{12}} - \frac{B}{r_{ij}^{6}}}$$

(1)

Where b is the bond length; b_0 its equilibrium value; θ is the angle with θ_o representing its equilibrium value; ω is the improper angle with ω_o representing its equilibrium value. In the dihedral term, φ is the torsion angle; φ_0 is 0 or 180 degrees, and n represents phase. K_b, K_θ, K_ω and K_t and force constants q_i and q_j denote partial charges of atoms not covalently bonded, and ϵ is the dielectric constant. r_{ij} is the distance between a pair of interacting atoms, and A and B are constants depending on the chemical nature of interacting atoms.

The constant forces and the bond and angle equilibrium values are taken from vibrational spectra, normal mode analysis or X-ray crystallography. In the case of torsional parameters, they are derived from QM data. The number and the form of the term in the potential energy function may differ with the force field. In particular, several bonded term can be added to the potential energy function to reinforce the geometry of groups (e.g. improper torsions in the amide planes of proteins). Popular atomistic and united force fields used to model surfactants are derived from CHARMM (Chemistry at HARvard Molecular Mechanics) [76], AMBER (Assisted Model Building and Energy Refinement), GAFF (General Amber Force Field) [77], GLYCAM [78] or OPLS (Optimized Potential for Liquid Simulations) [79] and GROMOS (GROningen MOlecular Simulation package) [80].

In Table 1, we present a (non-exhaustive) list of classical all-atoms and united atoms force fields previously used to model the AOT and PEG based surfactants (look in the next section for discussions about the surfactant models based on the coarse-grained force field). The earlier (1988) model of AOT was constructed by Brown and Clark [81] to simulate a simple model of RM in an apolar solvent. In this model, the charged and hydrophobic parts of the surfactant are modeled as a single Lennard-Jones site. A decade after, Derecskei et al. [146] have used two proprietary force fields based on (united atoms) UFF and (explicit atoms) ESFF to examine the geometries of representative AOT conformers and the interactions between individual AOT molecule and water in vacuum and in carbon tetrachloride (CCl_4). They showed that, in agreement with experiments, the interactions with water and CCl_4 modify modestly the AOT geometry and that AOT solvation by water is found to be exoergic (with >10 kcal/mol of interaction energy). A year after, Faeder et al. [82] used an implicit approach to model simple AOT RM where the SO_3^- part of the surfactant is represented by a single Lennard-Jones site and an alkyl chain by a dielectric continuum (see section 5.2 where this model is discussed).

The most used explicit force field to model AOT RM was initially developed by Bandyopadhyay et al. [83] for simulations of monolayer of AOT at an air/water interface or RM (see section 5). This model is based on the CHARMM27 force field for lipids [84] with the headgroup atomic charges obtained from DFT calculations. Later, Chowdhary and Ladanyi [85] used a model based the TraPPe united force field [86], [87]. But since this force field does not contain parameters for the sulfonate headgroup, the authors use the parameters and the atomic partial charges from the CHARMM force field [88] for the sulfur and oxygen atoms of AOT headgroups. More recently, Martinez et al. [89] use a model for AOT based on the GROMOS53A6 [80] united atom force field with the charge for the sulfur atom taken from dimethylsulfoxyde.

In case of the PEO-based surfactants, the force fields are also based on the classical CHARMM, OPLS and GROMOS force fields and combined with alkane parameters available in these force fields to obtain complete parameters of the surfactants. These force fields include generally parameters for the ether function that are able to reproduce accurately main thermodynamic and dynamic properties of simple monoether such as dimethylether (DME) in the liquid phase as well as in aqueous solutions. However, direct transfer of these parameters to similar compounds such as 1,2-dimethoxyethane (DXE), PEO and PEG are not guaranteed due to lack of an accurate description of the "gauche-effect" [90], [91], namely, a stereo-electronically induced preference of the OCCO dihedral angle of a vicinal diether for the two gauche over the trans configuration. In aqueous solutions, high dielectric screening as well as specific hydration (i.e. water-bridging) may also add up to the purely stereoelectronic gauche-effect [92], [93]. An appropriate description of the "gauche-effect" as well as an accurate description of the resulting PEG chain conformation and hydration in vacuum or in solution requires an accurate parameterization of the OCCO torsional-energy parameters and possibly the corresponding oxygen–oxygen third-neighbor nonbonded interaction parameters (including 1,4-LJ (dispersion and repulsion) and 1,4-electrostatic (repulsion, given the identical partial charges of the oxygen atoms) interactions. It was done along the years (see Table 1). Among the PEO and PEG models listed in Table 1, the Smith force field [94] is the oldest (1993) and it was refined over the years to improve its agreement with experimental thermodynamic properties and, more recently, to explicitly account for electronic polarizability [95]. The Tasaki model [96] is a variant of the Smith force field, with partial charges readjusted based on simulations of PEO in water and was used to simulate micelles and RM systems [97]. The Thomas [98] model was derived considering the properties of PEO crystals. The Müller-Plathe model [99], [100] based on the GROMOS37C4 (see [99], [100] and ref. herein) developed to model the properties of DXE with the aim of simulating PEO in the presence of lithium ions at high temperature. The Kolafa and Ratner [101] model is the oldest explicitly polarizable model and was designed considering density, dipole moments, dielectric constant, and QM calculations. The Anderson and Wilson [102] model compatible with OPLS-AA [79] was designed by recalibration of the OCCO torsional-energy parameters of DXE with QM calculations. The CHARMM force-field parameters (set C35) for linear and cyclic monoethers were revised in 2007 and extended for the description of diethers (set C35r) [103]. This model was validated in simulations of aqueous PEO and was found to reproduce very well a number of important experimental properties (dependence of the radius of gyration on the molecular weight, persistence length, hydrodynamic radius, and shape anisotropy). The Larson [104] model compatible with GROMOS45A3 [105] and involving modified non-bonded interaction parameters for the ether oxygen atom and OCCO torsional-energy parameters, was applied to study the interaction between PEO and sodium dodecyl sulfate (SDS) micelles. The Sadowski model [106] represents a modified version of the TraPPE-UA united-atom force field for ethers [107] and is based on the OCCO torsional-energy parameters developed earlier by Anderson and Wilson [102], and was applied in aqueous PEO simulations. The Boutin et al. [108] model is compatible with the AUA4 force field [109] and was designed for the study of phase-equilibrium and interfacial properties of liquid–vapor systems. The Bunker [110] model which is compatible with OPLS-AA [111] was developed for the investigation of PEGylated lipid bilayers. More recently, Roccatano and co-workers [91] have developed a new united-atom model for DXE, which is compatible with GROMOS. Finally, Fuchs et al. have recently updated the GROMOS53A6 parameters ($53A6_{OXY}$ [112] and $53A6_{OXY+D}$ [113]) for simulations of oxygen compounds (such as ethers, aldehydes, etc.) against available experimental data.

4.2.2. Coarse Grained Force Fields

Atomistic simulations of a large surfactant solution system during a long period of time may be today time consuming and computational expensive. Moreover, MD simulations using the "all-atoms" (AA) molecular model cannot be easily used to pursue non-equilibrium molecular processes (for example formation of self-organized mesostructure of amphiphiles) taking place in timescales in order of microseconds. To tackle these problems, simplified representation such as coarse-grained (CG) combined with MD or mesoscopic approaches (mainly Dissipative Dynamics Particles, DPD) can be used. In the CG approach, "pseudo-atoms" are used to represent groups of atoms instead of representing explicitly every atom of a system. Without any doubt, the most used coarse grained force field is the Martini force field [114–117]. It was developed by the groups of Marrink and Tieleman. Martini force field uses a four-to-one mapping (4:1 mapping), where; on average, four heavy atoms plus associated hydrogen are represented by a single interaction center. However, this mapping scheme can be too coarse to represent the correct geometry of small fragments or molecules (such as ring-like) and thus a higher resolution, up to 2 (i.e. two non-hydrogen atoms are equivalent to one Martini particle) is necessary.

The choice of this mapping scheme was dictated by computational efficiency and chemical representability. Water in Martini is modeled as one bead and is equivalent to 4 atomistic waters and an ion is modeled as a single bead by taking into account its first hydration shell. This mapping scheme reduces significantly the overall system size by a factor around 10 or more. Since, in the Martini force field (and in general all the coarse-grained based potentials) several atomistic degrees of freedom are missing compared to the atomistic potentials and thus coarse-grained interactions are much smoother compared to the atomistic counterpart, the energy landscape is highly simplified and thus allows a greatly increased sampling speed at the cost of a loss of detail. Inclusion of only short-range interactions and the use of smooth potentials allow to use large integration time steps of 20-40 fs for integration of the equation of motions [118]. The significant reduction of the simulated system size combined with the use of large time steps allows performing MD simulations with much longer time scales (>1 μs).

The Martini force field is versatile force field and covers a wide range of (bio)molecule types (for instance, amino-acids, peptides and proteins [116], [119], surfactants including phospholipids [114], [120], sterols [121], [122], polyethylene glycol based [123] and glycolipids [124]), sugars [125], [126], nucleic acids [127], polymers [128], [129], nanoparticles [130], [131], and more. MD simulations with surfactant CG models were successfully used to examine a wide range of phenomena, including lipid phase behavior (including formation of gel phases and inverted hexagonal and cubic phases, or transitions between micelles, bicelles, and vesicles, etc.), surfactant self-assembly [132], membrane peptide/protein lipid interplay [133], [134], membrane protein dimerization [135], self-assembly of soluble peptides/proteins and many others as discussed in reviews [115], [117]). Other CG force fields exist in literature, for example for the simulations of protein-membrane interactions [136], [137], large lipoprotein complexes [138] and amphiphilic diblock copolymers [139], [140]. These force fields differ mainly by the mapping scheme or the presence of different and additional terms in the potential energy function. Other promising approaches have also been developed to tackle the inherent limitation of the coarse grained approach: for example, to mix in the same simulation Martini and AA force fields [292].

Recently CG models of AOT and C_iE_j surfactants appeared in literature. The first model of AOT CG was constructed by Brodskaya and Mudzhikova [141–144] to simulate AOT RM. In their model, the AOT molecule is modeled with 7 beads instead of 66 atomic centers in the atomistic representation. Their CG model is similar to the Martini CG force field and was tested by examining structural and dynamical properties of AOT RM with different sizes (W_o up to 10), counterion types and simulation starting conditions (i.e. in preformed or self-assembled). More recently the group of Marrink has developed a new CG model of AOT based on Martini (personal communication). At this time, the model was only tested to examine the structures at different points of the AOT/Water/Octane ternary diagram. MD simulations of larger RM in currently are in progress (see below).

In case of the CG models for C_iE_j surfactants, the first one was developed by Shinoda et al. [155]. The authors were able to reproduce density and structural properties as calculated by all-atom simulations and the thermodynamic properties (surface tension, transfer and hydration free energies) as measured experimentally. In 2009, Lee et al. [156] have developed a coarse grained model based on Martini for PEO and PEG. These parameters were subsequently combined with the Martini parameters for alkane to simulate structural of $C_{12}E_j$ micelles in aqueous solution as a function of concentration and the hydrophilic headgroup chain length [157], [158].

However, these models suffer of two limitations: they have not been tested against the experimental phase of the surfactant and they can only be used with time steps smaller than or equal to 8 fs. To avoid these limitations, Rossi et al. [123] have recently developed a model for C_iE_j surfactants fully based on Martini allowing large time steps (20 – 25 fs), similar to the other molecules modeled with this force field. This model was tested against experimental data and all-atoms simulation results obtained for the self-assembly of two ternary mixtures water–surfactant mixtures.

Recently, we used the Martini AOT and C_iE_j CG models to simulate larger (up to $W_o >$ 11) AOT and C_iE_j RM systems (Figure 6). The originality of our approach compared to that of Brodskaya and Mudzhikova's is that we have firstly modeled the whole RM system into a coarse-grained representation to speed-up the surfactant aggregation process and subsequently converted the whole system into an atomistic representation for analysis of the RM characteristic properties (Figure 7). Our approach can be combined with the use of the

Martini force field for proteins, to model and simulate larger RM–protein complexes during timescales > 1μs unattainable with conventional MD simulations (unpublished results).

Yang et al. [159] also used a CG-based model for AOT (where the surfactant headgroup and two alkyl chains of the surfactant are modeled with one bead each) in the context of DPD simulations. With their simple model, these authors were able to characterize the various structures (i.e. lamellar, viscous isotropic and reverse hexagonal phases) formed by AOT at different points of the AOT/water phase diagram.

Table 1. Available force fields for AOT and Polyethyleneoxide (PEO) based surfactants. [a] For each model, the model name or author group, publication year, basis force field, force-field type, compatible water model and literature reference are indicated. [b] AA, all atom; UA, united atom; NP, non-polarizable, DP, polarizable and EP, explicit representation of electronic polarizability. [c] Compatible with GROMOS37C4. [d] Smith models with modified charges. Note that the different water models differ from each other by their charges bonded and non-bonded parameters. Adapted from [123]. Copyright 2012, American Chemical Society

Model[a]	Year	Basis force field[a]	type[b]	Water model	Ref.
AOT					
Brown and Clark	1988		LJ site	SPC[145]	[81]
Derecskei	1999	ESFF and UFF	UA/AA		[146]
Faeder	2000		LJ site	SPC/E[147]	[82]
Bandyopadhyay	2005	CHARMM27[88]	AA	TIP3P[148]	[83]
Ladanyi	2009	TraPPe[86], CHARMM27	UA	SPC/E	[85]
Martinez	2013	GROMOS53A6[80]	UA	SPC	[89]
Polyethyleneoxide (PEO)-based surfactants					
Smith	1993		AA/NP	TIP4P[148]	[94]
	1998		AA/NP	TIP4P	[90]
	2002		AA/NP	TIP4P	[96]
	2011		AA/EP	SWM4-DP[149]	[95]
Thomas	1994		AA/NP		[98]
Müller–Plathe [c]	1995	GROMOS37C4 [99]	UA/NP		[99], [100]
Tasaki [d]	1996	Smith model[94]	AA/NP	SPC	[150]
Kolafa and Ratnerg	1998		UA/EP		[101]
Anderson and Wilson	2004	OPLS-AA[79]	AA/NP	TIP4P	[102]
	2005		AA/NP	TIP4P	[151]
C35r	2008	CHARMMC35[152]	AA/NP	TIP3P	[103]
Larson	2008	GROMOS45A3[105]	UA/NP	SPC	[104]
Sadowski	2008	TraPPE-UA[107]	UA/NP	TIP4P-EW[153]	[106]
56A6CARBO	2010	GROMOS53A6	UA/NP	SPC	[154]
Boutin	2011	AUA4[109]	UA/NP		[108]
Bunker	2011	OPLS-AA	AA/NP	TIP3P	[110]
Roccatano	2011	GROMOS53A6 or OPLS-UA[111]	UA/NP	SPC or SPC/E	[91]

They were also able to show that the formation of a defective structure (i.e. pseudo reversed hexagonal phase) experimentally observed at intermediate AOT concentrations (about 40%) depends on the temperature. Interaction between two similar AOT RM was also considered by several authors by using the grand canonical ensemble Monte Carlo simulation (GCEMC) and by the linear response/Poisson–Boltzmann approximation (LPB) [160]. Their simulation results show that that the interaction force of two non-contacting micelles decreases in proportion to the logarithmic distance between them; moreover, the force depends substantially on the micellar size, the number and valence of ions, and the permittivity of the system.

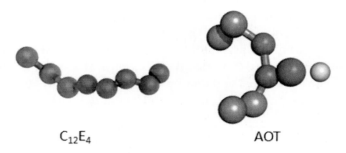

$C_{12}E_4$ AOT

Figure 6. (left) Martini coarse grained models for $C_{12}E_4$ based on ref. [123] and (right) AOT surfactants (unpublished results). In $C_{12}E_4$, each dark and light grey bead corresponds to CH_2OCH_2 group and C_4H_8 groups, respectively.

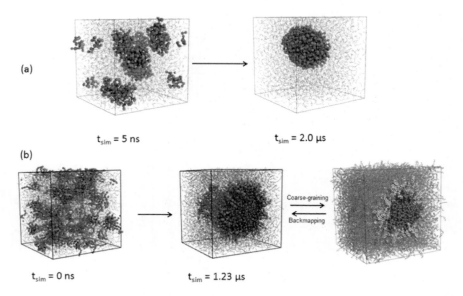

Figure 7. (a) Aggregation of a CG model of AOT RM with W_o=11. (b) CG model of $C_{12}E_4$ RM and comparison between the final coarse grain (CG) conformation of a $C_{12}E_4$ inverse micelle (W_o =11) in decane and its mapping to an all atom (AA) system. The number of atoms in the CG and all atom simulations are 14860 and 154606, respectively.

4.3. Simulation Methods

4.3.1. Quantum-Based Simulations

In quantum (*ab initio*) MD simulations such as Car–Parrinello MD (CPMD) [161] or other similar approaches [162], the electrons of the particles within the system are modeled explicitly and the atomic forces are calculated from first principles. Quantum Mechanics (QM) simulations give the most detailed modeling of interatomic interactions and allow examining phenomena such as chemical reactions (i.e. chemical bond breaking). Despite the recent advances in programming and the availability of large supercomputers, QM simulations remain nowadays, computational intensive and thus are generally limited to studies of small systems ($\sim 10^2$ particles) and during a short period of time (< 100 ps). To tackle these limitations, hybrid QM/MM (quantum mechanics/molecular mechanics) [163], [164] approaches can be used to combine the accuracy of the QM and the speed of molecular mechanics (MM). In the QM/MM simulations, a region of the system in which, for example a chemical process taking place is treated at an appropriate level of quantum chemistry theory, while the remainder is described by a molecular mechanics and a classical force field. Within this approach, chemical reactivity can be studied in the context of large systems (e.g. active site(s) of enzymes). Since a surfactant molecule is often composed of tens or hundreds of atoms and because surfactant solutions studies involve a large number of surfactant molecules, quantum simulations are not very much used to study surfactant solution behavior.

4.3.2. Classical Molecular Dynamics Simulations

In the classical MD simulations, the laws of classical mechanic are used to examine the motions of particles and atomic nuclei and treated using the classical mechanic. According to Newton's second law of motions, the forces $\mathbf{F}_i$ acting on each particle i are derivable from the potential energy function (also referred as a force field) of the system, $U(r_1, r_2, r_3, ... r_N)$, where N is the number of particles:

$$Fi = m_i \frac{d^2 r_i}{dt^2} = -\nabla U(r_1, r_2, r_3, ... r_N) \qquad (2)$$

The force field is a function of the nuclear position r_i where the electronic motions are taken into account according to the Born-Oppenheimer approximation. *From the knowledge of the force acting on each atom, it is possible to determine the acceleration of each atom in the system. Integration of the equations of motion then yields an (atomic) trajectory describing the positions, velocities and accelerations of the particles as they vary with time. The method is deterministic: once the positions and velocities of each atom are known, the state of the system can be predicted at any time in the future or the past. With molecular dynamics simulations, one can study both the thermodynamic properties and/or the time dependent (kinetic) phenomena [71]. A typical workflow used in MD studies is given in Figure 8.* Combined with coarse grained models of surfactant, these approaches can be used to simulate large surfactant complexes (such as vesicles or membrane domains) during long timescales. The atomic trajectories generated during the MD simulation production phase consist in a large number of system configurations (microscopic states) over time. The macroscopic observables (such as temperature, pressure) are related to the microscopic observables *via* the formalism of the statistical mechanics [71], [165]: physical observables are represented by averaging the microscopic states of the system (*ergodic hypothesis*) distributed according certain *ensembles* (*i.e.* collection of points in the space phase satisfying the conditions of a particular thermodynamic state). Initially MD simulations were carried out in the micro-canonical ensemble (i.e. NVE) where the number of atoms, N, the volume, V and the energy E are constant. During the end of the last century, different formulations and algorithms [71] appeared to simulate in other ensembles such as the canonical ensemble (NVT, characterized by a fixed number of atoms, N, volume, V and temperature, T), isobaric-isothermal ensemble (N*PT* where the number of atoms, N is fixed, as well as the pressure, P and the temperature) and generalized ensemble (e.g. replica exchange method (REMD)) [166], [167].

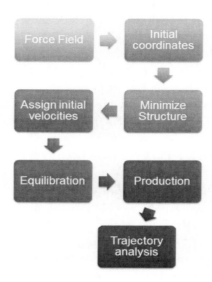

Figure 8. Simplified workflow during a MD simulation study. Minimization of the initial coordinates of the model according to the force field parameters in order to find the potential energy minimum. Initial velocities are assigned to each atom at a given temperature according to Boltzmann distribution and Newton's equations are integrated to propagate the system in time. Once the desired temperature is reached, the simulation continues and all properties (i.e. structure, energy, temperature, pressure, etc.) can be monitored. During the production phase, the coordinates (and velocities) are saved periodically for further structural and thermodynamic analysis of the simulated system.

Classical MD simulation has a number of important limitations to be kept in mind. Among these, the potential energy function requires a large number of parameters for partial charges, van der Waals interactions and equilibrium values for bonds, angles, dihedrals and force constants. These parameters should be adequately chosen from experimental or QM data to ensure that simple form potential energy function is able to describe correctly the modeled system and thus provide accurate simulation results. The omission of atomic polarizability in the commonly used force fields (i.e. atoms are represented as point charges) influences the force field parameters in such a way that average effects of polarizability are retained but detailed effects are not properly represented. In addition, some parameters like the dispersion in the van der Waals interactions and the height of the barriers in the dihedral potentials are difficult to determine, so that extensive tests and comparison with experimental data are needed to obtain the force field parameters.

4.3.3. Mesoscopic Simulations

To obtain phase structure information and hydrodynamic behavior of large systems containing millions of particles up to microseconds, one can use mesoscopic simulations such as Dissipative Particles Dynamics (DPD). DPD is a stochastic simulation technique introduced by Hoogerbrugge and Koelman [168] and the group of de Groot and Warren [169], [170]. In DPD, molecules, cluster or atomic regions are modeled according soft spheres or DPD beads and individual atoms or molecules are lumped together into quasi-particles, which interact via pairwise forces and obey the Newton equations of motion. To reproduce the molecule chemical structure and rigidity, the beads are connected by harmonic bond potentials $F^{(B)}_{ij}$. Random $F^{(R)}_{ij}$ and drag $F^{(D)}_{ij}$ forces take into account fluctuation and dissipation of energy and serve as the Langevin thermostat [171]. Beads can be connected to "molecules" by tying them together with soft springs allowing simulations of mesoscopic structure of surfactants and long polymers, with arbitrary branching and loop structure. DPD simulations are accurate methods for the studies of surfactant self-assemblies (i.e. micellization), polymer adsorption, polymer–surfactant interactions, mesophase formation of surfactant, etc. [172–175] and in recent reviews [176], [177].

4.3.4. Simulations of Surfactant Solutions

Finally, to carry out simulations of surfactants in solution, one needs to choose how the solvent phase is represented. Two approaches can be used to model the solvent phase (i.e. water or oil): in the first one, the solvent molecules are modeled explicitly with particles of different granularity (i.e. all atoms, united atom or coarse-grained) and with the use of periodic boundary conditions to mimic the bulk solvent phase. In this case, the simulation box size must be large enough to avoid boundary condition artifacts. In the second approach much less computational intensive, the solvent phase is modeled implicitly by using a mean-field and a defined dielectric constant. Examples of RM simulations using these two approaches are described in the next section.

5. COMPUTATIONAL SIMULATIONS OF REVERSE MICELLES

In this section, we provide a "cook-book" and a few rules to construct an experimentally correct reverse micellar system for subsequent simulation studies. We will take as example RM formed with AOT, but the approach and rules described below can be applied and generalized for other RM systems with confined peptide/protein with different molecular representation (i.e. atomistic or coarse grained).

5.1. How to Construct a RM System for Simulations Studies?

As indicated in the MD workflow depicted in Figure 8, before any simulation, it is prerequisite to construct an atomic model of the reverse micellar system. For this purpose, we have to choose between two approaches and different building protocols. The choice of the approach depends on aims of the study and the computational resources available for the simulations:

- In the first approach, the RM is modeled according to a simplified model where the RM aqueous core is represented by a spherical cavity with a rigid wall (Figure 9). The cavity is embedded in a continuous medium with a defined dielectric constant modeling the surfactant hydrophobic tails and the hydrocarbon solvent. In this representation, the surfactant headgroup is modeled as a single Lennard-Jones (LJ) site, uniformly distributed over the internal cavity. Each LJ site interacts with each other by LJ pair potential.

- Counterions and water modeled explicitly are fixed [178] or free to move [82], [85], [179–184] in the cavity. Interactions with the nonpolar shell are described with LJ potentials and interactions between the force centers are calculated employing the LJ and Coulombic interaction potentials. This approach was initially employed by Linse and Halle [178] for a model of RM formed with surfactants with a carboxylate headgroup and improved later by other authors [82], [85], [179–181], [185] for simulations of ionic [82], [85], [179–181], [183], [185] and nonionic surfactant-based RM [183], [186].

- In the second approach, each (or a part of) molecules in the micellar system are modeled explicitly with a different level of representation (e.g. with an explicit [97], [187–195], united [85], [89], [184], [186], [196–199] or coarse grained [142], [200]). With this approach, the RM system can be constructed by choosing between two protocols: "pre-assembled" or a "self-assembled".

In the "pre-assembled" approach, the RM is constructed by hand or with the help of a computational program, assuming that the RM and its water pool are spherical (Figure 9). For AOT RM, the number of surfactant, N_{AOT}, water molecules, N_{H2O} and the RM water core radius values, R_{H2O}, are chosen according to the W_o values and experimental data obtained, by SAXS, SANS, for instance. Firstly, a spherical water cluster with a radius of R_{H2O} containing N_{H2O} water is constructed. After that, the desired number of AOT monomers (including counterions) in extended (or planar) conformation is placed around the water sphere surface, the tails outside pointing toward the micelle. To avoid any steric clash between water and the AOT headgroups (here the SO_3^-), a slightly larger (± 3 Å) distance can be used for d_{AOT}. The resulting RM is then placed in a sufficiently large simulation box filled with the desired number of solvent molecules, N_{solv} to mimic a RM phase regime and to avoid any periodic artifacts due to the periodic boundary conditions.

It was recently found by several authors [89], [200–202] that to construct RM with a pre-assembled approach can be problematic if the RM are not spherical, in particular in case of RM with a small water loading. Moreover, since in this approach we have used a single conformation for the surfactant during the RM construction, and because the AOT tails are very flexible, long equilibration stages (i.e. dozens of ns) will be required to obtain stable RM aggregates [193], [194], [202]. However, previously simulations of AOT [97], [141–143], [184], [187], [189], [201–203] and C_iE_j [97], [186] water-free RM, a peptide [18], [89], [97] or protein containing RM [189] have used this approach. To tackle the "starting condition problem", we strongly suggest using the "self-assembled" approach to construct the RM system. In this approach, a defined number of surfactant monomers and water molecules (generally equal to the surfactant and water numbers needed to form a single micelle) are randomly placed in the simulation box filled with solvent molecules. This approach is largely more computationally expensive than the "preformed" one because of a long simulation time (> 100 ns or more if the concentration of solvent is large) is required to obtain a single RM with water forming a cluster and the surfactant around it. Due to the large increase of surfactant, water and solvent molecules with W_o, such approach is limited in practice in atomistic simulations of RM with $W_o < 11$. This approach can also be used to study the self-aggregation process of surfactants into RM or around peptides/proteins.

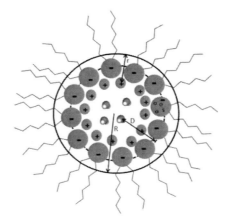

Figure 9. Model of a RM interior of Faeder and Ladanyi. The sulfonate headgroups, modeled as single negative sites, are constrained by radial-direction springs to remain close to the cavity surface, the surfactant tails and the nonpolar phase as a spherical nonpolar cavity. The solid circle marks the boundary of the hydrophobic cavity. The dotted circle shows the equilibrium positions of the headgroups, confined by a harmonic potential and also determines the van der Waals radius of the cavity. D marks the distance between an atomic center and the dotted circle, while d is the distance to the cavity boundary. R is the total radius of the cavity. Adapted from [82]. Copyright 2000, American Chemical Society.

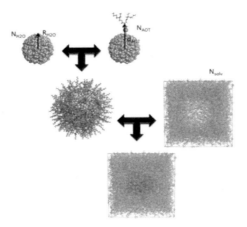

Figure 10. Successive steps for building a RM system with the pre-assembled protocol. N_{H2O}, N_{AOT}, N_{SOLV}, R_{H2O} and R_{AOT}, are the numbers of water, AOT and solvent molecules. R_{H2O}, R_{AOT}, are the water cluster and AOT radii assuming a spherical shape for the water core and the micelle.

5.2. History of Reverse Micelles Simulation

5.2.1. Simulations of Peptide/Protein-Free RM

During the last decades, a considerable amount of MD was devoted to study structural and dynamical properties of RM summarized in recent reviews [204], [205]. In this section, we will provide an overview of the RM previous models.

The earliest molecular dynamics (MD) simulation of a RM was carried out at the end of 80's by Brown and Clark [81] using single-site interaction models for the nonpolar solvent molecules, hydrocarbon tails (n-octane), and the positively charged headgroups. Their simulation time was short (100 ps), but they were able to examine the stability of the aggregate over time and the structural properties of water and ions. These simulations were followed by those of Linse [178] with a simplified model of RM and aqueous core. The system consisted of sodium ions and water molecules, spherically enclosed by a hydrophobic interface carrying carboxylate headgroups as depicted in Figure 9. A similar model in spirit was used by Faeder et al. [82], [179], [181], [185], Rosenfeld and Schmuttenmaer [182] and Biswas et al. [206] to study extensively and rigorously, the structural and dynamical properties of counterion and water in the aqueous core of AOT RM as a function of different parameters (aqueous core size, counterion nature or presence of charged chromophores). Later, the same group of authors [179], [181] and Pal et al. [207] using the same model, examined the counterion exchange (K^+, Na^+ and Cs^+) on the AOT RM structure. In another study, Faeder et al. [185] examined the effects of solute−headgroup electrostatic interactions on water solvation dynamics with two models of diatomic chromophores positively and negatively solvated in RM with a W_o value from 2 to 7.5. In a recent work by combining dynamic fluorescence and the Faeder-Ladanyi's RM model, Guchhait et al. [183] have studied the aqueous pool-size dependent solvation energy and rotational relaxations of a neutral dipolar solute, C153, trapped in AOT (charged) and IGPAL (neutral) RM.

The first atomistic simulations of aqueous RM, in which all components are explicitly modeled were probably those carried out by Griffiths and Heyes [208] and Tobias and Klein [196] on calcium carbonate. In their study, Tobias and Klein simulated a RM formed with 102 calcium carbonate, 11 calcium (2-hexadecyl)benzenesulfonate, and 22 water molecules in vacuum solvated in CCl_4 and octane.

The authors showed that in both solvents the RM has a similar structure and that when the micelle is simulated in vacuum, the surfactant tails collapse onto the surface of the core, producing a much more compact micelle.

The first MD simulation of AOT RM with a complete model of the surfactant was carried out in 1997 by Alaimo and Kumosinski [209]. The authors used an all-atom potential to simulate the surfactant, water and the apolar solvent (toluene) and they examined only the issue of the aggregation stability. In 2004, we performed the first atomistic simulations of small-size AOT RM in isooctane [187].

In these simulations, we examined the influence of the micellar size (W_o = 3 to 7) on the RM structure and water dynamics. In this work, the RM composition and the L_2 were rigorously modeled according to SAXS, high precision densimetry and ultrasound velocimetry data [210]. Later on, several authors [89], [201], [202] have shown that the simulation parameters the influence of different simulation parameters (i.e. force field, micelle construction and ion nature on the micelle structure) may influence strongly the simulation results in particular the micelle shape behavior. Chowdhary and Ladanyi [85],

[211] with a mixture of all-atom and united atom force fields but different aggregation numbers (from Eicke et Rehak [212]) for the micelle simulations similar to ours with a different aggregation number, they also examined the structure and the water dynamics.

MD of RM formed with fluoro-based surfactants [190–192], [197], [213–215] or an AOT analogue (AOK (aerosol-octyl-ketone), a non-fluorinated hydrocarbon surfactant with two symmetrical carbonyl groups in the tail) [216] in supercritical CO_2 (ScCO$_2$) were also carried out. In a first work, Salaniwal et al. [213] have examined the self-assembly and the stability of RM formed with a dichain flurosurfactant $(C_7F_{15})(C_7H_{15})CHSO_4^-Na^+$ in scCO$_2$. Their work demonstrated for the first time that MD simulations can be useful to examine the RM structure with this type of surfactant. In a second work [197], the same authors examined in detail the surfactant chemical structure, the water structure and the dynamics and the stability of the aggregate.

Furthermore by combining SANS and MD methods, Senapati et al. [191], [192] were able to demonstrate that a phosphate-based fluorosurfactant can form stable RM aggregates in ScCO2. Later, Chaitanya and Senapati [214] also showed that the aqueous core of phosphate-based fluorosurfactant RM can constitute a non-denaturing environment for proteins. In another work, Sanepati et Berkowitz [215] have studied the effect of the nature of counterions (Na^+, NH_4^+ and Ca^{2+}) on the structure of perfluorinated polyoxyethylene (FPE) RM (at W_o=8.4) and the state of water. They found that all RM were approximately spherical in shape, but that the nature of ion influences the interfacial intermolecular arrangements and the water dynamics. The first explicit simulations of a nonionic RM was carried out by Allen et al. [186] with a small model (W_o = 2.4) of $C_{12}E_2$ RM. They compared on their short simulation time (300 ps), the structural behavior of micelle and the water dynamic in vacuum and in decane. Several years after, we carried out longer simulations (3 ns) [97] with larger models of $C_{12}E_4$ RM (W_o = 3) to examine the effect of the surfactant headgroup conformation (i.e. helical and extended) on the RM microscopic properties (such as size and shape) and the confined water structural and dynamical properties.

5.2.2. Simulation of Reverse Micelles with Confined Peptides and Proteins

Simulations of RM with peptides or proteins appeared recently (2006) in literature and are scarce compared to simulations of peptide/protein-free RM, probably because important phenomena such as peptide/protein folding or denaturing effects induced by the RM environment require large reverse micellar systems and long simulations.

To the best of our knowledge, the first simulation of AOT RM with a confined peptide was carried out by us in 2006 [97] with a 8 residue-long alanine peptide (A8) in helical conformation, with the same model as in ref. [187]. The main goal of the work was to examine the influence of the AOT headgroups and RM water content on the A8 structural stability. A few years after, Tian and Garcia [194], Straub and co-workers [18] examined the localization the structure and of alanine amphipatic peptides in larger AOT RM (up to W_o = 11 and W_o = 6, respectively). At the same moment, Chaitanya and Senapati [214] carried out MD simulations of ionic RM (W_o = 8.4) formed with a dichain flurosurfactant (CF$_3$-(O-CF$_2$-CF(CF$_3$))$_3$-O-CF$_2$-COO-NH$_4^+$) in ScCO2 with a small model of protein (Trp-Cage, 20 residues long). They examined the aggregate stability and the protecting role the micelle aqueous core on the protein. Several years later with the increase of the computational resources, larger and longer simulations of AOT RM including confined proteins (i.e. Cytochrome c [189] and Ubiquitin [193]) appeared in literature (section 5.5). The main goal of these studies was to examine the effects of (i) the macromolecular insertion on the RM behavior and (ii) the effect of confinement and interactions between the peptides/proteins and the surfactant headgroups on the confined macromolecular stability as a function of the micelle size and water content.

5.3. Structural Properties of Reverse Micelles

Many different structural properties of the reverse micelle can be obtained from simulation trajectories that can be confronted with experiments. In this section, we will only discuss several of them often computed in the reverse micelles simulation studies.

5.3.1. Size of Reverse Micelles

The size of RM and its water core (including only the surfactant headgroup, water atoms), is often examined by computing the radius of gyration. This value can be compared with SAXS (in case of the water core) [217] and with DLS experiments (in case of the whole RM ([89], [201]). In most cases, the experimental linear dependence between the micelle core radius, R_w and the water-to-surfactant molar ratio is correctly reproduced by simulations [217].

5.3.2. Shape of Reverse Micelles

In the last decades, investigators working on RM have assumed a spherical shape for them. They have therefore constructed a geometric model of RM as a sphere displaying a central water core, of a radius increasing with the water content W_o, the water-to-surfactant molar ratio, all the surfactant being located at the water interface. This model has been referred to as the « aggregation » or the « equipartition » model (see ref. [5] for details and references herein). The model allows RM structural parameters to be deduced from purely geometrical considerations [51]. Experimental measurements using a wide range of physical techniques, i.e. spectral as well as scattering measurements [21] are consistent with the aggregation model. This is illustrated by Figure 3(c) where a linear relation between the water core radius R_w and W_o [29], measured by several techniques (DLS, SAXS, SANS, etc.) is found. However, the figure also suggests that at low W_o value (i.e. smaller than 10), the spherical model is not adequate to fit the experimental data and thus the applicability of the linear equation $R_w(W_o) = aW_o + b$ is limited. Indeed, since many parameters can affect the micelle shape (for instance, the effect of the ions [218], [219], temperature [42], [220], etc.) the nature of the micelle shape at low water content, remains still on debate [221]. Christ and Schurtenberger [43] have reexamined and refined the « aggregation » model taking into account the micellar polydispersity, γ, by using static and dynamic light scattering measurements. They estimated a polydispersity factor between 0.035 and 0.01 for AOT in decane. Similar polydispersity values were also found by Pal and co-workers [222] (around 0.04) and Tovstun and Razumov [223] (0.066) for AOT RM in isooctane at $W_o > 20$, with fluorescence correlation spectroscopy and DLS experiments, respectively. As indicated above, when the RM micelle is modeled by a rigid cavity embedded into a dielectric continuum as in Faeder and Landany's models, no information about the interactions between surfactant molecules or between the surfactant and the nonpolar solvent can be obtained. In addition, when the RM is spherically constrained, the possible deformation in shape of the RM (and its water core) cannot be examined.

In molecular dynamics when the RM are completely modeled, the shape of the aggregate can be characterized by computing the micelle semi-axis, a, b and c from the inertia tensor [187]. With these quantities, it is then possible to obtain the eccentricity factor, $e = \sqrt{(a^2 - c^2)/a^2}$ [224]. For a perfect sphere, $e \to 0$, whereas for a rod-like, $e \to 1$. These values can be used to compare the simulation results with the aggregate shape (and semi-axis values) deduced from the experimental SAXS and SANS data, for instance.

With the exception of the work of Nevidimov et Razumov [200] where the authors show that the shape of their AOT RM agree reasonably well with the spherical model described in experiments, all the previous explicit or CG RM simulations found that RM are not spherical but evolved quickly from a sphere to a rod-like or more surprisingly, a donut-like shape [89], [201] with an eccentricity around 0.6 – 0.8. In the latter study, the authors compared the micelle size obtained in their simualtions with DLS experiments [201] and found a fair agreement.

The effect on the salt ions (Zr^{4+}) on the shape of large AOT RM, was examined by Graeve et co-workers [201], [202] with atomistic simulations. They found that its size decreases and becomes less ellipsoidal when the concentration in salt increases in the RM. Mudzhikova and Brodskaya [144] using their coarse grained model investigated the properties of NaAOT, KAOT and Ca(AOT)$_2$ RM for $W_o = 10$. They found that the RM shape was larger for Ca(AOT) ($e = 0.62$) than KAOT ($e = 0.45$), whereas the NaAOT and KAOT were closer to a spherical shape. Distortions of the AOT RM shape (i.e. transition sphere *vs.* cylinder or *vice-versa*) with the ion exchange are consistent with experiments [225–228].

Several authors [89], [200–202], [229] have also examined with different models of AOT RM, the possible parameters which may influence the RM shape fluctuations in the simulations such as the protocol, the RM composition (i.e. number of surfactant and waters as function of W_o), the simulation time length and the nature of the counterion. For example, Gardner al. [202] and Nevidimov and Razumov [229] observed in their simulations significant deviations from the initial spherical shape for small RM ($W_o = 3$) within 1 ns of simulation time and in general, RM tend to be spherical at higher *water loading* values ($W_o = 15$) while at values of $W_0 < 5$ the shape tends to be more ellipsoidal or cylindrical, even if the simulation time length is large enough (here 425 ns). The authors concluded that starting from preassembled RM might not be appropriate if the simulations are run for relatively short times and if the aggregates are small (i.e. $W_o < 10$). In another work, Graeve et al. [201] and Martinez et al. [89] observed that the properties of the RM are more dependent on the size ($W_o = 6$ *vs.* 10) and on the force field (CHARMM27 and GROMOS53A6) used than on the absolute composition. The authors suggested that the difference of the micelle shape between simulations can be explained by the force field used. Indeed, in the GROMOS force field, all the aliphatic carbons have their partial charges set to 0, in contrast to CHARMM. The lack of Coulombic interactions between the water molecules and the AOT tails may avoid the diffusion of the confined water into the aliphatic tail region leading to a more compact and rigid structure of the water pool and by consequence a more rigid RM.

5.3.3. Reverse Micelle Interior

Simulations can be useful to provide data of the RM interior by locating the different components (i.e. water, counterions, surfactant headgroups and alkyl tails) of the system. This is done by computing the average radial density function $\rho(r)$ as function of distance r from the RM center of mass (COM). For the component a, the function $\rho_a(r)$ is defined such as [187]:

$$\rho(r)_a dr = \langle \sum_i \delta(r - r_i) \frac{m_i}{4\pi r^2} \rangle \qquad (3)$$

where the sum $\sum_i$ extends to all the atoms of the component a, m_i is the mass of the ith atom, and <...> is the ensemble average. Since ρ_a(r), is computed for a sphere, therefore we observe in case of a non-spherical aggregate broadening and overlap of these density functions and can differ significantly from RM modeled as a rigid cavity [82]. Figure 11 shows the ρ(r) curves obtained in case of the AOT RM with $W_o = 2 - 7$ [29], [187].

As can be seen, the density profiles of water in the interior of the RM are nonzero in a very broad hydrophilic core region and cross with $\rho_{AOT}(r)$ at distances increasing with the dimension of the reverse micelle. In all cases studied here, the water region contains the system ions.

The oil never penetrates into the interior of the micelles and the overlap between $\rho_{oil}(r)$ and $\rho_{H2O}(r)$ is very small. Moreover, overlaps of the $\rho_{oil}(r)$ and $\rho_{AOT}(r)$ profiles suggest that oil can penetrate into AOT alkyl tail layer. A similar profile can be also computed for nonionic RM [97].

5.3.4. Surfactant Headgroups and Counterion Hydration

The corresponding number of nearest neighbors (i.e. coordination number) of molecules near the RM headgroups, water or counterions can be computed by integrating until the first minimum following the first peak radial pair distribution functions, $g_o(r)$ between two atom pair. In short, the simulations showed that with the increase of water in RM, the number of Na^+-Na^+ pairs decreases (3.00 – 1.6 for RM $W_o = 2$ - 7.5) and the number of Na^+-water pairs increases (i.e. 1.50 - 2.3 for RM $W_o = 2$ - 7.5) [85].

The number of water oxygens in the first coordination shell of each Na^+ for $W_o = 2$ is 1.50 and increases up to 2.3 for $W_o = 7.5$. In case of the AOT headgroup hydration, an increase of the W_o value causes an increase of the water in AOT headgroup first shell (i.e. 2.6 – 10.0 for RM $W_o = 2$ - 7.5, respectively). Simulations [29], [85] also showed that the confined water can diffuse beyond the headgroups and hydrates significantly the C=O oxygen atoms of AOT.

In case of the polyoxyethylene alkyl ether RM, explicit simulations [97] showed that an hydration gradient along the surfactant headgroup exists where the number of waters near the oxygen atom of the headgroup increases with the proximity of the atom to the water pool. The hydration level of the headgroup depends on the headgroup conformation, since we found that the PEO headgroup in the all trans conformation is on average hydrated 2 fold higher that the same chain in the helix conformation, in agreement with experiments [230], [231].

The effect of the contention exchange on counterion and surfactant headgroup hydration was firstly examined by Faeder et al. [179] with their simple model of AOT RM at $W_o = 1 -$

10. They found that the main difference in the properties of the two types of RM is due to the fact that K^+ is larger and less hydrophilic than Na^+ and thus has a stronger tendency to coordinate to the headgroup rather than to water.

This leads K^+ ions to expel water to a larger extent than Na^+ ions from the headgroup region. In view of the weaker tendency of K^+ to coordinate water, interfacial mobility of water in KAOT was found to be higher than in NaAOT. Harpham et al. [181] found a similar trend in the case of CsAOT RM. In a similar study, Pal et al. [207] examined with the Faeder and Ladanyi's model the effect of adding alkali salts of Li^+, Na^+, K^+, and Cs^+ in the RM aqueous core. The main result of this work was that K^+ and Cs^+ had a tendency to replace Na^+ in the interfacial region, while Li^+ preferred to remain in the RM core and is solvated to the same extent as in bulk water.

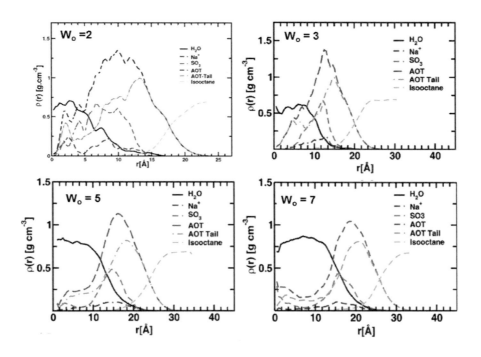

Figure 11. Radial density profiles with respect to the center of mass for the AOT RM with different water loading. Figures adapted from [29], [187]. Copyright 2004 American Chemical Society.

5.4. Water in Reverse Micelles

5.4.1. Water Structure

The unusual physical properties of water confined in RM have been the subject of a considerable amount of publications. The reader will find most of them in the bibliographic section, in particular in reviews [3], [8–10], [12], [232]. It was found that at low W_o values, the activity of micellar water decreased as well as its dielectric constant and polarity, preventing its freezing at 0°C: this property has been used in cryo-enzymologic studies [49]. Furthermore, micellar water at the surfactant surface in relatively small AOT micelles looks similar to interfacial water existing at membrane or protein surfaces, in fact very different from bulk water. At a W_o value above 10, two populations of water molecules have been described: the first one bound to the surfactant surface, the hydration layer, and the second one present in the central core, similar to what is called bulk water. As the value of W_o increases, the latter population increases at the same time. The high electrostatic interactions between the negative charges of the polar sulfonate headgroup and water induce electrostriction of water molecules. However the geometrical model used by most investigators requires all water molecules to occupy an identical average volume (30 Å³). Ultrasonic velocity measurements of water confined in RM in a range from $W_o = 2$ to 25 show a substantial variation of water adiabatic compressibility. Calculations indicate a decrease of water specific volume at low W_o values [233]. However, at very low values of W_o, the water volume obtained might be affected by a significant experimental error. Nevertheless, measured by neutron and X-ray solution scattering the density of the water at the surface of lysozyme is 15% denser than « bulk » water [234]. In another set of experiments carried out by X-ray solution scattering (SAXS) on solutions of *E. Coli* thioredoxin reductase, it was found that the average density of a first hydration shell had a density 10 % larger than « bulk » water [235], suggesting it might constitute a general property of aqueous charged interfaces. However, in our simulations [29], where we computed the Voronoi volume, V_{H2O}^v, [236], [237] of confined water in AOT RM in the range of $W_o = 2 - 7$ we found that the V_{H2O}^v does not change significantly. To the best of our knowledge we are not aware of other studies having examined this aspect, so far.

5.4.2. Water Dynamics: Interfacial and Bulklike Waters

Water dynamics in AOT RM has also been measured experimentally by a number of spectroscopic techniques such as ultrafast infrared spectroscopy [238], infrared vibrational pump-probe experiments [184], [239] and quasi-elastic neutron scattering (QENS) [180]. These investigations have shown that water environment inside the RM can be described by a two component model, as indicated in the previous section: a shell of interfacial waters that hydrate the AOT headgroup and a bulklike water core. By using this model, the group of Fayer [6], [180], [181], [239–246] has employed ultrafast IR spectroscopy of the hydroxyl stretch and given a detailed description of the dynamics of both the core bulklike and interfacial shells of water confined in RM. The results indicate that the core/shell model, adopted by a large number of investigators, reproduced accurately the experimental IR spectra and the vibrational lifetime OD stretch for all RM [6], [247]. In contrast, the orientational dynamics did not fit the same model. For the largest RM ($W_o = 46$) the IR spectrum is similar to bulk water, but slightly shifted to higher frequencies. Such a shift is more and more pronounced when the micelle size decreases to $W_o=2.0$. The interfacial water is blue shifted compared to bulk, defining thus two populations of water. In small RM ($W_o = 1 - 5$), water is considered mainly bound to the surfactant headgroups with a mobility strongly W_o dependent and quite different from bulk water mobility. At low W_o values (from 1 to 2.5) water is considered frozen with translational diffusion quasi-undetectable by QENS [180]. With their FTIR studies Das et al. [248] and Moilanen et al. [246] showed that the relative population of the surface-bound water molecules is higher in AOT RM compared to that in Igepal RM, and in mixed systems it also follows a linear trend with Igepal, indicating that physical properties of water in RM are mostly governed by the interfacial stoichiometry and water content.

Translational diffusion of the confined water. In MD simulations, the translational (or self) diffusion coefficient, D_{trans}, of molecules can be obtained from the Einstein relation with the mean square displacement (MSD) $(D_{trans} = \lim_{t\to\infty}[\langle r(t) - r(0)\rangle^2]/6t)$ or via the Green-Kubo relation and the velocity autocorrelation function [71]. It is known [249] that translational (or self) diffusion coefficient (and other dynamical properties) of the classical water models (i.e. TIP3P [145], SPC [147], SPC/E [147]) used in the RM simulations differ from experiments, therefore it is not expected that the simulation results closely match with the experimental ones, only qualitative information can be provided from the simulations.

As it was found previously in inhomogeneous media [250] and near protein or micelle surfaces [251], the mean square displacement (MSD) translational diffusion of the water in the RM presents a sub-diffusive regime which obeys a power law (i.e. $t^{\alpha} \propto [\langle r(t) - r(0)\rangle^2]$, where $\alpha < 1$) denoting a dispersive diffusion. Several authors [82], [97], [185], [217] have computed the water translational diffusion in RM. In our earlier work on AOT RM [187], we computed the water translational diffusion in AOT RM with $W_o = 2 - 7$ (Figure 12) and deduced the water retardation with the water residence time, τ_w, as a measure of the diffusion intensity. τ_w was defined as the time required for a water molecule to cover a distance equal to his own diameter (i.e. 3 Å). As can be seen, the water translational diffusion is strongly reduced in the smallest AOT RM (Figure 12(a)) and increases with the W_o value to reach the diffusion of the bulk water at larger W_o values. In the case of the $C_{12}E_4$ RM, we showed that the water diffusion is smaller than the bulk water and also depends on the surfactant conformation (Figure 12(b)).

However, in this work, we did not take into account the water different environment in the calculation and thus the computed water diffusion corresponds to the diffusion of all the water molecules wherever they are located within the RM core. A more rigorous approach was used by Faeder et al.[82][185] [179] [183] to compute the water dynamical properties in the RM. The authors separated the water into different sub-shells as function of their distance from the surfactant headgroup. They defined 6 regions (i.e. trapped, bound, free I, free II, free III and free IV, where for the three latter regions $4.5 < D < 7.5$ Å, $7.5 < D < 10.5$ Å, $10.5 < D < 13.5$ Å and $D > 13.5$ Å, respectively) according the distance D from the core surface. The main result of their studies is that water in the bound region is much more mobile than trapped water and has a mobility closer to that of free water, although the difference in mobility between the bound and free water increases with W_0. The water mobility within each region increases with micelle size. The mobility change is the largest for trapped water, which is about one order of magnitude less mobile in the micelle at $W_o = 1$ compared to the $W_o = 10$ micelle.

Confined Water Relaxation Shows Nonexponential Behavior. Not only is the water translational diffusion modified in RM, but also its rotational movement. This can be examined by computing the water dipole−dipole autocorrelation function, $C(t) = \langle\vec{\mu}(0).\vec{\mu}(t)\rangle/\vec{\mu}^2$.

The dipole rotational mobility trends are essentially the same as those observed for the translational diffusion. Further simulations [82], [181] showed that the water dipole reorientation is very slow at the interface but increases sharply in the bound layer and grows still further in the core. The mobility within each layer also increases with micelle size. The reorientation of water in RM is highly non-exponential, involving a long-lived tail that is pronounced in all regions but becomes very large near the interface. The water reorientation at the interface is enhanced by molecules moving out of the interfacial region, while the mobility on the interior appears slower because some molecules migrate to the interface, where they are essentially frozen.

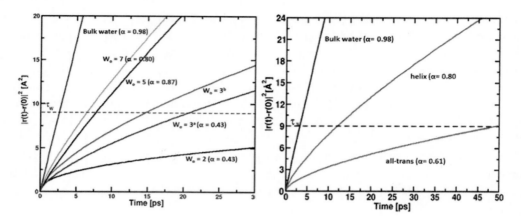

Figure 12. Plot of the mean square displacement of the confined water oxygen atoms in the AOT (left) and $C_{12}E_4$ (right) reverse micelles versus time, t, In AOT and $C_{12}E_4$ simulations, the TIP3P and SPC water models were used, respectively. τ_w is the water the residence time (see main text for details). Figures adapted from [29], [97], [187]. Copyright 2004 and 2006, American Chemical Society.

The rotational anisotropy correlation function (ACF) can also be computed from the dot product of the unit vectors, $\vec{u}$, in the direction of the O–H bonds, and then calculating the correlation function of the second Legendre polynomial, P_2, as :

$$C_2(t) = \langle P_2(\vec{u}(t).\vec{u}(0)) \rangle \qquad (4)$$

where $P_2(x) = (3x^2-1)/2$ and $x=\cos\theta = \langle \vec{u}(t).\vec{u}(0) \rangle$ [252]. The limit of $\langle P_2(x) \rangle \rightarrow 0$ indicates a random, isotropic system with fast decay times, whereas $\langle P_2(x) \rangle \rightarrow 1$ indicates a more ordered system with slow decay times. Experiments [184] show that confined water rotates slowly and has a long rotational anisotropy decay time. Rotational anisotropy decay times for water in RM can be extracted by fitting the ACF to exponential functions [184], [239], [253]. It was shown that the rotational anisotropy decay of bulk water and water in large RM ($W_o = 20, 40, 60$) can be fitted to a single exponential function. This is not the case for small reverse micelles ($W_o < 20$), where the rotational anisotropy decay cannot be fitted with a single exponential function but with multiple [206] or stretched exponentials (i.e. $e^{-(x/\tau)\beta}$) [184] with multiple relaxation times on short time scales ($\sim 10 - 20$ ps), and power law decay on longer time scales [254]. Piletic et al. [253] found that for RM of $W_o \leq 10$, the water orientational relaxation behaved bi-exponentially with long decay times of 50, 30, and 18 ps and short decay times of 0.9, 1.0, and 1.5 ps for RM of $W_o = 2, 5,$ and 10, respectively. In their simulations of AOT RM with $W_o = 6 - 10$, Martinez et al. [89] computed the ACF for the confined water, they found that ACF curves can be fitted with triexponential or a starched functions up to ~ 20 ps, but fail to capture the longer decay time features of the ACF. A fit of the ACF with multiple exponentials indicates multiple "types of water" in the RM water, each "type" being associated with a particular mean relaxation time [206].

The authors found τ values ranging from 0.61 to 0.85 ps and β values between 0.42 and 0.5 for the restrained and unrestrained RM. Pieniazek et al.[184] obtained β values ranging from 0.17 to 0.37, for RM of $W_o = 2$, 4, and 7.5, indicative of collective water behaviors. Finally, further MD studies [179], [181] in AOT RM with different counterion types (K^+ and Cs^+), also showed that the rotational movement at the interfacial water is affected by the nature of the ion, whereas in the micellar core water, no changes were found. Higher water mobility in AOT RM in the presence of NH_4^+ have been observed experimentally by measuring solvation dynamics of probe molecules via time-dependent fluorescence Stokes shift experiments [255].

5.5. Reverse Micelles Containing Confined Peptides/Proteins

Proteins in particular enzymes have been solubilized in the water pool of RM since decades [32]; the initial purpose of investigators was to monitor enzymatic kinetics as a function of hydration. In fact, enzymes display in RM a higher activity than in aqueous solutions, the degree of activation being modest [13]. A number of substrates could be solubilized in oil and the reaction was followed by spectroscopic measurements. Later on, investigators started to explore the conformational changes of incorporated peptides [256–261] and proteins, as well as the many interactions between the micellar shell and the macromolecular backbone [34], [262] taking advantage of the isotropic micellar solutions. Indeed optical transparency of the samples allows the use of a wide range of spectroscopic techniques: ultraviolet and infrared absorbance, fluorescence, circular dichroism to explore the conformational changes of confined peptides/proteins. Furthermore, confined water at low W_o values was suggested to mimic biological systems such as membranes and RM could be considered as a membrane-mimetic system. More than two decades ago, Nicot and Waks [263] established that RM could solubilize integral membrane proteins and were a good model for the study of membrane proteins at myelin interlamellar aqueous spaces. More recently NMR experiments and RM based systems were successfully used to study solubilized intrinsic membrane proteins [264], [265].

According to [20] a review devoted to conformational changes of proteins and peptides incorporated into RM, one can distinguish at least three different cases:

1. A number of proteins preserve their native structure. (e.g. ubiquitin, integral membrane proteins)
2. Basic proteins and peptides which have a tendency to unfold at least partially (ACTH (1-24) and Cytochrome C)
3. Proteins which reorganize into non-native conformations with minor structural changes. (Lysozyme, serum albumin, myoglobin).

In addition, it was found recently that RM can induce a fiber periodic structure in an Aβ21-30 amyloïd peptide [260].

The highly electrostricted environment in the water phase of RM is known to affect the thermodynamics and dynamics of water as noted in the previous section. It is also admitted that confining a protein/protein into a small inert space (a "cage") stabilizes the protein against reversible unfolding [17], [266–270]. To explain these facts, statistical thermodynamics [267], [269] and diffusional polymer models [268] were applied. It was shown that a major effect of confinement and crowding is excluded volume. In a confined space, conformations or positions in which parts of the protein chain lie outside the walls cannot be sampled. The unfolded state is more adversely affected, since in this state the conformations are more open and hence more likely to cross the walls of the confined space. In general, this is the reason why confinement is expected to favor the folded state and increase the folding stability. In term of protein stability, if one assumes that the protein may belong to only two thermodynamic states, the *unfolded* (U) and *folded* (F) typically its native state. In this case, the stability of the protein is simply the difference in Gibbs free energy, $\Delta\Delta G$, between the folded (ΔG_f) and the unfolded states (ΔG_u). The only factors affecting stability are the relative free energies of the folded (G_f) and the unfolded (G_u) states, ΔG. The larger and more positive $\Delta\Delta G_u$, the more resistant is the protein to denaturation.

Coming to peptides and proteins, we will now compare experimental results with MD simulations for polyalanine peptides and three proteins: Trp Cage (a 20 residue small model of protein), ubiquitin, a 76 residue long protein expressed in various eukaryotic cells, and Cytochrome c, a basic 104 residue long protein.

5.5.1. Small Alanine-Based Peptides

Sequence specific hydration of peptides has been involved in the stability of α-helices [271–273] where water dipoles compete with the α-helix hydrogen bonds. Mukherjee et al. [258], [259] used infrared spectroscopic measurements of Alanine-based peptides (i.e. AKA$_n$ peptide with n = 1, 2, 3, 5, and 6) and an amphipathic peptide (i.e. INWKGLAAMAKKLL) [256] in conjunction with a local infrared marker (i.e. amide I′ vibrational transitions) and circular dichroism (CD) to examine the peptide hydration environment and the folding in AOT/D$_2$O/isooctane RM as a function of water loading (W_o = 6 and 20) and temperature. They found that the AKA$_n$ + RM complexes produced two overlapping amide I′ transitions centered at 1634 and 1650 cm^{-1}, indicating in a helical conformation for the peptide. In the smallest RM the peptide backbone and hydrophobic side chains are mostly dehydrated and become partially hydrated at W_o = 20. The low peptide concentration favors formation of stable β-aggregates (in case of Alanine-based peptides) and an α-helical conformation (amphipathic peptide). In addition, these results also suggest that the amphipathic α-helices are oriented in such a way that its positively charged, lysine-rich, hydrophilic residues face points toward the negatively charged AOT head groups, while its hydrophobic face is directed toward the polar interior of the water pool.

Different MD simulations of AOT RM with confined Alanine-based peptides have been carried out. In a first study [274], we examined the secondary structure stability of an α-helical Alanine octapeptide (A8) in two sizes of RM (W_o = 4.8 and 6.9). Experimental [275] and theoretical [276], [277] studies have shown that this peptide displays an unfolded conformation in water, but can be stabilized in a restricted environment. We found that the size and shape of the RM was slightly affected by the presence of the peptide and in particular an elongated shape, as previously observed for a peptide-devoid AOT RM. Moreover, we observed a substantial slowing down of the translational motion of the water in the smaller RM in presence of the peptide compared to the same peptide-devoid RM. The diminished availability of water enhanced the peptide intramolecular hydrogen bonds, acting to preserve the peptide initial helical structure. No significant slowing down was observed for the water dynamics in the RM with $W_o = 6.9$. In the larger system, the peptide helical structure was not conserved. We concluded from this study that the major force affecting the stability of A8 is the competition for hydration water between the AOT headgroups and the peptide. At the lowest W_o value the amount of water bound to the sulfonate groups is very large, preventing the full hydration of A8 and its denaturation. Removing the AOT headgroup and the Na^+ ions leads to a fast unfolding of the peptide independently of the RM water content.

In another work, Tian et Garcia [194] employed self-assembly protocol to examine the structure of an helical amphipathic peptide (AK4, NH_3^+-YG(AKAAA)$_4$AG-COO$^-$) in two sizes of AOT RM ($W_o = 6$ and 11). The authors showed that, in agreement with the observations of Mukherjee et al. [258], after encapsulation by the RM, the peptide was more dehydrated compared to the peptide in bulk water and charged Lys side chains interact with the surfactant headgroup.

The helical peptide remained with its positively charged residues interacting with the negatively charged AOT headgroups. Finally in another work, Straub et al. [18] have simulated a peptide similar to that of Mukherjee et al. [259] and examined the influence of the shape of the AOT RM ($W_o = 6$) on the peptide environment (i.e. hydration) and stability. They simulated restrained and unrestrained RM: in the restrained model the micelle is kept spherical, whereas in the unconstrained one, the micelle shape can evolve freely. As previously, they showed that when no restrains are applied on the micelle, the RM evolves quickly into an ellipsoidal aggregate.

More interestingly, they also showed that the peptide secondary stability and the peptide environment are significantly affected by the shape of the micelle. In the restrained RM, the peptide keeps its helical conformation, whereas the secondary structure is partially lost when simulated in an unrestrained RM environment, in agreement with experiments of Mukherjee et al. [259]. Moreover, in the unrestrained RM, the peptides are largely in contact with the AOT tails and have thus fewer contacts with water. Interactions of the peptides with the AOT hydrophobic tail leads to a significant dehydration of the peptide backbone surrounded by a low dielectric environment. These results suggest that the small RM may have an environment similar to that of a lipid membrane in stabilizing the folded state of amphipathic helical peptides/proteins such as melittin [278].

5.5.2. Trp Cage

Supercritical carbon dioxide ($ScCO_2$) a low viscosity non polar solvent is known to have a strong deactivating effect on enzyme activity caused by two effects (i) by a direct effect pressure that leads to denaturation, and (ii) indirect effects of pressure on enzymatic activity and selectivity [279].

The direct effects are due to the harsh condition of high pressure on the enzyme structure. RM can be powerful tools to prevent these effects [280]. Chaitanya and Senapati [214] have examined this aspect by performing simulations of RM formed with a fluorosurfactant (PFPE) and the Trp cage confined. They showed that the protein remains confined in the RM aqueous core during all the simulation time (50 ns) and more interestingly, that protein structure remains unaffected in the RM aqueous core confirming experimental results showing that RM provides an aqueous environment for the protein similar to bulk water [281].

5.5.3. Cytochrome c

It has been established [282] that electrostatic interactions play a crucial role in the cellular redox potential by modulating the conformation and the dynamics of the protein. The interaction of positive charges disseminated on patches of the protein surface with the negatively charged AOT sulfonate groups determine the location and the orientation of the protein within RM. Investigators [283], [284] have demonstrated that the protein location is at the micellar interface, and the heme crevice located toward it. Circular Dichroism (CD) spectra in the Soret band and in the aromatic bands indicate that with increasing water load the structure of the protein is loosened.

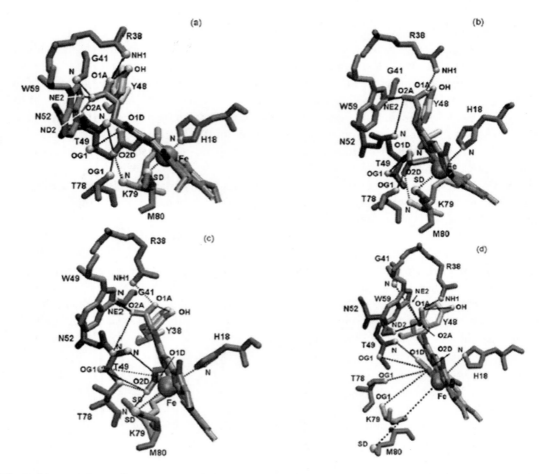

Figure 13. Average conformations of the heme environment for the last 4 ns of the simulations of each protein: Crystal (a), in water (b), in AOT RM at $W_o = 5.5$ (c) and $W_o=9.1$ (d). Hydrogen atoms are not shown for visual clarity and atom types are labeled according to the CHARMM force field. Distances between the hydrogen bond donor and the propionate atoms of the heme group and the iron are drawn as dashed lines. Figure from [189]. Copyright 2010 from Springer.

This fact was confirmed by CD spectra in the far ultraviolet. It was reported that the ellipticity value at 222 nm decreases from -14100° at a W_o value of 5, to -6700° at $W_o=40$. If the positively charged surfactant CTAB is used instead of AOT the ellipticity of the protein remains unchanged compared to its value in buffer [284]. This result indicates the role of electrostatic forces in the loosening of the forces which maintain the internal cohesion and the structure of cytochrome c (Cyt C) leading to the destabilization of the molecule. MD simulation [189] carried out with small model AOT RM at W_o = 5.5 and also 9.1 support these results. In particular, we observed that at lower hydration level, the protein displays a conformation close to its native state and is more stable than in water or in larger RM. Residues positively charged at the protein surface are in contact with the AOT headgroups. At a higher hydration level, the heme pocket is significantly distorted and opens with subsequent disruption of the Met80-Fe and His18-Fe bonds (Figure 13). We also observed large fluctuations of several protein loops involved in the stabilization of the heme native conformation. The distortion involves, at high W_o values, a partial opening of the prosthetic group crevice which becomes accessible to water. This result is in good agreement with modifications observed by spectroscopy in the Soret band [283]. However, the simulation time (10 ns) in this study was too short to observe any significant denaturation of the protein, as observed by CD [284] but only the initial steps of the denaturation process are visible. Indeed, recent NMR measurements [285] suggest that Cyt C in AOT RM, is substantially unfolded at W_o = 10.

5.5.4. Ubiquitin

In another work [193], Tian and Garcia examined by explicit and long (up to 400 ns) simulations in ambient conditions, the effects of confinement on ubiquitin structure, hydration, and the internal dynamics when encapsulated in AOT RM, at W_o = 12.5. Multidimensional solution NMR experiments have shown that ubiquitin, a 76 residue long highly conserved protein, can be encapsulated into RM without significant structural distortion [265]. The simulation results indicate that the solvation occurs in a few hundred picoseconds and that the protein becomes more rigid upon encapsulation in agreement with a previously reported experimental work on ACTH (1-24) [16]. In addition at the same time, a decrease in water coordination and an increase in coordination to the AOT headgroups is observed [286]. The simulation results also show that the RM displays two interfaces, one between the organic solvent and the AOT tails, another one between the AOT headgroups and water in the interior of the RM. The protein is located at the AOT headgroup/water interface of the RM, with several hydrophobic residues (Leu8, Ile44, and Val70) forming a hydrophobic patch making direct contacts with the surfactant positive charges, there are very few waters at the interface. This patch is recognized as ubiquitin binding domain physiologically active [287]. The face of the protein in contact with the positively charged residues is located at the RM interface near the AOT headgroups, the region of ubiquitin making contacts with the RM is partially dehydrated because of its location at the interface due to the strong electrostatic interactions. Examination of the ubiquitin dynamics in the RM was done by computing the backbone N-H relaxation and the order parameter S^2 as in NMR relaxation analysis. The results indicate, as expected, that the protein motions are restricted in the RM environment, compared to the same protein in bulk water, in agreement with experimental data [288]. Finally, with a potential of mean force calculations, the authors show the protein-RM interactions can be tuned by varying the ionic force of the RM aqueous core. At low excess salt conditions (0.187 M NaCl), ubiquitin is located at the interface of the RM through the hydrophobic patch with a driving bias as large as 17 kcal/mole whereas in an idealized RM, where the surfactant headgroup charges are neutralized, ubiquitin also prefers the interface region but with a much weaker driving bias of 1 kcal/mol. at higher excess salt conditions (1.0 to 2.5 M NaCl), where RM electrostatic interactions are significantly screened, ubiquitin samples the RM interior and exhibits fluctuations similar to those of the protein in bulk water. The authors conclude that the interactions of the protein with the confining environment may be stronger than the entropic effects due to confinement.

CONCLUSION

More than five decades of interdisciplinary work have accumulated a considerable amount of data about reverse micelles. However, it appears that in many instances, a number of results remain ambiguous or at least awaiting more precise answers. Indeed, even a series of experiments carried out in the best possible conditions can leave investigators frustrated.

In particular this is the case of the micellar shape determination; although all the simulations carried out agree with the fact that RM look like ellipsoidal aggregates, not a single MD simulation has provided a proof invalidating experimental results compatible with a spherical shape. In addition, micellar solutions, as indicated above, are polydisperse, while MD simulations are often carried out on isolated, stable micelles i.e. a monodisperse system at high solvent concentration. It should be therefore interesting to simulate RM systems at a very low solvent concentration, containing a large number of RM, in order to obtain a distribution in term of size and shape to get diffusion spectra comparable to experimental conditions. This would require the use of coarse grain simulations, or of systems similar to that used recently by LeBard [289] and Jusufi et al. [290] for modeling the self-assembly of alkyl sodium sulfate and tetradecyl trimethyl ammonium bromide (TDTAB) surfactants.

In the case of confined water properties, the important theoretical and experimental work of the Ladanyi, Fayer and Wand groups, for instance, have brought a better understanding of the dynamic phenomena of solvation in RM. The simulation results have been obtained with pairwise-additive potentials. Thus it would be interesting to determine via simulation to what extent polarizability contributes to the properties of these systems. As has been discussed in this review, the reverse micellear structure and the confined water properties depend on a delicate balance between counterion–water and counterion–headgroup interactions. Inclusion of the polarizability into the interaction model is likely to affect this balance by providing a better description of the subtle interactions between counterion–water counterion–headgroup and headgroup-water. Recently polarizable models of polar headgroups (sulfates, sulfonantes) [291] have been constructed and can serve as a starting point to obtain in the future better models of surfactant aggregates..

Finally, in this chapter, we have presented a limited number of results concerning peptides and proteins confined in RM. The scarcity of results obtained suggests that present simulation techniques are still limited to study efficiently these types of systems. Only a few properties taking place on a short time scale (< 1 microsecond) can be examined, such as solvation dynamics or for example local movements in proteins. Currently larger movements involved in folding/unfolding mechanisms cannot yet be studied. Mixed approaches such as CG/AA [292] could be used, where the confined macromolecule is modeled by an all atoms procedure and the rest of the system (RM, solvent) by using a coarse grain approach, in order to reduce significantly the size of the simulated systems and to attain higher time scales than the microsecond, and therefore narrowing the gap between experiments and computations.

REFERENCES

[1]   I. Danielsson and B. Lindman, "The definition of microemulsion," *Physicochemical and Engineering Aspects*, vol. 3, pp. 391–392, 1981.

[2]   P. D. I. Fletcher, A. M. Howe, and B. H. Robinson, "The kinetics of solubilisate exchange between water droplets of a water-in-oil microemulsion," *Journal of the Chemical Society, Faraday Transactions 1*, vol. 83, no. 4, p. 985, 1987.

[3]   M. P. Pileni, "Reverse micelles used as templates: a new understanding in nanocrystal growth," *J. Exp. Nanosci.*, vol. 1, no. 1, pp. 13–27, Mar. 2006.

[4]   P. L. Luisi, M. Giomini, M.-P. Pileni, and B. H. Robinson, "Reverse micelles as hosts for proteins and small molecules." *Biochimica et biophysica acta*, vol. 947, no. 1, pp. 209–46, Feb. 1988.

[5]   D. Langevin, "Structure of reversed micelles," in *Structure and Reactivity in Reversed Micelles*, vol. 65, M. P. Pileni, Ed. Amsterdam: Elsevier:, 1989, p. 13.

[6]   D. E. Moilanen, E. E. Fenn, D. Wong, and M. D. Fayer, "Water Dynamics at the Interface in AOT Reverse Micelles," *J. Phys. Chem. B*, vol. 113, no. 25, pp. 8560–8568, 2009.

[7]   D. C. Crans and N. E. Levinger, "The conundrum of pH in water nanodroplets: sensing pH in reverse micelle water pools.," *Accounts of chemical research*, vol. 45, no. 10, pp. 1637–1645, Oct. 2012.

[8]   B. Cohen, D. Huppert, K. M. Solntsev, Y. Tsfadia, E. Nachliel, and M. Gutman, "Excited State Proton Transfer in Reverse Micelles," *J. Am. Chem. Soc.*, vol. 124, no. 25, pp. 7539–7547, Jun. 2002.

[9]   P. Pratim Parui, D. Narayan Nath, and M. Chowdhury, "Determination of interfacial dielectric constant of AOT-based reverse micelle by probing magnetic field effect on pyrene–DMA exciplex luminescence," *Chem. Phys. Lett.*, vol. 396, no. 4–6, pp. 329–334, Oct. 2004.

[10] M. Hasegawa, T. Sugimura, Y. Suzaki, Y. Shindo, and A. Kitahara, "Microviscosity in Water Pool of Aerosol-OT Reversed Micelle Determined with Viscosity-Sensitive Fluorescence Probe, Auramine O, and Fluorescence Depolarization of Xanthene Dyes," *J. Phys. Chem.*, vol. 98, no. 8, pp. 2120–2124, Feb. 1994.

[11] T. L. Spehr, Frick, I. Grillo, and B. Stühn, "Supercooling of water confined in reverse micelles," *J. Phys.: Condens. Matter*, vol. 20, no. 10, p. 104204, Mar. 2008.

[12] P. Douzou, E. Keh, and C. Balny, "Cryoenzymology in aqueous media: Micellar solubilized water," *Proc. Natl. Acad. Sci. USA*, vol. 76, no. 2, pp. 681–684, 1979.

[13] C. Oldfield, "Enzymes in Water-in-oil Microemulsions ('Reversed Micelles'): Principles and Applications," *Biotechnology and Genetic Engineering Reviews*, vol. 12, no. 1, pp. 255–327, Dec. 1994.

[14] B. Orlich and R. Schomäcker, "Enzyme Catalysis in Reverse Micelles," in *Advances in Biochemical Engineering/Biotechnology*, vol. 75, 2002, pp. 185–208.

[15] C. Nicot, M. Vacher, L. Denoroy, P. C. Kahn, and M. Waks, "Limited Proteolysis of Myelin Basic Protein in a System Mimetic of the Myelin Interlamellar Aqueous Space," *J. Neurochem.*, vol. 60, no. 4, pp. 1283–1291, Apr. 1993.

[16] J. Gallay, M. Vincent, C. Nicot, and M. Waks, "Conformational aspects and rotational dynamics of synthetic adrenocorticotropin-(1-24) and glucagon in reverse micelles," *Biochemistry*, vol. 26, no. 18, pp. 5738–5747, 1987.

[17] H.-X. Zhou, "Protein folding in confined and crowded environments," *Archives of biochemistry and biophysics*, vol. 469, no. 1, pp. 76–82, Jan. 2008.

[18] A. V. Martinez, S. C. DeSensi, L. Dominguez, E. Rivera, and J. E. Straub, "Protein folding in a reverse micelle environment: the role of confinement and dehydration.," *J. Chem. Phys.*, vol. 134, no. 5, p. 055107, Feb. 2011.

[19] A. V. Kabanov, M. M. Khrutskaya, S. A. Eremin, N. L. Klyachko, and A. V. Levashov, "A new way in homogeneous immunoassay: Reversed micellar systems as a medium for analysis," *Anal. Biochem.*, vol. 181, no. 1, pp. 145–148, Aug. 1989.

[20] C. Nicot and M. Waks, "Proteins as Invited Guests of Reverse Micelles: Conformational Effects, Significance, Applications," *Biotechnology and Genetic Engineering Reviews*, vol. 13, no. 1, pp. 267–314, Dec. 1996.

[21] K. Vos, C. Laane, and A. J. W. G. Visser, "Spectroscopy of reversed micelles," *Photochem. Photobiol.*, vol. 45, no. s1, pp. 863–878, May 1987.

[22] A. S. Narang, D. Delmarre, and D. Gao, "Stable drug encapsulation in micelles and microemulsions.," *International journal of pharmaceutics*, vol. 345, no. 1–2, pp. 9–25, Dec. 2007.

[23] M. J. J. Lawrence and G. D. Rees, "Microemulsion-based media as novel drug delivery systems," *Adv. Drug Delivery Rev.*, vol. 64, no. 1, pp. 175–193, Dec. 2012.

[24] A. Kumar, A. Saxena, A. De, R. Shankar, and S. Mozumdar, "Controlled synthesis of size-tunable nickel and nickel oxide nanoparticles using water-in-oil microemulsions," *Advances in Natural Sciences: Nanoscience and Nanotechnology*, vol. 4, no. 2, p. 025009, Apr. 2013.

[25] P. Setua, A. Chakraborty, D. Seth, M. U. Bhatta, P. V. Satyam, and N. Sarkar, "Synthesis, Optical Properties, and Surface Enhanced Raman Scattering of Silver Nanoparticles in Nonaqueous Methanol Reverse Micelles," *J. Phys. Chem. C*, vol. 111, no. 10, pp. 3901–3907, Mar. 2007.

[26] J. C. Shelley and M. Y. Shelley, "Computer simulation of surfactant solutions," *Curr. Opin. Colloid Interface Sci.*, vol. 5, no. 1–2, pp. 101–110, Mar. 2000.

[27] B. Creton, C. Nieto-Draghi, and N. Pannacci, "Prediction of Surfactants' Properties using Multiscale Molecular Modeling Tools: A Review," *Oil & Gas Science and Technology – Revue d'IFP Energies nouvelles*, vol. 67, no. 6, pp. 969–982, Jan. 2013.

[28] M. L. Klein and W. Shinoda, "Large-scale molecular dynamics simulations of self-assembling systems.," *Science (New York, N.Y.)*, vol. 321, no. 5890, pp. 798–800, Aug. 2008.

[29] S. Abel, "Micelles inverses d'AOT et de C12E4: Structure et évaluation de leurs compressibilités par simulation de dynamique moléculaire," Universite Paris 6, Paris, 2007.

[30] P. A. Winsor, "Hydrotropy, solubilisation and related emulsification processes," *Transactions of the Faraday Society*, vol. 44, p. 376, 1948.

[31] K. Holmberg, B. Jönsson, B. Kronberg, and B. Lindman, *Surfactants and Polymers in Aqueous Solution*. Chichester, UK: John Wiley & Sons, Ltd, 2002, p. 547.

[32] K. Martinek, A. V Levashov, N. Klyachko, Y. Khmelnitzki, and V. Berezin, I, "Catalysis by water soluble enzymes in organic solvents. Solubilization of enzymes against denaturation through their inclusion in reversed micelles," *Dokl. Akad. Nauk. SSR*, vol. 236, pp. 920–923, 1977.

[33] P. L. Luisi and L. J. Magid, "Solubilization of enzymes and nucleic acids in hydrocarbon micellar solutions.," *CRC critical reviews in biochemistry*, vol. 20, no. 4, pp. 409–474, Jan. 1986.

[34] M. Waks, "Proteins and peptides in water-restricted environments.," *Proteins, structure, function, genetics*, vol. 1, no. 1, pp. 4–15, Sep. 1986.

[35] M. Fanun, *Microemulsions: Properties and Applications (Surfactant Science)*, 1st ed. CRC Press, 2008, p. 560.

[36] C. Stubenrauch, Ed., *Microemulsions*. Chichester, UK: John Wiley & Sons, Ltd, 2009.

[37] T. Hellweg, "Phase structures of microemulsions," *Curr. Opin. Colloid Interface Sci.*, vol. 7, no. 1–2, pp. 50–56, Mar. 2002.

[38] D. Langevin, "Micelles and Microemulsions," *Annu. Rev. Phys. Chem.*, vol. 43, no. 1, pp. 341–369, Oct. 1992.

[39] T. K. De and A. Maitra, "Solution behaviour of Aerosol OT in non-polar solvents," *Adv. Colloid Interface Sci.*, vol. 59, pp. 95–193, Aug. 1995.

[40] M.-P. Pileni, "Reverse micelles as microreactors," *J. Phys. Chem.*, vol. 97, no. 27, pp. 6961–6973, 1993.

[41] C. Cabos and P. Delord, "Etude d'un Système micellaire de Type inverse par Diffusion Centrale de Neutrons ," *J. Appl. Crystallogr.*, vol. 12, no. 6, pp. 502–510, 1979.

[42] M. Zulauf and H. F. Eicke, "Inverted Micelles and Microemulsions in the Ternary System H2O/Aerosol-OT/Isooctane as Studied by Photon correlation Spectroscopy," *J Phys. Chem.*, vol. 83, no. 4, pp. 480–486, 1979.

[43] S. Christ and P. Schurtenberger, "Optical Contrast Variation Experiments in Water-in-Oil Microemulsions: Size Distribution and Structure of Protein-Free and Protein-Containing Microemulsions," *J. Phys. Chem.*, vol. 98, no. 48, pp. 12708–12714, Dec. 1994.

[44] P. Ekwall, L. Mandell, and K. Fontell, "Some observations on binary and ternary aerosol OT systems," *J. Colloid Interface Sci.*, vol. 33, no. 2, pp. 215–235, 1970.

[45] U. Olsson, T. C. Wong, and O. Soederman, "Deuteron NMR study of sodium bis(2-ethylhexyl)sulfosuccinate in liquid crystals: acyl chain packing and effects of molecular chirality on quadrupolar splitting patterns," *J. Phys. Chem.*, vol. 94, no. 13, pp. 5356–5361, Jun. 1990.

[46] A. Yoshino, H. Okabayashi, and K. Kushida, "Dynamic Structure and Chirality Effects on 1H and 13C NMR Chemical Shifts for Aerosol OT in Reversed Micelles Assisted by NOESY, ROESY, and13C T1 Studies," *Journal Of Physical Chemistry*, vol. 100, no. 23, pp. 9592–9597, 1996.

[47] G. Zhou, Z. Guowei, L. Ganzuo, C. Wenjun, L. Anjing, and B. Meng, "FT-IR studies on the conformation and effective head-group area of AOT molecules in W/O microemulsions," *Science in China Series B: Chemistry*, vol. 45, no. 1, pp. 68–72, Dec. 2002.

[48] A. Maitra and H. F. Eicke, "Effect of rotational isomerism on the water-solubilizing properties of Aerosol OT as studied by hydrogen-1 NMR spectroscopy," *J. Phys. Chem.*, vol. 85, no. 18, pp. 2687–2691, 1981.

[49] J. Eastoe, B. M. H. Cazelles, D. C. Steytler, J. D. Holmes, A. R. Pitt, T. J. Wear, and R. K. Heenan, "Water-in-CO2 Microemulsions Studied by Small-Angle Neutron Scattering," *Langmuir*, vol. 13, no. 26, pp. 6980–6984, Dec. 1997.

[50] J. Chen, J. Zhang, B. Han, X. Feng, M. Hou, W. Li, and Z. Zhang, "Effect of compressed CO2 on the critical micelle concentration and aggregation number of AOT reverse micelles in isooctane.," *Chemistry (Weinheim an der Bergstrasse, Germany)*, vol. 12, no. 31, pp. 8067–8074, Oct. 2006.

[51] A. Maitra, "Determination of size parameters of water-Aerosol OT-oil reverse micelles from their nuclear magnetic resonance data," *J. Phys. Chem.*, vol. 88, no. 21, pp. 5122–5125, Oct. 1984.

[52] D. P. Acharya and P. G. Hartley, "Progress in microemulsion characterization," *Curr. Opin. Colloid Interface Sci.*, vol. 17, no. 5, pp. 274–280, Oct. 2012.

[53] M. Goto, Y. Ishikawa, T. Ono, F. Nakashio, and T. A. Hatton, "Extraction and activity of chymotrypsin using AOT-DOLPA mixed reversed micellar systems.," *Biotechnology progress*, vol. 14, no. 5, pp. 729–734, 1998.

[54] L. Klíčová, P. Sebej, P. Štacko, S. K. Filippov, A. Bogomolova, M. Padilla, and P. Klán, "CTAB/water/chloroform reverse micelles: a closed or open association model?," *Langmuir*, vol. 28, no. 43, pp. 15185–15192, Oct. 2012.

[55] R. Zana, J. Lang, and D. Canet, "Ternary water-in-oil microemulsions made of cationic surfactants, water, and aromatic solvents. 3. Self-diffusion studies in relation to exchange of material between droplets and percolation," *J. Phys. Chem.*, vol. 95, no. 8, pp. 3364–3367, Apr. 1991.

[56] D. M. Zhu, K. I. Feng, and Z. A. Schelly, "Reverse micelles of Triton X-100 in cyclohexane: effects of temperature, water content, and salinity on the aggregation behavior," *J. Phys. Chem.*, vol. 96, no. 5, pp. 2382–2385, Mar. 1992.

[57] S. Ghosh, "Comparative studies on brij reverse micelles prepared in benzene/surfactant/ethylammonium nitrate systems: effect of head group size and polarity of the hydrocarbon chain.," *Journal of colloid and interface science*, vol. 360, no. 2, pp. 672–680, Aug. 2011.

[58] M. Vasilescu, A. Caragheorgheopol, M. Almgren, W. A. Brown J., and R. Johannsson, "Structure and Dynamics of Nonionic Polyoxyethylenic Reverse Micelles by Time-Resolved Fluorescence Quenching," *Langmuir*, vol. 11, no. 8, pp. 2893–2898, 1995.

[59] K.-K. K. Fan, P. Ouyang, X. Wu, and Z. Lu, "Enhancement of the activity of papain in mixed reverse micellar systems in the presence of Tween80," *Journal of Chemical Technology & Biotechnology*, vol. 76, no. 1, pp. 27–34, Jan. 2001.

[60] M. A. Sedgwick, D. C. Crans, and N. E. Levinger, "What is inside a nonionic reverse micelle? Probing the interior of Igepal reverse micelles using decavanadate.," *Langmuir*, vol. 25, no. 10, pp. 5496–5503, May 2009.

[61] S. Doussin, N. Birlirakis, D. Georgin, F. Taran, and P. Berthault, "Novel zwitterionic reverse micelles for encapsulation of proteins in low-viscosity media.," *Chemistry (Weinheim an der Bergstrasse, Germany)*, vol. 12, no. 15, pp. 4170–4175, May 2006.

[62] P. Walde, A. M. Giuliani, C. A. Boicelli, and P. L. Luisi, "Phospholipid-based reverse micelles," *Chem. Phys. Lipids*, vol. 53, no. 4, pp. 265–288, Mar. 1990.

[63] T. Kinugasa, A. Kondo, S. Nishimura, Y. Miyauchi, Y. Nishii, K. Watanabe, and H. Takeuchi, "Estimation for size of reverse micelles formed by AOT and SDEHP based on viscosity measurement," *Colloids and Surfaces A: Physicochemical and Engineering Aspects*, vol. 204, no. 1–3, pp. 193–199, May 2002.

[64] K. S. Freeman, N. C. Beck Tan, S. F. Trevino, S. Kline, L. B. McGown, and D. J. Kiserow, "Size and Polydispersity Determinations of AOT/Bile Salt Reversed Micelles Obtained by Small-Angle Neutron Scattering," *Langmuir*, vol. 17, no. 13, pp. 3912–3916, Jun. 2001.

[65] S. Chatterjee, R. K. Mitra, B. K. Paul, and S. C. Bhattacharya, "Interface of AOT/Brij mixed reverse micellar systems: conductometric and spectrophotometric investigations.," *Journal of colloid and interface science*, vol. 298, no. 2, pp. 935–941, Jun. 2006.

[66] W. C. Griffin, "Classification of Surface-Active Agents by HLB," *Journal of the Society of Cosmetic Chemists* , vol. 1, p. 311, 1949.

[67] J. T. Davies, "A quantitative kinetic theory of emulsion type. 1 Physical Chemistry of the Emulsion Agent," in *Proceedings of 2nd International Congress Surface Activity, Butterworths, London 1957*, 1957.

[68] J. N. Israelachvili, "The science and applications of emulsions — an overview," *Coll. Surf. A*, vol. 91, pp. 1–8, 1994.

[69] K. Shinoda and H. Kunieda, *Encyclopaedia of Emulsion Technology*, Becher, P., vol. 1. New York.: Marcel Dekker, 1983.

[70] A. Merdas, M. Gindre, R. Ober, C. Nicot, W. Urbach, and M. Waks, "Nonionic Surfactant Reverse Micelles of C12E4 in Dodecane: Temperature Dependence of Size and Shape," *J. Phys. Chem.*, vol. 100, no. 37, pp. 15180–15186, Jan. 1996.

[71] D. Frenkel and B. Smit, *Understanding Molecular Simulation: From Algorithms to Applications*. Boston, MA: Academic Press, 2002.

[72] A. R. Leach, *Molecular Modelling: Principles and Applications*. Prentice Hall, 2001, p. 768.

[73] D. C. Rapaport, *The Art of Molecular Dynamics Simulation*, 2nd ed. New York, NY, USA: Press, Cambridge University, 1996, p. 564.

[74] A. Lyubartsev, Y. Tu, and A. Laaksonen, "Hierarchical Multiscale Modelling Scheme from First Principles to Mesoscale," *J. Comput. Theor. Nanosci.*, vol. 6, no. 5, pp. 951–959, May 2009.

[75] J. D. Durrant and J. A. McCammon, "Molecular dynamics simulations and drug discovery.," *BMC biology*, vol. 9, p. 71, Jan. 2011.

[76] S. S. Mallajosyula, O. Guvench, E. Hatcher, and A. D. MacKerell, "CHARMM Additive All-Atom Force Field for Phosphate and Sulfate Linked to Carbohydrates," *J. Chem. Theory Comput.*, p. 111226020902001, Dec. 2011.

[77] J. Wang, R. M. Wolf, J. W. Caldwell, P. A. Kollman, and D. A. Case, "Development and testing of a general amber force field.," *J. Comput. Chem.*, vol. 25, no. 9, pp. 1157–11574, Jul. 2004.

[78] B. L. Foley, M. B. Tessier, and R. J. Woods, "Carbohydrate force fields," *Wiley Interdisciplinary Reviews: Computational Molecular Science*, vol. 2, no. 4, pp. 652–697, Jul. 2012.

[79]   W. L. Jorgensen and J. Tirado-Rives, "The OPLS [optimized potentials for liquid simulations] potential functions for proteins, energy minimizations for crystals of cyclic peptides and crambin," *J. Am. Chem. Soc.*, vol. 110, no. 6, pp. 1657–1666, 1988.

[80]   C. Oostenbrink, A. Villa, A. E. Mark, and W. F. van Gunsteren, "A biomolecular force field based on the free enthalpy of hydration and solvation: the GROMOS force-field parameter sets 53A5 and 53A6.," *J. Comput. Chem.*, vol. 25, no. 13, pp. 1656–76, Oct. 2004.

[81]   D. Brown and J. H. R. Clarke, "Molecular dynamics simulation of a model reverse micelle," *J. Phys. Chem.*, vol. 92, no. 10, pp. 2881–2888, May 1988.

[82]   J. Faeder and B. M. Ladanyi, "Molecular Dynamics Simulations of the Interior of Aqueous Reverse Micelles," *J. Phys. Chem. B*, vol. 104, no. 5, pp. 1033–1046, Feb. 2000.

[83]   J. Chanda, S. Chakraborty, and S. Bandyopadhyay, "Monolayer of aerosol-OT surfactants adsorbed at the air/water interface: an atomistic computer simulation study.," *J. Phys. Chem. B*, vol. 109, no. 1, pp. 471–9, Jan. 2005.

[84]   B. R. Brooks, C. L. Brooks, A. D. MacKerell Jr., L. Nilsson, R. J. Petrella, B. Roux, Y. Won, G. Archontis, C. Bartels, S. Boresch, A. Caflisch, L. Caves, Q. Cui, A. R. Dinner, M. Feig, S. Fischer, J. Gao, M. Hodoscek, W. Im, K. Kuczera, T. Lazaridis, J. Ma, V. Ovchinnikov, E. Paci, R. W. Pastor, C. B. Post, J. Z. Pu, M. Schaefer, B. Tidor, R. M. Venable, H. L. Woodcock, X. Wu, W. Yang, D. M. York, and M. Karplus, "CHARMM: the biomolecular simulation program.," *J. Comput. Chem.*, vol. 30, no. 10, pp. 1545–1614, Jul. 2009.

[85]   J. Chowdhary and B. M. Ladanyi, "Molecular dynamics simulation of aerosol-OT reverse micelles.," *J. Phys. Chem. B*, vol. 113, no. 45, pp. 15029–15039, Dec. 2009.

[86]   M. G. Martin and J. I. Siepmann, "Novel Configurational-Bias Monte Carlo Method for Branched Molecules. Transferable Potentials for Phase Equilibria. 2. United-Atom Description of Branched Alkanes," *J. Phys. Chem. B*, vol. 103, no. 21, pp. 4508–4517, Apr. 1999.

[87]   J. J. Potoff and D. A. Bernard-Brunel, "Mie Potentials for Phase Equilibria Calculations: Application to Alkanes and Perfluoroalkanes," *J. Phys. Chem. B*, vol. 113, no. 44, pp. 14725–14731, 2009.

[88]   A. D. Mackerell, "Empirical force fields for biological macromolecules: overview and issues.," *J. Comput. Chem.*, vol. 25, no. 13, pp. 1584–1604, Oct. 2004.

[89]   A. V. Martinez, L. Dominguez, E. Malolepsza, A. Moser, Z. Ziegler, and J. E. Straub, "Probing the Structure and Dynamics of Confined Water in AOT Reverse Micelles.," *J. Phys. Chem. B*, vol. 117, no. 24, pp. 7345–7351, May 2013.

[90]   D. Bedrov and G. D. Smith, "Anomalous conformational behavior of poly(ethylene oxide) oligomers in aqueous solutions. A molecular dynamics study," *J. Chem. Phys.*, vol. 109, no. 18, pp. 8118–8123, 1998.

[91]   S. Hezaveh, S. Samanta, G. Milano, and D. Roccatano, "Structure and dynamics of 1,2-dimethoxyethane and 1,2-dimethoxypropane in aqueous and non-aqueous solutions: a molecular dynamics study.," *J. Chem. Phys.*, vol. 135, no. 16, p. 164501, Oct. 2011.

[92]   D. Bedrov, M. Pekny, and G. D. Smith, "Quantum-Chemistry-Based Force Field for 1,2-Dimethoxyethane and Poly(ethylene oxide) in Aqueous Solution," *J. Phys. Chem. B*, vol. 102, no. 6, pp. 996–1001, Feb. 1998.

[93] S. A. Wahab, T. Harada, T. Matsubara, and M. Aida, "Quantum Chemical Study of the Interaction of the Short-Chain Poly(oxyethylene)s CH$_3$(OCH$_2$CH$_2$)mOCH$_3$(C$_1$EmC; m = 1 and 2) with a Water Molecule in the Gas Phase and in Solutions," *J. Phys. Chem. A*, vol. 110, no. 3, pp. 1052–1059, 2006.

[94] G. D. Smith, R. L. Jaffe, and D. Y. Yoon, "Force field for simulations of 1,2-dimethoxyethane and poly(oxyethylene) based upon ab initio electronic structure calculations on model molecules," *J. Phys. Chem.*, vol. 97, no. 49, pp. 12752–12759, Dec. 1993.

[95] O. N. Starovoytov, O. Borodin, D. Bedrov, and G. D. Smith, "Development of a Polarizable Force Field for Molecular Dynamics Simulations of Poly (Ethylene Oxide) in Aqueous Solution," *J. Chem. Theory Comput.*, vol. 7, no. 6, pp. 1902–1915, Jun. 2011.

[96] G. D. Smith, O. Borodin, and D. Bedrov, "A revised quantum chemistry-based potential for poly(ethylene oxide) and its oligomers in aqueous solution.," *J. Comput. Chem.*, vol. 23, no. 15, pp. 1480–1488, Nov. 2002.

[97] S. Abel, M. Waks, M. Marchi, and W. Urbach, "Effect of surfactant conformation on the structures of small size nonionic reverse micelles: a molecular dynamics simulation study.," *Langmuir*, vol. 22, no. 22, pp. 9112–20, Oct. 2006.

[98] S. B. Neyertz and S. . B. Neyertz D.; Thomas, J. O., "Molecular dynamics simulation of crystalline poly(ethylene oxide)," *J. Chem. Phys.*, vol. 101, no. 11, pp. 10064–10073, 1994.

[99] F. Müller-Plathe, "Permeation of polymers: a computational approach," *Acta Polym.*, vol. 45, no. 4, pp. 259–293, Jul. 1994.

[100] F. Müller-Plathe and W. F. van Gunsteren, "Computer simulation of a polymer electrolyte: Lithium iodide in amorphous poly(ethylene oxide)," *J. Chem. Phys.*, vol. 103, no. 11, p. 4745, 1995.

[101] J. Kolafa and M. Ratner, "Oligomers of Poly(Ethylene Oxide): Molecular Dynamics with a Polarizable Force Field," *Mol. Simul.*, vol. 21, no. 1, pp. 1–26, Jul. 1998.

[102] P. M. Anderson and M. R. Wilson, "Molecular dynamics simulations of amphiphilic graft copolymer molecules at a water/air interface.," *J. Chem. Phys.*, vol. 121, no. 17, pp. 8503–8510, Nov. 2004.

[103] H. Lee, R. M. Venable, A. D. Mackerell, R. W. Pastor, and A. D. MacKerell Jr., "Molecular dynamics studies of polyethylene oxide and polyethylene glycol: hydrodynamic radius and shape anisotropy.," *Biophys. J.*, vol. 95, no. 4, pp. 1590–1599, Aug. 2008.

[104] B. Z. Shang, Z. Wang, and R. G. Larson, "Molecular dynamics simulation of interactions between a sodium dodecyl sulfate micelle and a poly(ethylene oxide) polymer.," *J. Phys. Chem. B*, vol. 112, no. 10, pp. 2888–2900, Mar. 2008.

[105] L. D. Schuler, X. Daura, and W. F. van Gunsteren, "An improved GROMOS96 force field for aliphatic hydrocarbons in the condensed phase," *J. Comput. Chem.*, vol. 22, no. 11, pp. 1205–1218, Aug. 2001.

[106] J. Fischer, D. Paschek, A. Geiger, and G. Sadowski, "Modeling of aqueous poly(oxyethylene) solutions: 1. Atomistic simulations.," *J. Phys. Chem. B*, vol. 112, no. 8, pp. 2388–2398, Feb. 2008.

[107] J. M. Stubbs, J. J. Potoff, and J. I. Siepmann, "Transferable Potentials for Phase Equilibria. 6. United-Atom Description for Ethers, Glycols, Ketones, and Aldehydes," *J. Phys. Chem. B*, vol. 108, no. 45, pp. 17596–17605, Nov. 2004.

[108] N. Ferrando, V. Lachet, J. Pérez-Pellitero, A. D. Mackie, P. Malfreyt, and A. Boutin, "A transferable force field to predict phase equilibria and surface tension of ethers and glycol ethers.," *J. Phys. Chem. B*, vol. 115, no. 36, pp. 10654–10664, Sep. 2011.

[109] P. Ungerer, C. Beauvais, J. Delhommelle, A. Boutin, B. Rousseau, and A. H. Fuchs, "Optimization of the anisotropic united atoms intermolecular potential for n-alkanes," *J. Chem. Phys.*, vol. 112, no. 12, p. 5499, 2000.

[110] M. Stepniewski, M. Pasenkiewicz-Gierula, T. Róg, R. Danne, A. Orlowski, M. Karttunen, A. Urtti, M. Yliperttula, E. Vuorimaa, and A. Bunker, "Study of PEGylated lipid layers as a model for PEGylated liposome surfaces: molecular dynamics simulation and Langmuir monolayer studies.," *Langmuir*, vol. 27, no. 12, pp. 7788–98, Jun. 2011.

[111] J. M. Briggs, T. Matsui, and W. L. Jorgensen, "Monte Carlo simulations of liquid alkyl ethers with the OPLS potential functions," *J. Comput. Chem.*, vol. 11, no. 8, pp. 958–971, Sep. 1990.

[112] B. A. C. Horta, P. F. J. Fuchs, W. F. van Gunsteren, and P. H. Hünenberger, "New Interaction Parameters for Oxygen Compounds in the GROMOS Force Field: Improved Pure-Liquid and Solvation Properties for Alcohols, Ethers, Aldehydes, Ketones, Carboxylic Acids, and Esters," *J. Chem. Theory Comput.*, vol. 7, no. 4, pp. 1016–1031,

[113] P. F. J. Fuchs, H. S. Hansen, P. H. Hünenberger, and B. A. C. Horta, "A GROMOS Parameter Set for Vicinal Diether Functions: Properties of Polyethyleneoxide and Polyethyleneglycol," *J. Chem. Theory Comput.*, vol. 8, no. 10, pp. 3943–3963, Oct. 2012.

[114] S.-J. Marrink, A. H. de Vries, and A. E. Mark, "Coarse Grained Model for Semiquantitative Lipid Simulations," *J. Phys. Chem. B*, vol. 108, no. 2, pp. 750–760, Jan. 2004.

[115] X. Periole and S.-J. Marrink, "The Martini coarse-grained force field.," *Methods in molecular biology*, vol. 924, pp. 533–565, Jan. 2013.

[116] D. H. de Jong, G. Singh, W. F. D. Bennett, C. Arnarez, T. A. Wassenaar, L. V. Schäfer, X. Periole, D. P. Tieleman, and S.-J. Marrink, "Improved Parameters for the Martini Coarse-Grained Protein Force Field," *J. Chem. Theory Comput.*, vol. 9, no. 1, pp. 687–697, Jan. 2013.

[117] S.-J. Marrink and D. P. Tieleman, "Perspective on the Martini model.," *Chemical Society reviews*, vol. 42, no. 16, pp. 6801–6822, Aug. 2013.

[118] S. J. Marrink, X. Periole, D. P. Tieleman, and A. H. de Vries, "Comment on 'On using a too large integration time step in molecular dynamics simulations of coarse-grained molecular models' by M. Winger, D. Trzesniak, R. Baron and W. F. van Gunsteren, Phys. Chem. Chem. Phys., 2009, 11, 1934.," *Physical chemistry chemical physics : PCCP*, vol. 12, no. 9, pp. 2254–2256, Mar. 2010.

[119] L. Monticelli, S. K. Kandasamy, X. Periole, R. G. Larson, D. P. Tieleman, and S.-J. Marrink, "The MARTINI Coarse-Grained Force Field: Extension to Proteins," *J. Chem. Theory Comput.*, vol. 4, no. 5, pp. 819–834, May 2008.

[120] S.-J. Marrink, H. J. Risselada, S. Yefimov, D. P. Tieleman, and A. H. de Vries, "The MARTINI force field: coarse grained model for biomolecular simulations.," *J. Phys. Chem. B*, vol. 111, no. 27, pp. 7812–7824, Jul. 2007.

[121] R. Baron, D. Trzesniak, A. H. de Vries, A. Elsener, S.-J. Marrink, and W. F. van Gunsteren, "Comparison of thermodynamic properties of coarse-grained and atomic-level simulation models.," *ChemPhysChem*, vol. 8, no. 3, pp. 452–461, Feb. 2007.

[122] J. D. Perlmutter and J. N. Sachs, "Inhibiting lateral domain formation in lipid bilayers: simulations of alternative steroid headgroup chemistries.," *J. Am. Chem. Soc.*, vol. 131, no. 45, pp. 16362–16363, Nov. 2009.

[123] G. Rossi, P. F. J. Fuchs, J. Barnoud, and L. Monticelli, "A coarse-grained MARTINI model of polyethylene glycol and of polyoxyethylene alkyl ether surfactants.," *J. Phys. Chem. B*, vol. 116, no. 49, pp. 14353–62, Dec. 2012.

[124] C. A. López, Z. Sovova, F. J. van Eerden, A. H. de Vries, and S.-J. Marrink, "Martini Force Field Parameters for Glycolipids," *J. Chem. Theory Comput.*, p. 130205132138001, Feb. 2013.

[125] C. A. López, A. J. Rzepiela, A. H. de Vries, L. Dijkhuizen, P. H. Hünenberger, and S.-J. Marrink, "Martini Coarse-Grained Force Field: Extension to Carbohydrates," *J. Chem. Theory Comput.*, vol. 5, no. 12, pp. 3195–3210, Dec. 2009.

[126] J. Wohlert and L. A. Berglund, "A Coarse-Grained Model for Molecular Dynamics Simulations of Native Cellulose," *J. Chem. Theory Comput.*, vol. 7, no. 3, pp. 753–760, Mar. 2011.

[127] S. Khalid, P. J. Bond, J. Holyoake, R. W. Hawtin, and M. S. P. Sansom, "DNA and lipid bilayers: self-assembly and insertion.," *Journal of the Royal Society, Interface / the Royal Society*, vol. 5 Suppl 3, no. 3, pp. S241–S250, Dec. 2008.

[128] G. Rossi, L. Monticelli, S. R. Puisto, I. Vattulainen, and T. Ala-Nissila, "Coarse-graining polymers with the MARTINI force-field: polystyrene as a benchmark case," *Soft Matter*, vol. 7, no. 2, p. 698, 2011.

[129] M. Hatakeyama and R. Faller, "Coarse-grained simulations of ABA amphiphilic triblock copolymer solutions in thin films.," *Physical chemistry chemical physics : PCCP*, vol. 9, no. 33, pp. 4662–4672, Sep. 2007.

[130] J. Wong-Ekkabut, S. Baoukina, W. Triampo, I.-M. Tang, D. P. Tieleman, and L. Monticelli, "Computer simulation study of fullerene translocation through lipid membranes.," *Nature nanotechnology*, vol. 3, no. 6, pp. 363–368, Jun. 2008.

[131] L. Monticelli, "On atomistic and coarse-grained models for C60 fullerene," *J. Chem. Theory Comput.*, vol. 8, no. 4, pp. 1370–1378, Mar. 2012.

[132] S. A. Sanders and A. Z. Panagiotopoulos, "Micellization behavior of coarse grained surfactant models.," *J. Chem. Phys.*, vol. 132, no. 11, p. 114902, Mar. 2010.

[133] C. Arnarez, J.-P. Mazat, J. Elezgaray, S.-J. Marrink, and X. Periole, "Evidence for cardiolipin binding sites on the membrane-exposed surface of the cytochrome bc1.," *J. Am. Chem. Soc.*, vol. 135, no. 8, pp. 3112–3120, Feb. 2013.

[134] M. Weingarth, A. Prokofyev, E. A. W. van der Cruijsen, D. Nand, A. M. J. J. Bonvin, O. Pongs, and M. Baldus, "Structural determinants aspects of specific lipid binding to potassium channels.," *J. Am. Chem. Soc.*, vol. 135, no. 10, pp. 3983–3988, Mar. 2013.

[135] X. Periole, A. M. Knepp, T. P. Sakmar, S.-J. Marrink, and T. Huber, "Structural determinants of the supramolecular organization of G protein-coupled receptors in bilayers.," *J. Am. Chem. Soc.*, vol. 134, no. 26, pp. 10959–10965, Jul. 2012.

[136] P. J. Bond, J. Holyoake, A. Ivetac, S. Khalid, and M. S. P. Sansom, "Coarse-grained molecular dynamics simulations of membrane proteins and peptides.," *Journal of structural biology*, vol. 157, no. 3, pp. 593–605, Mar. 2007.

[137] J. C. Shelley, M. Y. Shelley, R. C. Reeder, S. Bandyopadhyay, P. B. Moore, and M. L. Klein, "Simulations of Phospholipids Using a Coarse Grain Model," *J. Phys. Chem. B*, vol. 105, no. 40, pp. 9785–9792, Oct. 2001.

[138] A. Y. Shih, A. Arkhipov, P. L. Freddolino, and K. Schulten, "Coarse grained protein-lipid model with application to lipoprotein particles.," *J. Phys. Chem. B*, vol. 110, no. 8, pp. 3674–3684, Mar. 2006.

[139] G. Srinivas, J. C. Shelley, S. O. Nielsen, D. E. Discher, and M. L. Klein, "Simulation of Diblock Copolymer Self-Assembly, Using a Coarse-Grain Model," *J. Phys. Chem. B*, vol. 108, no. 24, pp. 8153–8160, Jun. 2004.

[140] W. Shinoda, R. H. DeVane, and M. L. Klein, "Coarse-grained molecular modeling of non-ionic surfactant self-assembly," *Soft Matter*, vol. 4, no. 12, p. 2454, 2008.

[141] E. N. Brodskaya and G. V Mudzhikova, "Molecular dynamics simulation of AOT reverse micelles," *Mol. Phys.*, vol. 104, no. 22–24, pp. 3635–3643, Nov. 2006.

[142] G. V Mudzhikova and E. Brodskaya, "Molecular simulation of an aerosol OT reverse micelle: 1. the shape and structure of a micelle," *Colloid J.*, vol. 68, no. 6, pp. 729–737, 2006.

[143] G. V Mudzhikova and E. Brodskaya, "Molecular simulation of an aerosol OT reverse micelle: 2. Energy and kinetic characteristics," *Colloid J.*, vol. 68, no. 6, pp. 738–742, 2006.

[144] G. V. Mudzhikova and E. N. Brodskaya, "Effect of counterions on the structure of reverse micelles according to the data of molecular-dynamic simulation," *Colloid J.*, vol. 71, no. 6, pp. 803–809, Dec. 2009.

[145] H. J. C. Berendsen, J. P. M. Postma, and W. F. van Gunsteren, *Intermolecular Forces*. Reidel Dodrecht: Pullman, B Ed., 1981, p. 331.

[146] B. Derecskei, A. Derecskei-Kovacs, and Z. A. Schelly, "Atomic-Level Molecular Modeling of AOT Reverse Micelles. 1. The AOT Molecule in Water and Carbon Tetrachloride," *Langmuir*, vol. 15, no. 6, pp. 1981–1992, Mar. 1999.

[147] H. J. C. Berendsen, J. R. Grigera, and T. P. Straatsma, "The missing term in effective pair potentials," *J. Phys. Chem.*, vol. 91, no. 24, pp. 6269–6271, Nov. 1987.

[148] W. L. Jorgensen, J. Chandrasekhar, J. D. Madura, R. W. Impey, and M. L. Klein, "Comparison of simple potential functions for simulating liquid water," *J. Chem. Phys.*, vol. 79, no. 2, pp. 926–935, 1983.

[149] G. Lamoureux, A. D. MacKerell, and B. Roux, "A simple polarizable model of water based on classical Drude oscillators," *J. Chem. Phys.*, vol. 119, no. 10, p. 5185, 2003.

[150] K. Tasaki, "Poly(oxyethylene)-Water Interactions: A Molecular Dynamics Study," *J. Am. Chem. Soc.*, vol. 118, no. 35, pp. 8459–8469, 1996.

[151] P. M. Anderson and M. R. Wilson *, "Developing a force field for simulation of poly(ethylene oxide) based upon ab initio calculations of 1,2-dimethoxyethane," *Mol. Phys.*, vol. 103, no. 1, pp. 89–97, Jan. 2005.

[152] I. Vorobyov, V. M. Anisimov, S. Greene, R. M. Venable, A. Moser, R. W. Pastor, and A. D. MacKerell Jr., "Additive and Classical Drude Polarizable Force Fields for Linear and Cyclic Ethers," *J. Chem. Theory Comput.*, vol. 3, no. 3, pp. 1120–1133, May 2007.

[153] H. W. Horn, W. C. Swope, J. W. Pitera, J. D. Madura, T. J. Dick, G. L. Hura, and T. Head-Gordon, "Development of an improved four-site water model for biomolecular simulations: TIP4P-Ew.," *J. Chem. Phys.*, vol. 120, no. 20, pp. 9665–9678, May 2004.

[154] H. S. Hansen and P. H. Hünenberger, "A reoptimized GROMOS force field for hexopyranose-based carbohydrates accounting for the relative free energies of ring conformers, anomers, epimers, hydroxymethyl rotamers, and glycosidic linkage conformers," *J. Comput. Chem.*, vol. 32, no. 6, pp. 998–1032, 2011.

[155] W. Shinoda, R. H. DeVane, and M. L. Klein, "Multi-property fitting and parameterization of a coarse grained model for aqueous surfactants," *Mol. Simul.*, vol. 33, no. 1–2, pp. 27–36, Jan. 2007.

[156] H. Lee, A. H. de Vries, S.-J. Marrink, and R. W. Pastor, "A Coarse-Grained Model for Polyethylene Oxide and Polyethylene Glycol: Conformation and Hydrodynamics," *J. Phys. Chem. B*, vol. 113, no. 40, pp. 13186–13194, Oct. 2009.

[157] M. Velinova, D. Sengupta, A. V Tadjer, and S.-J. Marrink, "Sphere-to-rod transitions of nonionic surfactant micelles in aqueous solution modeled by molecular dynamics simulations.," *Langmuir*, vol. 27, no. 23, pp. 14071–14077, Dec. 2011.

[158] M. Velinova, Y. Tsoneva, A. Ivanova, and A. V Tadjer, "Estimation of the Mutual Orientation and Intermolecular Interaction of C12Ex from MD Simulations.," *J. Phys. Chem. B*, vol. 116, no. 16, pp. 4879–4888, Mar. 2012.

[159] C. Yang, X. Chen, H. Qiu, W. Zhuang, Y. Chai, and J. Hao, "Dissipative particle dynamics simulation of phase behavior of aerosol OT/water system.," *J. Phys. Chem. B*, vol. 110, no. 43, pp. 21735–21740, Nov. 2006.

[160] D. Bratko, C. E. Woodward, and A. Luzar, "Charge fluctuation in reverse micelles," *J. Chem. Phys.*, vol. 95, no. 7, p. 5318, 1991.

[161] R. Car, "Unified Approach for Molecular Dynamics and Density-Functional Theory," *Phys. Rev. Lett.*, vol. 55, no. 22, pp. 2471–2474, Nov. 1985.

[162] A. Dreuw and M. Head-Gordon, "Single-reference ab initio methods for the calculation of excited states of large molecules.," *Chemical reviews*, vol. 105, no. 11, pp. 4009–4037, Nov. 2005.

[163] G. Groenhof, "Introduction to QM/MM simulations.," *Methods in molecular biology*, vol. 924, pp. 43–66, Jan. 2013.

[164] A. Warshel and M. Levitt, "Theoretical studies of enzymic reactions: dielectric, electrostatic and steric stabilization of the carbonium ion in the reaction of lysozyme.," *Journal of molecular biology*, vol. 103, no. 2, pp. 227–249, May 1976.

[165] D. Chandler, *Introduction to Modern Statistical Mechanics*, 1st ed. New York: , 1988, p. 288 pages.

[166] Y. Sugita and Y. Okamoto, "Replica-exchange molecular dynamics method for protein folding," *Chem. Phys. Lett.*, vol. 314, no. 1–2, pp. 141–151, Nov. 1999.

[167] Y. Okamoto, "Generalized-ensemble algorithms: enhanced sampling techniques for Monte Carlo and molecular dynamics simulations," *Journal of Molecular Graphics and Modelling*, vol. 22, no. 5, pp. 425–439, 2004.

[168] P. J. Hoogerbrugge and J. M. V. A. Koelman, "Simulating Microscopic Hydrodynamic Phenomena with Dissipative Particle Dynamics," *Europhysics Letters (EPL)*, vol. 19, no. 3, pp. 155–160, Jun. 1992.

[169] R. D. Groot and P. B. Warren, "Dissipative particle dynamics: Bridging the gap between atomistic and mesoscopic simulation," *J. Chem. Phys.*, vol. 107, no. 11, p. 4423, 1997.

[170] P. Español and P. Warren, "Statistical Mechanics of Dissipative Particle Dynamics," *Europhysics Letters (EPL)*, vol. 30, no. 4, pp. 191–196, May 1995.

[171] T. Schlick, R. Collepardo-Guevara, L. A. Halvorsen, S. Jung, and X. Xiao, "Biomolecularmodeling and simulation: a field coming of age.," *Q. Rev. Biophys.*, vol. 44, no. 2, pp. 191–228, May 2011.

[172] Z. Li and E. E. Dormidontova, "Kinetics of Diblock Copolymer Micellization by Dissipative Particle Dynamics," *Macromolecules*, vol. 43, no. 7, pp. 3521–3531, Apr. 2010.

[173] A. Vishnyakov, M.-T. Lee, and A. V. Neimark, "Prediction of the Critical Micelle Concentration of Nonionic Surfactants by Dissipative Particle Dynamics Simulations," *The Journal of Physical Chemistry Letters*, vol. 4, no. 5, pp. 797–802, Mar. 2013.

[174] J. C. Shillcock, "Spontaneous vesicle self-assembly: a mesoscopic view of membrane dynamics.," *Langmuir*, vol. 28, no. 1, pp. 541–547, Jan. 2012.

[175] E. Moeendarbary, T. Y. Ng, and M. Zangeneh, "Dissipative Particle Dynamics: Introduction, Methodology and Complex Fluid Applications - A Review," *International Journal of Applied Mechanics*, vol. 01, no. 04, pp. 737–763, Dec. 2009.

[176] Y. Li, Y. Guo, G. Xu, Z. Wang, M. Bao, and N. Sun, "Dissipative particle dynamics simulation on the properties of the oil/water/surfactant system in the absence and presence of polymer," *Mol. Simul.*, vol. 39, no. 4, pp. 299–308, Apr. 2013.

[177] E. Moeendarbary, T. Y. NG, and M. Zangeneh, "Dissipative Particle Dynamics in Soft Matter and Polymeric Applications — A Review," *International Journal of Applied Mechanics*, vol. 02, no. 01, pp. 161–190, Mar. 2010.

[178] P. Linse, "Molecular dynamics study of the aqueous core of a reversed ionic micelle," *J. Chem. Phys.*, vol. 90, no. 9, p. 4992, 1989.

[179] J. Faeder, M. V. Albert, and B. M. Ladanyi, "Molecular Dynamics Simulations of the Interior of Aqueous Reverse Micelles: A Comparison between Sodium and Potassium Counterions," *Langmuir*, vol. 19, no. 6, pp. 2514–2520, Mar. 2003.

[180] M. R. Harpham, B. M. Ladanyi, N. E. Levinger, and K. W. Herwig, "Water motion in reverse micelles studied by quasielastic neutron scattering and molecular dynamics simulations.," *J. Chem. Phys.*, vol. 121, no. 16, pp. 7855–7868, Oct. 2004.

[181] M. R. Harpham, B. M. Ladanyi, and N. E. Levinger, "The effect of the counterion on water mobility in reverse micelles studied by molecular dynamics simulations.," *J. Phys. Chem. B*, vol. 109, no. 35, pp. 16891–16900, Oct. 2005.

[182] D. E. Rosenfeld and C. A. Schmuttenmaer, "Dynamics of water confined within reverse micelles.," *J. Phys. Chem. B*, vol. 110, no. 29, pp. 14304–14312, Jul. 2006.

[183] B. Guchhait, R. Biswas, and P. K. Ghorai, "Solute and solvent dynamics in confined equal-sized aqueous environments of charged and neutral reverse micelles: a combined dynamic fluorescence and all-atom molecular dynamics simulation study.," *J. Phys. Chem. B*, vol. 117, no. 12, pp. 3345–3361, Mar. 2013.

[184] P. A. Pieniazek, Y.-S. Lin, J. Chowdhary, B. M. Ladanyi, and J. L. Skinner, "Vibrational spectroscopy and dynamics of water confined inside reverse micelles.," *J. Phys. Chem. B*, vol. 113, no. 45, pp. 15017–15028, Nov. 2009.

[185] J. Faeder and B. M. Ladanyi, "Solvation dynamics in reverse micelles: the role of headgroup-solute interactions.," *J. Phys. Chem. B*, vol. 109, no. 14, pp. 6732–6740, Apr. 2005.

[186] R. Allen, S. Bandyopadhyay, and M. L. Klein, "$C_{12}E_2$ Reverse Micelle: A Molecular Dynamics Study," *Langmuir*, vol. 16, no. 26, pp. 10547–10552, Dec. 2000.

[187] S. Abel, F. Sterpone, S. Bandyopadhyay, and M. Marchi, "Molecular Modeling and Simulations of AOT–Water Reverse Micelles in Isooctane: Structural and Dynamic Properties," *J. Phys. Chem. B*, vol. 108, no. 50, pp. 19458–19466, Dec. 2004.

[188] S. Abel, M. Waks, W. Urbach, and M. Marchi, "Structure, stability, and hydration of a polypeptide in AOT reverse micelles.," *J. Am. Chem. Soc.*, vol. 128, no. 2, pp. 382–383, Jan. 2006.

[189] S. Abel, M. Waks, and M. Marchi, "Molecular dynamics simulations of cytochrome c unfolding in AOT reverse micelles: The first steps.," *The European physical journal. E, Soft matter*, vol. 32, no. 4, pp. 399–409, Aug. 2010.

[190] S. Senapati, J. S. Keiper, J. M. DeSimone, G. D. Wignall, Y. B. Melnichenko, H. Frielinghaus, and M. L. Berkowitz, "Structure of Phosphate Fluorosurfactant Based Reverse Micelles in Supercritical Carbon Dioxide," *Langmuir*, vol. 18, no. 20, pp. 7371–7376, Oct. 2002.

[191] S. Senapati and M. L. Berkowitz, "Molecular Dynamics Simulation Studies of Polyether and Perfluoropolyether Surfactant Based Reverse Micelles in Supercritical Carbon Dioxide," *J. Phys. Chem. B*, vol. 107, no. 47, pp. 12906–12916, Nov. 2003.

[192] S. Senapati and M. L. Berkowitz, "Water structure and dynamics in phosphate fluorosurfactant based reverse micelle: A computer simulation study," *J. Chem. Phys.*, vol. 118, no. 4, p. 1937, 2003.

[193] J. Tian, A. E. García, and E. G. Angel, "Simulations of the confinement of ubiquitin in self-assembled reverse micelles.," *J. Chem. Phys.*, vol. 134, no. 22, p. 225101, Jun. 2011.

[194] J. Tian and A. E. Garcia, "An alpha-helical peptide in AOT micelles prefers to be localized at the water/headgroup interface.," *Biophys. J.*, vol. 96, no. 10, pp. L57–159, May 2009.

[195] M. Pomata, D. Laria, M. S. S. Skaf, M. D. D. Elola, and M. Pomata H. H., "Molecular dynamics simulations of AOT-water/formamide reverse micelles: Structural and dynamical properties," *J. Chem. Phys.*, vol. 129, no. 24, p. 244503, 2008.

[196] D. J. Tobias and M. L. Klein, "Molecular Dynamics Simulations of a Calcium Carbonate/Calcium Sulfonate Reverse Micelle †," *J. Phys. Chem.*, vol. 100, no. 16, pp. 6637–6648, Jan. 1996.

[197] S. Salaniwal, S. Cui, H. D. Cochran, and P. T. Cummings, "Molecular Dynamics Simulation of Reverse Micelles in Supercritical Carbon Dioxide," *Ind. Eng. Chem. Res.*, vol. 39, no. 12, pp. 4543–4554, Dec. 2000.

[198] C. D. Bruce, S. Senapati, M. L. Berkowitz, L. Perera, and M. D. E. Forbes, "Molecular Dynamics Simulations of Sodium Dodecyl Sulfate Micelle in Water: The Behavior of Water," *J. Phys. Chem. B*, vol. 106, no. 42, pp. 10902–10907, Oct. 2002.

[199] L. Lu and M. L. Berkowitz, "Molecular dynamics simulation of a reverse micelle self assembly in supercritical CO_2.," *J. Am. Chem. Soc.*, vol. 126, no. 33, pp. 10254–10255, Aug. 2004.

[200] A. V Nevidimov and V. F. Razumov, "Molecular dynamics simulations of AOT reverse micelles' self-assembly," *Mol. Phys.*, vol. 107, no. 20, pp. 2169–2180, 2009.

[201] V. R. Vasquez, B. C. Williams, and O. A. Graeve, "Stability and comparative analysis of AOT/water/isooctane reverse micelle system using dynamic light scattering and molecular dynamics.," *J. Phys. Chem. B*, vol. 115, no. 12, pp. 2979–2987, Mar. 2011.

[202] A. Gardner, V. R. Vásquez, A. Clifton, and O. A. Graeve, "Molecular dynamics analysis of the AOT/water/isooctane system: Effect of simulation time, initial configuration, and model salts," *Fluid Phase Equilib.*, vol. 262, no. 1–2, pp. 264–270, Dec. 2007.

[203] M. Javanainen, H. Hammaren, L. Monticelli, J.-H. Jeon, M. S. Miettinen, H. Martinez-Seara, R. Metzler, and I. Vattulainen, "Anomalous and normal diffusion of proteins and lipids in crowded lipid membranes," *Faraday Discuss.*, 2013.

[204] G. V Mudzhikova and E. N. Brodskaya, "Computer simulation of reverse micelles and water-in-oil microemulsions," *Colloid J.*, vol. 74, no. 3, pp. 269–279, Jun. 2012.

[205] B. M. Ladanyi, "Computer simulation studies of counterion effects on the properties of surfactant systems," *Curr. Opin. Colloid Interface Sci.*, vol. 18, no. 1, pp. 15–25, Feb. 2013.

[206] R. Biswas, T. Chakraborti, B. Bagchi, and K. G. Ayappa, "Non-monotonic, distance-dependent relaxation of water in reverse micelles: propagation of surface induced frustration along hydrogen bond networks.," *J. Chem. Phys.*, vol. 137, no. 1, p. 014515, Jul. 2012.

[207] S. Pal, G. Vishal, K. S. Gandhi, and K. G. Ayappa, "Ion exchange in reverse micelles.," *Langmuir*, vol. 21, no. 2, pp. 767–778, Jan. 2005.

[208] J. A. Griffiths and D. M. Heyes, "Atomistic Simulation of Overbased Detergent Inverse Micelles," *Langmuir*, vol. 12, no. 10, pp. 2418–2424, Jan. 1996.

[209] M. H. Alaimo and T. F. Kumosinski, "Investigation of Hydrophobic Interactions in Colloidal and Biological Systems by Molecular Dynamics Simulations and NMR Spectroscopy," *Langmuir*, vol. 13, no. 7, pp. 2007–2018, 1997.

[210] A. Amararene, M. Gindre, J.-Y. Le Huérou, W. Urbach, D. Valdez, and M. Waks, "Adiabatic compressibility of AOT [sodium bis(2-ethylhexyl)sulfosuccinate] reverse micelles: Analysis of a simple model based on micellar size and volumetric measurements," *Statistical Nonlinear and Soft Matter Physics*, vol. 61, no. 1, pp. 682–689, Jan. 2000.

[211] J. Chowdhary and B. M. Ladanyi, "Molecular Simulation Study of Water Mobility in Aerosol-OT Reverse Micelles," *J. Phys. Chem. A*, p. null–null, 2011.

[212] H. F. Eicke and J. Rehak, "On the formation of water/oil microemulsions," *Helv. Chim. Acta*, vol. 59, no. 8, 1976.

[213] S. Salaniwal, S. T. Cui, P. T. Cummings, and H. D. Cochran, "Self-Assembly of Reverse Micelles in Water/Surfactant/Carbon Dioxide Systems by Molecular Simulation," *Langmuir*, vol. 15, no. 16, pp. 5188–5192, Aug. 1999.

[214] V. S. V. Chaitanya and S. Senapati, "Self-assembled reverse micelles in supercritical CO2 entrap protein in native state.," *J. Am. Chem. Soc.*, vol. 130, no. 6, pp. 1866–1870, Feb. 2008.

[215] S. Senapati and M. L. Berkowitz, "Computer Simulation Studies of Water States in Perfluoro Polyether Reverse Micelles: Effects of Changing the Counterion †," *J. Phys. Chem. A*, vol. 108, no. 45, pp. 9768–9776, Nov. 2004.

[216] B. Wu, X. Yang, and Z. Z. Xu, "Molecular dynamics simulation of self-assembly structure for AOK based reverse micelle in supercritical CO2," *Colloids and Surfaces A: Physicochemical and Engineering Aspects*, vol. 367, no. 1–3, pp. 148–154, Sep. 2010.

[217] S. Abel, "Propriétés structurales de l'Alanine octapeptide confinée dans des micelles inverses d'AOT: Une étude de simulation de dynamique moléculaire," in *Meeting annuel du GDR 2478 « □Protéines membranaires et assemblages Colloïdaux*, 2004.

[218] J. Eastoe, G. Fragneto, B. H. Robinson, T. R. Towey, R. K. Heenan, and J. L. Frank, "Variation of surfactant counterion and its effect on the structure and properties of Aerosol-OT-based water-in-oil microemulsions," *J. Chem. Soc., Faraday Trans.*, no. 88, pp. 461–471, 1992.

[219] M. J. Hou, M. Kim, and D. O. Shah, "A light scattering study on the droplet size and interdroplet interaction in microemulsions of AOT-oil-water system," *J. Colloid Interface Sci.*, vol. 123, no. 2, pp. 398–412, 1988.

[220] J. Eastoe, B. H. Robinson, D. C. Steytler, and D. Thorn-Leeson, "Structural studies of microemulsions stabilised by aerosol-OT," *Adv. Colloid. Interface Sci.*, vol. 36, pp. 1–31, 1991.

[221] L. Arleth and J. S. Pedersen, "Droplet polydispersity and shape fluctuations in AOT [bis(2-ethylhexyl)sulfosuccinate sodium salt] microemulsions studied by contrast variation small-angle neutron scattering," *Phys. Rev. E*, vol. 63, no. 06, pp. 1406–1424, 2001.

[222] N. Pal, S. Dev Verma, M. K. Singh, and S. Sen, "Fluorescence correlation spectroscopy: an efficient tool for measuring size, size-distribution and polydispersity of microemulsion droplets in solution.," *Analytical chemistry*, vol. 83, no. 20, pp. 7736–7744, Oct. 2011.

[223] S. A. Tovstun and V. F. Razumov, "On the composition fluctuations of reverse micelles.," *Journal of colloid and interface science*, vol. 351, no. 2, pp. 485–492, Nov. 2010.

[224] H. V Tartar, "A Theory of the Structure of the Micelles of Normal Paraffin-Chain Salts in Aqueous Solution," *J. Phys. Chem.*, vol. 59, no. 12, pp. 1195–1199, 1955.

[225] J. Eastoe, G. Fragneto, B. H. Robinson, T. F. Towey, R. K. Heenan, and F. J. Leng, "Variation of surfactant counterion and its effect on the structure and properties of Aerosol-OT-based water-in-oil microemulsions," *Journal of the Chemical Society, Faraday Transactions*, vol. 88, no. 3, pp. 461–471, 1992.

[226] J. Eastoe, T. F. Towey, B. H. Robinson, J. Williams, and R. K. Heenan, "Structures of metal bis(2-ethylhexylsulfosuccinate) aggregates in cyclohexane," *J. Phys. Chem.*, vol. 97, no. 7, pp. 1459–1463, Feb. 1993.

[227] C. Petit, P. Lixon, and M. P. Pileni, "Structural change in AOT reverse micelles induced by changing the counterion," in *Trends in Colloid and Interface Science VI*, Steinkopff, 1992, pp. 328–331.

[228] E. Bardez, Nguyen Cao Vy, and T. Zemb, "Counterion-Driven Sphere to Cylinder Transition in Reverse Micelles: A Small Angle X-ray Scattering and Conductometric Study," *Langmuir*, vol. 11, no. 3374–3381, 1996.

[229] A. V. Nevidimov and V. F. Razumov, "Molecular dynamics simulation of reverse micelles: A search for the most efficient strategy," *Colloid J.*, vol. 75, no. 2, pp. 191–197, Mar. 2013.

[230] H. Caldararu, A. Caragheorgheopol, M. Vasilescu, and I. Dragutan, "Structure of the Polar Core in Reverse Micelles of Nonionic Poly(oxyethylene) Surfactants, As Studied by Spin Probe and Fluorescence Probe Techniques," *J. Phys. Chem.*, vol. 98, no. 20, pp. 5320–5331, 1994.

[231] A. Caragheorgheopol, J. Pilar, and S. Schlick, "Hydration and Dynamics in Reverse Micelles of the Triblock Copolymer EO13PO30EO13 in Water-Xylene Mixtures: A Spin Probe Study," *Macromolecules*, vol. 30, no. 10, pp. 2923–2933, 1997.

[232] T. L. Spehr, B. Frick, M. Zamponi, and B. Stühn, "Dynamics of water confined to reverse AOT micelles," *Soft Matter*, vol. 7, no. 12, pp. 5745–5755, 2011.

[233] A. Amararene, M. Gindre, J.-Y. Le Huérou, C. Nicot, W. Urbach, and M. Waks, "Water Confined in Reverse Micelles: Acoustic and Densimetric Studies," *J. Phys. Chem. B*, vol. 101, no. 50, pp. 10751–10756, 1997.

[234] F. Merzel and J. C. Smith, "High-density hydration layer of lysozymes: molecular dynamics decomposition of solution scattering data.," *Journal of chemical information and modeling*, vol. 45, no. 6, pp. 1593–1599, 2005.

[235] D. I. Svergun, S. Richard, M. H. J. Koch, Z. Sayers, S. Kuprin, and G. Zaccai, "Protein hydration in solution: Experimental observation by x-ray and neutron scattering," *Proc. Natl. Acad. Sci. USA*, vol. 95, no. 5, pp. 2267–2272, 1998.

[236] M. Marchi, "Compressibility of Cavities and Biological Water from Voronoi Volumes in Hydrated Proteins," *J. Phys. Chem. B*, vol. 107, no. 27, pp. 6598–6602, Jul. 2003.

[237] G. Voronoi, "Nouvelles applications des paramètres continus à la théorie des formes quadratiques. Deuxième mémoire. Recherches sur les parallélloèdres primitifs.," *Journal für die reine und angewandte Mathematik (Crelles Journal)*, vol. 1908, no. 134, pp. 198–287, Jan. 1908.

[238] J. Zheng, K. Kwak, and M. D. Fayer, "Ultrafast 2D IR vibrational echo spectroscopy.," *Accounts of chemical research*, vol. 40, no. 1, pp. 75–83, Jan. 2007.

[239] M. D. Fayer, "Dynamics of water interacting with interfaces, molecules, and ions.," *Accounts of chemical research*, vol. 45, no. 1, pp. 3–14, Jan. 2012.

[240] M. D. Fayer, "Water in a Crowd," *Physiology*, vol. 26, no. 6, pp. 381–392, Dec. 2011.

[241] T. Howe-Siang, I. R. Piletic, R. E. Riter, N. E. Levinger, and M. D. Fayer, "Dynamics of Water Confined on a Nanometer Length Scale in Reverse Micelles: Ultrafast Infrared Vibrational Echo Spectroscopy," *Phys. Rev. Lett.*, vol. 94, no. 5, p. 57405, 2005.

[242] S. Bagchi, D. G. Thorpe, I. F. Thorpe, G. A. Voth, and M. D. Fayer, "Conformational Switching between Protein Substates Studied with 2D IR Vibrational Echo Spectroscopy and Molecular Dynamics Simulations," *J. Phys. Chem. B*, vol. 114, no. 51, pp. 17187–17193, 2010.

[243] I. R. Piletic, H.-S. Tan, M. D. Fayer, and T. Howe-Siang, "Orientational dynamics of water confined on a nanometer length scale in reverse micelles.," *J. Chem. Phys.*, vol. 122, no. 45, pp. 17450/1–174501/9, 2005.

[244] E. E. Fenn, D. B. Wong, and M. D. Fayer, "Water dynamics at neutral and ionic interfaces," *Proc. Natl. Acad. Sci. USA*, vol. 106, no. 36, pp. 15243–15248, 2009.

[245] D. E. Moilanen, E. E. Fenn, D. Wong, M. D. Fayer, E. M. David, E. F. Emily, W. Daryl, and D. F. Michael, "Water dynamics in large and small reverse micelles: from two ensembles to collective behavior.," *J. Chem. Phys.*, vol. 131, no. 1, p. 014704, Jul. 2009.

[246] D. E. Moilanen, N. E. Levinger, D. B. Spry, and M. D. Fayer, "Confinement or the nature of the interface? Dynamics of nanoscopic water.," *J. Am. Chem. Soc.*, vol. 129, no. 46, pp. 14311–14318, Nov. 2007.

[247] D. E. Moilanen, E. E. Fenn, D. Wong, M. D. Fayer, E. M. David, E. F. Emily, W. Daryl, and D. F. Michael, "Water dynamics in large and small reverse micelles: from two ensembles to collective behavior.," *J. Chem. Phys.*, vol. 131, no. 1, p. 014704, Jul. 2009.

[248] A. Das, A. Patra, and R. K. Mitra, "Do the physical properties of water in mixed reverse micelles follow a synergistic effect: a spectroscopic investigation.," *J. Phys. Chem. B*, vol. 117, no. 13, pp. 3593–602, Mar. 2013.

[249] P. Mark and L. Nilsson, "Structure and dynamics of the TIP3P, SPC, and SPC/E water models at 298 K," *J. Phys. Chem. A*, vol. 105, no. 43, pp. 9954–9960, 2001.

[250] M. Christensen and J. B. Pedersen, "Diffusion in inhomogeneous and anisotropic media," *J. of Chem. Phys.*, vol. 119, no. 10, pp. 5171–5175, 2003.

[251] B. Bagchi, "Water dynamics in the hydration layer around proteins and micelles," *Chemical reviews*, vol. 105, no. 9, pp. 3197–219, Sep. 2005.

[252] R. W. Impey, P. A. Madden, and I. R. McDonald, "Spectroscopic and transport properties of water," *Mol. Phys.*, vol. 46, no. 3, pp. 513–539, Jun. 1982.

[253] I. R. Piletic, D. E. Moilanen, D. B. Spry, N. E. Levinger, and M. D. Fayer, "Testing the core/shell model of nanoconfined water in reverse micelles using linear and nonlinear IR spectroscopy.," *The journal of physical chemistry. A*, vol. 110, no. 15, pp. 4985–99, Apr. 2006.

[254] D. Laage and W. H. Thompson, "Reorientation dynamics of nanoconfined water: power-law decay, hydrogen-bond jumps, and test of a two-state model.," *J. Chem. Phys.*, vol. 136, no. 4, p. 044513, Jan. 2012.

[255] R. E. Riter, E. P. Undiks, and N. E. Levinger, "Impact of Counterion on Water Motion in Aerosol OT Reverse Micelles," *J. Am. Chem. Soc.*, vol. 120, no. 24, pp. 6062–6067, Jun. 1998.

[256] S. Mukherjee, P. Chowdhury, W. F. DeGrado, and F. Gai, "Site-Specific Hydration Status of an Amphipathic Peptide in AOT Reverse Micelles," *Langmuir*, vol. 23, no. 22, pp. 11174–11179, 2007.

[257] H. Raghuraman and A. Chattopadhyay, "Organization and Dynamics of Melittin in Environments of Graded Hydration: A Fluorescence Approach," *Langmuir*, vol. 19, no. 24, pp. 10332–10341, 2003.

[258] S. Mukherjee, P. Chowdhury, and F. Gai, "Tuning the Cooperativity of the Helix-Coil Transition by Aqueous Reverse Micelles," *J. Phys. Chem. B*, vol. 110, no. 24, pp. 11615–11619, 2006.

[259] S. Mukherjee, P. Chowdhury, and F. Gai, "Infrared Study of the Effect of Hydration on the Amide I Band and Aggregation Properties of Helical Peptides," *J. Phys. Chem. B*, vol. 111, no. 17, pp. 4596–4602, 2007.

[260] P. S.-W. Yeung and P. H. Axelsen, "The crowded environment of a reverse micelle induces the formation of β-strand seed structures for nucleating amyloid fibril formation.," *J. Am. Chem. Soc.*, vol. 134, no. 14, pp. 6061–6063, Apr. 2012.

[261] P. S.-W. Yeung, G. Eskici, and P. H. Axelsen, "Infrared spectroscopy of proteins in reverse micelles.," *Biochimica et biophysica acta*, Oct. 2012.

[262] P. L. Luisi, L. J. Magid, and J. H. Fendler, "Solubilization of Enzymes and Nucleic Acids in Hydrocarbon Micellar Solution," *Crit. Rev. Biochem. Mol. Biol.*, vol. 20, no. 4, pp. 409–474, Jan. 1986.

[263] C. Nicot and M. Waks, "Reverse Micelles as a model for the study of membrane proteins at myelin interlamellar aqueous species," in *Structure and reactivity in reverse micelles*, M.-P. Pileni, Ed. Elsevier, 1989, pp. 340–362.

[264] W. D. Van Horn, M. E. Ogilvie, and P. F. Flynn, "Use of reverse micelles in membrane protein structural biology.," *Journal of biomolecular NMR*, vol. 40, no. 3, pp. 203–211, Mar. 2008.

[265] C. R. Babu, P. F. Flynn, and A. J. Wand, "Validation of protein structure from preparations of encapsulated proteins dissolved in low viscosity fluids.," *J. Am. Chem. Soc.*, vol. 123, no. 11, pp. 2691–2, Mar. 2001.

[266] T. Giesa and M. J. Buehler, "Nanoconfinement and the strength of biopolymers.," *Annual review of biophysics*, vol. 42, pp. 651–673, Jan. 2013.

[267] A. P. Minton, "The Influence of Macromolecular Crowding and Macromolecular Confinement on Biochemical Reactions in Physiological Media," *Journal of Biological Chemistry*, vol. 276, no. 14, pp. 10577–10580, Apr. 2001.

[268] H. X. Zhou and K. A. Dill, "Stabilization of Proteins in Confined Spaces," *Biochemistry*, vol. 40, no. 38, pp. 11289–11293, 2001.

[269] A. P. Minton, "Confinement as a determinant of macromolecular structure and reactivity. II. Effects of weakly attractive interactions between confined macrosolutes and confining structures.," *Biophys. J.*, vol. 68, no. 4, pp. 1311–22, Apr. 1995.

[270] K. A. Dill, "Dominant forces in protein folding," *Biochemistry*, vol. 29, no. 31, pp. 7133–7155, Aug. 1990.

[271] J. A. Vila, D. R. Ripoll, and H. A. Scheraga, "Physical reasons for the unusual alpha-helix stabilization afforded by charged or neutral polar residues in alanine-rich peptides.," *Proc. Natl. Acad. Sci. USA*, vol. 97, no. 24, pp. 13075–13079, Nov. 2000.

[272] A. E. García and K. Y. Sanbonmatsu, "Alpha-helical stabilization by side chain shielding of backbone hydrogen bonds.," *Proc. Natl. Acad. Sci. USA*, vol. 99, no. 5, pp. 2782–2787, Mar. 2002.

[273] R. A. G. D. Silva, J. Y. Nguyen, and S. M. Decatur, "Probing the effect of side chains on the conformation and stability of helical peptides via isotope-edited infrared spectroscopy.," *Biochemistry*, vol. 41, no. 51, pp. 15296–15303, Dec. 2002.

[274] S. Abel, "Molecular Simulations of the Stability of An Alanine Octapeptide confined in Small Size AOT Reverse Micelles," in *49th Biophysical Society Annual Meeting*, 2005.

[275] S. Chakrabarty and B. Bagchi, "Self-Organization of n-Alkane Chains in Water: Length Dependent Crossover from Helix and Toroid to Molten Globule," *J. Phys. Chem. B*, vol. 0, no. 0, 2009.

[276] W. Weber, P. H. Hünenberger, and A. J. McCammon, "Molecular Dynamics Simulations of a Polyalanine Octapeptide under Ewald Boundary Conditions: Influence of Artificial Periodicity on Peptide Conformation," *J. Phys. Chem. B*, vol. 104, no. 15, pp. 3668–3675, Apr. 2000.

[277] C. J. Margulis, H. A. Stern, and B. J. Berne, "Helix Unfolding and Intramolecular Hydrogen Bond Dynamics in Small Alpha-Helices in Explicit Solvent," *J. Phys. Chem. B*, vol. 106, no. 41, pp. 10748–10752, 2002.

[278] M. Bachar and O. M. Becker, "Melittin at a membrane/water interface: Effects on water orientation and water penetration," *J. Chem. Phys.*, vol. 111, no. 18, p. 8672, 1999.

[279] Z. Wimmer and M. Zarevúcka, "A review on the effects of supercritical carbon dioxide on enzyme activity.," *International journal of molecular sciences*, vol. 11, no. 1, pp. 233–253, Jan. 2010.

[280] J. Zhang and B. Han, "Supercritical CO2-continuous microemulsions and compressed CO2-expanded reverse microemulsions," *The Journal of Supercritical Fluids*, vol. 47, no. 3, pp. 531–536, Jan. 2009.

[281] K. P. Johnston, K. L. Harrison, M. J. Clarke, S. M. Howdle, M. P. Heitz, F. V. Bright, C. Carlier, and T. W. Randolph, "Water-in-Carbon Dioxide Microemulsions: An Environment for Hydrophiles Including Proteins," *Science*, vol. 271, no. 5249, pp. 624–626, Feb. 1996.

[282] G. R. Moore and G. W. Pettigrew, *Cytochromes c. Evolutionary, Structural, and Physicochemical Aspects.* . Berlin, Heidelberg and New York.: Springer Verlag, 1990.

[283] P. Brochette, C. Petit, and M.-P. Pileni, "Cytochrome c in sodium bis(2-ethylhexyl) sulfosuccinate reverse micelles: structure and reactivity," *J. Phys. Chem.*, vol. 92, no. 12, pp. 3505–3511, Jun. 1988.

[284] K. Vos, C. Laane, S. R. Weijers, A. Hoek, C. Veeger, and A. J. W. G. Visser, "Time-resolved fluorescence and circular dichroism of porphyrin cytochrome c and Zn-porphyrin cytochrome c incorporated in reversed micelles," *Eur. J. Biochem.*, vol. 169, no. 2, pp. 259–268, 1987.

[285] R. W. Peterson, K. Anbalagan, C. Tommos, and A. J. Wand, "Forced folding and structural analysis of metastable proteins.," *J. Am. Chem. Soc.*, vol. 126, no. 31, pp. 9498–9, Aug. 2004.

[286] N. V Nucci, M. S. Pometun, and A. J. Wand, "Mapping the hydration dynamics of ubiquitin.," *J. Am. Chem. Soc.*, vol. 133, no. 32, pp. 12326–12329, Aug. 2011.

[287] L. Hicke, H. L. Schubert, and C. P. Hill, "Ubiquitin-binding domains.," *Nature reviews. Molecular cell biology*, vol. 6, no. 8, pp. 610–621, Aug. 2005.

[288] A. K. Simorellis and P. F. Flynn, "Fast local backbone dynamics of encapsulated ubiquitin.," *J. Am. Chem. Soc.*, vol. 128, no. 30, pp. 9580–9581, Aug. 2006.

[289] D. N. LeBard, B. G. Levine, P. Mertmann, S. A. Barr, A. Jusufi, S. A. Sanders, M. L. Klein, and A. Z. Panagiotopoulos, "Self-assembly of coarse-grained ionic surfactants accelerated by graphics processing units," *Soft Matter*, vol. 8, no. 8, p. 2385, 2012.

[290] A. Jusufi, A. Kohlmeyer, M. Sztucki, T. Narayanan, and M. Ballauff, "Self-Assembly of Charged Surfactants: Full Comparison of Molecular Simulations and Scattering Experiments.," *Langmuir*, vol. 28, no. 51, pp. 17632–17641, Dec. 2012.

[291] G. Stirnemann, E. Wernersson, P. Jungwirth, and D. Laage, "Mechanisms of Acceleration and Retardation of Water Dynamics by Ions.," *J. Am. Chem. Soc.*, vol. 135, no. 32, pp. 11824–11831, Aug. 2013.

[292] T. A. Wassenaar, H. I. Ingólfsson, M. Priess, S. J. Marrink, and L. V Schäfer, "Mixing MARTINI: electrostatic coupling in hybrid atomistic-coarse-grained biomolecular simulations.," *J. Phys. Chem. B*, vol. 117, no. 13, pp. 3516–3530, Apr. 2013.

[293] B. Tamamushi and N. Watanabe, "The formation of molecular aggregation structures in ternary system: Aerosol OT/water/iso-octane," *Colloid and Polymer Science Kolloid Zeitschrift & Zeitschrift für Polymere*, vol. 258, no. 2, pp. 174–178, Feb. 1980.

[294] M. Kotlarchyk, S. H. Chen, J. S. Huang, and M. W. Kim, "Structure of three-component micoemulsions in the critical regions determined by small-angle neutron scattering," *Phys. Rev. A*, vol. 29, no. 4, pp. 2054–2068, 1984.

[295] M. Hirai, R. K. Hirai, H. Iwase, S. Arai, S. Mitsuya, T. Takeda, H. Seto, and M. Nagao, "Dynamics of w/o AOT microemulsions studied by neutron spin echo," *J. Phys. Chem. Solids*, vol. 60, no. 8–9, pp. 1359–1361, 1999.

[296] K. M. Larsson and M. P. Pileni, "Interactions of native and modified cytochrome c with negatively charged reverse micellar liquid interface," *Eur. Biophys. J.*, vol. 21, no. 6, pp. 409–416, 1993.

[297] H. B. Bohidar and M. Behboudnia, "Characterization of reverse micelles by dynamic light scattering," *Colloids and Surfaces A: Physicochemical and Engineering Aspects*, vol. 178, no. 1–3, pp. 313–323, 2001.

ISBN: 978-1-62948-444-0
© 2014 Nova Science Publishers, Inc.

Chapter 3

THERMODYNAMIC ASPECTS OF MICELLES

Hiroshi Maeda[*]

Professor Emeritus, Kyushu University, Japan

ABSTRACT

In this Chapter, thermodynamic aspects of micelles are discussed with particular emphasis on electric interaction (ionic micelles) and two-component mixed micelles. In the first section, the dual nature of micelles, a collection of small systems or a pseudophase is discussed followed by a brief history of the concept of surfactant micelles. In Section II, the free energy of micelle formation is described which is the basis of the micelle stability and related to the critical micelle concentration (*cmc*). Various contributions other than the electric interaction are discussed. The electrostatic free energy is described in Section III together with the electric potential in the solutions evaluated by the Poisson-Boltzmann equation where no further advanced approach is introduced. Stability of micelles mainly depends on the length of the nonpolar chain and the kind of polar head groups. the topic is discussed in Section IV. The integral and the differential chemical potentials are discussed. In Section V, effects of salt concentration, temperature and pressure on the stability of micelles are discussed. The size (the aggregation number) and the shape of micelles are important and they are determined by the condition of the free energy minimum but geometrical considerations are able to provide us with a simple but useful approach to the problem. The pioneering idea of Tanford was developed into 'the packing parameter' by Israelachvili-Mitchell-Ninham as described in Section VI, followed by a brief description on the light scattering and osmometry which are used for the determination of the aggregation numer of micelles. Rod-like or worm-like micelles are discussed also in Section VI. Mixed micelles are discussed extensively throughout Section VII though limited to the two-component mixed micelles, in particular, to ionic/nonionic mixed micelles. The micellar Gibbs-Duhem relation and several phenomenological approaches to analyze the *cmc* data are described. A 'phase diagram' is presented to describe the mixing behavior. As a special example of ionic/nonionic mixed micelles, the hydrogen ion titration of micelles is discussed in Section VIII.

---

[*] E-mail: maeda@chem.kyushu-univ.jp, maedahrs@cap.bbiq.jp.

I. INTRODUCTION

1. Dual Nature of Micelles; a Collection of Small System or a Pseudophase

Amphiphiles are those molecules consisting of two (or more) portions of different chemical natures, one is compatible with the molecules constituting the surrounding medium (solvent) and the other part is not compatible with it. They show surface activity by adsorbing at solution/air interface and hence called surfactant (surface active agent). When the concentration of amphiphiles reaches a certain level, several tens of the molecules begin to aggregate to form particles called micelle [1-10]. Although the aggregation processes follow the mass action law, the aggregate formation takes place in a narrow concentration range, known as the critical micelle concentration (cmc), i.e., the micelle formation is a cooperative association subject to the mass action law. In aqueous media, hydrocarbon chains or other nonpolar parts of the molecules form an oil droplet covered with polar head groups that separates, though not completely, the oil core from aqueous environment. At the cmc, various properties of the solution undergo significant changes: surface tension, osmotic pressure (or solvent activity), light scattering (turbidity), viscosity, density and electrical conductivity in the case of ionic surfactants [1-4]. Micellization is a kind of cooperative phenomena that resembles phase separation like crystallization. A nucleation process is certainly involved to in the micelle formation. However, micellization differs from ordinary phase separation in the respect that the micelle is not a macroscopic phase but a small system consisting of several tens or hundreds molecules except for the case of long rodlike micelles. The stability of micelles against macroscopic phase separation generally originates from the condition that the aggregate size is, at least in one dimension, limited to the length related to the amphiphile molecule in the extended conformation. Geometrical packing constrains dictate, in many cases, curved interface of the aggregates and aggregates cannot grow indefinitely into a macroscopic phase with curved interfaces. Curvatures of the final stable aggregates are determined by several interactions such as electrostatic repulsion, steric repulsion among head groups, attraction among hydrocarbon chains and so on. These factors are summed up into one parameter called the packing parameter[3] or the shape factor[3] or surfactant parameter or surfactant number [4]. This is one of key parameters controlling the size and shape of aggregates and discussed in Section VI.

Aside from the small system nature of micelles described above, on the other hand, the surface tension of the solution of surfactants shows little change when the concentration exceeds the cmc. According to the Gibbs adsorption isotherm, this well known behavior suggests the chemical potential of the surfactant molecule to be practically constant when micelles are present to a significant amount. Accordingly, a tempting view comes up that micelles can be approximated as a pseudophase. These two different views on micelles are referred to here *the mass action model* and *the pseudophase model*. Since micelles cannot be a true phase as is evident from the phase rule consideration, the mass action model is correct and the pseudophase model is approximate. However, to apply the mass action model, we need to know the aggregation number with its standard deviation, micellar shape and its distribution, the dependence of the electric surface potential on the size and the shape of the micelle in the case of ionic micelles, and so on. On the other hand, we can analyze the obtained experimental data by applying the pseudophase model with fewer data than required in the mass action model. The two approaches should be complementary and we make use of them interchangeably in the present study. Throughout the present chapter, references are not complete at all.

2. A Brief History of the Concept of Surfactant Micelle

In the last decade of the 19th century, Krafft intensively investigated the physico-chemical properties of soap solutions, therby noting both the 'crystalloid' and the 'colloid' nature of soap solutions [11-13]. Krafft and Wiglow found that the solubilities of soaps in water increased sharply in a narrow temperature range (the Krafft temperature) that is significantly lower than the melting point of the corresponding fatty acid [12a]. In the subsequent paper, they discovered the aggregation of soap molecules from the molecular weight determination by the boiling point elevation [12b]. The aggregation of hexadecylammonium chloride was also observed [13]. Very small values of the boiling point elevation at rather high concentrations observed on soap solutions were correctly associated with the same behavior of glue and rubber, natural polymeric compounds known at that time [12b]. Measurements of the boiling point of aqueous soap solutions are hampered by the bubble formation and small differences could not be accurately determined. Freezing point depression method is not applicable for many soap solutions because their Krafft temperatures are higher than the melting point of water. Later, Smitz confirmed the aggregation by the measurements of the vapor pressure depression [14] and the aggregation of soaps in water was finally confirmed. However, nobody including Krafft seemed to present any model for the soap aggregates. Another flaw of Krafft's work arose from the point that Krafft regarded the soap as a neutral molecule instead of an electrolyte consisting of anionic fatty acid (carboxylate) plus a counterion (Na^+ or K^+). Later, the work of Krafft was severely criticized by McBain. In one of his papers, McBain wrote as follows, "Krafft's well known work is completely erroneous" [15a]. Nevertheless, it is Krafft who first discovered the aggregation of soap ions in aqueous solutions, the colloidal nature of aqueous soap solutions. On the other hand, McBain correctly recognized soap aggregates to be a kind of colloidal electrolytes and used the term 'micelle' for the aggregates. In the frequently cited reference, an issue of Transactions of the Faraday Society in 1913 [15b], the term 'micelle' appeared, not conspicuously, in the discussion part.

In the same year, 1913, in the study on the physicochemical properties of solutions of soaps or cetylsulfonic acid, Reychler used the term 'micelle (Mizellen)'. Moreover, Reychler has presented the concepts of amphiphiles, of hydrophilic and lipophilic, in addition to a model for the micelle where nonpolar groups are inside and polar head groups cover them forming a spherical entity [16]. McBain considered the micelle something like a crystalline plate-like aggregates (lamellar colloid) in which the sate of hydrocarbon chain is considered to be close to the crystalline state. The micelle model of McBain was inevitably polydisperse and no sharp *cmc* was associated with their formation. On the other hand, Hartley considered spherical micelles where hydrocarbon chains are in the liquid state. Spherical micelles are expected to be rather monodisperse with well defined *cmc* values [17]. Extensive data in support of Hartley's revised concept of micellar structure have since been provided by numerous studies. On the other hand, rod-like micelles were first suggested by Debye and

Anacker on the basis of the analysis of the dissymmetry of scattered light [18]. An extensive descriptions on the history of the study on amphiphiles is found elsewhere [6].

II. THE FREE ENERGY OF MICELLE FORMATION ΔG_M*

1. Fundamental Relations

For the Gibbs free energy of the whole system containing N_w water molecules, N_i^s molecules/ions in the solution part, N_i^m molecules/ions in the micelles and N micelles, we have eq (2.1.1) at an absolute temperature T, a pressure P and the subdivision potential ε for the micelles under the assumption that the equilibrium among micelles of different compositions and the aggregation numbers is established.

$$dG = VdP - SdT + \Sigma\mu_i^s dN_i^s + \Sigma\mu_i^m dN_i^m + \varepsilon\, dN. \tag{2.1.1}$$

Here suffix i refers to any species including water. The contribution from the electrostatic free energy, if present, is included in chemical potentials μ_i. Let us define G_m and the average number of ith-species per micelle m_i as follows.

$$m_i = N_i^m/N, \tag{2.1.2}$$

$$G_m = \Sigma\, m_i\mu_i^m + \varepsilon. \tag{2.1.3}$$

Eq (2.1.1) is now rewritten as eq (2.1.4) in terms of m_i and G_m.

$$dG = VdP - SdT + \Sigma\mu_i^s dN_i^s + N\Sigma\mu_i^m dm_i + G_m dN. \tag{2.1.4}$$

It is found that $G_m = (\partial G/\partial N)_{T, P, Nis, mi}$ and hence G_m represents the chemical potential of the micelle. From eq (2.1.3), we have eq (2.1.5) where the summation with respect to j extends over all species other than i.

$$(G_m - \Sigma m_j\, \mu_j^m)/m_i = \mu_i^m + \varepsilon/m_i. \tag{2.1.5}$$

The lhs of eq (2.1.5) represents the 'integral' chemical potential of the i-th species in the micelle [19, 20], which does not coincide with μ_i^m, the 'differential' chemical potential [19, 20]. For any macroscopic system, however, these two chemical potentials are identical.

By integration of eq (2.1.4) at constant T, P, and m_i, we have

$$G = \Sigma N_i^s\mu_i^s + N\, G_m. \tag{2.1.6}$$

For any change under constant T, P and the total number of i-th species $N_i^t (= N_i^s + N_i^m)$, dG of eq (2.1.4) reduces to eq (2.1.7) with a relation $dN_i^s + N\, dm_i + m_i\, dN = d\, N_i^t = 0$.

$$dG = \Sigma(\mu_i^s - \mu_i^m)\, dN_i^s + \varepsilon\, dN = \Sigma(\mu_i^s - \mu_i^m)\, dN_i^s + [G_m - \Sigma\mu_i^m\, m_i]\, dN \qquad (2.1.7)$$

At equilibirum, $dG = 0$ and we have,

$$\mu_i^s = \mu_i^m, \qquad (2.1.8)$$

$$G_m = \Sigma\, m_i\, \mu_i^m, \qquad (2.1.9)$$

$$\varepsilon = 0. \qquad (2.1.10)$$

As shown by eq (2.1.9), the two chemical potentials, 'integral' and 'differential', become identical as far as the equilibrium relations $\mu_i^s = \mu_i^m$ and $\varepsilon = 0$ are established. From eqs (2.1.8) and (2.1.9), the following equilibrium relation is obtained between the micelles and the constituting species in the solution part.

$$G_m = \Sigma m_i \mu_i^s. \qquad (2.1.11)$$

The analysis in this section indicates that micelles are essentially polydisperse with respect to both the composition and the aggregation number. In the rest of the present study, however, monodisperse approximation will be employed frequently only for the sake of simplicity.

2. The Stability of Micelles ΔG_M^* Relative to the Monomers

2-1. One-component Nonionic Micelle

Eq (2.1.11) becomes eq (2.2.1) where m and μ_1^s denote, respectively, the average aggregation number and the chemical potential of the monomer in the solution part.

$$G_m = m\, \mu_1^s \qquad (2.2.1)$$

Assuming the ideal behavior of the monomer, we have eq (2.2.2) in terms of the monomer concentration in the solution part X_1.

$$\mu_1^s = \mu_1^{s*} + RT \ln X_1. \qquad (2.2.2)$$

The chemical potential of the micelle G_m is written as follows in terms of the micelle concentration X_m as far as inter-micellar interactions are negligible.

$$G_m = G_m^* + RT \ln X_m. \qquad (2.2.3)$$

The reference chemical potentials of the monomer μ_1^{s*} and the micelle G_m^* are defined as hypothetical pure states (unit mole fraction) at infinite dilution in water, $\mu_1^{s*}(T, P)$ and $G_m^*(T, P)$.

In the pseudo-phase approximation, micelles are approximated as a macroscopic phase and hence the effects of the concentration term $\ln X_m$ are ignored. Then, the chemical potential of the surfactant in the 'micelle phase' μ_M is introduced as a function of T and P, $\mu_M(T, P)$. The equilibrium condition is eq (2.2.4) instead of eq (2.2.1).

$$\mu_M = \mu_1^s \tag{2.2.4}$$

The stability of the micelle relative to the monomer in solution is given by the free energy of micelle formation ΔG_M^* which is defined as $G_m^*/m - \mu_1^{s*}$, or $\mu_M - \mu_1^{s*}$.

$$\Delta G_M^* = G_m^*/m - \mu_1^{s*} = RT \ln [X_1/(X_m^{1/m})] \tag{2.2.5}$$

Under the approximation that $X_m^{1/m} \sim 1$ [For $X_m = 1 \times 10^{-6}$ and $m = 100$, $X_m^{1/m} = 0.87$], we have $\Delta G_M^* = RT \ln X_1$. In the pseudo-phase approximation, $\Delta G_M^* = \mu_M - \mu_1^{s*} = RT \ln X_1$. In the expression, X_1 is the monomer concentration in equilibrium with the micelles. If X_1 is approximated with the *cmc*, we have

$$\Delta G_M^* = RT \ln cmc. \tag{2.2.6}$$

Here, the concentration unit of the *cmc* is the mole fraction but other units can be used with concomitant changes of the definition of the standard state [21, 22]. We adopt either the mole fraction or the molarity interchangeably in the rest part of the present study.

2-2. One-component Ionic Micelle Only Consisting of the Surfactant Ion

In the case of ionic micelles, there are two different approaches regarding the micelle composition: whether or not the counterions are included as a constituent of the micelle. When counterion activity does not change appreciably in the course of the micellization reaction, micelles can be defined as only consisting of surfactant ions, and eq (2.2.1) holds. The condition of constant activity of counterions is satisfied either in salt solutions or at very low micelle concentration in water. The reference state of the micelle G_m^* is now defined at infinite dilution not in water but in the solution containing ΣN_i^s molecules/ions, i. e., $G_m^*(T, P, \xi)$. As an environmental variable ξ, counterion concentration X_g or salt concentration X_s will be taken where the salt is assumed to consist of the same counterion species as the surfactant. In the charged pseudo-phase approximation, we have the following relations. When the salt is present in excess, $X_s \gg X_1^s$,

$$\Delta G_M^* = \mu_M (T, P, X_s) - \mu_1^{s*}(T, P, X_s) = RT \ln cmc. \tag{2.2.7}$$

In water, on the other hand, ξ is taken as X_g^* the counterion concentration at the *cmc*.

$$\Delta G_M^* = \mu_M (T, P, X_g^*) - \mu_1^{s*}(T, P, X_g^*) = RT \ln cmc. \tag{2.2.8}$$

It is to be noted that ΔG_M^* is not a proper quantity when we wish to compare the stability among different ionic micelles in water or at low X_s, inasmuch as X_g^* values differ generally for different surfactants. It is indispensable to correct for the effect of different C_g^*. This topics will be discussed later in Section VII-6.

2-3. One-component Ionic Micelle Consisting of the Surfactant Ion and the Counterions

When a fraction v of micellar charges is compensated by the counterion binding, eq (2.2.1) is to be replaced with eq (2.2.9), in terms of the chemical potential of the counterion μ_g [23, 24].

$$G_m = m \, (\mu_l^s + v\mu_g^s) \tag{2.2.9}$$

Another measure for the stability ΔG_M^{**} will be introduced as below, in place of ΔG_M^*.

$$\Delta G_M^{**} = G_m^*/m - [\mu_l^{s*}(T, P, X_g^*) + v\mu_g^{s*}]. \tag{2.2.10}$$

Under situations that the counterion activity a_g can be approximated with the concentration X_g, $a_g = X_g = X_1 + X_s$, we have the following equation by ignoring the micelle concentration term.

$$\Delta G_M^{**}/RT = \ln X_1 + v \ln a_g = \ln X_1 + v \ln (X_1 + X_s). \tag{2.2.11}$$

When salt is absent (X_s=0),

$$\Delta G_M^{**}/RT = (1 + v) \ln X_1 = (1 + v) \ln cmc. \tag{2.2.12}$$

Effects of different X_g^* values for different ionic micelles are expected to be small by the introduction of v values. Thus, comparison of the micelle stability of different ionic surfactants can be effected in terms of ΔG_M^{**} without any correction. This will be a great advantage to ΔG_M^{**}. To obtain ΔG_M^{**}, however, v should be evaluated in addition to the cmc. It is to be noted that ΔG_M^{**} contains the contribution from the counterion $(\mu_g^m - \mu_g^{s*})$ while ΔG_M^* does not. As is evident, eq (2.2.12) does not hold in the presence of salt. On the other hand, ΔG_M^* can be used not only in salt solutions but also in water and hence it is useful when we discuss the effect of the salt concentration X_s on the micelle stability.

In the case of charged pseudo-phase approximation, we have $d(\mu_l^s + v\mu_g^s) = dG^* = 0$ from eq (2.2.9). In water, the following relation has been found in the concentration range higher than the cmc with a practically constant v value [25].

$$\ln a_l^s = -v \, \ln a_g^s + \text{constant} \tag{2.2.13}$$

An assessment of v is possible by means of eq (2.2.13).

3. Various Nonelectric Contributions to the Micelle Stability

ΔG_M^* will be divided into the nonelectric contribution ΔG_{non}^* and the electric one ΔG_{el}. The electric free energy ΔG_{el} will be discussed in Section III. In the molecular thermodynamics approach to the stability of micelles, developed by Blankschtein [26-29], Nagarajan-Ruckenstein [30-32], Erikkson-Bergström [20, 33] and others, ΔG_M^* is divided into several contributions as follows.

$$\Delta G_M^* = \Delta G_{non}^* + \Delta G_{el} = G_{tr} + G_{int} + G_{pack} + G_{head} + \Delta G_{el} \qquad (2.3.1)$$

Here, G_{tr} is related to the transfer of the nonpolar group from aqueous solution to the micelle. G_{int} is the 'interfacial' free energy of micelles, which takes the situation into account that a part of the hydrocarbon chains is exposed to aqueous environment. G_{pack} is associated partly with the restriction of one end of the alkyl tail at the micelle surface and partly with the constraint to pack chains within a limited space of the micelle core. G_{head} is related to the interactions between polar head groups at the micelle surface. The steric repulsion is ubiquitous and important to limit the aggregation number finite in the case of noncharged micelles. Other possible contributions to G_{head} include the hydrogen bonding and/or dipole-dipole interaction between the neighboring head groups.

As to G_{tr}, it is estimated by the transfer free energy of a saturated hydrocarbon from the pure liquid state to the aqueous solution (infinitely dilute). The associated free energy ΔG_ℓ^w per mole of methylene group is about 3.8 kJ/mol (900 cal/mol) at 298 K, calculated from the solubility data of alkanes [1, 23, 76]. The following expression has been proposed by Blankschtein for an alkyl chain consisting of n_C carbon atoms [27].

$$\Delta G_\ell^w/RT = - (4.09 - 1.05\ n_C)(298/T) + (4.62 + 0.44\ n_C) \qquad (2.3.2)$$

It is to be noted that the transfer free energy G_{tr} of an alkyl chain from the aqueous environment to the micelle core is less negative than $- \Delta G_\ell^w$ due to a positive G_{pack} contribution. A value about $- 2.9$ kJ/mol (-700 cal/mol) per methylene group has been proposed [23]. As to the linearity shown in eq (2.3.2), the transfer free energy of undissociated fatty acids from n-heptane to water at room temperature varied linearly up to $n_C = 22$ [1].

The surface free energy of micelles G_{int} is given by the product of the surface area of the hydrocarbon core in contact with water and the microscopic interfacial tension $\gamma_{HC/w}$. Of the area per surfactant molecule a, a part denoted as a_0 is screened by the head group. Accordingly, G_{int} is given as $(a - a_0)\ \gamma_{HC/w}$. Although few convincing reasoning has been proposed regarding appropriate estimates of $\gamma_{HC/w}$, values 20-50 mN/m seem accepted currently [34]. The following expression has been proposed [27] in terms of the surface tension of the curved interface given by Tolman[35].

$$\gamma_{HC/w} = \gamma_{HC/w}^0 / [1 + (S-1)\ \delta/l_c] \qquad (2.3.3)$$

Here, $\gamma_{HC/w}^0$ is the surface tension of the planar interface. S and l_c are, respectively, a shape factor (3 for spheres and 2 for cylinders) and the radius of the nonpolar core for a sphere or a cylinder. As to the Tolman distance δ for micelles consisting of hydrocarbon chains of n_C carbon atoms, the following relation has been proposed [27] in terms of the fully extended alkyl chain length l_{max}, which is given later by eq (6.1.1).

$$\delta/nm = 0.225 \, l_{max}(n_C)/ \, l_{max}(n_C=12). \tag{2.3.4}$$

As to G_{pack}, according to the mean-field theory assuming the isotropic core and the uniform curvature, any chain is forced to be squeezed out by neighboring chains and hence tend to stretch.[27].

The Gibbs free energy of the micelle formation discussed above consists of the enthalpy $\Delta H_M{}^*$ and the entropy $\Delta S_M{}^*$ parts. Experimentally, $\Delta H_M{}^*$ has been evaluated by measuring the heat of dilution of micellar solutions. For nonionic surfactants, heat of dilution is generally negative, i.e., $\Delta H_m > 0$. For ionic surfactants, $\Delta H_{el} > 0$ and hence ΔH_m is expected to be more positive than those of nonionic micelles, but the reported values(-3 to 9 kJ mol^{-1} for ionic surfactants) are inconsistent with the expectation [2], suggesting the contribution from polar head groups. Also, the temperature dependence of $\Delta G_M{}^*$ or the *cmc* will provide us with the information on $\Delta H_M{}^*$ and $\Delta S_M{}^*$. This will be discussed in Section V-2.

III. THE ELECTROSTATIC FREE ENERGY

1. The Electrostatic Free Energy G_{el}

In the medium of a proper ionic strength where the interaction among charged colloids can be ignored, G_{el} can be evaluated by the charging up the colloid under a constant pressure. When, on the other hand, charged colloids are dispersed in water or in the medium of low ionic strengths, the electrostatic free energy of the whole solution has been frequently evaluated using the cell model [36-38]. According to the cell model, a solution containing N_p charged colloids is divided into N_p cells each containing one colloid particle at the center of the cell. A cell is electroneutral and electric field is zero at the cell surface. In the following we consider the quantities of a single cell and denote them with a superscript 'cell'. The electric free energy of the whole solution is given by $N_p \, G_{el}{}^{cell}$.

The Gibbs free energy G of the whole solution containing N_i molecule or ions is given as follows assuming the ideal behavior in the absence of the electric interaction.

$$G = \Sigma N_i \mu_i{}^{id} + N_p \, G_{el}{}^{cell}. \tag{3.1.1}$$

The electrostatic energy $U_{el}{}^{cell}$ is given as follows in terms of the electric potential ψ and the charge density ρ.

$$U_{el}{}^{cell} = (\varepsilon\varepsilon_0/2) \int(grad\,\psi)^2 \, dv = (1/2)\int_V \psi(r)\,\rho(r) \, dr + (1/2)\,q\,\psi_0 \tag{3.1.2}$$

Here, ψ_0, q, ε, and ε_0 denote, respectively, the surface electric potential and the total charge of a colloid particle and the dielectric constant of the medium and the permittivity of vacuum. Due to the electric interaction of the colloid ion with small ions, the distribution of small ions is not uniform but it forms a diffuse electrical double layer around the colloid ion. The electrostatic entropy associated with this uneven distribution of small ions S_{el}^{cell} is given as follows in terms of the average concentrations $<C_+>$ and $<C_->$.

$$- T S_{el}^{cell} = RT [\int \; C_+(r) \ln \{C_+(r)/<C_+>\} \; dv + \int \; C_-(r) \ln \{C_-(r)/<C_->\} \; dv]. \qquad (3.1.3)$$

Here, $C_+(r)$ or $C_+(r)$ is proportional to $\exp\{- e_0 \psi(r)/kT\}$ or $\exp\{ e_0 \psi(r)/kT\}$, respectively, in terms of the protonic charge e_0 and the Boltzmann constant k. From eqs (3.1.2) and (3.1.3), the electrostatic Helmholtz free energy F_{el}^{cell} is given as $F_{el}^{cell} = U_{el}^{cell} - T S_{el}^{cell}$ [39, 40]. It has been shown that F_{el}^{cell} is equivalently given by the charging up procedure at a constant volume V, as shown in eq (3.1.4) where λ denotes the charging up parameter [41, 42].

$$F_{el}^{cell} = 2\int_0^1 [U_{el}(\lambda)/\lambda]d\lambda . \qquad (3.1.4)$$

On the other hand, the electric chemical potential of the colloid ion G_{el}^{cell} can be obtained by charging up the colloid particle at a constant pressure in the solution where all small ions carry their full charges, the Güntelberg method [41]. When the activities of small ions scarcely change during the charging up of the colloid, as is the case in the presence of excess salt, the following familiar expression is obtained [42].

$$G_{el}^{cell} = \int_0^1 \psi_0(q\lambda)qd\lambda \qquad (3.1.5)$$

For the ionic micelle consisting of m univalent surfactant cations, $G_{el}^{cell} = G_{el}^{micelle}$ and we have

$$G_{el} = G_{el}^{micelle} = \int_0^1 e_0\psi_0(\lambda)md\lambda \qquad (3.1.6)$$

In the micelle solutions without added salt, this equation could be used at surfactant concentrations not far from the *cmc* so that monomeric surfactant ions and counterions are regarded as a 'salt'. The differences between the two electrostatic free energies, Gibbs and Helmholtz is often ignored, Then, $G_{el}^{cell} \sim F_{el}^{cell}$[43]. Although the term ΔG_{el} is given by the difference $G_{el} - (\mu_l^s)_{el}$, the monomer contribution is usually ignored and ΔG_{el} is often approximated to G_{el}.

2. The Electric Potential ψ and the Poisson-Boltzmann Equation

In order to evaluate G_{el}^{cell} or F_{el}^{cell}, we should know the electric potential ψ in the solution and the colloid surface ψ_0. To obtain these electric potentials, the Poisson – Boltzmann (P-B) equation is solved for a given shape of micelles with appropriate boundary conditions. The P-

B equation is written as follows in the case of the solutions containing ionic species of the valence z_i. The origin of the co-ordinates is taken at the center of gravity of the colloid ion.

$$-\varepsilon\,\varepsilon_0\,\Delta\psi = e_0\,\Sigma\,z_i\,n_i\,\exp(-z_i\,e_0\,\psi/kT). \tag{3.2.1}$$

Here, n_i represents the number concentration of i-th ion at $\psi = 0$ or in the absence of electric field due to the colloid (micelle) charges. When the number of counterions to neutralize the micelle charges is much smaller than the total number of the counterions in the system, the P-B equation is written as follows for the case of a uni-uni valent salt present at a number concentration n_S.

$$\varepsilon\,\varepsilon_0\,\Delta\psi = 2\,e_0\,n_S\,\sinh(e_0\,\psi/kT). \tag{3.2.2}$$

A popular boundary condition set is (1) the Gauss theorem connecting the normal component of the electric displacement vector at the micelle surface to the charge q of a micelle, and (2) zero electric field at a point in the bulk solution distant from the micelle surface or at the cell surface in the case of the cell model.

In many cases, the Gouy – Chapman type diffuse electrical double layer is considered and the smeared charge model with a uniform surface charge density σ is assumed for micelles. The use of the smeared charge model is shown to give too large electrostatic free energy [44]. A diffuse micelle model is proposed where micelle charges are not distributed on a surface but in a shell [45].

The P-B equation is solved analytically for an infinitely large plane in water [46, 47] or in the presence of sufficient salt [42]. Another analytical solution of the P-B equation has been known for an infinitely long cylinder in water [36, 48]. In the presence of sufficient amount of supporting electrolyte, the P-B equation can be linearized which is well known as the Debye–Hückel (DH) approximation. Under the DH approximation, the analytical expressions are available [49] for an infinite rod and a sphere. Several analytical expressions have been proposed and examined for the potentials in the media of moderate salt concentrations beyond the DH approximation [50-52].

Experimentally, the surface electric potential of the micelle is evaluated by a couple of measurements; the hydrogen ion titration, electrophoresis and others. In the electrophoresis, zeta potentials are obtained which represent the potential at the slipping plane, not at the micelle surface. As will be discussed in Section VIII, the hydrogen ion titration of micelles is able to provide us with the surface potential and the electric free energy of micelles. However, the procedure can be applied to limited groups of surfactants. Measurements of the probe potential ψ_{probe} of acid-base indicators adsorbed onto micelle surfaces are applicable to micelles in general. Healy et al. reported that ψ_{probe} of three ionic micelles in the presence of salts, dodecyltrimethylammonium ($C12TA^+$), dodecylsulfate ($C12OSO_3^-$) and decylsulfate ($C10OSO_3^-$), changed linearly with log C_g up to as high as $C_g = 4M$, C_g denoting the counterion concentration [53].

$$\psi_{probe} = \pm\,k_{phi}\,\log C_g + \text{constant} \tag{3.2.3}$$

Here, the plus (minus) sign is for anionic (cationic) micelles. Values of k_{phi} are 35.9, 40.3, and 42.2 mV for C12TACl/NaCl, C12TABr/NaBr, and C12OSO$_3$Na/NaCl, respectively. On the other hand, log cmc also varies linearly with log C_g, known as the Corrin-Harkins relation, eq (4.1.2). When ψ_{probe} is correlated to log cmc, however, all these data gave a single straight line with a slope of about 59 mV. The result suggests ψ_{probe} is a good measure of the surface potential ψ_0.

IV. STABILITY OF MICELLES RELATED TO CHEMICAL STRUCTURES OF SURFACTANT

1. Dependence of the Stability of Micelles on the Nonpolar Chain Length

1-1. Nonionic Micelles

For a homologous series of amphiphiles with a common polar head group, dependence of G_{tr} on the hydrocarbon chain length n_C is important. As far as G_{tr} is a linear function of n_C as shown by eq (2.3.2), values of log cmc is expected to be a linear function of n_C. For nonionic micelles, the linear relations have observed [1, 2] described by the following empirical relation [2].

$$\log cmc = a - b\, n_C. \tag{4.1.1}$$

The coefficient b is expected to be contributed mostly from G_{tr} per methylene group. The coefficient a includes the contribution from G_{head}. For nonionic micelles at 25^{0}C in water, b is 0.49 - 0.5 for hexa- and octa- oxyethylene alkylether [2] and 0.48 for alkyldimethylamine oxide [54]. We thus see that the cmc of a nonionic surfactant decreases by nearly one order by increasing two methylene groups in the hydrocarbon chain. The free energy (per methylene group) of transfer of a nonionic surfactant from the micelle to water, $\Delta G_m^{w}/CH_2$, is 2.9 kJ/mol (700 cal/mol) when calculated as 2.303RT b with $b = 0.5$. This estimate $\Delta G_m^{w}/CH_2$ is referred to in Section II-3.

1-2. Ionic Micelles

In the case of ionic micelles, the dependence of G_{el} on n_C is generally non-linear. Furthermore, the counterion concentration C_g depends on the cmc at low salt concentrations. In water ($C_s = 0$), however, a linear relation has been observed for ionic micelles [2, 4]. For ionic micelles where the salting-out effect is negligible, log cmc varies linearly with log C_g, a relation well known as the Corrin-Harkins relation [55, 56].

$$\log cmc = a_{CH} - k_{CH} \log C_g. \tag{4.1.2}$$

The Corrin-Harkins (CH) relation will be discussed in Section V-1.2. Combining the CH relation with eq (4.1.1), we have

$$\log cmc = a - b\, n_C + a_{CH} - k_{CH} \log (cmc + C_s). \tag{4.1.3}$$

Eq (4.1.3) shows a nonlinear relation between log *cmc* and n_C for ionic micelles in the presence of a salt and the extent of nonlinearity increases with C_s [40, 57]. In water ($C_s = 0$), however, eq (4.1.3) reduces to eq (4.1.4)

$$\log cmc \text{ (ionic micelle in water)} = a' - b' n_C, \tag{4.1.4}$$

where a' and b' are given as follows.

$$a' = (a + a_{CH})/(1 + k_{CH}) \text{ and } b' = b/(1 + k_{CH}). \tag{4.1.5}$$

Values of b' are 0.29 for potassium salts of fatty acids ($RCOO^-K^+$), 0.30 for sodium alkylsulfates ($ROSO_3^-Na^+$) and 0.32 for trimethylammonum bromide ($RN^+Me_3Br^-$) [2]. These values of b' are smaller than 0.5 found for b values for nonionic micelles. With an increase in n_C, size and charge amount of the micelle both increase and hence G_{el} increases accordingly. This effect makes the micelle unstable with increasing n_C, which makes b' value smaller than b value. If we can approximate that $b/b' \approx 5/3$, then, k_{CH} is predicted to be about 2/3. This value is close to those observed for typical ionic micelles. When the relation $b/b' = 1 + k_{CH}$ is introduced into eq (4.1.4), we have $(1 + k_{CH}) \log cmc = \text{constant} - b n_C$. Thus the same slope b is obtained for ionic micelles in water as for nonionic micelles when $(1 + k_{CH}) \log cmc$, instead of log *cmc*, is plotted against n_C. In the presence of excess salt, on the other hand, the following linear relation will be expected.

$$\log cmc \text{ (ionic micelle in the excess salt)} = a'' - b''(C_s) n_C. \tag{4.1.6}$$

Here, $a'' = a + a_{CH} - k_{CH} \log C_s$. The coefficient b'' is expected not to be much affected by G_{el} but it now depends on C_s when the salting-out effect is significant. In the above analysis, we assume that k_{CH} value does not vary with n_C significantly. Similar results presented in this section have been reported previously by Funasaki through a somewhat different approach [57].

2. Effects of the Head Group

For nonionic micelles, bulky head groups make micelle unstable and some correlation between the size of the head group and the *cmc* was observed [23].

The electrostatic free energy of ionic micelles with a given nonpolar chain depends on the kind of charged head – counterion pair. For a cationic micelle of dodecyltrimethylammonium bromide (C12TAB) in 0.5M NaX, values of the *cmc* (mM) are as follows [23].

$$8.4(F^-) > 6.0 (HCOO^-) > 5.1(IO_3^-) > 3.8(Cl^-) > 3.3(BrO_3^-) > 1.9(Br^-) > 0.8 (NO_3^-) \tag{4.2.1}$$

The result can be compared with the standard Hofmeister series, $F^- > Cl^- > Br^- > NO_3^-$ [58]. For dodecylsulfate micelles at 25°C, the following *cmc* values (mM) are found [59].

$$8.5(Li^+) \sim 8.3(Na^+) > 7.8 (K^+, 40°C) > 6.2 (NH_4^+) \sim 6.2 (H^+) > 4.8\text{-}5.5 [N^+(CH_3)_4]. \tag{4.2.2}$$

Here the temperature for the hydrogen ion is not specified. As shown above, specificity with respect to the head group - counterion pair is significant for cationic micelles. One of the mechanisms leading to this kind of specificity is the specific binding of counterions. To analyze this effect, the Stern type electrical double layer is required.

It is found that the *cmc* is lower if the charge of the head group is more distant from the α- carbon atom of the nonpolar chain [60]. For three anionic head groups, the distances are in the following order, $-OSO_3^-$ (0.36 nm) > $-SO_3^-$ (0.23 nm) > $-CO_2^-$ (0.21 nm) . Differences of ln *cmc* referred to the sulfate surfactant are 0.32 and 0.65 for the surfactants of the head group $-SO_3^-$ and $-CO_2^-$, respectively [60]. On micellization, the charge of the head group is brought from the aqueous environment to the water-hydrocarbon core interface. The self-energy of the charge increases as the distance from the interface becomes short. When an electric charge locates near an interface between two media of different dielectric constants, the charge experiences a force that is called the image charge force. Consider a point ion carrying the electric charge q located at a distance x from a plane interface between two media, water (ε_w) and oil (ε_{HC}). The effect of the interface can be simply replaced with that of an image charge q' located at the position -x in the oil phase that is the mirror image point of the ion considered in water. The image charge q' is given by

$$q' = q \ (\varepsilon_w - \varepsilon_{HC}) \ / \ (\varepsilon_w + \varepsilon_{HC}) \tag{4.2.3}$$

Since $\varepsilon_w > \varepsilon_{HC}$, q and q' have the same sign and the image force acts to repel the ion from the interface.

3. The Integral Stability and the Differential Stability [20, 44]

Because of the small system nature of micelles, the chemical potential of a surfactant in the micelle can be defined in the following two different ways and they are not identical. In the pseudophase model, the difference between the two chemical potentials is ignored and they are approximated to be independent of m, and denoted as μ_M as introduced in Section II. To simplify the discussion, we consider the one-component micelle. The integral chemical potential μ^{int} and the differential chemical potential μ^m are defined as follows.

$$\mu^{int}(m) = \ G_m/m = G_m^*/m + (kT/m) \ln X_m \tag{4.3.1}$$

$$\mu^m(m) = \partial G_m/\partial m = \partial G_m^*/\partial m = \partial(m\mu^{int})/\partial m = \mu^{int} + \partial\mu^{int}/\partial \ln m. \tag{4.3.2}$$

The differentiation is carried out under constant T, P, N_i^s the monomer concentration ($\sim cmc$), and the micelle concentration X_m. For the most stable micelle, G_m^*/m takes the minimum value at the equilibrium aggregation number m, i.e., $\partial(G_m^*/m)/\partial m \sim 0$ and then $\partial G_m^*/\partial m \sim G_m^*/m$. From eq (4.3.2),

$$\mu^m(m) = \partial G_m^*/\partial m \sim G_m^*/m = \mu^{int}(m) - (kT/m) \ln X_m. \tag{4.3.3}$$

When eq (4.3.2) and eq (4.3.3) are compared, the term $\partial \mu^{int}/\partial \ln m$ is of the order of the term $[- (kT/m) \ln X_m]$, which is claimed to be about $- 0.2 \, kT$ for a typical spherical micelle [20]. For a cmc (mole fraction) of $X_1 = 10^{-4}$, $\mu^{int} - \mu_1^{s*} \sim - 9.2 \, kT$ and hence the contribution from the term $\partial \mu^{int}/\partial \ln m$ is negligibly small compared with $\mu^{int}(m)$.

Stigter has discussed a different aspect of the problem at hand [44]. For the micellization equilibrium,

$$\Delta G_M^* = G_m^*/m - \mu_1^{s*} = RT \ln [X_1/(X_m^{1/m})] \sim RT \ln X_1. \tag{2.2.5}$$

For the micelle growth reaction equilibrium,

$$(G_{m+\Delta m}^* - G_m^*)/\Delta m - \mu_1^{s*} = RT \ln [X_1/(X_{m+Dm}/X_m)^{1/\Delta m}] \sim RT \ln X_1. \tag{4.3.4}$$

From the above two equations, we have $(G_{m+\Delta m}^* - G_m^*)/\Delta m = G_m^*/m$. $\tag{4.3.5}$

The lhs and the rhs of eq (4.3.5) correspond, respectively, to the differential chemical potential μ^m and the integral chemical potential μ^{int}, hence $\mu^m = \mu^{int} = \mu_M$. For an ionic micelle, $G_m^* = G_m^{non} + G_m^{el}$. Then, we have

$$(G_m^{non} + G_m^{el})/m - \mu_1^{s*} = RT \ln X_1, \tag{4.3.6}$$

$$(G_{m+\Delta m}^{non} - G_m^{non})/\Delta m + (G_{m+\Delta m}^{el} - G_m^{el})/\Delta m - \mu_1^{s*} = RT \ln X_1. \tag{4.3.7}$$

Stigter has calculated G_m^{el}/m and $(G_{m+\Delta m}^{el} - G_m^{el})/\Delta m$ as $\partial G_m^{el}/\partial m$ and has found the following inequality for spherical micelles with the surface potential ψ_0 [44].

$$e_0 \psi_0 > e_0 \psi_0 + (\partial G_m^{el}/\partial a)_m (\partial a/\partial m) > \int_0^1 e_0 \psi_0(\lambda) d\lambda \tag{4.3.8}$$

where a represents the radius of a spherical micelle. Let us consider the three quantities appearing in inequality (4.3.8). The term $e_0 \psi_0$ corresponds to the quantity $\partial G_m^{el}/\partial m = \mu_M^{el}$ in the case of the pseudophase approximation. The quantity $[e_0 \psi_0 + (\partial G_m^{el}/\partial a)_m (\partial a/\partial m)]$ corresponds to $\partial G_m^{el}/\partial m$ and the integral gives G_m^{el}/m. Hence, the relation (4.3.8) is rewritten as follows

$$\mu_M^{el} \text{ (pseudophase)} > \mu^{m,el} > \mu^{int,el} \tag{4.3.9}$$

Accordingly, the quantity $(G_{m+\Delta m}^{non} - G_m^{non})/\Delta m = \mu^{m,non}$ was more negative than $G_m^{non}/m = \mu^{int,non}$. Although μ^m and μ^{int} are nearly identical as shown by eq (4.3.5), it is not always the case for each component constituting them.

V. EFFECTS OF SALT, TEMPERATURE AND PRESSURE

1. Effects of Salt

Effects of salt on the micelle stability can be examined by the effect of salt on various terms constituting $\Delta G_M{}^*$ in eq (2.3.1). In the case of nonionic micelles, both G_{tr} and G_{int} significantly change with the salt concentration. In the case of ionic micelles, on the other hand, the salt effect on G_{el} is the most important. The effect on G_{el} is dominant at low salt concentrations, while the effects on G_{tr} and G_{int} become significant at high salt concentrations.

1-1. Nonionic Micelles

For the nonionic micelles, the log cmc decreases linearly with the salt concentration C_S in most cases examined.

$$\log [cmc_0/cmc_0(C_S = 0)] = - K_S C_S \qquad (5.1.1)$$

The salt effect is also written as follows.

$$\text{RT} \ln [cmc_0/cmc_0 (C_S = 0)] = \text{RT} \, \Delta \ln cmc_0 = \Delta(G_m{}^*/m) - \Delta\mu_1{}^*. \qquad (5.1.2)$$

Since the nonionic head groups is expected not to be much influenced by salt, the salt effect mostly originates from the term G_{tr} and G_{int}.

The parameter K_S is closely related to the salting-out effect [23, 61]. For alkylbetaines of octyl, decyl, and dodecyl chains in NaCl at 27°C, $K_S(\text{M}^{-1})$ were 0.134, 0.215, and 0.291, respectively [62]. For alkyldimethylamine oxides (CnDMAO) of dodecyl and tetradecyl chains in NaCl at 25°C, $K_S(\text{M}^{-1})$ were 0.33 [63] and 0.40 [64], respectively. For hexaoxyethylene alkyl ether (NaCl, 20°C of octyl, decyl, and dodecyl chains, K_S (M^{-1}) were 0.23, 0.33, and 0.43, respectively [65]. These data show the increment of K_S per methylene group to be about 0.04 for the first two groups and 0.05 for the hexaoxyethylene head group. The constant K_S is closely related to the salting-out constant (the Setschenow constant) k_S of nonpolar substances measured by the change of the solubility S with salt concentration in aqueous solutions, as is described by the Setschenow equation, eq (5.1.3).

$$\log [S/S(C_S = 0)] = - k_S C_S. \qquad (5.1.3)$$

Increment of k_S (M^{-1}) per methylene group in the case of amides at 25°C are 0.065, 0.053 and 0.038 for NaCl, NaBr, and NaI, respectively [66]. For NaCl at 25°C, values of K_S (0.04 - 0.05) above are significantly smaller than the value of 0.065 from the solubility of amides. One possible interpretation would be such that the hydrocarbons in the micelle are not completely shielded from water but a certain fraction of the surface of the hydrocarbon core of the micelle is in contact with water. On the contrary, the methylene group of amides in the solid state is completely shielded from water or surface contribution is small for solid precipitates. Hence the salt effect on the solubility $S(C_S)$ of a solute can be expressed as follows in terms of the reference chemical potential in water $\mu_1{}^*(C_S = 0)$.

$$\mu_l^*(C_S) - \mu_l^*(C_S = 0) = \Delta\mu_l^* = - RT \Delta\ln S = 2.303 \ RT \ k_S \ C_S \qquad (5.1.4)$$

In the case of nonionic micelles, on the other hand, the salt effect on the micelle cannot be ignored and we have

$$\Delta\mu_l^* - \Delta(\mu_m^*/m) = - RT \ \Delta\ln \ cmc = 2.303 \ RT \ K_S \ C_S. \qquad (5.1.5)$$

If $\Delta\mu_l^*$ in eqs (5.1.4) and (5.1.5) can be equated, we have

$$\Delta(\mu_m^*/m) = 2.303 \ RT \ (k_S - K_S) \ C_S. \qquad (5.1.6)$$

As shown above, the salting-out constant k_S of the solubility measurements represents essentially the effect of C_S on μ_l^* under the constant chemical potential of the solid precipitates. On the contrary, K_S of micelles includes the effect of C_S both on μ_m^*/m and μ_l^*.

1-2. Ionic Micelles

The *cmc* values of many ionic surfactants have been known to follow the Corrin -Harkins (C-H) relation in the low salt concentration range, smaller than about $0.1 - 0.2$ M for uni-uni valent salts [55, 56]. The relation eq (4.1.2) is again shown below.

$$\log \ cmc = a_{CH} - k_{CH} \log C_g. \qquad (4.1.2)$$

Since the discovery of the empirical Corrin–Harkins relation, a number of attempts have been made to elucidate theoretical foundations of the relation. Nevertheless, the theoretical foundations are not yet established [51, 67, 68]. The C-H relation is related to the dependence of the electrostatic free energy G_{el} on the counterion concentration C_g, $C_g = C_S + cmc$. From eq (2.2.7), we have $RT \ln cmc = \Delta G_M^* = \Delta G_{non}^* + \Delta G_{el}$. Differentiation of both sides of this equation with respect to $\ln C_g$ yields,

$$- k_{CH} = (\partial \ln cmc \ /\partial \ln C_g) \sim (1/RT) \ (\partial \ G_{el} \ /\partial \ln C_g) \qquad (5.1.7)$$

Here $(\partial\mu_l^{el} /\partial \ln C_g)$ is approximated to be negligible. Also, an approximation that $\partial \ \Delta G_{non}^*/\partial \ln C_g = 0$ is an indispensable condition for the C-H relation to hold.

From eq (2.2.13), on the other hand, we have the following relation between the *cmc* and C_g if activities can be approximated with the concentrations.

$$\ln cmc + \nu \ln C_g = \text{constant} \qquad (5.1.8)$$

From the comparison of equations, (4.1.2) and (5.1.8), it is clear that the Corrin-Harkins coefficient k_{CH} is identical with the degree of counterion binding ν. In the approach to the C-H relation in terms of eq (5.1.8), it is essential to confirm ν to be independent of C_S. The dressed micelle model [51] or the point excess concept [68] has been introduced for the purpose.

The experimentally observed dependence of the *cmc* on C_g should include the contribution from the salting out effect on the hydrocarbon tail in addition to the salt effect on the electrostatic interaction [23, 63, 69, 70]. An empirical extended Corrin–Harkins equation has been proposed to describe the salt effect [63, 70].

$$\log (cmc/\text{mM}) = - k_{CH} \log (C_g /\text{M}) - (K_S)_{ion} (C_S /\text{M}) + \text{constant} \tag{5.1.9}$$

Sometimes it is claimed that the effect of salt on the aqueous solution/hydrocarbon core interface should be taken into account by introducing a new term 'interfacial tension' [69]. In the case of the nonionic micelles, however, the effect is included in the term K_S of eq (5.1.1), as discussed above in relation to eq (5.1.6). Hence, the effect should be also included in the term K_S in eq (5.1.9) in the case of ionic micelles and no new term need be introduced. Fitting procedures of the data to eq (5.1.9) are done essentially using a single adjustable parameter $(K_S)_{ion}$. Also, a good estimate of k_{CH} is possible in most cases from the slope (d log cmc / d log C_g) in the range of low C_g. The best fit to the obtained data gave $(K_S)_{ion} = 0.24$ in the case of dodecyldimethylhydroxy ammonium (C12DMAOH$^+$) as shown in Figure 1 [63]. Values of K_S of the surfactants carrying a common nonpolar chain, dodecyl group, but different head groups are as follows [62, 63, 65, 69].

$$0.43 \text{ (hexaoxyethylene)} > 0.33 \text{ (dipolar, -NO)} > 0.29 \text{ (betaine)} >$$
$$0.24 \text{ (-NOH}^+\text{)} > 0.20 \text{ (-NH}_3^+\text{)}. \tag{5.1.10}$$

For this comparison, we should use $(K_S)_{ion}$ of Eq.(5.1.9), but the result of dodecylammonium chloride K_S was obtained by a different equation including a term 'interfacial tension' [69]. Inequality (5.1.10) shows that K_S value decreases as the head group becomes more polar. The result maybe related to different extents of perturbation of water structure in the micelle surface region by different head groups.

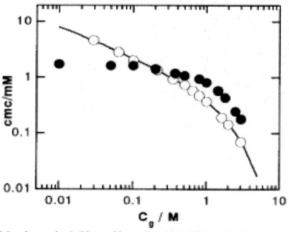

Figure is taken from H. Maeda et al., J. Phys. Chem. B, 101 (1997) 7378-7382, with permission.

Figure 1. Dependence of the logarithm of the critical micelle concentration on the logarithm of the counterion concentration C_g. For the cationic species (open circles), a solid curve is drawn according to eq (5.1.9) with $(K_S)_{ion} = 0.24$. For the nonionic species (filled circles), C_g denotes the salt concentration.

Nonlinear Corrin-Harkins plots can be interpreted in terms of the salting-out effect as described above. At the same time, however, shape/size changes of ionic micelles have been observed occasionally in the range of C_S where the deviations from the linear Corrin-Harkins relation are significant. The two factors, salting-out and micelle shape/size change may be correlated somehow.

2. Effects of Temperature

The Gibbs free energy of the micelle formation $\Delta G_M{}^*$ consists of the enthalpy $\Delta H_M{}^*$ and the entropy $\Delta S_M{}^*$ parts. Effects of the temperature on the micelle stability is related to the temperature dependence of $\Delta G_M{}^*$ or the *cmc*. A couple of examples have been known where the *cmc* decreases with increasing temperature. Among them are, tetra- and hepta-oxyethylene dodecyl ethers in the range 283K-313K [2], tetradecyldimetylamine oxide in water, where *cmc* values were 149μM(283K), 130(288K), 124(293K), 122(298K), 120(303K), 118(308K), 115(313K) [71], alkyl betaines in the range 283K-333K [62] and sodium soaps [72]. A couple of ionic micelles, on the other hand, indicate the minimum of the *cmc* around room temperature. In the case of alkyltrimethylammonium salt, the minimum temperature decreases with increasing nonpolar chain length [73].

For macroscopic phase changes or for chemical reactions of well defined stoichiometry, the enthalpy contribution can be evaluated from the temperature dependence of the free energy by the use of the Gibbs-Helmholtz relation.

$$\Delta H_M{}^* = [\partial(\Delta G_M{}^*/T)/\partial(1/T)] = - RT^2\, \partial(\ln cmc)/\partial T. \tag{5.2.1}$$

For micelles which are small systems, the aggregation number m and the degree of counterion binding v for ionic micelles are both temperature-dependent, at least conceptually. For nonionic micelles, eq (5.2.1) may be used under the pseudophase approximation. In the case of alkyl betaines, for example, ΔH_m was positive when eq (5.2.1) was applied : ΔH_m (kcal/mol) = 0.67(C8), 0.57(C10), 0.55(C12) [62].

Various contributions are also included in $\Delta H_M{}^*$ and $\Delta S_M{}^*$ as for $\Delta G_M{}^*$ shown in eq (2.3.1). Here we consider only the transfer contribution H_{tr} and S_{tr}. For aliphatic hydrocarbons, The enthalpy $\Delta H_\ell{}^w$ ($= -H_{tr}$) and the entropy $\Delta S_\ell{}^w (= -S_{tr})$ of the transfer of alkanes from pure liquid state to water (at infinite dilution) is approximately expressed as follows in the temperature range where the transfer of the heat capacity $\Delta(C_p)_\ell{}^w$ is assumed to be constant independent of temperature [74, 75].

$$\Delta H_\ell{}^w = \Delta(C_p)_\ell{}^w\,(T- T_h), \tag{5.2.2}$$

and

$$\Delta S_\ell{}^w = \Delta(C_p)_\ell{}^w\,\ln(T/T_s). \tag{5.2.3}$$

Since $\Delta H_\ell{}^w (T_h) = 0$ by definition, T_h is determined from the temperature dependence of $\Delta G_\ell{}^w$, known from the solubility, as $[\partial \Delta G_\ell{}^w/\partial T]_{T=Th} = 0$. Then, $\Delta S_\ell{}^w$ can be evaluated from the relation $\Delta S_\ell{}^w = (\Delta H_\ell{}^w - \Delta G_\ell{}^w)/T$. Accordingly, T_s can be also determined from eq (5.2.3).

For *n*-pentane, $\Delta C_{p\ell}^{w} = 400$ J/(mol K), $T_h = 303$K and $T_s = 385$K. Calculated values of ΔG_{ℓ}^{w}, ΔH_{ℓ}^{w} and ΔS_{ℓ}^{w} for *n*-pentane are indicated in Fig. 2. Near the room temperature, $\Delta H_{\ell}^{w} \sim 0$ and ΔG_{ℓ}^{w} is contributed practically from the entropy, the entropy-driven process. At high temperatures, on the other hand, $\Delta S_{\ell}^{w} \sim 0$ and ΔG_{ℓ}^{w} is contributed practically from the enthalpy. Correspondingly, the *cmc* is expected to show a shallow minimum around T_s with increasing T, if the effect on polar head groups is insignificant. However, the minimum of the *cmc* is rarely observed for nonionic surfactants partly because the measured temperature ranges are considerably lower than T_s and partly because the interaction of hydrophilic head groups with water may become less favorable with increasing temperature. The *cmc* of micelles consisting of oxyethylene head groups generally decreases with increasing temperature [2].The hydrophilicity of oxyethylene group decreases with increasing T and a phase separation eventually takes place known as a cloud point or LCST(lower critical solution temperature).

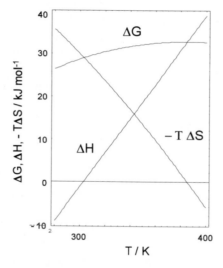

Figure 2. Transfer free energy ΔG_{l}^{w}, enthalpy ΔH_{l}^{w} and entropy ΔS_{l}^{w} of *n*-pentane from the liquid state to the water as functions of temperature. ΔH_{l}^{w} and entropy ΔS_{l}^{w} are calculated according to equations (5.2.2) and (5.2.3). Employed parameter values are $\Delta C_{p\ell}^{w} = 400$ J/(mol K), $T_h = 303$K and $T_s = 385$K.

Contrary to nonionic micelles, a couple of ionic micelles indicate the minimum of the *cmc* around room temperature. This suggests a factor other than the transfer contribution that destabilizes the micelle in the temperature range higher than the minimum temperature. The increase of G_{el} with increasing T will therefore be expected to be significant, partly due to a decrease of the dielectric constant and/or dissociation of bound counterions.

As to the chain length dependence of ΔH_{ℓ}^{w} and ΔS_{ℓ}^{w}, the following relations have been frequently used evaluated at 298 K [26, 76].

$$\Delta H_{\ell}^{w}/RT = - [3.04 - 1.05(n_C - 1)] \qquad (5.2.4)$$

$$\Delta S_{\ell}^{w}/R = - [5.06 - 0.44(n_C - 1)] \qquad (5.2.5)$$

3. Effects of Pressure

The partial molar volume of surfactants generally shows a steep increase in a concentration range around the *cmc*, such as for alkyl sulfates/sulfonates [77] and dodecyl polyoxyethylene ethers [78]. The result shows that the volume of micellization Δv_m is positive. This is consistent with negative ΔV_ℓ^w values of alkanol (for example, - 6.3cc/mol at 293 K for pentanol) [1]. For the nonionic surfactants, the partial molar volume in the micelle state is close to that of the volume of pure surfactant liquid [78], supporting the traditional view of the liquid state hydrocarbons in the micelle core. On the other hand, the partial molar volume of some anionic surfactants in the hydrated solid state (below the Krafft temperature) is smaller than that of singly-dispersed monomer [77].

For ionic surfactants, the *cmc* generally increases with pressure P, goes through the maximum at $P = P^*$ and then decreases with P[79,80]. Values of P^* at 278 K were: about 1000 atm for sodium dodecylsulfate (SDS) [79], 1200 atm for both sodium decylsulfate (SDeS) and decyltrimethyl ammonium bromide (C10TAB) [80]. In correspondence to the pressure dependence of the *cmc*, the volume of micellization Δv_m decreased with P, became zero at P^* and then Δv_m was negative and decreased further with P [80]. Positive values of Δv_m in the pressure region d *cmc*/d $P > 0$ will suggest negative ΔV_ℓ^w values of alkane. Another contribution for positive Δv_m will be dehydration of ionic head groups and counterions as a result of counterion binding to the micelle surface. On the other hand, one of mechanisms responsible for the behavior d *cmc*/d $P < 0$ or negative Δv_m values is associated with the solidification of alkyl chains under high pressure in the micelle core.

VI.   THE SIZE AND THE SHAPE OF MICELLES

1. Geometric Considerations

The size or the aggregation number m and the shape of micelles are determined as a result of the minimization of the free energy of the micelle formation ΔG_M^*. There are a couple of approaches of predictive nature. Here we confine ourselves in the case of surfactants with single saturated hydrocarbon chain consisting of n_C carbon atoms. According to Tanford [1], the maximum length l_{max} of the chain in the hydrocarbon core is given as follows.

$$l_{max}/\text{nm} = 0.15 + 0.127 \, (n_C - 1). \tag{6.1.1}$$

Here, the 0.127 nm comes from the C-C bond length (0.154 nm) projected onto the direction of the chain in the fully extended conformation. The length from the center of the first carbon atom (C_1) to the end of the chain is therefore $0.127 \, (n_C - 1) + 0.21$, where 0.21 nm is the van der Waals radius of the end methyl group. If the half of the length C_1-C_2 (0.127/2), 0.06 nm, is not included in the hydrocarbon core, then this amount should be subtracted and eq (2.4.1) results. The actual chain length l will be somehow related to l_{max}. For hydrocarbon liquids where both ends of the chain are not anchored, $l = 0.75 \, l_{max}$ at room temperature [1]. The hydrocarbon volume V_c of a micelle of the aggregation number m is given as follows in terms of the volume per monomer v_m [1].

$$V_c/\text{nm}^3 = m\, v_m = m\, 10^{-3}\, (27.4 + 26.9\, n_C).$$ (6.1.2)

Here, the volume of a methylene group is 26.9×10^{-3} nm^3 and the terminal methyl group has the volume nearly twice that of a methylene group. When the radius of a spherical micelle core r_c is taken to be l_{max}, a rough estimate of m is obtained for a given surfactant containing n_C carbon atoms in an alkyl chain by $V_c = (4\pi/3)\, r_c^3$. For selected values of n_C, calculated values of l_{max} and m are given in Table 1. An important geometrical parameter is the area per monomer a. For large n_C values, the ratio v_m/l_{max} approaches $26.9/127 = 0.21$ nm^2 which is the minimum cross-sectional area of a saturated hydrocarbon chain. Although both v_m and l_{max} are evaluated by eqs (6.1.1) and (6.1.2), a will vary depending on the kind of the polar head group resulting in different shapes. Conversely, if the optimum value of a, a_0, is specified for a given surfactant, a set of geometrical parameters (v_m, l_{max}, a_0) can limit the range of possible size and shape of the micelle comprising from the surfactant.

The geometric considerations of Tanford [1] were developed later by Israelachvili, Mitchell and Ninham [3, 81, 82] who have proposed an important parameter, the packing parameter p defined as

$$p = v_m/(l_c\, a_0).$$ (6.1.3)

Here, l_c is a critical chain length, i.e., the maximum chain length that a given hydrocarbon chain can take, $l_c \leq l_{max}$. The parameter p is sometimes called as the shape factor or the surfactant number [4]. For a given molecule, it can form a spherical micelle if $p < 1/3$, a non-spherical shape including a rod if $1/3 < p < 1/2$, a rod or a plate-like structure if $1/2 < p < 1$ and inverted structures if $p > 1$. As to the micelle shape for surfactants of $1/2 < p < 1$, many theoretical and experimental studies have been reported. Nevertheless, the stability of oblate-shaped or disc-like micelle has been a controversial subject which is re-examined recently [83].

For a given hydrocarbon chain, aggregation numbers differ significantly for head groups while values of cmc are rather similar [Table 8-1 of ref.1]. A large difference of the size/shape is not associated with a large free energy difference in many cases. The aggregation number m of dodecylammonium chloride (DAC) increases significantly with the salt concentration while that of dodecyltrimethylammonium chloride (DTAC) does not increase significantly [Figure 8-1 of ref 1].

The result suggests that a_0 of DTAC is determined mostly by the steric interaction among head groups while that of DAC is determined much more by the electric repulsion. With an increase of the salt concentration, a_0 of DAC decreases and hence the packing parameter p increases leading to the sphere-to-rod shape change [98].

Table 1. Aggregation numbers m of spherical micelles carrying a hydrocarbon chain of n_C carbon atoms, predicted by the geometrical consideration according to Tanford [1]

n_C	8	10	12	14	16	18
l_{max}/nm	1.04	1.29	1.55	1.80	2.06	2.31
m	19.3	30.6	44.3	60.6	79.4	100.8

The concept of the average packing parameter is introduced for mixed micelles [84, 85]. For non-complexing pairs, the average p_{av} is defined by the number-averaged value, $p_{av} = x_A p_A + x_B p_B$. For lipid-surfactant (double chain-single chain) mixtures or mixtures of cationic and anionic surfactants where strong catanionic complexes are expected to be formed, reasonable estimates of the packing parameter for the complex could be possible. When the p value of one component is well assumed, p value of the other component could be determined experimentally by observing the change of shapes with changing mixing ratio. Consequently, the average packing parameter could provide us with a useful experimental procedure to determine the packing parameter of individual surfactant experimentally.

2. Determination of the Aggregation Number of Micelles

The aggregation number or the micellar weight can be determined by a couple of methods familiar in the polymer science. Among them are the light scattering, osmometry and sedimentation equilibrium. Fluorescence probe method is applicable to micelles. Transport properties such as diffusion or viscosity can be used to assess the shape/size of colloidal particles including micelles. These topics are described in many textbooks [1, 3, 4]. Here, only the light scattering and the osmometry will be briefly described.

2.1. Light Scattering

For isotropic two-component solutions containing colloid particles (the molecular weight M) at a weight concentration c (gr/cc = 10^3kg/m^3) is briefly described below [86].

According to the fluctuation theory for two-component solutions, the excess scattering intensity of the solution over that of the solvent ΔR_θ at a scattering angle θ is given as follows in terms of the optical constant K_0 and the molar volume V_w and the chemical potential μ_w of solvent water.

$$\Delta R_\theta = K_0 \, V_w \, c \, /[- \, \mathrm{d}(\mu_w/RT)/\mathrm{d}c] \tag{6.2.1}$$

In terms of the virial expansion of μ_w, we have

$$- \, \mathrm{d}(\mu_w/RT)/\mathrm{d}c = V_w \, (1/M + 2Bc + \text{higher virial terms}). \tag{6.2.2}$$

Combination of eq (6.2.1) and eq (6.2.2) and introduction of the shape factor $P(\theta)$, we have

$$K_0 \, c/\Delta R_\theta = 1/[M \, P(\theta)] + 2Bc + \text{higher virial terms}. \tag{6.2.3}$$

Here B is expressed in mole cm^3/gr^2 = mole m^3/kg^2. The shape factor $P(\theta)$ takes the intra-particle optical interference into account and tends to unity at zero scattering angle θ. The molecular weight M is obtained as $1/[K_0 \, c/\Delta R_\theta]_{q \to 0, \, c \to 0}$, where the two kinds of extrapolations are facilitated by the use of the Zimm plot. The optical constant K_0 is given as follows in terms of the wavelength of the unpolarized incident light λ_0 and the Avogadro number N_A.

$$K_0 = [2\pi^2 n_0^2/(N_A\lambda_0^4)]\, (dn/dc)^2.$$ (6.2.4)

where n_0 and n denote, respectively, the refractive indices of the solvent and the solution. (dn/dc) denotes the refractive increment of the solution. Generally, the second virial coefficient B is related to the excluded volume u of the particle as $B = uN_A/(2M^2)$. For a sphere of radius r and a rod (a diameter d and a length L), values of u are given by $32\pi r^3/3$ and $\pi d L^2/2$, respectively.

For colloidal ions in the media of sufficient ionic strengths, correlation of the concentration fluctuations between the colloidal ion and small ions is expected to be not significant. The above results hold for colloidal ions as long as electroneutral fluctuations are considered. However, $(dn/dc)^2$ should be evaluated at a constant chemical potential of the salt by equilibrium dialysis. Also, the second virial coefficient B contains the Donnan term in addition to the excluded volume term. In the case of the ideal Donnan, the Donnan term is given as $10^3(Z/M)^2/(4Cs)$ where Z denotes the charge number carried by a colloid particle and Cs is given in molarity.

For micelles, $[K_0\,(c\text{-}cmc)/\Delta R_\theta]_{\theta\to0}$ is obtained from the intercept of the plot $[K_0\,(c\text{-}cmc)/\Delta R_\theta]$ against $[\sin(\theta/2)]^2$. From the slope of the plot we can evaluate R_G, the radius of gyration of micelles. In terms of $[K_0\,(c\text{-}cmc)/\Delta R_\theta]_{\theta\to0}$, we have eq (6.2.5) by ignoring the higher order virial terms.

$$[K_0\,(c\text{-}cmc)/\Delta R_\theta]_{\theta\to0} = 1/M + 2B(c\text{-}cmc).$$ (6.2.5)

When the Debye plot, $[K_0\,(c\text{-}cmc)/\Delta R_\theta]_{\theta\to0}$ vs $(c\text{-}cmc)$, gives a straight line, we can determine the micellar weight M from the intercept and B from the slope. When $[K_0\,(c\text{-}cmc)/\Delta R_\theta]_{\theta\to0}$ decreases with c, on the other hand, it is an indication of micelle growth unless the second virial coefficient is negative. In the case of ionic micelles, however, there is a problem about determination of $(dn/dc)^2$ by the equilibrium dialysis. Vrij and Overbeek have proposed a procedure to evaluate the molecular weight in terms of the $(dn/dc)^2$ values obtained under a constant salt concentration Cs not a constant chemical potential of the salt [87]. The aggregation number of ionic micelles in water is not easy to be determined correctly and counterion binding is often assumed to facilitate the evaluation. The introduction of the counterion binding gives the aggregation number greater than that obtained in the otherwise case by 5-15% in many cases.

2.2. Osmometry

The main problem in the application of the osmometry to micelle solutions arises from the condition of non-equilibrium because of the dissociation of micelles into the monomers which are not retained by the semi-permeable membrane. To circumvent the difficulty, a certain amount of the surfactant is added to the 'solvent' compartment as the 'background surfactant', thereby suppressing dissociation of micelles and minimizing the monomer contribution to the osmotic pressure. The observed osmotic pressure Π^{obs} is given as follows in terms of the micellar molecular weight M and the second virial coefficient B [88].

$$\Pi^{obs}/RT = c/M + B[c^2 + 2c(c_0 - cmc)]$$ (6.2.6)

Here, c and c_0 denote, respectively, the excess surfactant concentrations and the background concentration in kg/m^3. In deriving eq (6.2.6), the following two assumptions are made among others. (1) The effective Staverman coefficient is assumed to be unity, which is the measure of the micelle penetration through the membrane. (2) The monomer concentrations in the sample and the solvent compartments are set equal to the cmc. It is to be noted that the surfactant concentration in the solution compartment is $(c+c_0)$. By plotting (Π^{pbs}/cRT) against c, we can get M and B from the intercept ($c \rightarrow 0$) and the slope, respectively. Aggregation numbers of some ionic and nonionic micelles were determined by the osmometry [88, 89]. The described procedure is pertinent for nonionic micelles and ionic micelles in the media containing a sufficient amount of a salt. For ionic surfactants in the media of low ionic strengths, uneven distribution of salt contributes to the osmotic pressure. The Donnan distribution of salts was shown to be handled in the similar way as for the osmotic pressure by introducing the background surfactant [90].

The above results found in the osmometry of micelle solutions suggests that micelles can be dialyzed, though in an approximate sense. When a micelle solution is brought contact with the solvent, a fraction of the surfactant will diffuse into the outer solvent phase. The diffusion will be greatly reduced, however, as far as the surfactant concentration in the solvent phase reaches the cmc or a bit higher than the cmc.

3. Rod-like Micelles

For a surfactant having a value of the packing parameter (or the surfactant parameter) greater than 1/3, spherical micelles become unfavorable compared to rod-like micelles. Long rod-like micelles are sometimes called worm-like micelles and their solutions exhibit similar properties as solutions of linear polymers. A worm-like micelle is characterized as a polymer of freely-jointed chain consisting of virtual bonds and the bond length is twice the persistence length L_p. When the total micelle length L_t is much larger than L_p, the micelle behaves like a flexible polymer chain. On the other hand, the micelle is more or less rigid rod-like if $L_t < L_{p,}$. The persistence length of micelles is a complicated function of the surfactant concentration and the interactions among them. Typical values of L_p are in the range 10-30 nm [91] but larger values are also suggested [92]. The persistence length is characteristic to a given polymer but for micelles it may depend on the surfactant concentration c. However, apparent concentration dependence of L_p is likely to arise from the neglect of the inter-micelle interaction in the analysis. In the semi-dilute regime, the solutions become visco-elastic due to entanglement of worm-like micelles. Visco-elastic properties of the solutions of the worm-like micelles differ, however, from those of polymer solution because of the dynamic nature of micelles, (1) the monomer exchange between micelles and the solution part, and (2) the average lifetime of micelles [93]. For example, relaxation times of the polymer solutions generally have a wide spectrum, while single Maxwell type relaxation has been frequently observed in the micelle solutions [93]. As another example, polymers are used to reduce the frictional dissipation in the transport of solutions, the drag reduction. However, degradation of polymer chains takes place under a high shear stress but worm-like micelles can be formed again after they are broken under shear into smaller micelles or monomers.

A rod-like micelle will be modeled to consist of a cylinder part and two semi-spherical caps. In the below, we consider nonionic micelles first. We denote the standard chemical potentials of a surfactant molecules packed in the cylindrical and the spherical parts as μ_{cyl} and μ_{cap}, respectively. When μ_{cap} is larger than μ_{cyl}, the end cap energy E_{cap} is positive, which is denoted as $kT\,\delta$. The chemical potential of a rod-like micelle G_m consisting of m monomers including m_0 monomers in the two hemi-cap regions is written as follows in terms of the mole fraction X_m of the m-mer when the ideal solution is assumed [5, 94].

$$G_m = G_m^* + kT \ln X_m. \tag{6.3.1}$$

The reference free energy G_m^* includes the end cap energy

$$G_m^* = m\,\mu_{cyl} + kT\,\delta, \tag{6.3.2}$$

where $kT\,\delta = m_0\,(\mu_{cap} - \mu_{cyl}) = m_0\,E_{cap}$.

The end cap energy E_{cap} or the parameter δ is regarded as a kind of the nucleation barrier for the rod-like micelle formation when it is positive. From the equilibrium condition

$$G_m = G_m^* + kT \ln X_m = m\mu_1, \tag{6.3.3}$$

we have

$$X_m = \exp[(m\,\mu_1 - G_m^0)/kT] = \exp[m\,(\mu_1 - \mu_{cyl})/kT - \delta] = e^{-m\alpha}\,e^{-\delta}, \tag{6.3.4}$$

where $\alpha = (\mu_{cyl} - \mu_1)/kT \ll 1$. The total micelle concentration X_t is given by the summation with m greater than m_0.

$$X_t = \Sigma\, mX_m = e^{-\delta}\,\Sigma\, m\, e^{-m\alpha} \sim e^{-\delta}/\alpha^2. \tag{6.3.5}$$

Here, $\Sigma\, e^{-m\alpha} = \exp(-m_0\alpha)/(1 - e^{-\alpha}) \sim 1/\alpha$ and $\Sigma\, m\, e^{-m\alpha} \sim 1/\alpha^2$. Since X_m decreases exponentially with m, the probable value m^* will be evaluated by the maximization of (mX_m) or (m^2X_m): $d(mX_m)/dm = 0$ or $d(m^2X_m)/dm = 0$ at $m = m^*$. Then, $m^* = 1/\alpha = (X_t\,e^{\delta})^{1/2}$ or $2/\alpha = 2(X_t\,e^{\delta})^{1/2}$. Under the situation that rod-like micelles prevail, the total surfactant concentration is well approximated with X_t. Thus the (average or probable) micelle size m^* is proportional to the square root of the surfactant concentration $X_t^{1/2}$ or $C^{1/2}$ [5, 94]. The rod length L_t can be evaluated from the shape factor $P(\theta)$ at a given c, and the functional dependence of L_t on c can be detected.

With the increasing concentration, rod-like micelles become unstable due to the excluded volume effect and micelle growth is enhanced to reduce the effect. As the concentration goes higher, however, long rod-like micelles eventually undergo a transition from the isotropic solution (L_1) to the nematic liquid crystalline phase (H), thereby reducing the orientational entropy of rods.

The growth parameter δ is somehow related to the packing parameter p. For $p < 1/3$, δ will be negative. In the case of a large positive δ, micelle growth is favored. but when δ is too large, the branching of rod-like micelle, proposed by Porte [95] and observed [96, 97], is likely to occur to reduce the number of end caps. Branching of rod-like micelles is related to the formation of L3 phase.

Up to here we discuss the non-charged rod-like micelles. For ionic surfactants, the electric free energy of the micelle G_{el} increases with the aggregation number m and hence the micelle growth becomes unfavorable. Long rods tend to break into short rods when the charge amount increases. Eq (6.3.2) is now modified as follows.

$$G_m^* = m\,\mu_{cyl} + kT\,\delta + G_{el} \tag{6.3.6}$$

where

$$G_{el} = (m - m_0)\,\mu_{cyl}^{el} + m_0\,\mu_{cap}^{el} = m\,\mu_{cyl}^{el} + kT\,\delta^{el}, \tag{6.3.7}$$

and

$$kT\,\delta' = kT\,\delta + kT\,\delta^{el} = m_0\,(\mu_{cap} + \mu_{cap}^{el} - \mu_{cyl} - \mu_{cyl}^{el}) = m_0\,(E_{cap} + E_{cap}^{el}). \tag{6.3.8}$$

Electric repulsion favors a structure of larger curvature and hence E_{cap}^{el} is negative and $\delta' < \delta$. Eq (6.3.4) is now rewritten as

$$X_m = \exp[(m\,\mu_1 - G_m^*)/kT] = e^{-m\alpha}\,e^{-\delta}\,\exp(-\,G_{el}/kT). \tag{6.3.9}$$

Since the dependence of G_{el} on m is generally not linear, the concentration dependence of the size m^* cannot be derived in the same way as for the nonionic micelles to which $m^* \sim C^{1/2}$. For an infinitely long rod where $G_{el} \sim m\,\mu_{cyl}^{el}$, the linearized P-B equation gives the result $G_{el} \sim m\,(g\,kT)$ with a constant g. Then, eq (6.3.9) can be written as follows in terms of α': $\alpha' = \alpha + g > \alpha$.

$$X_m = e^{-m\alpha}\,e^{-\delta}\,\exp(-\,gm) = e^{-m\alpha'}e^{-\delta}. \tag{6.3.10}$$

Then, $m^* = 1/\alpha'$ or $1/\alpha'$ and the relation $m^* \sim C^{1/2}$ becomes valid for ionic micelles. Since $\alpha' > \alpha$, the average size m^* becomes smaller by the introduction of electric charges. With the addition of a salt, however, electric repulsion is shielded and the sphere-to-rod change will take place as Cs increases [98]. The sphere-to-rod change also occurs with increasing surfactant concentration under proper ionic strengths observed as the second cmc.

VII. MIXED MICELLES

In many products or processes, two or more surfactants are used together to improve the properties, such as the lowering of the cmc, interfacial tension and the Krafft point or elevating the cloud point of solutions of nonionic surfactants. Improvement of the foamability/foam stability by mixing surfactants is also expected [99-101]. In some cases, interaction between different polar head groups, such as the hydrogen bond, leads to a complex formation. We consider here only two-component micelles. If the mixture cmc is lower than the cmc values of the pure components in a certain range of the composition, the mixture is said to exhibit synergism. In opposite situation, the mixture is said to exhibit negative synergism [2]. However, a different definition of the synergism on the basis of the excess free energy will be used in this study. Surfactant mixtures usually form a group of mixed micelles of similar compositions but under some conditions, they form two classes of mixed micelles of significantly different compositions, as found for the mixtures of hydrocarbon and fluorocarbon surfactants. This is a kind of phase separation of mixtures. In some lipid/surfactant mixtures (double chain/single chain mixtures) a kind of phase separation has been reported.

Two-component mixed micelles will be classified into three groups: nonionic / nonionic, nonionic /ionic, ionic / ionic. Generally, the *cmc* will decrease when a nonionic surfactant is added to an ionic micelle, by lowering the electric repulsion among charged head groups. When, on the other hand, the *cmc* decreases by the addition of an ionic surfactant to a nonionic micelle, a probable mechanism will be relaxation of the steric repulsion between bulky nonionic head groups. Mixtures of a cationic surfactant and an anionic one tend to form strong complex like vesicles [102] or to precipitate. However, worm-like micelles become stable by tuning the mixing ratio and/or the difference in the alkylchain lengths [103]. Accordingly, vesicle-micelle change can be induced by changing one of these factors.

Thermodynamic analyses of the obtained experimental data are expected to help us to predict (1) the *cmc* of the mixture from the *cmc* values of the pure one-component micelles, (2) the micelle composition at the *cmc*, (3) nonelectric interaction between the two components, and (4) dependence of the electrostatic free energy on the micelle composition in the case of ionic mixed micelles. Many references can be found on the thermodynamics of mixed micelles [29, 31-33, 99-120].

In the case of surfactants carrying a head group of weak electrolyte nature, such as soaps (carboxylic acid), amine oxides and alkylphosphates, micelles are actually mixed micelles consisting of the ionized and the non-ionized head groups where the composition varies with pH/ionic strengths. The hydrogen ion titration of these micelles will be discussed in Section VIII.

1. Fundamental Thermodynamic Relations of Mixed Micelles

1-1. The Reference State and the Excess Free Energy G^{ex}

Consider a mixed micelle of the total aggregation number $m = m_A + m_B$ consisting of m_A species A and m_B species B. Values of the *cmc* of the one-component micelles for the two species are denoted as cmc_A and cmc_B. We assume the relation $cmc_A > cmc_B$. The micelle-mole fraction of the species A, x, is given as m_A/m, which is taken to represent the micelle composition. The mixed micelle formation reaction is written as eq (7.1.1) not only for nonionic mixtures but also for ionic/nonionic mixtures. In the case of ionic/nonionic mixed micells, the ionic component and the nonionic component are denoted as I and N, respectively, and hence x refers to m_I/m.

$$m_A A + m_B B = \text{Micelle}\,(m_A, m_B) = \text{Micelle}\,(m, x). \tag{7.1.1}$$

The chemical potential of the mixed micelle G_m and that of each component in the mixed micelle, $\mu_A{}^m$ or $\mu_B{}^m$, are related as follows from eq (2.1.9).

$$G_m(m, x)/m = G_m^*(m, x)/m + (RT/m) \ln X_m = x \, \mu_A^m + (1- x) \, \mu_B^m \qquad (7.1.2)$$

Throughout the present Section VII, we neglect the contributions from the micelle concentration X_m. Then, we define $g(x)$ as follows.

$$g(x) = G_m(m, x)/mRT = G_m^*(m, x)/mRT. \qquad (7.1.3)$$

To relate $g(x)$ or $G_m^*(m, x)$ to those of pure one-component micelles, they all should be defined in the same environment T, P, and ξ which is independent of x. In the most of this section, except Subsection VII-6, we discuss the situations where ξ is expected to be independent of x and $g(x{:}\xi)$ is simply written as $g(x)$.

In the case of the ideal mixed micelle, $g(x)^{id}$ will be defined as follows.

$$g(x)^{id} = x \, g(x{=}1) + (1- x) \, g(x{=}0) + g_{mix}^{id}. \qquad (7.1.4)$$

$$g_{mix}^{id} = x \ln x + (1{-}x) \ln (1{-}x). \qquad (7.1.5)$$

For ideal mixed micelles, both the *cmc* and the micelle composition x can be evaluated as follows [104] in terms of cmc_A and cmc_B, and the monomer composition x_1 (the surfactant-only mole fraction of A species) in the solution part, i.e., $x_1 = N_A^s/(N_A^s + N_B^s)$.

$$cmc/cmc_A = x/x_1, \qquad (7.1.6a)$$

$$cmc/cmc_B = (1{-}x)/(1{-}x_1). \qquad (7.1.6b)$$

$$1/cmc = x_1/cmc_A + (1{-} x_1)/cmc_B. \qquad (7.1.7)$$

$$cmc = x \, cmc_A + (1{-} x) cmc_B. \qquad (7.1.8)$$

For mixed micelles exhibiting deviations from the ideal mixing behavior, the excess free energy $g(x)^{ex}$ is defined as follows.

$$g(x)^{ex} = g(x) - g(x)^{id}. \qquad (7.1.9)$$

At the *cmc*, the equilibrium condition eq (7.1.1), together with eq (7.1.3), yields the following equation.

$$\begin{aligned} RTg(x) &= x \, \mu_A^s + (1- x) \, \mu_B^s \\ &= x \, \mu_A^{s*} + (1- x) \, \mu_B^{s*} + RT[x \ln(x_1 cmc) + (1{-}x) \ln \{(1{-} x_1) \, cmc \}]. \end{aligned} \qquad (7.1.10)$$

The free energy of the mixed micelle formation ΔG_M^* is defined as follows.

$$\Delta G_M^* = RTg(x) - [x \, \mu_A^{s*} + (1{-}x) \, \mu_B^{s*}]. \qquad (7.1.11)$$

Then,

$$\Delta G_M{}^*/RT = x \ln x_1 + (1-x) \ln (1-x_1) + \ln (cmc). \tag{7.1.12}$$

To obtain $\Delta G_M{}^*/RT$ experimentally in the case of mixed micelles, we need to evaluate the micelle composition x in addition to the observed values of cmc and x_1. As to the electric interaction contribution $g^{ex,el}(x)$, it is explicitly written as follows in the case of ionic/nonionic micelles.

$$g^{ex,el}(x) = g^{el}(x) - g^{el,id}(x) = g^{el}(x) - x\, g^{el}(x{=}1). \tag{7.1.13}$$

1-2. Activities of Components in the Mixed Micelles

In conformity with the definition of the excess free energy eq (7.1.9), the reference state for the chemical potential of each component in mixed micelles is taken as the pure one-component micelle placed in the same solvent condition as the mixed micelle under consideration. The activity coefficients in the mixed micelle are denoted as γ_A and γ_B with the condition that $\gamma_A(x{=}1) = 1$ and $\gamma_B(x{=}0) = 1$.

$$\mu_A{}^m (x) = \mu_A{}^m(x{=}1) + RT \ln (x\, \gamma_A), \tag{7.1.14a}$$

$$\mu_B{}^m (x) = \mu_B{}^m(x{=}0) + RT \ln \{(1{-}x)\gamma_B\}. \tag{7.1.14b}$$

From eqs (7.1.3, 7.1.9, 7.1.12, and 7.1.14), $g(x)^{ex}$ is expressed in terms of γ_A and γ_B as follows.

$$g(x)^{ex} = x \ln \gamma_A + (1{-}x) \ln \gamma_B. \tag{7.1.15}$$

For monomers in the solution, the concentration of component A is given by $x_1 C_1$ in terms of the total monomer concentration C_1. Unless otherwise stated, we assume the ideal behavior of the monomer in the solution part.

$$\mu_A{}^s(x_1) = \mu_A{}^{s^*} + RT \ln (x_1 C_1), \tag{7.1.16a}$$

$$\mu_B{}^s(x_1) = \mu_B{}^{s^*} + RT \ln \{(1{-}x_1)C_1\} \tag{7.1.16b}$$

The following equilibrium conditions hold at the cmc.

$$\mu_A{}^m(x) = \mu_A{}^s(x_1 cmc), \tag{7.1.17a}$$

$$\mu_B{}^m (x) = \mu_B{}^s(x_1 cmc), \tag{7.1.17b}$$

and

$$\mu_A{}^m(x{=}1) = \mu_A{}^s(cmc_A), \tag{7.1.18a}$$

$$\mu_B{}^m (x{=}0) = \mu_B{}^s(cmc_B). \tag{7.1.18b}$$

Then, we have

$$cmc/cmc_A = \gamma_A \, x/x_1,$$ (7.1.19a)

$$cmc/cmc_B = \gamma_B \, (1-x)/(1-x_1).$$ (7.1.19b)

$$1/cmc = (x_1/\gamma_A)/\, cmc_A + \{(1- x_1)/\gamma_B\}/cmc_B.$$ (7.1.20)

$$cmc = x\gamma_A \, cmc_A + (1- x)\gamma_B cmc_B.$$ (7.1.21)

We can evaluate the activity coefficients of the constituting species and the excess free energy referred to the ideal mixing case, if the micelle compositions are known. Stability and the micelle composition near the *cmc* are fundamental properties of micelles, which are free from inter-micelle interactions. Micelle compositions can be determined by proper experimental methods such as e. m. f. measurements using surfactant ion specific electrodes [118, 121, 122] or NMR [123(a,b), 124] or others.

1-3. The Electric Synergism

For ionic mixed micelles, the electrostatic interaction constitutes a main contribution to the excess free energy g^{ex}. The corresponding contribution $g^{ex,el}(x)$ is generally negative leading to a synergistic effect (electric synergism) in the case of ionic/nonionic mixtures [28, 29, 111, 115, 116]. A mechanism of reducing the electric repulsion among ionic head groups by intervening nonionic head groups has been frequently suggested for a mechanism of the electric synergism. It is to be noted, however, this mechanism does exist even in the case of the ideal mixing and hence it does not always lead to the synergetic effect. It is the difference of the shielding effect between the actual mixed micelle $g^{el}(x)$ and the ideal mixing case $g^{el,id}(x)$, that leads to the synergism, as is clearly shown in eq (7.1.13). With $f(x)$ defined as the electrostatic free energy per charge, we have $g^{el}(x) = x\, f(x)$ and then $g^{ex,el}(x) = x\, [f(x) - f(x=1)]$. Since $f(x)$ is an increasing function of x, $g^{ex,el}(x)$ cannot be positive. It may be said that the true mechanism resides in positive curvatures of $g^{el}(x)$, $d^2 g^{el}(x)/dx^2 > 0$ [125]. In Figure 3, $f(x)$, $g^{el}(x)$ and $g^{el,id}(x)$ are compared schematically to show their characteristic dependencies on x.

1-4. Different cmc Values Obtained from Different Methods in the Case of Mixed Micelles

It is reported that solution density and electric conductivity measurements gave higher *cmc* values than that from the surface tension measurements for mixed micelles of sodium dodecylsulfate and sodium decylsulfate, although the three methods gave nearly identical *cmc* values for each single-component micelles [126]. Significant amounts of micelles are required to detect them by density or electric conductivity measurements. This situation does not always lead to overestimate of the *cmc*, however, since reasonable *cmc* values have been obtained in the case of single-component micelles. In the total concentration range $C_t > cmc$ at a given total composition x_t, x is larger than the x value at the *cmc* for many mixed micelles. Also, *cmc* increases with x in many cases. Thus, evaluations of the *cmc* from the measurements at $C_t > cmc$ are apt to result in higher *cmc* values. On the other hand, values of *cmc* from the surface tension measurements are in many examples the lowest among those determined by various methods. This is because the surface tension method relies on practically constant nature of the chemical potential (it should not be constant in the exact sense) and hence it is relatively insensitive to the amount of micelles. Mixed micelles in the concentration range higher than the *cmc* were discussed elsewhere [106, 120].

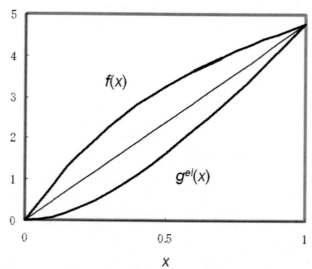

Figure is taken from H. Maeda, Adv. Colloid Interface Sci., 156 (2010) 70-82 with permission.

Figure 3. Schematic representations of three electrostatic free energies as functions of the mole fraction of the ionic species x in the ionic /nonionic mixed micelles. $f(x)$: the electrostatic free energy per charge, $g^{el}(x) = xf(x)$: the average electrostatic free energy per monomer. A straight line represents $g^{el,id}(x) = xg^{el}(x=1)$, the average electrostatic free energy per monomer in the case of ideal mixing. The surface charge density is assumed to be proportional to x.

2. The Micellar Gibbs-Duhem (MGD) Relation

For the mixed micelles consisting of an ionic and a nonionic surfactants, the following micellar Gibbs-Duhem (MGD) relation has been given. [127, 128].

(type 1) $x \, d\mu_I^m + (1-x) \, d\mu_N^m + \nu x \, d\mu_g^s = 0.$ (7.2.1)

Here, μ_I^m, μ_N^m, μ_g^s, and ν denote, respectively, the chemical potentials of the ionic and the nonionic surfactant species in the micelle, the chemical potential of counterions in the solution, and the degree of counterion binding defined as (number of thermodynamically bound counterions)/(number of ionic species in a micelle averaged over all kinds of micelles present in the solution). When the chemical potential of counterions μ_g^s can be approximated to be constant ($d\mu_g^s = 0$) irrespective of the micelle composition x, eq (7.2.1) reduces to eq (7.2.2).

(type 2) $x \, d\mu_I^m + (1-x) \, d\mu_N^m = 0.$ (7.2.2)

The MGD of type 2, eq (7.2.2), can be applied to nonionic mixed micelles and ionic/nonionic mixed micelles in the media of high ionic strengths. From the equilibrium condition, $\mu_A{}^m = \mu_A{}^s$ and $\mu_B{}^m = \mu_B{}^s$, eq (7.2.3) has been derived from the type 2 MGD rerlation [108].

$$x = x_1 \left[1 - (1 - x_1)\, d\ln cmc\, /dx_1\right]. \tag{7.2.3}$$

The micelle composition x can be experimentally evaluated if the *cmc* is measured as a function of the monomer composition x_1, according to eq (7.2.3). Then, $\Delta G_M{}^*/RT$ is obtained from eq (7.1.12). Eq (7.2.3) indicates that compositions of the micelle and the monomer coincide ($x = x_1$) at the minimum (or the maximum) of the *cmc*. This relation could be used to examine the validity of type 2 MGD relation. It is to be noted that the term $\mu_I{}^m$ in eq (7.2.2) cannot be replaced with that of the corresponding salt Ig, $\mu_{Ig}{}^m$ ($\mu_{Ig} = \mu_I + \mu_g$), simply because micelles are small systems and hence the electroneutrality condition cannot be applied. Accordingly, eq (7.2.2) should not be confused with the following macroscopic GD relation ($\nu = 1$).

$$x\,d\mu_{Ig}{}^m + (1 - x)\,d\mu_N{}^m = 0. \tag{7.2.4}$$

From eq (7.2.4), we have eq (7.2.5) instead of eq (7.2.3).

$$2x/(1+x) = x_1 \left[1 - (1 - x_1)\, d\ln cmc\, /dx_1\right]. \tag{7.2.5}$$

The MGD relation for ionic/nonionic mixed micelles proposed by Motomura et al. yields eq (7.2.5) [108] and hence it is similar to the macroscopic GD, as noted earlier [129]. For an arbitrary ν, type 1 MGD should be applied and we have eq (7.2.6).

$$\frac{(1+x\nu)\,cmc\,x_1 + Cs}{(cmc\,x_1 + Cs)}\,d\ln cmc + \left[\frac{x}{x_1}\left\{1 + \frac{\nu cmc\,x_1}{cmc\,x_1 + Cs}\right\} - \frac{1-x}{1-x_1}\right]dx_1 = 0 \tag{7.2.6}$$

In the case of no added salt ($Cs = 0$), eq (7.2.6) reduces to eq (7.2.7).

$$x = x_1 \left[1 - (1 - x_1)\, d\ln cmc\, /dx_1\right] / \left[1 + \nu(1 - x_1)\{1 + x_1 d\ln cmc\, /dx_1\}\right]. \tag{7.2.7}$$

In the application of eq (7.2.7) to evaluate x from the *cmc*, ν must be known as a function of x_1 or x, which is not likely the case except a few examples [130]. Approximate analyses of the *cmc* data are possible for such mixed micelles, however, in terms of the following relation which has been shown to describe approximately the dependence of ν on the micelle composition x. Here ν_0 denotes the degree of counterion binding of the pure ionic micelle.

$$\nu(x) = x\nu_0 / (1 - \nu_0 + x\nu_0) \tag{7.2.8}$$

Eq (7.2.8) was originally proposed on purely empirical grounds [131] and later its theoretical basis was given [132]. When eq (7.2.8) is substituted in eq (7.2.7), x should be solved in an iterative manner starting from the first guess x. Unique x values will be obtained after two or three iterative cycles [133].

For ionic/nonionic mixed micelles in the media of low ionic strengths, neither eq.(7.2.3) nor eq.(7.2.5) holds but eq.(7.2.6) or eq (7.2.7) should be applied [133]. To obtain x in terms of any one of above equations, it is essential to evaluate a quantity d $\ln(cmc)/dx_1$ from the experimental cmc data. A problem related to this procedure was discussed [120].

3. The Regular Solution Model

When the interactions between the two species in the micelle are of short-range and isotropic nature, we can treat a mixed micelle as the regular solution and the excess free energy g^{ex} can be written as follows in terms of a single interaction parameter β [99, 100, 107, 110].

$$g^{ex} = \beta x (1-x) \tag{7.3.1}$$

Although the regular solution model (RSM) is defined not by eq (7.3.1) in the exact sense [134], we take the eq (7.3.1) as a definition of the RSM. Eq (7.3.1) is expected to be valid for many nonionic mixed micelles where $\beta = \beta^{ion}$. According to RSM, the activity coefficients γ_A and γ_B. are given as follows.

$$\gamma_A = \exp [\beta (1-x)^2], \tag{7.3.2a}$$

$$\gamma_B = \exp [\beta x^2]. \tag{7.3.2b}$$

Introducing the results into Eqs(7.1.19 a, b),

$$cmc/cmc_A = (x/x_1) \exp [\beta(1-x)^2] \tag{7.3.3a}$$

$$cmc/cmc_B = [(1-x)/(1-x_1)] \exp(\beta x^2) \tag{7.3.3b}$$

By fitting the eqs(7.3 3 a and b) to the experimentally determined cmc values as a function of the monomer composition x_1, we can determine both the interaction parameter β and the micelle composition x at cmc [99, 100, 107, 110]. The parameter β represents the stability of the mixed micelle relative to the ideal mixing case. In some instances, the cmc data are well described by the regular solution approach when plotted against the monomer composition but not when plotted against the micelle composition [135].

For ionic/nonionic mixed micelles in the media of high ionic strengths, it was suggested that the g^{el} can be well approximated with a quadratic function of the ionic component mole fraction x, i.e., $g^{el} = a_1 x^2$ [28, 112], as has been experimentally found in the hydrogen ion titration of dodecyldimethylamine oxide [112]. Then, from eq (7.1.13),

$$g^{ex,el} = a_1 x^2 - a_1 x = -a_1 x (1-x). \tag{7.3.4}$$

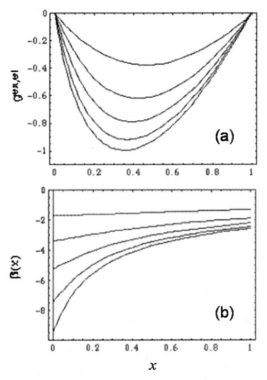

Figures are taken from H. Maeda, J. Phys. Chem. B, 108 (2004) 6043-6051, with permission.

Figure 4. Electrostatic contribution to the excess free energy $g^{ex,el}$ (a) and the corresponding β values (b) in the case of a spherical ionic/nonionic mixed micelle at different salt concentrations. The radius of a sphere is $R = 1.81$ nm and the area per charge at $x=1$ is 0.58 nm^2, corresponding to sodium dodecyl sulfate (SDS) micelle in 0.03M NaCl solution. The parameter β is defined as $\beta(x) = g^{ex}/\{x(1-x)\}$ where x denotes the mole fraction of the ionic component in the mixed micelle. Values of salt concentration (M) of uni-univalent salt are, from top to bottom, 1, 0.1, 0.01, 1 x 10^{-3} and 1 x 10^{-4}.

Thus, eq (7.3.1) holds for ionic/nonionic mixed micelles in the media of high ionic strengths with $\beta = \beta^{non} - a_1$. Since a_1 is positive, the electric interaction makes a negative contribution to β (electric synergism) [28, 112]. As the charge density increases or the salt concentration decreases, $g^{ex,el}(x)$ becomes more negative (stronger electric synergism) and the position of the minimum of $g^{ex,el}(x)$ shifts toward a smaller x value. Under the situation, β^{el} and hence β become a function of x, $\beta(x)$. Generally, $\beta(x)$ increases (becomes less negative) with x. The dependence is more or less linear in the range of large x values but deviations from the linearity become more significant as x approaches zero due to the asymmetric dependence of $g^{ex,el}(x)$ on x. An example is shown in Figure 4 [125].

Some models predict the linear dependence of $\beta(x)$ on x [115, 118]. The linear approximation is valid under a variety of conditions but within a limited range of x. Non-linear $\beta(x)$ functions have been reported in a study where x was determined by means of potentiometry [122]. It was predicted that $d\beta(x)/dx$ increases as x approaches 0 [125]. It is important to exclude a range of small x values ($x < 0.1 - 0.15$), therefore, to have a wide range of the linear approximation to $\beta(x)$. For small x, terms of the order x^2 are neglected. Then,

$g^{ex,el}(x) \sim - xg^{el}(x{=}1)$ and $g^{ex}(x) \sim \beta x$. Accordingly, we have $\beta(x{=}0) = - g^{el}(x{=}1)$, the relation first noted by Reif and Somasundaran [115].

In the solutions of low ionic strengths, $\beta(x)$ generally increases with x as shown schematically in Figure 4. An average $<\beta>$ value over a certain range of x has been often reported in the literature. Different ranges employed for the averaging, however, make reasonable comparison difficult in terms of $<\beta>$ among different mixed micelles.

4. Other Phenomenological Approaches

4-1. The Method of Eads and Robosky

Eads and Robosky have proposed an important model [124]. They determined experimentally the micelle composition x by means of NMR and they found that the experimentally evaluated activity coefficients did not fit the RSM but are well described by the van Laar type expression which is derived by taking into account different volumes of two species I and N, e.g., v_I and v_N. According to the model, g^{ex} and activity coefficients are given as follows in terms of an interaction parameter ω and $\rho = v_I / v_N$.

$$g^{ex} = \omega\rho \; x(1{-}x) / (x\rho + 1{-}x). \tag{7.4.1}$$

$$\ln \gamma_I = \omega\rho(1{-}x)^2 / (x\rho + 1{-}x)^2, \tag{7.4.2a}$$

$$\ln \gamma_N = \omega(\rho x)^2 / (x\rho + 1{-}x)^2. \tag{7.4.2b}$$

Eqs(7.4.2 a and b) are equivalent to Eqs. 3 and 4 of ref [124]. In the case of $\rho = 1$, eq (7.4.1) reduces to eq (7.3.1) with $\omega = \beta$. It is to be noted that ω in the present paper is not ω_{NI} but it is β_{NI} in the notation of ref [124]. Although long-range electrostatic interactions are not considered in the model, Eads and Robosky applied the analysis to anionic/nonionic mixtures, sodium dodecylsulfate (SDS)/pentaethyleneglycol alkylether (CnE5). Activity coefficients of SDS and C8E5 showed deviations from the behavior expected in the case of the RSM. For SDS/C8E5, $\omega = - 2.67$ and $\rho = 2.28$ and for SDS/C12E5, $\omega = - 1.47$ and $\rho = 2.93$. Since head groups are the same for both mixtures, the authors ascribed the different results to the effects arising from different alkyl chain lengths. It is likely, however, that obtained different values of the interaction parameters suggest a significant contribution from electric interaction originating from different sizes and/or shapes of the two mixed micelles.

4-2. The method of Georgiev

Georgiev has proposed a model in which only the nearest neighbor interactions are considered [136]. Mixed micelle formation was treated in analogy with the copolymerization by translating the kinetic treatment into the equilibrium version. A mixed micelle is treated as if it were a one dimensional two-component solid (alloy), while it is actually best approximated as a two component liquid-like mixture. To facilitate understanding his model, it may be pertinent to examine the model on purely thermodynamic grounds. By eliminating the term *cmc* from eqs(7.1.19 a and b), we have eq (7.4.3) for ionic(I)/nonionic(N) mixed micelles.

$$x\,(1-x_I)/[x_I(1-x)] = \gamma_N\,cmc_N\,/(\gamma_I\,cmc_I) \tag{7.4.3}$$

On the other hand, the following equation is given by Georgiev, Eq 22 of ref. [136].

$$x\,(1-x_I)/[x_I(1-x)] = (g_I x_I + 1 - x_I)/[g_2(1-x_I) + x_I] \tag{7.4.4}$$

From these two equations, we can obtain the following relations which provide us with the physical meaning of the Georgiev parameters g_I and g_2.

$$g_I = \gamma_N\,(x{\rightarrow}1)\,cmc_N\,/cmc_I, \tag{7.4.5a}$$

$$g_2 = \gamma_I\,(x{\rightarrow}0)\,cmc_I\,/cmc_N, \tag{7.4.5b}$$

$$g_I\,g_2 = \gamma_N\,(x{\rightarrow}1)\,\gamma_I\,(x{\rightarrow}0). \tag{7.4.6}$$

Accordingly, we find $g_I = cmc_N\,/cmc_I = 1/g_2$ in the case of ideal mixing. In the case of RSM, $g_I = (cmc_N\,/cmc_I)e^{\beta}$ and $g_2 = (cmc_I\,/cmc_N)e^{\beta}$. Solving eq (7.4.4) for the micelle composition x, we have,

$$x = x_I\,(g_I x_I + 1 - x_I)/q(x_I),\ 1-x = (1-x_I)\,[g_2(1-x_I) + x_I]/\,q(x_I), \tag{7.4.7}$$

where $q(x_I) = g_2(1-x_I)^2 + 2x_I(1-x_I) + g_I x_I^2$. Activity coefficients γ_N and γ_I are expressed as follows.

$$\gamma_I = (cmc/cmc_I)\,q(x_I)/(g_I x_I + 1 - x_I), \tag{7.4.8a}$$

$$\gamma_N = (cmc/cmc_N)\,q(x_I)/\{g_2(1-x_I) + x_I\}. \tag{7.4.8b}$$

In the application of the method, x should be known in advance. Both g_I and g_2 can be evaluated using eq (7.4.4) in a modified form: $(v-1)/w = g_I - g_2(v/w^2)$, where $v = x\,/(1-x)$ and $w = x_I/(1-x_I)$ [136]. It is interesting to note that parameter $\ln g_2$ is identical with a parameter B_I discussed in Section VII-7 which has been proposed to represent the contribution of the non-electric interactions in ionic/nonionic mixed micelles [112].

5. Mixing Behavior and the 'Phase Diagram'

5-1. Phase Diagram

As one of the ways to characterize mixing behaviors, representations by 'phase diagram' will be useful, in which values of the *cmc* are plotted against both the compositions of the micelle x_m and the monomer x_I simultaneously. Some typical examples of 'phase diagram' of two-component mixed micelles are shown in Figure 5.

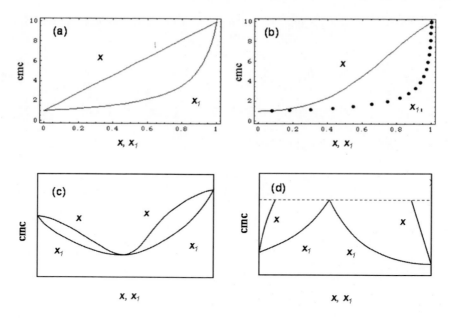

Figure 5. Some typical examples of 'phase diagram' of two component mixed micelles.

(a) Ideal mixing case. (b) Attractive interaction: $\beta = -2.0$, $x_0 < 0$. (c) Azeotrope : $\beta < 0$, $0 < x_0 < 1$. (d) Repulsive: $\beta > 2$ ('phase separation'). In panels (a) - (c), the mole fractions of micelle x and that of monomer x_1 refer to the component (H) having the higher cmc value. The regular solution model parameter β is defined by eq (7.3.1) and $x_0 = [\beta + \ln(cmc_H/cmc_L)]/(2\beta)$. An example for the behavior shown in panel (d) is the mixtures consisting of a hydrocarbon chain and a fluorocarbon chain.

We discuss here within the framework of the regular solution model (RSM). The ideal behavior ($\beta = 0$) is shown in panel(a). In the case of attractive interactions between the two components ($\beta < 0$), two different behaviors are predicted depending on the value of a parameter x_0 defined as follows: $x_0 = [\beta + \ln(cmc_H/cmc_L)]/(2\beta)$ where $cmc_H > cmc_L$ [120]. An example for $x_0 < 0$ is shown in panel (b) where $\beta = -2.0$ and $x_0 < 0$. On the other hand, a kind of azeotrope type phase diagram is obtained for $0 < x_0 < 1$ as shown in panel (c). When the cmc has the minimum when plotted against x_1, this kind of azeotrope will be predicted by eq (7.2.3) (type 2 MGD). According to eq (7.2.3), $x_m > x_1$ for d cmc/d$x_1 < 0$ and vise versa. Similarly, when the cmc has the maximum corresponding to the case $\beta > 0$ and $0 < x_0 < 1$, the reversed type of the azeotrope will be obtained.

5-2. Conditions for the Instability for Mixtures of Two Surfactants

In analogy with the binary solution mixtures, the condition for stable mixing will be given by the condition: $d^2(G_m/mRT)/dx^2 > 0$ at any composition. For mixed micelles in the pseudophase model, $G_m/m = x_A \mu_A^m + x_B \mu_B^m$ from eq (7.1.2). The first and the second derivatives of the free energy with respect to x are as follows where $\Delta\mu^0 = \mu_A^m(x=1) - \mu_B^m(x=0)$,

$$d(G_m/m\,RT)/dx = \Delta\mu^0/RT + \ln[x/(1-x)] + x\,d\ln\gamma_A/dx + (1-x)\,d\ln\gamma_B/dx + \ln(\gamma_A/\gamma_B)$$

$$(7.5.1)$$

and

$$d^2(G_m/m\,RT)/d\,x^2 = 1/\,[x\,(1-x)] + x\,d^2 \ln \gamma_A/d\,x^2$$
$$+ (1-x)\,d^2 \ln\gamma_B/d\,x^2 + 2\,d \ln (\gamma_A/\gamma_B)/\,d\,x \qquad (7.5.2)$$

From the Gibbs – Duhem relation eq (7.2.2), we have $x\,d \ln \gamma_A + (1-x)\,d \ln \gamma_B = 0$. Then,

$$d^2(G_m/m\,RT)/d\,x^2 = 1/\,[x\,(1-x)] + d \ln (\gamma_A/\gamma_B)/\,d\,x_A \qquad (7.5.3)$$

In case that the regular solution approximation is valid, the activity coefficients are explicitly given as follows.

$$\ln (\gamma_A/\gamma_B) = \beta\,(1-x)^2 - \beta x^2 = \beta\,(1-2\,x) : d \ln (\gamma_A/\gamma_B)/d\,x = -2\beta \qquad (7.5.4)$$

The condition $d^2(G_m/mRT)/d\,x^2 < 0$ now reduces to $1/[x\,(1-x)] < 2\beta$. The term $[1/\{x\,(1-x)\}]$ takes the minimum value of 4 at $x = 1/2$. Consequently, in case that $2 < \beta$, demixing into two types of micelles of different compositions will take place in the composition range of $[1 - \{1 - (2/\beta)\}] / 2 < x < [1 + \{1 - (2/\beta)\}] / 2$ as far as the regular solution model can be applied. An example of the demixing case ($\beta > 2$) is shown in panel (d) of Figure 5 in the case of surfactants mixtures of a hydrocarbon and a fluorocarbon. In panel (d), x and x_1 refer to the mole fractions of the fluorocarbon surfactant.

The demixing corresponds to a bimodal composition distribution. The distribution of composition among mixed micelles was discussed on the basis of the statistical mechanics [134].

6. Charged Mixed Micelles in the Media of Low Ionic Strengths

For ionic/nonionic mixed micelles in the media of low ionic strengths, the counterion concentration C_g increases with x as x refers to m_1/m. Because of the definition of the reference state, both g^{ex} and the activity coefficient γ_1 for ionic/nonionic mixed micelles include the effects of varying ionic strength with x. Now an environmental factor ξ discussed in section 1 enters, which is the counterion concentration C_g in the present context. We write $g^{ex,el}$ explicitly as follows.

$$g^{ex,el} = g^{el}(x) - x\,g^{el}\,(x{=}1) = g^{el}\,[x : C_g(x)] - x\,g^{el}\,[x{=}1: C_g(x{=}1)]. \qquad (7.6.1)$$

We define $g^{ex,el}*$ as follows as a quantity that takes the effect of varying C_g into account.

$$g^{ex,el}* = g^{el}\,[x : C_g(x)] - x\,g^{el}\,[x{=}1: C_g(x)]. \qquad (7.6.2)$$

Since the difference $g^{ex,el} - g^{ex,el}* = x\,g^{el}\,[x{=}1: C_g(x)] - xg^{el}\,[x{=}1: C_g(x{=}1)]$ can be approximately evaluated in terms of the Corrin-Harkins relation eq (4.1.2) for the ionic micelle in question.

$$d\, g^{el}(x{=}1) = -\,k_{CH}\, d\ln C_g.$$ (7.6.3)

As a good approximation, we have $g^{ex} - g^{ex}* = g^{ex,el} - g^{ex,el}*$. Then,

$$g^{ex} - g^{ex}* = x\, g^{el}\,[x{=}1{:}\,C_g(x)] - x\, g^{el}\,[x{=}1{:}\,C_g(x{=}1)] = -\,x\, k_{CH}\ln[cmc(x_1)\,x_1/cmc_1].$$ (7.6.4)

In Figure 6(a), g^{ex} and $g^{ex}*$ are compared for three alkyltrimethylammonium bromide (C_nTAB) /TritonX100 mixed micelles [133, 137]. In the case of $C_{16}TAB$, $g^{ex}*$ is more negative than g^{ex}, $g^{ex}*/\, g^{ex} \sim 2$. Also, significant chain length dependence that was observed for g^{ex} becomes much reduced for $g^{ex}*$. In conformity with $g^{ex}*$, the activity coefficient of the ionic species after the correction, γ_I*, is given as follows which was originally proposed by Funasaki [57].

$$\ln[\gamma_I*\,x] = (1+ k_{CH})\ln\,[cmc\,x_1/cmc_I]$$ (7.6.5)

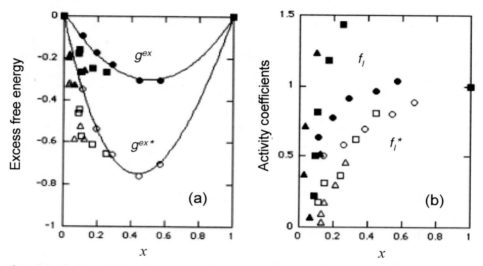

Taken from Maeda H, J. Phys. Chem. B, 109 (2005) 15933-15940, with permission.

Figure 6. Ionic/nonionic mixed micelles of alkyltrimethyammonium bromide (CnTAB) – Triton X100 mixed micelles.

Circles (C16TAB), squares (C14TAB) and triangles (C12TAB). (a) The excess free energy g^{ex} ($g^{ex}*$). Filled and open symbols represent g^{ex} and $g^{ex}*$, respectively. Solid curves are drawn for C16TAB according to $g^{ex} = -1.20\, x\,(1- x)$ and $g^{ex}* = (-3.71+1.51\, x)\, x\,(1- x)$. (b) Activity coefficients of CnTAB - Triton X100 mixed micelles. Filled and open symbols represent f_I and f_I*, respectively.

In Figure 6(b) γ_I and γ_I* are compared. While γ_I values exceed unity, no such behavior is seen for γ_I*. As shown in Figures 6(a) and (b), effects of varying ionic strength with x are significant. Although the correction is not always significant, it is pertinent to examine the effect when the measurements are carried out without added salt. The idea of the correction described above is essentially the same as proposed for ionic/ionic mixed micelles of like charges [104, 138, 139].

It is pertinent to introduce three regimes with respect to the ionic strength of the media to examine the validity of different types of the MGD relations and the implications of β of the RSM. For nonionic mixed micelles and ionic/nonionic mixed micelles in high ionic strengths, type 2 MGD relation and the standard RSM both hold. This is Regime 1. For ionic/nonionic mixed micelles in Regime 2(medium ionic strengths), the chemical potential of the counterion μ_g is well approximated to be independent of x. Then, type 2 MGD holds but the parameter β of the RSM is a function of x. For ionic/nonionic mixed micelles in Regime 3(water or low ionic strengths), μ_g varies with x. Then, type 2 MGD does not hold but type 1 MGD should be used and the parameter β of the RSM is a function of x. These results are summarized in Table 2.

Table 2. Three regimes with respect to the counterion concentration for ionic/nonionic mixed micelles

Regime	Ionic strength	Counterion Activity	Electric interaction	Micellar Gibbs-Duhem relation	The regular solution Model
(1)	high	Constant	Short range	Type 2	β is constant
(2)	medium	Constant	Long range	Type 2	β varies with x, $\beta(x)$
(3)	low	varies with x	Long range	Type 1	β varies with x, $\beta(x)$

x denotes the mole fraction of the ionic species in the mixed micelles.

7. Assessment of the Non-Electric Contributions to the Stability of Ionic/Nonionic Mixed Micelles

Interactions between constituting surfactant species in mixed micelles are generally represented by the reduced excess free energy per surfactant g^{ex} defined by eq (7.1.9). In ionic/nonionic mixed micelles, the electric contribution $g^{ex,el}$ is usually predominant thereby masking the non-electric contribution $g^{ex,non}$. It will be informative if $g^{ex,non}$ can be extracted. Two different attempts have been presented for the purpose [112, 122].

7-1. The Method of Peyre

A pioneering approach has been proposed by Peyre et al.[122]. They studied two kinds of the ionic/nonionic mixed micelles having a common cationic component C12TAB while nonionic species is partially hydrogenated fluorooctyl chain (F6) in one group but it is dodecyl chain (H12) in the other group. The two nonionic species have a common head group of lactobionamide. In their study, the *cmc*, compositions of the micelle x and the monomer x_1, they were all determined experimentally, by the potentiometry with a cationic surfactant-selective membrane electrode and the surface tension measurements. Then, the activity coefficients γ_1 and γ_N and g^{ex} can be determined by, respectively, eq (7.1.19) and eq (7.1.15). In the analysis of the obtained data, the RSM was employed and β values were obtained from g^{ex} by eq (7.3.1). Values of β were negative for both mixed micelles. It was found that β increased with x in 0.1 M NaBr, linearly for C12TAB/H12 but nonlinearly for C12TAB/F6. Negative β values for C12TAB/F6 suggests the electric synergism is stronger than the repulsive interaction between hydrocarbon and fluorocarbon chains. In other words, the electric synergism makes the two components to mix.

For C12TAB/H12, the non-electric interaction mostly arises from the head group steric interaction since the nonpolar core consists of only dodecyl chains and we put $\beta = \beta^{el} + \beta^{head}$. For C12TAB/F6, on the other hand, the non-electric contribution β^{ion} mostly arises from the mixing of hydrocarbon chains and fluorocarbon chains, in addition to β^{head}. Consequently, their difference, β (C12TAB/F6) - β (C12TAB/H12), is expected to give the contribution (β^{ion} - β^{head}) for (C12TAB/F6) mixed micelle. The obtained values of (β^{ion} - β^{head}) were slightly positive except in a narrow range of very small x. The positive value is expected to give a quantitative measure of the repulsive interaction between hydrocarbon and fluorocarbon chains. Although the macroscopic Gibbs-Duhem relation was used to ionic/nonionic mixed micelles in their analysis (See Section VII.7.2), the method by Peyre is undoubtedly promising and important.

7-2. A Phenomenological Approach

7-2-1. The Parameter B_1

We have proposed a parameter B_1 that does not contain the electric contribution, which is related to the standard free energy change ΔG^* of the following hypothetical exchange reaction (I) where a possible change of micelle shape/size associated with the reaction is not considered [112].

A nonionic micelle (aggregation number m) + An ionic monomer $\rightarrow$

A nonionic monomer + A mixed micelle containing only one ionic species   (I)

In terms of the chemical potential of the micelle $G_m(i, j)$ containing i ionic species and j nonionic species, chemical potentials of the ionic and the nonionic species (μ_I and μ_N), we have the following relations.

$$\Delta G^* = [G_m(1, m-1) + \mu_N^{s*}] - [G_m(0, m) + \mu_I^{s*}], \tag{7.7.1}$$

$$G_m(1, m-1) - G_m(0, m) = [(m-1) \mu_N^{m*} + \mu_I^{m}(i{=}1)] - m \mu_N^{m*}, \tag{7.7.2}$$

$$\Delta G^* = (\mu_N^{s*} - \mu_N^{m*}) + [\mu_I^{m}(i{=}1) - \mu_I^{s*}]. \tag{7.7.3}$$

The chemical potential of the ionic species in the micelle containing only one ionic species is denoted as $\mu_I^{m}(i{=}1)$ and it is written as follows by eq (7.1.14)

$$\mu_I^{m}(i{=}1) = \mu_I^{m}(x{=}1) + RT \ln [x_0 \gamma_I(x_0)]. \tag{7.7.4}$$

Here, the limiting value of x is not zero but $x_0 (=1/m)$ and $\gamma_I(x = x_0)$ is written as $\gamma_I(x_0)$. On the other hand, $(\mu_N^{s*} - \mu_N^{m*}) = - RT \ln (cmc_N)$ and $(\mu_I^{s*} - \mu_I^{m*}) = - RT \ln (cmc_I)$. Eq (7.7.3) reduces to the following.

$$\Delta G^* / RT = \ln (cmc_I/cmc_N) + \ln [x_0 \gamma_I(x_0)]. \tag{7.7.5}$$

We define a parameter B_1 as follows:

$B_1 \equiv \Delta G^*/RT - \ln x_0$

$= \ln (cmc_I/cmc_N) + \ln \gamma_I(x_0).$ (7.7.6)

As a possible way to assess B_1 experimentally, we consider the *cmc* in the range of small x, $cmc \sim cmc_N$. By expanding the *cmc* around cmc_N, we have,

$$\ln [cmc(x_1)/cmc_N] = (d \ln cmc /d x_1)_{(x_1=0)} x_1 + O(x_1^2) \qquad (7.7.7)$$

Eq (7.7.7) reduces to eq (7.7.8) after some manipulations using eqs(7.1.19) and eq (7.4.3).

$$\ln [cmc(x_1)/cmc_N] = [1+ (d \ln \gamma_N/d x_1)_{(x_1=0)} - \exp(-B_1) + x_0 (d \ln\gamma_I/d x_1)_{(x_1=0)}] x_1 + O(x_1^2)$$
$$(7.7.8)$$

If we evaluate the two derivative terms according to the RSM, then, $(d \ln \gamma_N/d x_1)_{(x_1=0)} \sim -x_0 (d \ln\gamma_I/dx_1)_{(x_1=0)} \sim 2 x_0\beta \exp(-B_1)$ ignoring terms of the order of x_0^2 and higher. We have finally eq (7.7.9) if the two derivative terms in eq (7.7.8) are ignored.

$$\ln[cmc(x_1)/cmc_N] = [1 - \exp(-B_1)] x_1 + O(x_1^2). \qquad (7.7.9)$$

Or, the following alternative equation can be used.

$$cmc(x_1)/cmc_N = \exp [\{1 - \exp(-B_1)\} x_1] = 1 + \{1 - \exp(-B_1)\} x_1 . \qquad (7.7.10)$$

These equations indicate that $cmc(x_1)/cmc_N < 1$ for negative B_1 and vice versa. Unfortunately, accurate measurements of the *cmc* in the region of small x_1 have been rarely reported so far.

7-2-2. Analysis in Terms of the RSM

As discussed in Sections VII.3 and VII.6, the regular solution model (RGM) holds for ionic/nonionic mixed micelles in the media of high ionic strengths, Regime(1) in Table 2. From eq (7.3.2a), we have $\ln \gamma_I(x_0) = \beta (1-x_0)^2 \sim \beta$ and we have the following expression for B_1 [112]

$$B_1 = \ln (cmc_I/cmc_N) + \beta = \beta^{ion} + [\ln (cmc_I/cmc_N) + \beta^{el}] \qquad (7.7.11)$$

Only when the quantity in the square bracket is small, B_1 can be a reasonable measure of β^{ion}.

Values of B_1 obtained on several ionic/nonionic mixed micelles in the media of high ionic strengths were reported and various contributions to B_1 were discussed [112].

In Regime (2), the following relation is generally obtained.

$$\ln \gamma_I = g^{ex}(x) + (1-x) dg^{ex}/dx. \qquad (7.7.12)$$

If we extend the RSM to allow the expression $g^{ex}(x) = \beta(x)x(1-x)$, we have

$$\ln \gamma_I = (1-x)^2 [\beta(x) + xd\beta/dx]. \qquad (7.7.13)$$

In the limit $x \to x_0$, we have the following relation if $d\beta^{non}/dx = 0$ is assumed.

$$\ln \gamma_1(x_0) = \beta(x_0) + x_0(d\beta/dx)_{x=x0} = \beta(x_0) + x_0(d\beta^{el}/dx)_{x=x0}. \tag{7.7.14}$$

In terms of $f(x)$ defined as g^{el}/x, $\beta^{el} = [f(x) - f(x=1)]/(1-x)$. Then,

$$(d\beta^{el}/dx)_{x=x0} = (df/dx)_{x=x0} + f(x_0)/(1-x_0)^2 = (df/dx)_{x=x0}. \tag{7.7.15}$$

Here $f(x_0) = 0$ by the definiton of the electric free energy g^{el}. Finally, we have
$$\ln \gamma_1(x_0) = \beta(x_0) + x_0(df/dx)_{x=x0}. \tag{7.7.16}$$

The term $x_0(df/dx)_{x=x0}$ cannot be ignored generally in spite of small x_0 (~ 0.02 if $m = 50$), because the term $(df/dx)_{x=x0}$ is expected to be large.

In summary, to assess B_1 in terms of the RGM, eq (7.7.11) is the only proper relation for the moment and the measurements should be carried out in the media of high ionic strengths.

VIII. HYDROGEN ION TITRATION OF MICELLES

The electrostatic free energy of micelles (per monomer) g^{el} can be evaluated by the molecular thermodynamic approach based on molecular parameters and size and shape of micelles. In the phenomenological approach, g^{el} is expressed as a function of x in terms of one or two parameters. For a particular group of mixed micelles, however, g^{el} can be determined experimentally by the hydrogen ion titration.

We consider the following proton dissociation reaction between a cationic (RH^+) and a nonionic (R) surfactant species.

$$RH^+ = R + H^+ \tag{8.1}$$

The degree of ionization x is identical with the mole fraction of the ionic species (RH^+), defined in the same manner as throughout Section VII. The proton dissociation constant of the monomer K_1 is defined as follows.

$$pK_1 = pH + \log [x_1 / (1 - x_1)]. \tag{8.2}$$

Let us define the apparent dissociation constant K_a and the intrinsic dissociation constant K_0 on the surface of the colloidal particle (either micelles or linear polymers) as follows.

$$pK_a = pH + \log [x/(1-x)]. : pK_0 = pK_a (x \to 0). \tag{8.3}$$

From the thermodynamics of hydrogen ion titration of linear polyelectrolytes, the free energy accompanying the dissociation of hydrogen ions is $\Delta g(x) = g(x) - g(x=0)$, which is directly given as follows [37, 140].

$$\Delta g(x)/ (\ln 10) = \int_0^x (pK_0 - pK_a)\, dx. \qquad (8.4)$$

If the electrostatic contribution is dominant in $\Delta g(x)$ as in the case of linear polyions [141], then the lhs of eq (8.4) can be approximated to $g^{el}/(\ln 10)$. Also, the electric surface potential ψ_0 is given as $e_0\psi_0 /kT \equiv \phi_0 = (\ln 10) (pK_0 - pK_a) = (\ln 10) \Delta pK_a$. The integral in eq (8.4) corresponds to the area A indicated in Figure 7. The area A' in panel (a) of Figure 7 is shown to represent $- \log \gamma_N : A' = - \log \gamma_N$ [142].

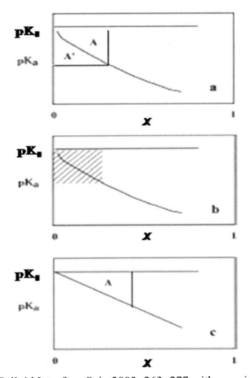

Taken from Maeda, H., J. Colloid Interface Sci., 2003; 263: 277 with permission.

Figure 7. Schematic representations of the titration curves.

(a) Covalently bonded colloids (linear polymers). At a given x, $pK_a - pK_0$ corresponds to $\phi_0/\ln 10$ if electric work is predominant in Δg. The area A and A' are equal to $g^{ex}/\ln 10$ and $(- \log \gamma_N)$, respectively. (b) Associative colloids like micelles. The hatched area (A+A') is equal to $[g^{ex}/\{\ln 10\} - \log \gamma_N]$. (c) Mixed micelles to which the regular solution model is applicable. pK_a is a linear function of x: $pK_a = pK_0 - (2\beta /\ln 10)\, x$.

Hydrogen ion titrations of surfactant micelles have been carried out on alkylamine oxides and others [143]. In the titration of surfactant micelles, however, there are several characteristics to be considered in contrast with the case of linear polyions described above. For example, the aggregation number m, a counterpart of the degree of polymerization of polyelectrolytes, varies with ionization x. Also, the equilibrium between the micelles and the monomeric species in the solution is always maintained during the titration. Accordingly, the concentrations of both monomers and micelles also change with pH. A thermodynamic analysis of the hydrogen ion titration of micelles has been presented to take these issues into account [142]. For colloids including micelles under the dissociation-association equilibrium, the sum of the area (A +A') indicated as a hatched region in panel(b) of Figure 7 corresponds to $[\Delta g(x)/(\ln 10) - \log \gamma_N]$ and each area A or A' cannot be equated to $\Delta g(x)/(\ln 10)$ or $- \log \gamma_N$, separately [142]. However, when the micellar Gibbs-Duhem (MGD) relation of type 2 holds for the mixed micelle consisting of RH^+ and R, the same procedure as applied to linear polyelectrolytes becomes valid for micelles [142]. So, g^{el} and ψ_0 can be experimentally obtained. Results for dodecyldimethylamine oxide micelles (C12DMAO), to whish type 2 MGD is shown to be applicable [144] are: g^{el} = 2.56 and 2.33, ϕ_0 = 4.63 and 4.38 for 0.1M and 0.2 M NaCl.

As another conclusion of the study[142], for those micelles to which the regular solution model (RSM) holds, the titration curve (pK_a vs x) becomes a straight line with a slope proportional to β, as shown schematically in panel (c) of Figure 7.

$$pK_0 - pK_a = (2\beta/\ln 10)\, x. \tag{8.5}$$

Experimental results for the case of C12DMAO micelles are shown in Figure 8. In the example shown in Figure 8, we have $\beta = (-2.11/2)\ln 10 = -2.4$. The value is slightly different from - 2.08 obtained from the *cmc* analysis, indicating the approximate nature of the RSM. It has turned out that the above results from the thermodynamic analysis [142] are consistent with later achievements by the molecular thermodynamic approach [145]. The linear approximation in the titration curves corresponds to averaging $\beta(x)$ values to provide a constant β value. In ordinary *cmc* analyses in terms of either MGD relations or model approaches, the range of x covered is usually narrower than that in the hydrogen ion titrations.

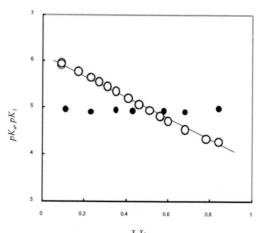

Taken from Maeda, H., J. Colloid Interface Sci., 2003; 263: 277 with permission.

Figure 8. The titration curve of dodecyldimethylamine oxide in 0.2 M NaCl solutions at 25^0C. Open and filled circles refer to pK_a and pK_1, respectively. A straight line is drawn according to the relation pK_a = 6.03 - 2.11 x.

Consequently, titration curves provide us with a useful criterion whether or not the RSM can be applied.

Introduction of pK_0 and pK_a was once criticized [144]. The criticism was not wrong but misleading in the sense that it overlooked valuable information obtained by the introduction of pK_0 and pK_a. The criticism has been dismissed by proper arguments [142].

It is important to carry out blank titration experiments to assess correct pK_0 values [70]. Once correctly evaluated, pK_0 provides useful information as shown below. For a couple of micelles, pK_0 differs significantly from that of the monomer pK_1 [143], while we have generally $pK_0 = pK_1$ for linear polyelectrolytes. The difference between pK_0 and pK_1 provides us with information about the environment of an ionic species RH^+ in the nonionic micelle. The issue is closely related to the 'differentiating influence of micelles' on proton dissociation equilibrium of various acids (indicator dyes), as reviewed by Mchedlov-Petrossyan [146]. For example, pK values of lauric acid incorporated in micelles are as follows [147a].

7.4 (LiDS) > 7.2 (NaDS) > 6.7 (C12E8) > 6.2 (C12TAB) >5.8 (C12TAC)

The observed trend is consistent with the expected electric interaction. However, the values of pK for a nonionic and even for two cationic micelles are much greater than that of octanoic acid in water, 4.85. In the case of nonionic micelles, ubiquitous mechanisms will be (a) the image charge effect and (b) effective dielectric constant ε_{eff} of the 'mixed solvent' consisting of solvent water and head groups of the nonionic surfactant. These two mechanisms will disfavor the charged state and hence increase the pK value. Similar but significantly smaller pK values (6.1 - 6.4) of myristic acid in alkylpolyglucoside (APG) micelles are reported which is smaller than the pK value in C12E8 (6.7) [147b]. The result would suggest more polar nature of glucoside groups ($\varepsilon_{eff} \sim$ 33-40) than oxyethylene group ($\varepsilon_{eff} \sim$27). It is not clear at present whether larger pK values in the nonionic micelles than that in water can be understood in terms of the above two ubiquitous mechanisms or it is further contributed from another effect such as the hydrogen bond between -COOH and -O- (C12E8) and/or -OH (glucose).

In the case of amine oxide surfactants, we have always the relation $pK_0 > pK_1$ [70, 143], opposite to the expectation from the image charge effect. The following two mechanisms have been considered as responsible for the effect $pK_0 > pK_1$ [70]: (a) the hydrogen bond and (b) dipole-dipole repulsion.

In the hydrogen bond mechanism, bound hydrogen ions $-NOH^+$ are stabilized by the hydrogen bond to the neighboring -NO group. Some results of spectroscopic measurements have supported the proposed hydrogen bond [148, 149].

The dipole-dipole interaction in the nonionic (non-protonated) amine oxide micelles makes the *cmc* about one order higher than those of other nonionic micelles of the same alkyl chain lengths. The dipole repulsion is greatly reduced by protonation and this effect leads to $pK_0 > pK_1$ [70, 145, 150]. Various values have been proposed for the dipole moment of NO group. Dielectric dispersion measurements give 4.9-5.0 D in nonpolar solvent [151a] and 4.1-4.5 D in aqueous media [151b] and the surface electric potential of a monolayer suggests 5.0 D [151c]. From quantum chemical *ab initio* calculations, 4.2 D is suggested for a dihydrate amine oxide [151d].

A molecular thermodynamic study using a value of 6.38 D and ignoring the hydrogen bond contribution predicts ΔpK_m ($= pK_0 - pK_1$) values of about 0.5 for dodecyldimethylamine oxide (C12DMAO) [145a], which is nearly half of the observed value ($\Delta pK_m \sim 1$). Experimentally, the *cmc* of C12DMAO in NaCl solutions of 0.1-0.2 M takes the minimum at *x* around 0.5 [70] which is consistent with the hydrogen bond mechanism. The molecular thermodynamic study without taking the hydrogen bond into account predicts the minimum of the *cmc* at *x* around 0.2-0.3.

ACKNOWLEDGMENTS

The publication cost of the present chapter is assisted by the Grant-in-Aid for Scientific Research (C) (No. 22500727) from Monbu-Kagakushou Japan

REFERENCES

[1]   Tanford, C. "The Hydrophobic Effect: Formation of micelles and biological membranes", 2nd Ed., John Wiley & Sons Inc.(1980).

[2]   Rosen, J. "*Surfactants and Interfacial Phenomena*", 2nd Ed., John Wiley & Sons Inc.(1989).

[3]   Israelachvili, J. "*Intermolecular & Surface Forces*", 2nd Ed., Academic Press (1992).

[4]   Evans, DF and Wennerström, H, "*The Colloidal Domain*", VCH, (1994).

[5]   "Micelles, Membranes, Microemulsions, and Monolayers", W. M. Gelbart, A. Ben-Shaul, D. Roux Eds., Springer, New York (1994)

[6]   Laughlin, R. G., The Aqueous Phase Behavior of Surfactants, Academic Press, 1994.

[7]   Rusanov, A. I., "*Micellization in Surfactant Solutions*", Harwood Academic Publishers, 1997.

[8]   Tsujii, K., "*Surface Activity-Principles, Phenomena, and Applications*", Academic Press 1998.

[9]   Wennerström, H., Lindman, B., *Micelles, Physical Chemistry of Surfactant Association, Physics Report*, 52, (1979) 1-86.

[10]   Maeda, H., *Thermodynamic Analysis of Micellar Systems*, Encyclopedia of Surface and Colloid Science, Hubbard A. Ed. Marcel Dekker, Inc., 2002. 5312-5325.

[11]   (a) Krafft, F., Stern, A., *Ber.*, 27 (1894) 1747-1754: 1755-1761.
       (b) Krafft, F., *Ber.*,29 (1896) 1334-1344.

[12]   (a) Krafft, F., Wiglow, H., *Ber.*, 28 (1895) 2566-2573.
       (b) Krafft, F., Wiglow, H., *Ber.*, 28 (1895) 2573-2582.

[13]   Krafft, F., Strutz, A., *Ber.*, 29 (1896)1328-1334.

[14]   Smits, A., *Z. phys. Chem.*, 45 (1903) 608-612.

[15]   (a) McBain, J. W, Salmon, C. S., *J. Am. Chem. Soc.*, 42 (1920) 426-460.
       (b) McBain, J. W., *Transactions of the Faraday Society*, 9 (1913) 100.

[16]   Reychler, A., *Kolloid-Z.*, 12, (1913) 277-283 : 252-254.

[17]   Hartley, G. S., "*Aqueous Solutions of Paraffin-Chain Salts*", Hermann & Cie, Paris, 1936.

[18]   Debye, P, Anacker, E.W., *J. Phys. Colloid Chem.*, 55 (1951) 644-655.
[19]   Hill, T. L., *"Thermodynamics of Small Systems"*, Dover 1994
[20]   Eriksson, J. C., Bergström, M, Persson, M., *Russ. J. Phys. Chem.*, 77 (2003) S87-S94.
[21]   Ben-Naim, A., *J. Phys. Chem.*, 82 (1978) 792-803.
[22]   Tanford, C. *J. Phys. Chem.*, 83 (1979) 1802-1803.
[23]   Mukerjee, P., *Adv. Colloid Interface Sci.*, 1 (1967) 241-275.
[24]   Zana, R., *Langmuir*, 12 (1996) 1208-1211.
[25]   Sasaki, T, Hattori, M, Sasaki, J, and Nukina, K, *Bull. Chem. Soc. Jpn.*, 48 (1975) 139-1403.
[26]   Puvvada, S, Blankschtein, D, *J. Chem. Phys.*, 92 (1990) 3710-3724.
[27]   Puvvada, S., Blankschtein, D, *J. Phys. Chem.*, 96 (1992) 5579-5592.
[28]   Puvvada, S, Blankschtein, D, *J. Phys. Chem.*, 96 (1992) 5567-5579.
[29]   Shiloach A, Blankschtein D, *Langmuir*, 14 (1998) 7166-7182.
[30]   Nagarajan R, Ruckenstein, *J. Colloid Interface Sci.*, 60 (1976) 221-231.
[31]   Nagarajan R, Ruckenstein, *J. Colloid Interface Sci.*, 71 (1979) 580-604.
[32]   Nagarajan, R, *Colloids Surfaces A*, 71 (1993) 39-64.
[33]   Bergström M, Jonsson P, Persson M, Eriksson J Ch, *Langmuir*, 19 (2003) 10719-10725.
[34]   Zana, R., *Langmuir*, 11 (1995) 2314-2315.
[35]   Tolman, RC, *J. Chem. Phys.*, 17(1949) 333-337.
[36]   Fuoss, RM, Katchalsky, A, and Lifson, S, *Proc. Natl. Acad. USA*, 37 (1951) 579-589.
[37]   Marcus, RA, *J. Chem. Phys.*, 23 (1955) 1057-1068.
[38]   Jonssön, B, Wennerström, H, *J. Colloid Interface Sci.*, 80 (1981) 482-496.
[39]   Lifson, S, and Katchalsky, A, *J. Polym. Sci.*, 13 (1954) 43-55.
[40]   Gunnarsson G, Jönsson B, Wennerström H., *J. Phys. Chem.*, 84(1980) 3114-3121.
[41]   Fowler, R, Guggenheim, EA, "*Statistical Thermodynamics*", Cambridge Univ. Press, 1949. §922.
[42]   Verwey, EJW, and Overbeek, J. Th. G., "*Theory of the Stability of Lyophobic Colloids*", Chapter III, Elsevier, Amsterdam, (1948).
[43]   Fowler, R, Guggenheim, EA, "*Statistical Thermodynamics*", Cambridge Univ. Press, 1949. §917.
[44]   Stigter, D, *J. Colloid Interface Sci.,* 47 (1974) 473-482.
[45]   Gilanyi, T, *Coll. Surfaces* A. 104 (1995) 119-126.
[46]   Engström, S, Wennerström, H, *J. Phys. Chem.*, 82 (1978) 2711-2714.
[47]   Maeda, H, Oosawa, F, *J. Phys. Chem.*, 83 (1979) 2911-2918.
[48]   Alfrey Jr, T, Berg, PW, Morawetz, H., *J. Polym. Sci.*, 7 (1951) 543-547.
[49]   Tanford, C., "*Physical Chemistry of Macromolecules*", John Wiley & Sons, 1961. Chapter 7,
[50]   Ohshima, H, Healy, TW, White, LR, *J. Colloid Interface Sci.*, 90 (1982) 17-26.
[51]   Evans, DF, Mitchell, DJ, Ninham, BW, *J. Phys. Chem.*, 88 (1984) 6344-6348.
[52]   Hayter, J. B., *Langmuir*, 8 (1992) 2873-2876.
[53]   Healy, TW, Drummond, CJ, Grieser, F, Murray, BS, *Langmuir*, 6 (1990) 506-508.
[54]   Herrmann, KW, *J. Phys. Chem.*, 66 (1962) 295-300.
[55]   Corrin, ML, Harkins, WD, *J. Am. Chem. Soc.*, 69 (1947) 683-688.
[56]   Corrin, ML, *J. Colloid Sci.*, 3 (1948) 333-338.
[57]   Funasaki, N, *J. Colloid Interface Sci.*, 67 (1978) 384-386.

[58] Collins, K, Washabaugh, MW, *Quat. Rev. Biophys.*, 18 (1985) 323-422.

[59] Mukerjee, P, Mysels, C., NSRDS-NB36 (1971).

[60] Stigter, D., *J. Phys. Chem.*, 78 (1974) 2480-2485.

[61] Mukerjee, P, *J. Phys. Chem.*, 69 (1965) 4038-4040.

[62] Tori, K, Nakagawa,T, Kolloid - Z. Z. - *Polym.*, 189 (1963) 50-55.

[63] Maeda, H, Muroi, S, Kakehashi, R, *J. Phys. Chem. B*, 101 (1997) 7378-7382.

[64] Maeda, H, Kanakubo,Y, Miyahara, M, Kakehashi, R, Garamus, V, Pedersen, JS, *J. Phys. Chem. B*, 104 (2000) 6174-6180.

[65] Nishikido, N, Matuura, R, *Bull. Chem. Soc. Jpn.*,50 (1977) 1690-1694.

[66] Schrier, EE, Schrier, EB, *J. Phys. Chem.*, 71 (1967) 1851-1860.

[67] Maeda, H., *J. Colloid Interface Sci.*, 241(2001) 18-25.

[68] Rusanov, A. I., Kuni, F. M., Shchekin, A. K., *Russ. J. Phys. Chem.*, A83, (2009) 223-230.

[69] Chan, CC, Mukerjee, P, cited in Franchini, MK, Carstensen, JT, *J. Pharm. Sci.*, 85 (1996) 220-227.

[70] Maeda, H, Kakehashi, R, *Adv. Colloid Interface Sci.*, 88 (2000) 275-293.

[71] Gorski, N, Kalus, N, Meier, G, Schwahn, D., *Langmuir*,15 (1999) 3476-3482.

[72] de Mul, MNG, Davis, HT, Evans, DF, Bhave, AV, Wagner, JR., *Langmuir*, 16 (2000) 8276-8284.

[73] Zielinski, R, Ikeda, S, Nomura, H, Kato, S, *J. Colloid Interface Sci.*, 129 (1989) 175-184.

[74] Baldwin, R. L., *Proc. Natl. Acad. Sci.*, 83 (1986) 8069-8072.

[75] Privalov, P. L., Gill, S. J., *Adv. Protein Chem.*, 39 (1988) 191-234.

[76] Abraham, MH, *J. Chem. Soc. Faraday Trans.* 1, 80 (1984) 153-181.

[77] Shinoda, K, Soda, T., *J. Phys. Chem.*, 67 (1963) 2072-2074.

[78] Harada, S, Nakagawa, T, *J. Solution. Chem.*, 8 (1979) 267-276.

[79] Hamann, SD, JPC, 66 (1962) 1359-1361.

[80] Tanaka, M, Kaneshina, S, Shin-no, K, Okajima, T, Tomida, T., *J. Colloid Interface Sci.*, 46 (1974) 132-138.

[81] Israelachvili, J. N., Mitchell, JD, Ninham, BW., *J. Chem. Soc. Faraday Trans.* II, 72 (1976) 1525-1568.

[82] Mitchell, JD, Ninham, BW., *J. Chem. Soc. Faraday Trans.* 2, 77 (1981) 601-629.

[83] Iyer, J, Blankschtein, D., *J. Phys. Chem.* B116 (2012) 6443-6454.

[84] Rosen, MJ, Wang, H, Shen, P, Zhu, Y., *Langmuir*, 21 (2005) 3749-3756.

[85] Manohar, C, Narayanan, J., *Colloid Surface* A, 403 (2012) 129-132.

[86] Tanford, C., *"Physical Chemistry of Macromolecules"*, John Wiley & Sons, 1961. Chapter 5.

[87] Vrij, A, Overbeek, J.Th G, *J. Colloid. Sci.*, 17 (1962) 570-588.

[88] Coll, H, *J. Phys. Chem.*, 74 (1970) 520-528.

[89] Attwood, D, Elworthy, PH, Kayne, SB, *J. Phys. Chem.*, 74 (1970) 3529-3534.

[90] Kakehashi, R, Kanakubo, Y, Yamamoto, A, Maeda, H., *Langmuir*, 15 (1999) 4194-4197.

[91] Ezrahi, S, Tuval, E, Aserin, A., *Adv. Colloid Interface Sci.*, 128-130 (2006) 77-102.

[92] Magid, JL, *J. Phys. Chem. B*, 102 (1998) 4064-4074.

[93] Rehage, H, Hoffmann, H., *Mol. Phys.*, 74 (1991) 933-973.

[94] Mukerjee, P, *J. Phys. Chem.*, 76 (1972) 565-570.

[95] Porte, G, Gomati, R, Appel, HE, Marignan, J., *J. Phys. Chem.*, 90 (1986) 5746-5751.

[96] Danio, D., Talmon, Y., Levy, H., Zana, R., *Science*, 269 (1995) 1420-1421.

[97] Lin, Z, *Langmuir*, 12 (1996) 1729-1737.

[98] (a) Ikeda, S, Ozeki, S, Tsunoda, M, *J. Colloid Interface Sci.*, 73 (1980) 27-37.
(b) Ozeki, S, Hyomen, 20 (1982) 632-648 (A review in Japanese).

[99] Rubingh, DN, Mixed Micelle Solutions, in Solution Chemistry of Surfactants, Mittal K., Ed., Plenum, NY, 1979, p337-354.

[100] Mixed Surfactant Systems, Holland, PM and Rubingh, DN, Eds., ACS Symposium Series 501, ACS, Washington DC (1992).

[101] (a) Mixed Surfactant Systems, Ogino, K and Abe, M, Eds., Marcel Dekker, (1993).
(b) Mixed Surfactant Systems, Abe, M, Scamehorn, J F., Eds., Marcel Dekker, (2005).

[102] Kaler, EW, Murthy, AK, Rodriguez, BE, Zasadzinski, JA, *Science*, 245 (1989) 1371-1374.

[103] Kaler, EW, Harrington, KK, Murthy, AK, Zasadzinski, JA, *J. Phys. Chem.*, 96 (1992) 6698-6707.

[104] H. Lange, *Kolloid-Z.*, 131 (1953) 96-103.

[105] Clint, JH, *J. Chem. Soc., Faraday*, 71 (1975) 1327-1334.

[106] Funasaki, N, Hada, S, *J. Phys. Chem.*, 83 (1979) 2471-2475.

[107] Holland, PM, Rubingh, DN, *J. Phys. Chem.*, 87 (1983) 1984-1990.

[108] Motomura, K, Yamanaka, M, Aratono, M, *Colloid Polym. Sci.*, 262 (1984) 948-955.

[109] Nagarajan R, *Langmuir*, 1 (1985) 331-341.

[110] Holland, PM, *Adv. Colloid Interface Sci.*, 26 (1986) 111-129.

[111] Hoffmann, H, Pössnecker, G, *Langmuir*, 10 (1994) 381-389.

[112] Maeda, H, *J. Colloid Interface Sci.*,172 (1995) 98-105.

[113] Kronberg B, *Curr. Opin, Colloid Interface Sci.*, 2 (1997) 456-463.

[114] Shiloach A, Blankschtein D, *Langmuir*, 14 (1998) 1618-1636.

[115] Reif I, Somasundaran P, *Langmuir*,15 (1999) 3411-3417.

[116] Bergström M, Eriksson J. Ch, *Langmuir*, 16 (2000)7173-7181.

[117] Hines J. D., *Curr. Opin, Colloid Interface Sci.*, 6 (2001) 350-356.

[118] Peyre, V., *Langmuir*, 18 (2002) 1014-1023.

[119] Smirnova N. A., *Russ. J. Phys. Chem.*, 80 (2006) 1809-1818.

[120] Maeda, H. *Adv. Colloid Interface Sci.*, 156 (2010) 70-82.

[121] Palous J. L., Turmine, M., Letellier, P., *J. Phys. Chem. B*, 102 (1998) 5886-5890.

[122] Peyre V, Patil S, Durand G, Pucci B, *Langmuir*, 23 (2007) 11465-11474.

[123] (a) Carlfors J, Stilbs P, *J. Phys. Chem.*, 88 (1984) 4410-4414.
(b) Nordstierna L, Furo I, Stilbs P, *J. Am. Chem. Soc.*, 128 (2006) 6704-6712.

[124] Eads C. D., Robosky L. C., *Langmuir*, 15 (1999) 2661-2668.

[125] Maeda H, *J. Phys. Chem. B*, 108 (2004) 6043-6051.

[126] Szymczyk K, Janczuk B, *Langmuir*, 25 (2009) 4377-4383.

[127] Hall D. G., *J. Chem. Soc. Faraday Trans.* 87 (1991) 3529-3533.

[128] Maeda H, *J. Colloid Interface Sci.*, 364 (2011) 413-416.

[129] Attwood D, Patel J, *J. Colloid Interface Sci.*, 129 (1989) 222-230.

[130] Treiner C, Khodja A. A., Fromon M, *J. Colloid Interface Sci.*, 128 (1989) 416-421.

[131] Hall D. G., Meares P, C. Davidson, E. Wyn-Jones, J. Taylor, in ref.[100], Chapter 7, 128-141.

[132] Maeda H, *J. Colloid Interface Sci.*, 258 (2003) 390-395.

[133] Maeda H, *J. Phys. Chem.* B,109 (2005) 15933-15940.

[134] Barzykin, AV, Almgren, M., *Langmuir*, 12 (1996) 4672-4680.

[135] Garamus, V, Kameyama, K, Kakehashi, Maeda, H, *Colloid Polym. Sci.*, 277 (1999) 868-874.

[136] Georgiev G. S., *Colloid Polym. Sci.*, 274 (1996) 49-58.

[137] Ruiz C. C., Aguiar J, *Langmuir*, 16 (2000) 7946-7953.

[138] Lange H, Beck, KH, *Kolloid-ZZ. Polym.*, 251 (1973) 424-431.

[139] Shinoda K, *J. Phys. Chem.*, 58 (1954) 541-543.

[140] (a) Katchalsky A, Gillis J, *Rec. trav. chim.*, 68 (1949) 879-897.

   (b) Arnold R, Overbeek J. Th G, *Rec. trav. chim.*, 69 (1950)192-206.

[141] Kotin L, Nagasawa M, *J. Chem. Phys.*, 36 (1962) 873-879.

[142] Maeda H, *J. Colloid Interface Sci.*, 263 (2003) 277-287.

[143] Section 6 of ref [120]

[144] Rathman J. F., Christian S. D., *Langmuir*, 6 (1990)391-395.

[145] (a) Goldsipe A, Blankschtein D, *Langmuir*, 22 (2006) 3547-3559.

   (b) Goldsipe A, Blankschtein D, *Langmuir*, 22 (2006) 9894-9904.

[146] Michedlov-Petrossyan, N. O., *Pure Appl. Chem.*, 80 (2008)1459-1510.

[147] (a) da Silva F. L. B, Bogren D, Söderman O, Åkesson T, Jönsson B, *J. Phys. Chem.* B, 106 (2002) 3515-3522.

   (b) Whiddon C. R., Bunton C. A., Söderman O, *J. Phys. Chem.* B, 107 (2003) 1001-1005.

   (c) Söderman O, Jönsson B, Olofsson G, *J. Phys. Chem.* B, 110 (2006) 3288-3293.

[148] Rathman J. F., Scheuing D R, *ACS Symp. Ser.*, 447 (1990)123-142.

[149] Kawasaki H, Maeda H, *Langumir*, 17 (2001) 2278-2281.

[150] Terada Y, Maeda H, Odagaki T, *J. Phys. Chem.* B, 101 (1997) 5784-5788.

[151] (a) Linton E. P., *J. Am. Chem. Soc.*, 62 (1940) 1945-1948.

   (b) Shikata T, Itatani S, *J. Solution Chem.*, 31 (2002) 823-844.

   (c) Goddard, E. D., Kung, H. C., *J. Colloid Interface Sci.*, 43 (1973) 511-520.

   (d) Itatani S, Doctoral Dissertation, Osaka University, 2008.

In: Micelles
Editors: Danielle Bradburn and Tom Bittinger

ISBN: 978-1-62948-444-0
© 2014 Nova Science Publishers, Inc.

Chapter 4

MICELLIZATION OF GEMINI SURFACTANTS IN AQUEOUS SOLUTIONS

Barbara Trzebicka,[1,] Andrzej Dworak,[1] Julia Hawranke,[2] Edyta Kuliszewska,[2] and Zofia Hordyjewicz-Baran[2]*

[1]Centre of Polymer and Carbon Materials, Polish Academy of Sciences, Zabrze, Poland
[2]Institute of Heavy Organic Synthesis "Blachownia", Kedzierzyn-Kozle, Poland

ABSTRACT

Over the past few years, intensive studies have been performed on the synthesis and solution behavior of surfactants with more than one tail. Among these surfactants, the most widely studied are the gemini surfactants, which consist of two (or more) amphiphilic moieties connected at or close to the head group and separated by a spacer group. Gemini surfactants can be orders of magnitude more active than their single tail analogues.

All surfactants self-organize in solutions into different structures with interesting morphologies. Above a certain concentration, known as the critical micelle concentration *(CMC),* the molecules spontaneously associate to form larger aggregates of colloidal dimensions – micelles.

A considerable amount of research on gemini surfactants is currently being conducted in both academic institutions and in chemical companies because of an insufficient understanding of their fundamental properties and in view of their actual or envisaged applications. Over the past 25 years, many different types of gemini surfactants have been synthesized. At first, studies on the catalysis of chemical reactions in micellar solutions of cationic dimeric surfactants and the use of such solutions as antimicrobial agents were reported. Later, unique properties concerning not only the surface properties but also the molecular aggregation were demonstrated. Currently, the relationships between the structure and the properties have been widely investigated for cationic, anionic, zwitterionic and nonionic gemini surfactants.

This chapter describes the issues related to the aggregation behavior of new members of the gemini family of surfactants in solutions based on the latest research.

---

*Corresponding author: Barbara Trzebicka, Centre of Polymer and Carbon Materials, Polish Academy of Sciences, M. Curie-Sklodowskiej 34, 41-819 Zabrze, Poland. E-mail: btrzebicka@cmpw-pan.edu.pl.

The structures of newly synthesized gemini surfactants are reported. The properties of the micelles of the gemini surfactants (ionic and nonionic) and their micellar solutions are reviewed. The following properties are discussed: the micelle shape, dispersity and size, micelle ionization degree, microstructure in solution and kinetics/dynamics of gemini surfactant micelles. In addition, the influence of additives, especially organic and inorganic salts, on the surface-active properties and aggregation behavior of surfactants are reviewed.

The current state of progress in solubilization studies of the hydrophobic compounds in micellar gemini surfactant solutions is also presented.

The experimental methods used in the determination of micellar properties are discussed. Examples of the determination of *CMC* values with the use of surface tension, light scattering, and fluorescence and UV spectroscopies are presented. The use of static light scattering, small angle neutron scattering and fluorescence methods for determining the aggregation number of self-assembled gemini structures is reported. The information derived from cryo-transmission electron microscopy, which provides a direct visualization of micelles and the highly organized structures of gemini surfactants, is presented.

The application of aggregated structures of gemini surfactants and their potential future in technology are also described.

INTRODUCTION

The amphiphilic nature of surfactants enables their self-organization into micelles in aqueous solutions. Gemini surfactants are defined as surfactants composed of two amphiphilic moieties that consist of two hydrophobic tails and two hydrophilic head groups. Those two moieties are covalently attached through a spacer group, which can be hydrophilic or hydrophobic, flexible or rigid. Compared with their corresponding single-tail surfactants, gemini surfactants are generally more efficient in lowering surface tension, have a much lower critical micelle concentration, and possess specific rheological and unusual aggregation properties. By varying the nature of the spacer, hydrophobic tails, and head groups, the molecular structures of gemini surfactants can be tailored, which may provide a new way to control their performance, including the properties of their micellar solutions.

Different types of gemini surfactants, viz. anionic, cationic, zwitterionic and nonionic have been synthesized and investigated for their solution behavior and performance-based properties. This chapter describes issues related to the aggregation behavior of new members of the gemini family in solution based on the latest research. In most surfactant applications, surfactants with additives, rather than pure surfactants, are used. Moreover, such systems often exhibit exceptional properties. The influence of the most common additives (salts, alcohols, and amines) on the surface-active properties and aggregation behavior of surfactants is reviewed. Additionally, studies on the improvement of the solubility of hydrophobic compounds caused by micellar solutions of geminis are described.

STRUCTURES OF GEMINI SURFACTANTS

Gemini surfactants represent a new class of surfactants composed of two amphiphilic moieties connected at the head group or very close to the head group by a spacer (Figure 1).

The chemical character of the spacer can vary: short (two methylene groups), long (20 or more methylene groups), hydrophobic (aliphatic or aromatic), hydrophilic (polyether), rigid (stilbene) or flexible (polymethylene group). Surfactants with dissymmetrical hydrophobic tails, dissymmetrical head groups, or both are called heterogemini surfactants (Figure 1B). Surfactants with a spacer connecting the two amphiphilic moieties in the middle or at the end of tail are called bolaform surfactants [1] (Figure 1C).

Bolaform structures will not be discussed here.

Gemini surfactants have considerable potential for structural variability. They can be cationic, anionic, zwitterionic or nonionic, with all types of chemical character in the spacer group [2]. The most widely studied ionic gemini surfactants, with alkyl tails and alkyl spacers, are referred to as $m\text{-}s\text{-}m,2X$ or as $C_m\text{-}C_s\text{-}C_m,2X$, where C indicates a carbon atom, m is the carbon number of the alkyl tail, s is the number of carbon atoms in the spacer, and X represents the counterions.

The second acronym is often used to distinguish a partially fluorinated portion of a gemini surfactant, such as $C_{12}\text{-}C_3fC_6C_3\text{-}C_{12}$, where f is the number of fluorinated carbon atoms. Gemini surfactants with different tails have been referred to as $m\text{-}s\text{-}m',2X$. Gemini surfactants with an oligooxyethylene spacer are denoted as $m\text{-}EO_n\text{-}m,2X$, where n is the number of oxyethylene units. Zwitterionic, nonionic and gemini surfactants with peculiar chemical structures have been described using the following chemical formulas: $[Br^-,C_{12}H_{25} (CH_3CH_2)_2N^+CH_2C(O)NHCH_2CH_2S]_2$ or $C_{12}H_{25}OP(O^-)(=O)OCH_2CH_2N^+(CH_3)_2C_{14}H_{29}$, or for gemini with fluoro atoms, $[Cl^-,C_8F_{17}N^+(CH_3)_2 C_2H_4S]_2$.

The first scientific report on gemini surfactants was from Bunton et al. [3] in 1971. His work was followed by Devinsky et al. [4, 5], who synthesized bis-quaternary ammonium surfactants with a large variety of structures, and by Okahara et al. [6], who synthesized a large number of anionic gemini surfactants.

The most thoroughly investigated group of gemini surfactants is the N,N,N',N'-tetramethyl-α,ω-alkylenediamine dihalides [7-9]. Several new structures of spacers have been introduced into gemini surfactant molecules. Alkyl spacer groups can be replaced by hydrophilic groups, such as an oxyethylene chain [10-13] or substituted with hydroxyl group (s) [14-16].

These groups can also be introduced into the short chain [15] within the quaternary ammonium group. In most cases, the synthesis paths are similar. In general, gemini surfactants are obtained by the quaternization of the diamine with an alkyl halide or dihalide.

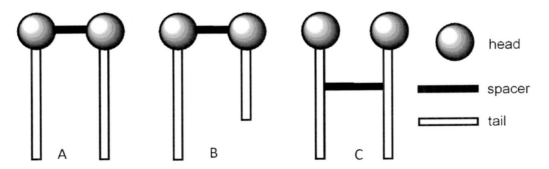

Figure 1. Schematic representation of gemini surfactants: symmetrical gemini surfactant (A), heterogemini surfactant (B) and bolaform surfactant (C).

Natural products have also been incorporated into the structure of gemini surfactants, a development important from an environmental perspective. Amino acids [17-20] and sugar moieties [21-23] (Figure 2) imparted gemini surfactants with interesting and useful properties. The introduction of an amide or an ester linkage [24-29] into the lipophilic tail of gemini surfactants favored the decomposition of the structure in the natural environment.

The introduction of additional amphiphilic groups into the structure of the surfactant caused multitail surfactants to become intermediates between gemini and polymeric surfactants. Menger et al. [30] named the synthesized multitail surfactants "multiarmed" (Figure 3).

Wu et al. [31] called the three-tailed cationic surfactants with amide groups in the spacer "star-like". Zhang et al. [32] synthesized a three-tailed quaternary ammonium salt containing polyoxyethylene chains. Laschewsky et al. [33] synthesized three series of multitailed surfactants with rigid, fixed spacers.

Asymmetrical geminis with different head groups or different tails [34] have also been obtained. The last class of cationic gemini surfactants consists of the fluorocarbon [35, 36] and the perfluoroalkyl [37] tail surfactants.

Chiral cationic gemini surfactants with two methoxy groups in the spacer were synthesized to study the kinetics of micellization [38]. Peptide-based chiral cationic gemini surfactants were used in gene transfection [39, 40].

Anionic gemini surfactants [41] have four main types of head groups: phosphate, sulfonate, sulfate and carboxylate. Functional groups can be located in the tail or in the spacer. Tyagi and Tyagi [42] synthesized a series of dialkyldiphosphate gemini surfactants with octadecyl carbon chains, a flexible spacer and phosphate as the head group.

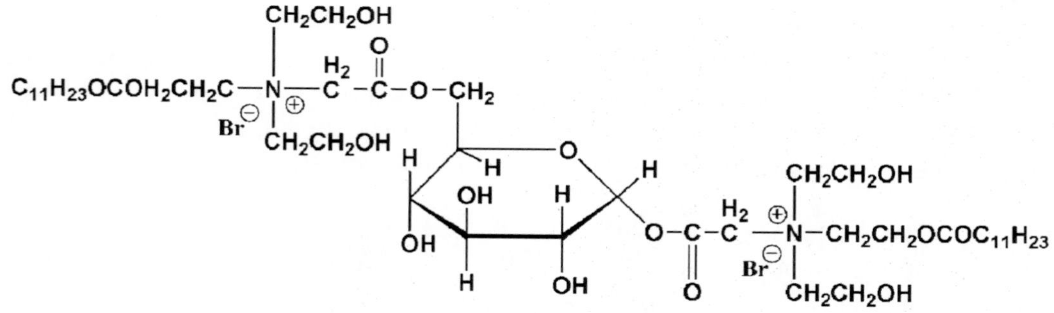

Figure 2. Sugar cationic gemini surfactant.

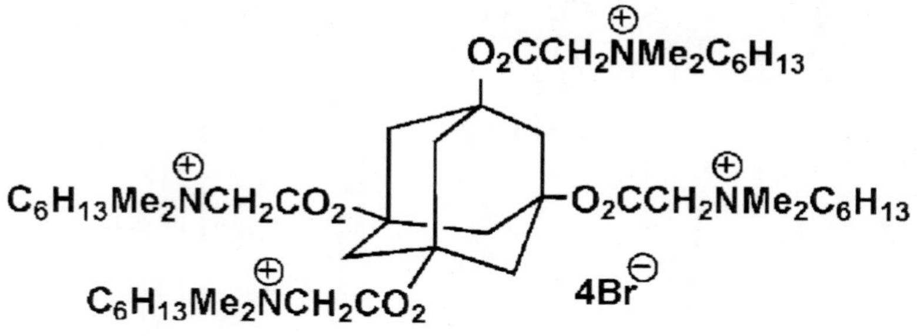

Figure 3. Four-tailed "multiarmed" gemini surfactant structure.

Jaeger et al. [43] obtained two series of pyrophosphate-based gemini surfactants containing the shortest possible spacer - a single oxygen atom. Adewuyi et al. [44] prepared phosphate-hydroxy ethanolamide gemini surfactants using naturally occurring raw materials. Takamatsu et al. [1] presented a new class of gemini surfactants with dissymmetric hydrocarbon tails containing phosphate or hydroxyl head groups. The sulfonated anionic gemini surfactants are represented by a large group of aryl sulfonates. Du et al. [45] synthesized novel alkylbenzene sulfonates where the sulfonate group was in the *para*-position to the alkylbenzene. Linear dodecyl diphenyl ether sulfonate gemini surfactants were described by Hujun et al. [46]. In these compounds, the sulfonate group is in *ortho*- or *meta*-position to the linear alkyl diphenyl ester. This author also described [47] linear alkylated diphenylmethane sulfonate gemini surfactants with sulfonate groups located in the *ortho*- or *meta*- position. Liu et al. [48] synthesized linear alkylated diphenyl chains linked by an oxyethylated spacer with sulfonated groups in the *ortho*- position to the spacer. Ge et al. [49] presented a new class of *para*- position sulfonated alkylated anilines linked by the nitrogen atom of the aniline to a diamidalkyl spacer. Disulfonate gemini surfactants with an aryl spacer linking two dialkyls not directly at the level of the head groups were presented by Zaijun et al. [50]. Sulfonated gemini surfactants with two triazine moieties were described by Li et al. [51].

Alkyl sulfate surfactants are among the oldest known anionic surfactants. Gemini surfactants with alkyl sulfate head groups can be regarded as analogues of the conventional single chain surfactant sodium dodecyl sulfonate. Tai et al. [52] presented a multi-step synthetic route leading to alkyl sulfate gemini surfactants.

A series of anionic gemini surfactants with two carboxylated groups were synthesized by Yoshimura et al. [53] and Chen et al. [29]. Song et al. [54] described the synthesis of carboxylated gemini surfactants with an azobenzene spacer. An interesting compound representing the anionic gemini surfactants was obtained by Acharya et al. [55]. They linked two alkyl tails by an ester bond with two carboxylate groups without a spacer group. Yoshimura et al. [56] partially replaced hydrogen atoms in hydrocarbon alkyl chains with fluorine to produce a partially fluorinated carboxylate anionic gemini.

In the class of nonionic gemini surfactants, the most popular are those with an amide [57, 58] or polyoxyethylene [59-62] in the head or spacer group. Recently, sugar-based nonionic gemini surfactants have played an increasingly important role in surfactant chemistry. Starting from D-glucose, Mariano et al. [63] connected two sugar moieties via a diesteralkyl bond. Laska et al. [64] used an ethylenediamine spacer to link two D-glucose moieties. Warwel et al. [65, 66] connected *N*-alkyl glucamines by hydroxyalkyl- or epoxy hydroxyalkyl spacers. A new family of glucosamide-based trisiloxane gemini surfactants was obtained by Han et al. [67].

Zwitterionic surfactants incorporate both negative and positive charges in the hydrophilic head. These surfactants exhibit pH-dependent behavior; they show anionic character at high pH and cationic properties at low pH. In the literature, there have been reports on the synthesis of gemini surfactants possessing nonidentical hydrophilic head groups, such as ammonium-phosphodiester [68], sulfate-polyoxyethylene [69-71] and hydroxyl-polyoxyethylene [72]. Zwitterionic gemini surfactants with two identical head groups, such as a pair of carboxybetaines [73] or a pair of sulfobetaines [74, 75], have potential industrial importance. Bordi et al. [76] reported the synthesis of a new class of double alkyl chain *N*-oxides linked by poly(ethylene glycol) spacers of different lengths.

SELF-ASSEMBLING OF GEMINI
SURFACTANTS IN AQUEOUS SOLUTION

The amphiphilic character of surfactant molecules causes their characteristic arrangement at water-air surfaces [77]. The adsorption of surfactant from the solution onto a surface depends on the concentration. At very low concentration the surfactant molecules are randomly located at the air-water interface. With increasing concentration, the number of the surfactant molecules on the surface increases. The area accessible to the molecules is limited, so the molecules orient themselves in a certain way. At higher concentrations, the surfactant molecules fully cover the surface.

This particular concentration is called the critical micelle concentration (*CMC*). Once the concentration is greater than the *CMC*, micelles of surfactants can be formed (Figure 4).

In most cases gemini have significantly lower values of *CMC* compared to single-tail analogues (example in Figure 4). They more effectively reduce the surface tension of water and are better soluble in water.

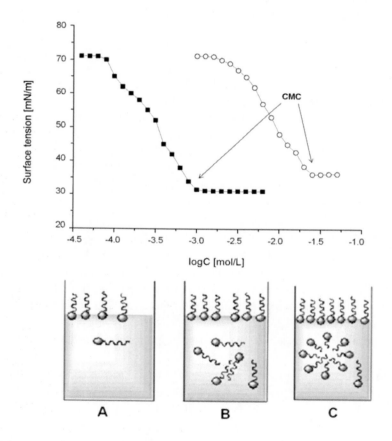

Figure 4. Schematic illustration of the behavior of surfactant molecules in aqueous solution as a function of concentration, (■) gemini surfactant 12-2-12 (○) conventional surfactant DTAB.

Gemini Surfactants in Solution at Concentrations below *CMC*

Adsorption on the Interface

The behavior of gemini surfactants in aqueous solution at concentrations below the *CMC* is dependent on the distance between the neighboring molecules. The surface area *a* occupied by one surfactant molecule at the water-air interface is determined from the correlation of the surface tension *γ* with the surfactant concentration *C*. Equation (1) links the surface excess *Γ* and *a* on the basis of Gibbs law:

$$a = \frac{1}{\Gamma N_A} = \left(\frac{nRT}{N_A}\right)\left(\frac{d\gamma}{d\ln C}\right)^{-1} \tag{1}$$

where *R* is the gas constant, *T* is the absolute temperature, N_A is Avogadro's number, and *n* (called Gibbs prefactor) is a constant that depends on the dissociation degree of the gemini surfactant.

At concentrations below the *CMC*, the geminis can be completely dissociated, giving one doubly-charged ion and two counterions, or, if the dissociation is not complete, there is partial binding between the gemini head and one counterion. The Gibbs prefactor *n* takes a value of 1 for zwitterionic gemini surfactants because they carry no counterions. A value of 2 occurs in the case of non-completely dissociated gemini surfactants; for completely dissociated gemini surfactants, the value is 3. For ionic three-tails surfactants, the value is 4 [70, 78, 79]. The behavior of gemini surfactants at concentrations below the *CMC* depends on the potential for hydrophobic interactions between their two tails. At the air-water interface, the hydrophobic interaction of the tails plays an important role in the adsorption behavior, especially with regards to the increasing length of the hydrophobic spacer. The area per molecule measured from the surface tension for alkyl *m-s-m* gemini surfactants shows a maximum value for 10-12 carbon tails [80] (Figure 5). This effect is explained by the increasing hydrophobicity of the spacer. In the range of *s*<10, the spacer lies at the water-air surface. With increasing length (*s*≥10-12) of the spacer, the spacer group moves to the air side, causing the approach of the head groups, and the surface area of the molecules decreases. In the case of the polyoxyethylene spacers EO_n, with an increasing *n*, *a* slowly increases [81] (Figure 5).

Diamant and Andelman [82] described an experiment-based model to explain the nonmonotonic dependence of gemini surfactants on the specific area per surfactant at the air-water interface. They found that three major factors determine the area occupied by molecules at the water-air interface: the geometrical effect, the interaction among the surfactant tails and the conformational entropy of the spacer.

For nonionic gemini surfactants with an open sugar ring [83], the average thickness of the water-interface layer remains constant at concentrations from *CMC*/30 to *CMC*. The alkyl tails are oriented normal to the surface at a concentration of *CMC*/400, but at the *CMC*, they show an angle of tilt of approximately 35°.

Neutron reflectometry has been used to study the adsorption of two symmetrical cationic (dimethyl ammonium bromides) gemini surfactants with two dodecyl tails and partially fluorinated spacers at the air-water interface [84].

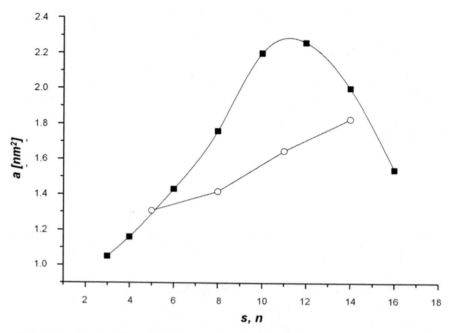

Data from [81] Dreja, M.; Pyckhout-Hintzen, W.; Mays, H.; Tieke, B. Langmuir 1999, 15, 391-399 and
   [80] Alami, E.; Beinert, G.; Marie, P.; Zana, R. Langmuir, 1993, 9, 1465-1467).

Figure 5. Surface area a occupied by one gemini molecule at the air–water interface. Variation with the
spacer carbon number s at 25°C for 12-s-12 surfactants (■) and 12-EO_n-12 (○).

The area per molecule for two fluorocarbon geminis, $C_{12}-C_3fC_6C_3-C_{12}$ and
$C_{12}-C_4fC_4C_4-C_{12}$, had considerably lower values compared to that of $C_{12}-C_{12}-C_{12}$. This
result is explained by the positioning of the fluorocarbon spacers away from the underlying
water and the more efficient packing at the interface compared to the hydrocarbon gemini.

It was reported that adsorption at the air-water interface of anionic [85], cationic [83],
nonionic [86] and a mixture of conventional/gemini surfactants is diffusion controlled.
Geminis with flexible spacers adsorbed faster than gemini surfactants with a rigid spacer. For
cationic gemini surfactants derived from disulfur betaine [87], a very large barrier to
adsorption at the air-water interface was found.

Wegrzynska et al. [88] proposed a model of adsorption of bis- and tris-ammonium salts
assuming the formation of multiple surfactant ion–counterion complexes and their influence
on the interfacial properties.

For conventional surfactants, the addition of electrolyte into a surfactant solution
decreased the surface tension more compared to pure surfactant solution at the same
concentration [89, 90]. This effect can be explained by the formation of a surfactant-
counterion complex, which neutralizes the surface charge and thus lowers the electrostatic
barrier for adsorption at the interface.

Li et al. [91] developed a quantitative model to explain the variations of the Gibbs
prefactor for bis-ammonium salts with different spacer and tail lengths. The area per molecule
increases with the tail length. The longer the tails, the more they interfere with each other and
the less effectively they decrease the surface tension of water.

Ion-Pairing

Ionic gemini surfactants at concentrations below the *CMC* can be completely dissociated or can occur as one double ion and two counterions or with partial binding of one double ion to one counterion. The ion-pairing effects are attributed to the Coulombic interaction between the charged head group of the amphiphiles and counterions. Ion binding increases with the surfactant concentration.

Electrical conductivity is a very accurate parameter for studying ion-pairing in solution [9]. The conductivity plots of 8-3-8 and 8-6-8 geminis show significant deviation from linearity below the *CMC*.

A conductance variation with the surfactant concentrations for the 10-3-10 and 10-8-10 also show a deviation from linearity below the *CMC,* but the deviation is less pronounced than for the 8-*s*-8 surfactants [92] (Figure 6). Ion-pairing has been observed for gemini surfactants with high *CMC* values containing 8 or 10 carbon atoms in the tails as the low concentration break of the function conductance vs. concentration.

Geng et al. [93] studied ion pairing in aqueous solution for the gemini surfactants 12-*s*-12,2Br⁻, where s = 2-4 CH_2 groups. The experiment resulted in the quantitative estimation of the molarities of interfacial bromide (Br_m) and water (H_2O_m), the fraction of free and paired head groups and counterions, and the net head group charge. They found that Br_m increases and H_2O_m decreases as the spacer length decreases and that the two cationic charges are close together. The effect that forces the aggregate morphology is not the balance of free energies between the hydrophobic repulsion but the specific head group counterion pair and ion hydration interaction.

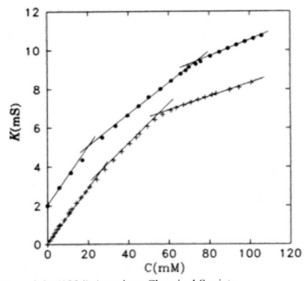

Figure 6. Variation of the electrical conductance with the surfactant concentration for 8-3-8 gemini (+) and 8-6-8 gemini (●) at 25°C. The *CMC* corresponds to the high concentration break.

Premicellar Aggregation

Premicellar aggregation exists for conventional surfactants with tails longer than 14 carbon atoms. Premicellar aggregation occurs when surfactant molecules arrange their hydrophilic groups at opposite sites with their hydrophobic tails oriented towards each other, similar to a small bilayer.

In addition to bringing about a low aggregation number, premicellar aggregation also disrupts the adsorption on the surface. Menger and Littau [94] observed premicellar association in a solution of anionic and cationic gemini surfactants. The premicellar structure of geminis is shown in Figure 7.

Song and Rosen [95] studied cationic gemini surfactants of various chemical characters. For shorter homologues, a regular increase in the surface activity with increasing spacer length was observed, but the surfactants with spacers longer than 16 carbon atoms showed anomalous behavior related to the formation of premicellar structures.

Hadgiivanova et al. [96, 97] developed a thermodynamic model of the mechanism of premicellar aggregation. They found that the more hydrophobic the surfactant is, the wider the range of stability of the premicellar structures.

Tiwari et al. [98] studied the premicellar aggregation of gemini surfactants with hydroxyl groups in the spacer using steady-state fluorescence spectroscopy. The occurrence of premicellar aggregation for these surfactants with 12 carbon atoms in the tail and with a short spacer substituted with a hydroxyl group is attributed to the induced intermolecular hydrogen bonding. The premicellar aggregates transform into micelles with increasing surfactant concentrations.

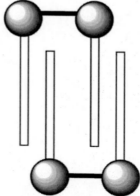

Adapted with permission from Song et al. [95]. Copyright (1996) American Chemical Society.

Figure 7. Schematic representation of a premicellar structure of gemini surfactants.

Gemini Surfactants in Solution at and above the *CMC*

The *CMC* is the concentration above which surfactant molecules assemble into organized structures - micelles. At the *CMC*, the physical properties of the surfactant aqueous solution, such as the surface tension, molar conductivity, osmotic pressure, turbidity and solubilization ability, rapidly changes (Figure 8).

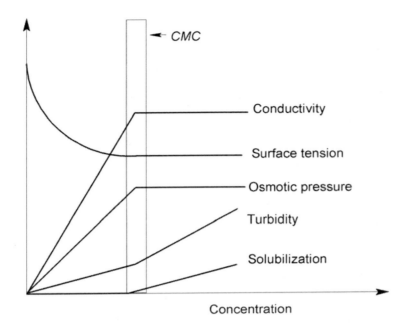

Figure 8. Physical properties of surfactants as a function of concentration.

Micelle Structures and Sizes

The *CMC* does not provide information about size and shape of formed micelles. In contrast to single-chain surfactants the sizes of aggregated structures of gemini surfactants significantly vary with concentration. Micelles of conventional surfactants have aggregation numbers (N_{agg} - number of molecules per micelle) less than 100. Their sizes vary only slightly with the surfactant concentration.

The most complete sets of aggregation numbers as a function of the concentration were obtained for several 10-*s*-10 [99, 100] and 12-*s*-12 [92, 101] gemini surfactants. In all cases, N_{agg} depended significantly on the concentration. For 10-*s*-10, the N_{agg} increases linearly with increasing surfactant concentration. For 12-*s*-12, the values of N_{agg} at the *CMC* for all surfactants are between 25 and 30, which corresponds to 50-60 dodecyl tails per micelle. Therefore, at concentrations near the *CMC*, the micelles of 12-*s*-12 surfactants are spherical or nearly spherical.

The same is observed for micelles of the 10-*s*-10 series. With increasing concentration above the *CMC*, the N_{agg} increases, which is indicated as growth of the micelles. The micelle growth for the 12-*s*-12 series was more rapid than for the 10-*s*-10 gemini surfactants.

Bernheim-Groswasser et al. [102] studied the micellar growth of the 12-2-12 gemini surfactants in aqueous solution using a cryo-TEM technique. The cryo-TEM images showed mainly spheroidal micelles at very low concentration (0.26 wt %). As the concentration increased, elongated micelles appeared.

At higher concentrations, the micelles branched (Figure 9). Quaternary ammonium surfactants with long spacers, 12-16-12 and 12-20-12, formed vesicles at higher concentrations. The sequence of the structures was as follows: elongated micelles → spheroidal micelles → vesicles.

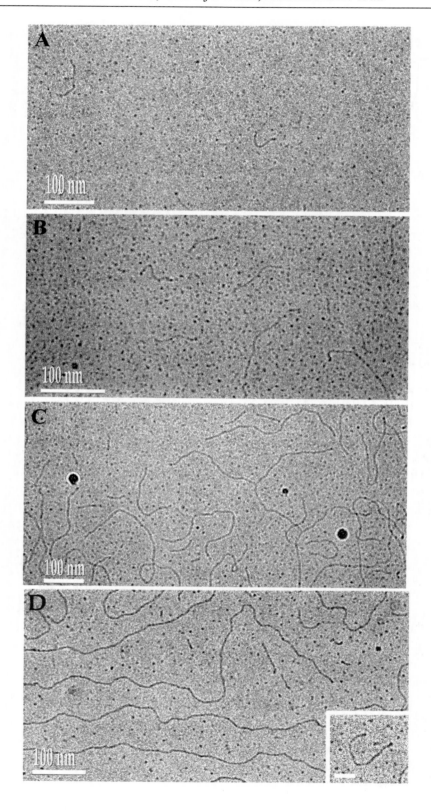

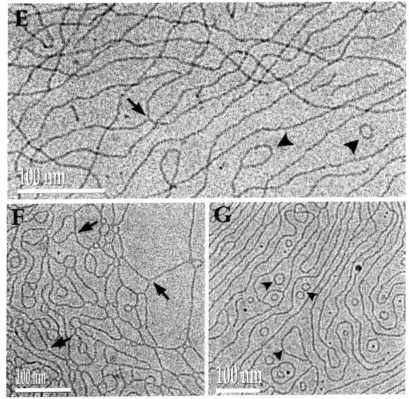

Figure 9. Cryo-TEM images of 12-2-12 solutions at 25 °C:☐ (A) at 0.26 wt % (B) at 0.50 wt %, (C) at 0.62 wt %, 12-2-12 and (D) at 0.74 wt % (E) at 1 wt % 12-2-12, (F) at 1.5 wt %, (G) at 1.5 wt %, vesicles are detected.

Lu et al. [103] reported an important role of a short hydrocarbon part at the head group on the aggregation microstructure of the cationic gemini surfactants. The aggregation behavior of the 12-s-12 gemini surfactant with a diethyl tail at the quaternary ammonium group (C_{12}-C_s-C_{12}(Et)) was compared to the C_{12}-C_s-C_{12}(Me) with a dimethyl group.

Compared with the C_{12}-C_s-C_{12}(Me) series ($s = 4$, 6, 8, 10, 12), for which the TEM micrographs showed only densely packed spherical micelles, vesicles or elongated micelles could be observed in case of C_{11}-C_s-C_{12} (Figure 10).

In et al. [104] measured the aggregation numbers of 12-s-12 gemini surfactants and three-tailed surfactants referred to as 12-s-12-s-12,3Br⁻ at various temperatures. Increased temperature caused repulsion between the micelles, and smaller aggregates were observed.

Zhu et al. [105] determined the aggregation numbers of anionic gemini surfactants based on nonylphenol with alkyl spacers. The aggregation numbers increased with increasing spacer length.

These results are explained by the high flexibility of the spacer, which reduced the Coulombic repulsion between the head groups and allowed the molecule to arrange into larger structures. The aggregation number increased with the surfactant concentration and then decreased, which is explained by the formation of the liquid crystal phase (Figure 11).

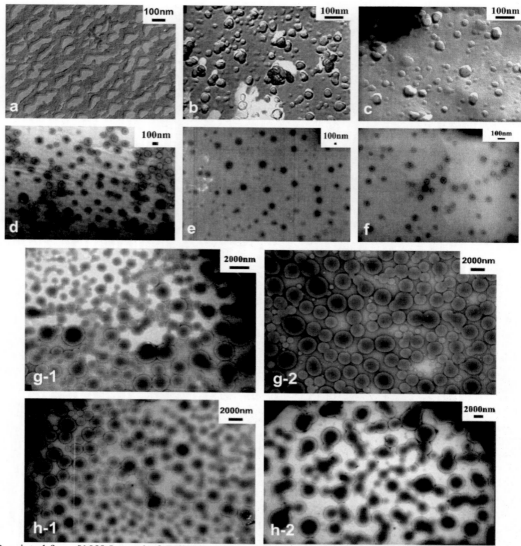

Figure 10. TEM micrographs of the aqueous solutions of $C_{12}C_sC_{12}$ (Et): (a) 20 mmol/L $C_{12}C_sC_{12}$ (Et); (b–f) 10 mmol/L $C_{12}C_sC_{12}$(Et) s = 4, 6, 8, 10, 12; (g–1) 1 mmol/L $C_{12}C_{16}C_{12}$ (Et); (g-2) 10 mmol/L $C_{12}C_{16}C_{12}$ (Et); (h-1) 1 mmol/L $C_{12}C_{20}C_{12}$ (Et); (h-2) 5 mmol/L $C_{12}C_{20}C_{12}$ (Et).

The aggregation numbers of anionic gemini surfactants with nonylphenol tails and alkyl and alkoxylated groups as spacers were studied by Cao et al. [106]. N_{agg} increased with the concentration for all surfactants. For surfactants with an alkyl spacer, the increase in N_{agg} with concentration is relatively small compared to the gemini surfactants with alkoxylated spacer groups. The authors agreed with the theory of Zhu et al. [105] that higher spacer flexibility reduces the repulsion between the head groups and forces the formation of larger aggregates than in the case of the conventional surfactants.

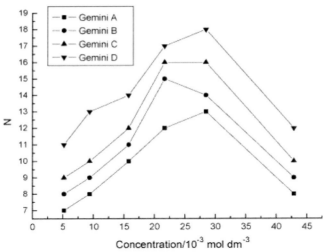

Reprinted from [105] Colloids and Surfaces A: Physicochemical and Engineering Aspects 281, S. Zhu et al., "Anionic Gemini surfactants: Synthesis and aggregation properties in aqueous solutions", p. 35-39, Copyright (2006) with permission of Elsevier.

Figure 11. Plots of the aggregation numbers versus the concentrations of gemini surfactants ($N=N_{agg}$); Gemini A, $s = 2$; Gemini B; $s = 3$, Gemini C, $s = 4$; Gemini D, $s = 6$.

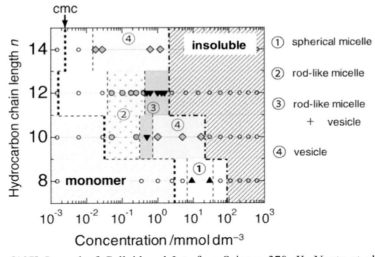

Reprinted from [107] Journal of Colloid and Interface Science 370, K. Nyuta et al., "Zwitterionic heterogemini surfactants containing ammonium and carboxylate headgroups 2: Aggregation behavior studied by SANS, DLS, and cryo-TEM", p. 80-85, Copyright (2012) with permission of Elsevier.

Figure 12. Phase diagram of the aggregates formed by heterogemini surfactants with ammonium and carboxylate head groups in aqueous solution.

Nyuta et al. [107] studied the aggregation behavior of zwitterionic heterogemini surfactants with ammonium and carboxylate head groups in aqueous solutions. They found that the aggregation behavior strongly depends on the tail length and the surfactant concentration.

This class of gemini surfactants exhibits unique aggregation behavior, such as the formation of spherical micelles → rod-like micelles → rod-like micelles and coexistent vesicles → vesicles, with increasing hydrocarbon chain lengths and surfactant concentrations (Figure 12).

Kinetics of Micellization

At the *CMC*, the surfactants molecules form micelles that are in dynamic equilibrium with individual molecules in the bulk solvent [108-110]. The kinetics of micellization have been studied by temperature-jump [111], pressure-jump [112], ultrasonic absorption [92, 113], and self-diffusion NMR [114-116].

There are two relaxation processes that occur during micellar disruption. The first is the fast relaxation process (τ_1), which can be measured on the microsecond time scale. It is associated with the fast exchange of monomers between the micelles and the surrounding bulk phase (Figure 13A). The second process is the long relaxation time process (τ_2), which is on the order of milliseconds and is attributed to complete micelle formation and dissolution, as shown in Figure 13B. For conventional surfactants, the rate constant k^- and k^+ are related to diffusion-controlled exit and entry of the surfactant molecules from and to the micelles, respectively.

The lifetime of micelles has a significant influence on technological processes involving rapid modifications at the interface area, such as foaming, wetting, emulsification, solubilization, and detergency. The exchange kinetics in micellar systems consisting of gemini surfactants were studied by Ulbricht and Zana [112]. They demonstrated that gemini surfactants with a short spacer showed micellization kinetics that were similar to those of conventional surfactants.

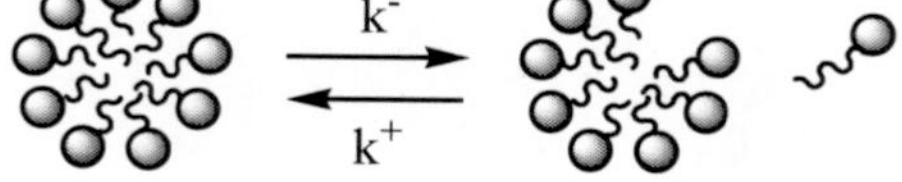

A: fast relaxation process

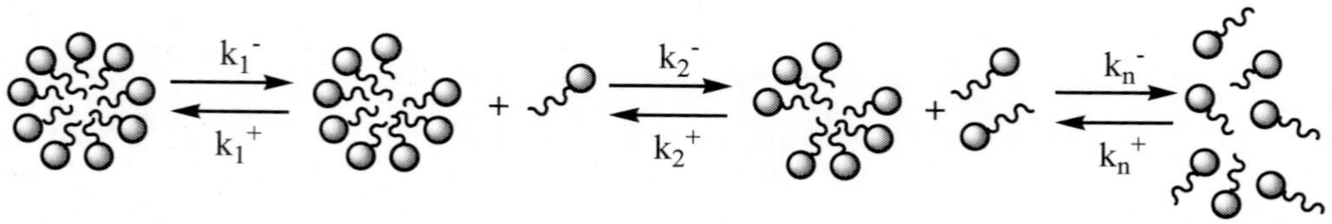

B: long relaxation process

With kind permission from Springer Sciences + Business Media: Journal of Surfactants and Detergents, Importance of Micellar Relaxation Time on Detergent Properties, 2,1999, 317-324, Patist, A.; Jha, B.K.; Oh, S.G.; Shah, D.O, Figure 2.

Figure 13. Mechanism of the fast (A) and the slow (B) micelle relaxation processes for conventional surfactants.

However, fast relaxation times (τ_1) are approximately 10^3 times longer for geminis. This behavior could be induced by the short spacer, which causes steric hindrance and forces the symmetrical molecule to adopt a conformation in which the two alkyl chains are in a position *trans* to each other. With increased spacer length, the steric hindrance and the relaxation time τ_1 decrease.

The slow relaxation time (τ_2) kinetics of gemini surfactants was studied by Groth et al. [115] using a stopped-flow method employing alkanediyl-α,ω-bis(dodecyldimethyl-ammonium bromides) (*m-s-m, s* = 2-4). They showed that the equilibrium time for gemini surfactants is much longer than for conventional surfactants and that the equilibrium time increases with decreasing spacer length. The micelle lifetime was determined to be on the order of tens of seconds and decreased with increasing spacer length. The results are explained by the steric hindrance of an individual chain in the molecule, as well as the molecular packing within the micelle. Gemini surfactants with a short spacer groups, *s* = 2, are able to pack more tightly in the micelle and in the monolayer than those with longer spacers, *s* = 4.

The long relaxation time of gemini surfactants in a micelle is related to the distribution of the distances between the heads d_T (Figure 14). In conventional surfactants, the molecules are randomly distributed on the micelle surfaces separating the aqueous phase. Surfactant molecules are placed in the micellar hydrophobic core with a distance d_T between their heads, which is determined thermodynamically (Figure 14A). In the case of a gemini surfactant, the distance between the head groups of neighbor molecules is not expected to differ significantly from the value for conventional surfactants. The second distance, d_s, is the distance between the head groups of the same molecule, which is determined by the spacer length (Figure 14B).

The distribution of gemini surfactants in a micelle depends on the spacer size. Short spacers lead to the preferred *trans* or *gauche* orientations of the two alkyl chains because for *s*<4, the spacer length is smaller than the diameter of the alkyl tail. The *cis* position of the alkyl tail becomes possible for *s* greater than 4.

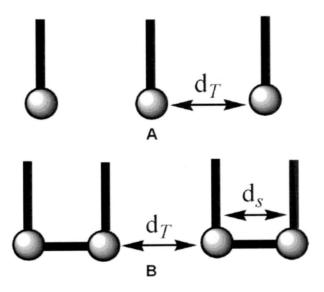

Figure 14. Schematic representation of the distance distributions between the head groups: A) conventional surfactants, B) gemini surfactants.

With increased spacer length, the effect of steric hindrance decreases. With smaller steric hindrance, the formation of micelles requires a lower concentration, so the CMC values decrease. A further aspect of the behavior at the CMC is connected to the flexibility of the hydrocarbon spacer. In gemini surfactants with short spacers $s<4$, the spacer group is straight and rigid, which forces the hydrocarbon groups toward repulsive contact with water. With an increase of the spacer length, it becomes more flexible, and the whole group is able to penetrate into the micellar hydrophobic core.

Thermodynamics of the Micellization of Gemini Surfactants

The free energy of micellization $\Delta G°_M$ of a surfactant is usually obtained from the CMC value (equation 2).

$$\Delta G_M^o = RT \ln CMC \tag{2}$$

The value of $\Delta G°_M$ of cationic gemini surfactants can be calculated from equation 3.

$$\Delta G°_M \approx 2RT(1.5 - \alpha) \ln CMC \tag{3}$$

where α is the micelle ionization degree [117].

The thermodynamics of the micellization of 12-s-12 and 16-s-16 surfactants have been studied using the same set of CMC but a different set of α values [118, 119]. The α values thus obtained are more reliable that those obtained by the first methods. The value ($-\Delta G°_M$) for the 12-s-12 series varies relatively little with the spacer length. The much lower CMC value of the 16-s-16 surfactants results in a significantly more negative value of ($-\Delta G°_M$) than for the 12-s-12 surfactant series. The free energy of micellization $\Delta G°_M$ was measured for a series of gemini surfactants of m-EO$_n$-m (m = 8, 10, 12, 14 and 16 and n = 1, 2, 3) [120] The ($-\Delta G°_M$) barely changed in the series with the same spacer length, but a small increase of the ($-\Delta G°_M$) is observed with increasing tail length.

In a system where premicellization occurs, the CMC value increases, resulting in a less negative value of ($-\Delta G°_M$). When premicellization occurs, some of the water – alkyl tail contacts are eliminated and do not contribute to the free energy of micellization.

Enthalpies of micellization ($\Delta H°_M$) can be obtained from the temperature dependence of the CMC (equation 4) [121]:

$$\Delta H_M^o = R \frac{d(\ln CMC)}{d\left(\frac{1}{T}\right)} \tag{4}$$

Calorimetric measurements are an accurate and rapid technique for investigating the enthalpy of micellization. Grosmaire et al. [122] studied the effect of the spacer carbon number and temperature on the enthalpy of micellization. The ($\Delta H°_M$) value was in all cases negative and became more negative when the temperature increased. The ($\Delta H°_M$) value was strongly dependent on the spacer length.

The entropy of micellization ($\Delta S°_M$) can be obtained from equation 5.

$$\Delta S_M^o = \Delta H_M^o - \frac{\Delta G_M^o}{T}$$

(5)

The entropy of micellization becomes more negative with increasing temperature. Grosmaire investigated the (ΔS°_M) obtained from the (ΔH°_M) and (ΔG°_M) data. The results showed that in all cases $T\Delta S^\circ_M > - \Delta H^\circ_M$.

The thermodynamic properties of micellization of sulfobetaine-type zwitterionic gemini surfactants in aqueous solution were investigated by Liu et al. [123]. They found that micellization is a spontaneous and entropy-driven process.

Effect of the Molecular Structure on the Aggregation of Gemini Surfactants in Aqueous Solution

The nature, length, and structure of a spacer, and the head group effect are the most important factors determining the aggregation of gemini surfactants in aqueous solution [114, 124]

Effect of the Spacer
The chemical structure and nature of the spacer gives gemini surfactants unique properties. The spacer shields the hydrophobic core of the micelles from contact with water, limits the distance between the head groups and controls the charge distribution. A long hydrophobic spacer can be immersed into the micellar core and increase the hydrophobic interactions [125].

Manipulation of the spacer, such as increasing or decreasing its length, or the introduction of new functional groups causes modification either in the hydrophobic/ hydrophilic balance of the surfactants or in the electrostatic interaction between two head groups.

For gemini surfactants (*m-s-m* structures) with alkyl spacers, the *CMC* increases for shorter spacers and reaches a maximum value for 4-5 carbon atoms. The *CMC* then decreases, first nonlinearly in the range of $5<s<10$ and then linearly for spacers longer than 10 methylene groups [9]. In the case of a short spacer, the electrostatic repulsion between the heads and the relatively inflexible spacer hinders the aggregation process. With increasing spacer length, micelle formation is more favorable.

Danino et al. [101], using a cryo-TEM technique, found that gemini surfactants with short spacers, 12-2-12, formed giant threadlike micelles, whereas gemini surfactants with spacers of $s>6$ self-assembled into small spherical or spheroidal micelles. Borse et al. [126, 127], using small-angle neutron-scattering (SANS), investigated the aggregation number and micelle dimensions of bis-quaternary ammonium salts with $s = 4, 6, 8, 10$. They observed a decrease in the aggregation number when the spacer length increased from 4 to 6. For longer spacers, only a small variation in the aggregation number was observed. They attributed this behavior to conformational changes in the spacer at the water-micelle interface. For compounds with alkyl spacers of $s<6$ methylene groups, the spacer remains in the extended form in the micelle. When the spacer is longer than 6 methylene units, it immerses towards the hydrophobic core of the micelles.

Bergstrom and Garamus [128] determined the geometrical shape of cationic gemini ammonium salts of different spacer lengths using the SANS method. They observed that gemini surfactants with a short spacer (12-3-12 and 12-4-12) formed elongated ellipsoidal micelles; gemini with longer spacers $6<s<12$ assembled into spherical particles. Generally, for gemini surfactants with rigid spacers, with an increasing length of the spacer, the micelle size decreases.

Pisarcik et al. [129] investigated the area per surfactant molecule at the liquid/ hydrophobic solid and the liquid/air interface as a function of the spacer length for bis-quaternary ammonium salts 12-s-12, where $s = 2, 4, 6, 8, 10, 12$. The area per surfactant molecule at the liquid/air interface increased with increasing spacer length up to $s = 6$-8 and was approximately constant for $s>8$. This result was explained by the prone position of the short spacer at the interface, which with extension by each -CH_2- group in the spacer, caused an increase in the area per surfactant molecule. When $s \leq 8$, the spacer becomes more flexible, and the increased hydrophobicity directs the spacer towards the air phase, which results in a decrease of the area per surfactant molecule. The authors described a correlation between the area per surfactant molecule at the interface with the micellar growth. The aggregation number for surfactants with $s = 8$-10 did not increase with the concentration. The 12-8-12 gemini surfactants formed only spherical and spheroidal micelles, even at very high concentrations.

Pei et al. [130] compared the aggregation properties of gemini surfactants with and without a hydroxyl group in the alkyl spacer. They found that intermolecular hydrogen bonding strongly promoted micellar growth. Gemini surfactants with a hydroxyl group in the spacer formed longer wormlike micelles.

The behavior of gemini surfactants with an oligo(oxyethylene) spacer was investigated by Dreja et al. [81] using SANS. They observed that the aggregation number of micelles decreased with increasing spacer length. One or two oxyethylene groups in the spacer led to an elongated ellipsoidal shape, whereas compounds with three or four oxyethylene groups formed spherical micelles. The effect increased with increasing surfactant concentrations.

The surface area per molecule was investigated by Zhang et al. [131] for two gemini surfactants with different spacer rigidities. The spacer in the first case contained two ester groups and, in the second case, there was a double bond between the two ester groups. The sizes of the aggregates were determined by dynamic light scattering. The flexible spacer of the gemini surfactants with two ester groups adsorbed at the water/air interface changed the conformation and looped into the air. This effect caused the approach of the cationic groups, resulting in a smaller area per molecule for the gemini surfactants with a double bond between the two ester groups. Gemini surfactants with two flexible ester groups in the spacer formed spherical micelles whose size increased with the concentration in solution. Surfactants with a rigid spacer between the ester group formed micelles at low concentrations, which transformed into vesicles at increased concentrations. The various micelle distribution was connected with the different spacer rigidities.

The effect of the spacer on the aggregation process of three structures of gemini surfactants, with the same quaternary ammonium heads and alkyl tail lengths but different chemical natures of the spacer, was investigated by Wang et al. [132]. The lowest *CMC* value and the highest micelle aggregation number were found for a diethyl ether spacer. The easier micellization process was explained by the formation of hydrogen bonds between the oxygen atom in the spacer and water.

Gemini surfactants with flexible hydrocarbon spacers showed intermediate values of *CMC* and micelle aggregation number. The highest value of *CMC* and aggregation number occurred for the gemini surfactants with a rigid xylyl spacer, which was explained by the steric hindrance that perturbs the incorporation of the compound into micelles.

Effect of the Tail

The alkyl tails play a key role in the determination of the hydrophobic/hydrophilic interaction and micellization. Gemini surfactants can contain two identical tails (symmetric geminis), or two tails of different lengths or chemical natures (dissymmetric geminis).

Zana et al. [9] investigated symmetrical gemini surfactants with $m = 12$ and 16 hydrocarbon units in the alkyl tail. The *CMC* values for 16-*s*-16 geminis are one order of magnitude lower than for 12-*s*-12. They found that, within this range of tail length, the alkyl chain did not influence the internal organization of the micelle [8].

Li et al. [133] studied the process of micellization for a series of *m*-6-*m* gemini surfactants, where $m = 7, 8, 9, 10, 11, 12$ and 16. The log *CMC* decreased linearly with the increasing alkyl tail length (Figure 15), which was explained by the increasing hydrophobicity of the surfactant molecules. Micellization was accompanied by various endothermic to exothermic values.

Considerable attention has been focused on dissymmetrical gemini surfactants. Fan et al. [134] studied the micellization process of dissymmetrical cationic *m*-6-6 gemini surfactants where $m = 12, 14$, and 16. The *CMC* values decreased with increasing m. For all compounds, (ΔH_M) was exothermic and increased with increasing m. The electrostatic repulsion between the two different alkyl tails was relatively weak.

Oda et al. [135] studied the properties of cationic gemini surfactants possessing one or two perfluoroalkyl tails.

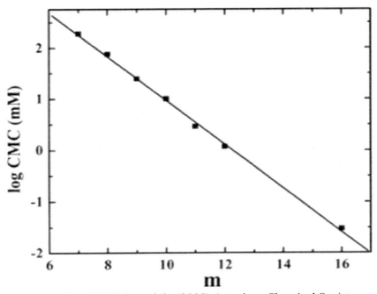

Reprinted with permission from [133] Copyright (2005) American Chemical Society.

Figure 15. Variation of the log *CMC* with the number of carbon atoms in the alkyl tail or $C_mC_6C_mBr_2$ at 303.15 K.

The *CMC* of the fluorinated gemini surfactants was almost 2 orders of magnitude lower than for hydrocarbon compounds. The fluorinated gemini surfactants assembled in various structures, including stable lamellar vesicles.

Yoshimura et al. [75] studied sulfobetaine-type zwitterionic gemini surfactants with hydrocarbon tails with $m = 6$, 8, and 10. Despite the poor water solubility of this class of compounds, the surfactants had low *CMC* values. Due to the steric hindrance with increasing tail length, the zwitterionic gemini surfactants formed small micelles.

Zwitterionic gemini surfactants with dihydroxy sulfate betaine were studied by Geng et al. [74]. Elongation of the tail from dodecyl to tetradecyl led to the formation of surfactant aggregates with different shapes, from vesicles to elongated fiber-like micelles.

Du et al. [45] synthesized a series of alkylbenzene sulfonate geminis. The *CMC* values increased with increasing tail length. The *CMC* value for the surfactant with a dodecyl tail and four methylene units in the spacer was two orders of magnitude lower than the *CMC* value of corresponding 12-4-12 bis-quaternary ammonium surfactants. The surface area per molecule for the alkylbenzene sulfonate decreased slightly with tail length.

Chen et al. [29] investigated a series of carboxylate gemini surfactants that contained two hydrocarbon tails linked by an amide, two carboxylate groups and a flexible alkyl spacer. The *CMC* values for the carboxylated gemini surfactants were lower compared to the corresponding quaternary ammonium surfactants. The carboxylated gemini surfactants formed compact micelles.

FitzGerald et al. [136] synthesized nonionic gemini surfactants, varying in the length of the ethoxy chains, linked by a flexible alkyl spacer. The tail length strongly influenced the shape of the surfactant aggregates. Gemini with longer ethoxy chains formed spherical micelles, whereas surfactants with shorter ethoxy tails assembled in rods and vesicles.

Effect of the Head Group

Gemini surfactants contain either two identical or two different head groups. In the first case, the gemini surfactants are called homogemini; the asymmetrical gemini surfactants are called heterogemini.

Borse et al. [126, 127] studied the influence of the head group on the aggregation properties of bis-quaternary ammonium salts. The quaternary nitrogen atom was substituted by two methyl groups, one methyl and one hydroxyethyl group and two hydroxyethyl groups. The increasing polarity of the head group caused a significant decrease in the *CMC* values. The hydroxylation of the head group led to Coulombic repulsion between the charged heads and facilitated the aggregation. The increased head group polarity of the cationic gemini favored micellar growth.

Seredyuk et al. [137] investigated the aggregation properties of asymmetrical zwitterionic surfactants with two hydrophilic and two hydrophobic groups. One hydrophilic group was a phosphodiester anion, and the other was a quaternary ammonium salt. The heads were connected by an alkyl spacer. The more symmetrical gemini surfactants gave very low values of surface area per molecule on the hydrophobic surface, indicating a very tight packing of the surfactant molecules. The zwitterionic geminis showed a strong tendency to self-assemble at very low concentrations. Menger and Peresypin [138] studied the self-assembly of ten asymmetric gemini surfactants with the general structure:□long-chain/phosphate/2-carbon spacer/quaternary nitrogen/short-chain. The asymmetrical gemini surfactants self-assembled into vesicles, which, in turn, self-assembled into gels.

The influence of counterions on the aggregation process was studied by Jiang et al. [139]. They investigated the micellization of 12-6-12,2X cationic gemini surfactants with various counterions ($X = $ F$^-$, Cl$^-$, Br$^-$, Ac$^-$, NO$_3^-$ and ½ SO$_4^{2-}$) in aqueous solution. The nature of the counterion significantly influenced the aggregation process.

This result is related to the different hydration situations. A decreasing hydrated radius of the anion is accompanied by an increasing polarizability. This resulted in enhancement of the binding of the counterion at the micellar surface and a decrease of the electrostatic repulsion between the head groups of the surfactant molecules.

METHODS FOR THE INVESTIGATION OF THE MICELLIZATION OF GEMINI SURFACTANTS IN AQUEOUS SOLUTIONS

The self-organization of gemini surfactants into micelles in aqueous solution is of primary importance for their function and application. The methods used to follow this process are not different from those applied for other self-organizing colloidal systems, namely spectroscopic, tensiometric, microscopic, and electrical conductivity measurements. In general, the self-organization influences many macroscopic properties of the solution. Most of the macroscopic properties change abruptly after reaching the *CMC* of the surfactant. Many of the methods used to follow the gemini surfactant micellization processes have been comprehensively described by Zana [140]. Here, they will only be discussed briefly.

Electrical Conductivity

The number and mobility of charge carriers change abruptly when the ionic surfactants aggregate into micelles; therefore, the conductivity measurements of the gemini surfactant solutions in various concentrations are useful for determining the *CMC*. The effect of different conductivity values below and above the *CMC* is related to the different ionization degrees α of non-aggregated surfactant molecules and micelles.

The *CMC* is taken as the intersection of the linear parts of the plots of conductivity versus surfactant concentration [141-145]. The micelle ionization degree α can be obtained as the ratio of the slopes of the plots of the specific conductivity versus surfactant concentration above and below the obtained *CMC* [141, 142].

Tensiometry

The surface tension of water decreases with the addition of surfactant until the aggregation process begins, after which the surface tension remains constant. This principle is also true for gemini surfactant solutions, and surface tension measurements are the most commonly applied technique to determine *CMC* values [143-153]. The *CMC* is taken as the breakpoint in the plot of the surface tension versus the logarithm of surfactant concentration.

When there is more than one breakpoint in the plot, the breakpoints at lower concentrations are considered to be the effects of premicellar aggregation. The behavior of the surfactants in solution and at the water-air interface is described in detail in the previous part of this chapter.

Scattering Methods

When a radiation beam hits a particle, the radiation is scattered in coherent and non-coherent ways. The way in which the radiation is scattered depends on the size of the particles, their shape, mobility and to some extent, their chemical structure. For studying self-organization, in most cases, neutrons and light are scattered. The fundamentals of the scattering methods are described in [154, 155]

In the case of gemini self-assembly, small-angle neutron scattering (SANS) is applied to determine the micelle diameter [136], micelle shape [143], and microstructure of the aggregates in the solution. Dynamic light scattering (DLS) enables the determination of the hydrodynamic radii (R_h) [150] and dispersity of a colloidal system. It also provides the size distribution of the surfactant aggregates [156, 157]. Static light scattering (SLS) may deliver information about the molar mass of the micelles formed, their sizes, radius of gyration R_g, and shape of the micelles from the R_g/R_h ratio. The aggregation number can also be determined for gemini micelles.

Spectroscopic Methods

The fluorescence emission spectra of pyrene [55, 158] or Nile Red [157] as a fluorescent probe are useful in determining the aggregation numbers (N_{agg}) of gemini surfactants in solution [103, 143, 157, 159, 160], in evaluating the size and dispersity of micelles [161] and in determining the CMC [55, 157]. At the CMC, the pyrene probe starts to be surrounded by surfactant tails forming the micellar core, and a break in the plot of the fluorescence intensity ratio I_1/I_3 (the first and the third vibrational bands in the emission spectra of the probe) versus the surfactant concentration is observed using a simple spectrofluorimeter.

For the determination of N_{agg}, two fluorescence techniques are used: time-resolved fluorescence quenching (TRFQ) and steady-state fluorescence quenching (SSFQ). The fundamental rules are described in [162].

In these methods, probe molecules (for example pyrene) are solubilized in micelles, and their emission is measured before and after the addition of a second species, a quencher. It is assumed that the presence of the single quencher molecule in the micelle will deactivate all probe molecules in that micelle. N_{agg} can be obtained from the fluorescence intensities in the absence, I_0, and in the presence of a quencher, I.

In the case of solubilization studies, UV/VIS absorption spectra are useful in determining the concentration of the solubilized/dispersed substance in the surfactant micellar solution [143, 156, 163, 164] and in helping to investigate the microenvironment of the solubilized substance to determine the solubilization site [156, 165]. The observation of the spectra over time provides information to help evaluate the stability of the system [166].

Visualization Methods

Microscopy provides visual images of the particles. In transmission electron microscopy, the image is formed from the interaction of electrons transmitted through the specimens. To avoid possible distortion of particle size and number due to the evaporation of water, cryo-TEM is used. This technique uses a special method of shock-freezing called vitrification, in which the water is displaced by sublimation, minimizing possible changes [167, 168]. TEM provides direct visualization of the micelles and their structure in surfactant solution, as well as for gemini surfactant solutions [103, 169] and their nanoparticle dispersions [151].

THE INFLUENCE OF ADDITIVES ON THE MICELLIZATION OF GEMINI SURFACTANTS IN AQUEOUS SOLUTION

In most applications, surfactants are mixed with different additives (such as salts, alcohols, and amines) to improve surfactant performance. In the case of single tail ionic surfactants the additives exert a strong influence on the *CMC, N_{agg}*, and the size and shape of the aggregates of ionic surfactant systems [170-175].

The effect of the nature of the salt on the physicochemical properties of amphiphiles was first observed by Hofmeister [176]. The Hofmeister series [177] was defined and is commonly used in surfactant science. The place of the ion in this series depends on the ion capability to interact with water molecules and to disturb the hydrogen-bonded structure of bulk water. Generally, ions in the Hofmeister series have been classified according to their effectiveness as either salting-in or salting-out agents.

An example of the ordering of some of the cations and anions taken from the Hofmeister series are shown in Figure 16. The species to the left of Cl⁻ are called kosmotropes, whereas those to its right are referred to as chaotropes.

The strongly hydrated kosmotropes, ('water structure makers') cause salting-out effects on proteins and macromolecules. Chaotropes ('water structure breakers') destabilize proteins and cause salting-in behavior. The addition of ions to the solution determines structural changes in a water network. In water, chaotropic/hydrophobic counterions are bound more strongly to the micellar surface than kosmotropic/hydrophilic counterions.

Hofmeister series

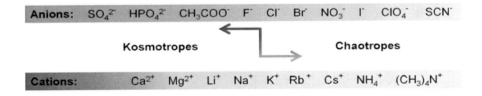

Figure 16. The Hofmeister series.

Chaotropic ions are also more effective in promoting the micellar growth of ionic single-tail surfactants. Generally, higher values of *CMC* for water/surfactant/additive system are observed with increasing hydrophilicity or decreasing hydrophobicity of added ions [93, 178]. The size and nature of counterions affect the shape of micelles. Usually, for single-chain surfactants, spherical micelles are formed in the presence of halide ions. The addition of other inorganic salts may lead to the changes of micelle shape from globular to rod-like or worm-like [179]. Aromatic ions often cause the formation of worm-like micelles at relatively low surfactant and ion concentrations.

Reports on mixtures of ionic gemini surfactants and counterions have been rare. Studies of gemini surfactants in the presence of different classes of additives is a new area of research in surfactant science.

Wattebled and Laschewsky [180] described the effect of adding sodium salts with various organic anions to a series of cationic gemini surfactants with dodecyl tails and different spacer groups. The stoichiometric addition of the organic salts to the gemini surfactants resulted either in clear solutions or in phase separation/precipitation, depending on the detailed nature of the added counterions and on the spacer group of the gemini surfactant. Clear aqueous solutions were obtained for gemini/salt mixtures based on benzoate and benzene dicarboxylates counterions and their derivatives. However, the addition of more hydrophobic counteranions (tosylate, sulfonate) induced turbidity in the surfactant solution followed by precipitation. The geminis with long, flexible and polar spacers were less prone to precipitation in the presence of aromatic salts. Moreover, aromatic anions induced synergistic effects in the gemini micellization, strongly reducing the *CMCs*.

The micellization of the cationic gemini surfactant ethanediylbis (dimethyltetra-decylammonium) 14-2-14 was investigated in the presence of inorganic and organic salts: (1) small and inorganic counterions taken from the Hofmeister series (halide ions, nitrate, acetate, etc.), (2) aliphatic carboxylate counterions, (3) aromatic carboxylate counterions with different positions of substitutions, and (4) other counterions that do not belong to the first three groups (orphan) [181]. It was observed that the higher the hydrophilicity of a counterion, the more unfavorable its effect on micellization, leading to high *CMCs*. The study demonstrated the importance of the hydration of the counterion and the resulting entropy variation during aggregation due to dehydration. For halide anions, the hydration number was directly related to the hydrophilicity; the more hydrophilic the anions, the lower the polarizability and the higher the hydration number. The investigation of aromatic carboxylate anions and orphan anions revealed that the presence of a hydrophobic aromatic ring as well as the replacement of a hydrocarbon by a fluorocarbon resulted in a decrease of the *CMCs*. In the case of benzoates with a different number and position of hydroxyl groups, the *CMC* depended on resonance stabilization of the negative charge and on steric hindrance. When the hydroxyl group was placed in the *ortho* position to the carboxylate of the aromatic anion, micellization was stabilized, whereas if it was in *para* position, its localization inside the apolar core of the micelles caused its destabilization. The authors concluded that ion pairing cannot be accurately described using one single parameter. The opposing effects (e.g., ion hydration, ion polarizability, intramolecular hydrogen bonding, and steric hindrance) all affect the entropy gain upon micellization and the tendency of the counterions to form ion pairs with the surfactant head groups. Two ions with similar hydrophilicity but with different polarizability and/or with different structures may lead to very different *CMCs*.

The group of Huang has studied the effect of the hydrotropic salt sodium salicylate (NaSal) on the micellization of the cationic gemini surfactant dimethylene-1,2-bis(dodecyl-diethylammonium bromide) (12-2-12(Et)) [182]. In a pure surfactant solution, elongated micelles with a diameter of 20–30 nm were observed by freeze-fracture transmission electron microscopy (FF-TEM). DLS measurements indicated that the elongated micelles coexisted with the spherical micelles, which were the predominant form.

The addition of NaSal to the gemini surfactant solution induced micelle growth and the transformation of spherical micelles into elongated micelles and vesicles (Figure 17) with increasing molar ratios of NaSal to surfactant (R): spherical/elongated micelles ($R = 0$, Figure 17a) $\rightarrow$ longer elongated micelles ($R = 0.3$, Figure 17b) $\rightarrow$ overlapping micelles ($R = 0.5$, Figure 17c) $\rightarrow$ three-dimensional network ($R = 0.75$, Figure 17d) $\rightarrow$ densely packed vesicles ($R = 1$, Figure 17e) $\rightarrow$ lamellar structures and small vesicles ($R = 2$, Figure 17f). The rich aggregation behavior resulted from the penetration of aromatic counterions into the head group region of the surfactants and led to the reduction of head group repulsions and facilitated micellar growth.

Siddiqui et al. [183] investigated the micellization of a series of cationic gemini surfactants (14-s-14; s = 4–6) in the presence of inorganic (KBr, KNO$_3$ and KSCN) and organic salts (NaBenz and NaSal). An increase of the salt concentration resulted in a structural transition of the gemini micelles from spherical to nonspherical, depending on the nature and size of the added counterion.

The inorganic counterions affected the micellar growth following the Hofmeister series (Br$^-$<NO$_3^-$<SCN$^-$). The aromatic counterions, having a greater ability to penetrate the head group region, led to micellar growth at lower concentrations compared to the weakly penetrating inorganic counterions. NaSal was found to be more effective in micelle growth compared to NaBenz. The growth of gemini micelles followed the order of the shorter spacer being more effective (s = 4>5>6) because of the large molecular packing parameter and the small surface area occupied per head group.

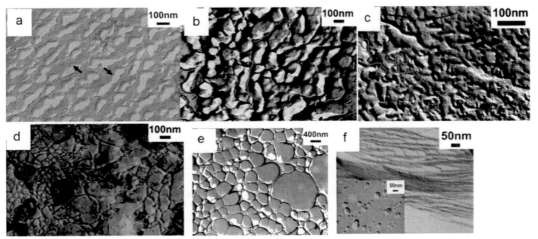

Adapted with permission from [182] Copyright (2008) American Chemical Society.

Figure 17. FF-TEM micrographs for 20 mM C$_{12}$C$_2$C$_{12}$(Et) with varying molar ratios of NaSal to C$_{12}$C$_2$C$_{12}$(Et):□ (a) $R = 0$ (b) $R = 0.3$, (c) $R = 0.5$, (d) $R = 0.75$, (e) $R = 1$, (f) $R = 2$.

The same group described the influence of salts on the micellar structure changes for the micellization of the butanediyl-1,4-bis(dimethyldodecylammonium bromide) (12-4-12) surfactant. The ability to promote aggregation decreased in the order KBr>KNO$_3$>KSCN> NaBenz>NaSal [184]

The effects of inorganic (NaCl and Na$_2$SO$_4$) and organic salts (NaBenz and sodium terephthalate (p-C$_6$H$_4$(COONa)$_2$) were investigated for cationic gemini surfactants with hydrophobic 12-4-12 and hydrophilic spacers 12-4(OH)$_2$-12 [185]. The *CMC* value of 12-4(OH)$_2$-12 without any added salt was lower than that of 12-4-12 due to intermolecular hydrogen bonding, which may effectively promote the aggregation of 12-4(OH)$_2$-12 molecules. In the presence of inorganic and organic salts, the *CMC* values of both surfactants decreased with an increase in the ionic strength. The ability to reduce the *CMC* decreased in order of C$_6$H$_5$COONa>p-C$_6$H$_4$(COONa)$_2$>Na$_2$SO$_4$>NaCl. For gemini with a hydrophobic spacer 12-4-12, the penetration of the C$_6$H$_5$COO$^-$ anions into the surfactant micelles and the charge neutralization induced a morphology change from spherical micelles to vesicles (Figure 18a), whereas the other salts only slightly increased the sizes of the micelles. The gemini with a hydrophilic spacer 12-4(OH)$_2$-12, changed from the micelle/vesicle coexistence to vesicles with the addition of C$_6$H$_5$COONa, (Figure 18b) whereas the other salts transformed the 12-4(OH)$_2$-12 solution from micelle/vesicle coexistence to micelles.

Ryhanen et al. [186] reported on the transition of cationic gemini surfactant 16-4(OH)$_2$-16 from small vesicles to large vesicles at the proper NaCl concentration and a specific temperature. With increasing concentration, the optically clear solution turned opalescent and slightly bluish ([NaCl] = 1.5 and 2 M, at 60 °C) and then cloudy, even at ambient temperature ([NaCl] = 3 M). Cooling the dispersion in [NaCl] = 1.5 and 2 M back to ambient temperature resulted in optically clear solutions. With increasing temperature of the surfactant solution at [NaCl] = 2 M, the following transition was observed: micelles/small vesicles (24 °C) → large tubular structures (29 °C) → giant vesicles (33 °C). The authors stated that the two positive charges in the head groups of the gemini acted as a nucleating surface for Cl$^-$ counterions to form a planar pseudocrystalline lattice corresponding to the 111-facet for Cl$^-$ in a NaCl crystal and associated with the vesicle surface.

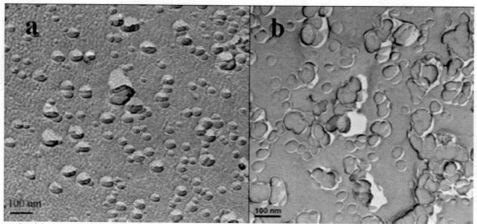

Reprinted with permission from [185] Copyright (2010) American Chemical Society.

Figure 18. FF-TEM micrograph: (a) 5 mM 12-4-12 solution with 20 mM C$_6$H$_5$COONa and (b) 5 mM 12-4(OH)$_2$-12 solution with 8 mM C$_6$H$_5$COONa.

However, the role of the orientation of the hydroxyl groups in the spacer and changes in the hydration of the head groups of the gemini needs investigation.

The unique morphology of gemini surfactant-counterion systems, based on the cationic 16-2-16 gemini amphiphile (ethanediyl-1,2-bis(hexadecyldimethylammonium) and chiral tartrate counteranions, were described by Oda et al. [187-189]. Non-chiral cationic gemini surfactant in the presence of tartrate enantiomers formed twisted multilayered ribbons in solution. Over time, the twisted ribbons slowly transformed to helical ribbons and then to tubules (Figure 19).

Among various additives, alcohols and amines have an important role in the preparation of microemulsions. The Kabir-ud-Din group observed the effects of salts (KBr, KNO$_3$ NaSal and NaTos) and organic additives (alcohols and amines) on the microstructure of cationic gemini surfactants with different spacer lengths [190, 191] and alkyl tail lengths [192]. The primary alcohols (butanol, pentanol and hexanol) caused the sphere-to-rod transition by the formation of gemini–alcohol mixed micelles with alcohol molecules embedded between the hydrophobic tails and increasing the volume of the micellar core. The presence of longer chain alcohols induced formation of larger micelles. The combined presence of KBr and alcohols or n-hexylamine revealed a synergistic effect on the size of the 16–4–16 micelle solution. Micellar growth that does not occur in the presence of either the salt or the additive alone was observed [190]. The synergistic effect was also observed for gemini 14-s-14 in the presence of KNO$_3$ salt with alcohols and amines, [191] as well as for gemini m-2-m (m = 10, 12, 14) in the presence of the organic salts NaSal and NaTos and high chain length alcohols/ amines (C$_6$-C$_8$) [192].

When comparing the influence of alcohol and amine on micellar growth, alcohol was found to be more effective. Graciani et al. [193] studied the micellization and micellar growth of cationic gemini surfactants 12-s-12, s = 3, 4, and 6, in the presence of medium-chain length alcohols (1-butanol, 1-pentanol, and 1-hexanol).

The presence of alcohol in the micellar solution led to a decrease in the average micellar aggregation number. Similarly, Chavda et al. [194] investigated the qualitative and quantitative effects of butanol on cationic single chain tetradecyltrimethylammonium bromide (C$_{14}$TAB) and gemini surfactant (12-4-12) solutions. In both cases, the alcohols affected the micellization and micellar properties of the surfactants. For butyl alcohols, the *CMC* decreased in the order: primary>secondary>tertiary.

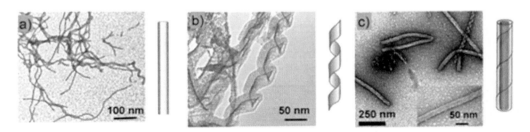

Adapted with permission from [189] Copyright (2007) American Chemical Society.

Figure 19. TEM micrographs and schematic representations of the evolution of the morphologies of the fibrous structures of 16-2-16 (10 mM in H$_2$O) with time. (a) Ill-defined fibers are observed after 2 h. (b) These fibers evolved into helical ribbons after 3 h, (c) which closed to form tubules after 36 h.

Ethanol, ethanediol, and 1,4-butanediol increased the *CMC* value more strongly for gemini surfactants [195]. The effect of short chain length alcohols on the micellization behavior of the cationic gemini surfactant 16-10-16 compared to single-chain surfactants was investigated by Kumar et al. [196]. The *CMC* values of the cationic surfactants increased with the increasing chain length of alcohols (methanol and ethanol) and decreased with 1-propanol.

SOLUBILIZATION OF HYDROPHOBIC COMPOUNDS IN GEMINI SURFACTANTS MICELLES

The solubility of hydrophobic organic compounds in water increases if the substance is captured inside a surfactant aggregate. This phenomenon is called micellar solubilization and is widely applied. Some surface properties of gemini surfactants and their ability to self-assemble into micelles at very low concentrations indicate better solubilization properties than those of the conventional surfactants. Research on aqueous solubility improvement is particularly important because of future uses of the new surfactants as emulsifiers, detergents and also as carriers in drug delivery systems.

Various parameters are used to quantify solubilization, which is usually investigated by spectroscopic methods (UV-VIS, light-scattering, fluorescence, and turbidimetry). The solubilization efficiency can be called the solubilization power (S_e), which is the amount of hydrophobic compound solubilized in one mole of micellized surfactant, as calculated in equation 6 [157].

$$S_e = \frac{C_{so}}{C_s - CMC}$$

(6)

where C_{so} is the concentration of substance solubilized in micelles and C_s is the surfactant concentration.

The solubilization capacity [158] Σ, can be correlated with S_e and N_{agg} (equation 7).

$$\Sigma = N_{agg} S_e$$

(7)

Below the *CMC*, the solubility of hydrophobic compounds in a surfactant solution is usually very low. Above the *CMC*, the solubility increases, usually linearly with the concentration of micellized surfactant [197]. The slope of the plot of the surfactant concentration of solubilized hydrophobe against the surfactant concentration expresses the effectiveness of the solubilization. The molar solubilization ratio, *MSR*, defined by Chaiko et al. [198] as the number of moles of the insoluble compound solubilized per mole of the surfactant present in solution, is represented by (equation 8):

$$MSR = \frac{S_t - S_{CMC}}{C_t - CMC}$$

(8)

where S_t, S_{cmc}, and C_t, are, respectively, the solubility of the solubilizate in the surfactant solution at a particular surfactant concentration above CMC (C_t), the solubility of solubilizate at the CMC, and the particular concentration of the surfactant above the CMC.

The solubilization effectiveness can be described by the partition coefficient K_m, which is the distribution of the mole fraction of the hydrophobic compound between the surfactant micelles (X_m) and the aqueous phase (X_a) (equation 9) [146].

$$K_m = \frac{X_m}{X_a}$$

(9)

The position of the hydrophobe in the micelle (solubilization site) can be obtained by UV-VIS spectroscopy, fluorescence spectroscopy [157, 164], or NMR [199]. The solubilizate may be placed on the surface of the micelle (1), in the palisade layer between the hydrophilic groups and the first few carbon atoms in the hydrophobic group (2), or in the inner core of the micelle (3) (Figure 20).

The selected studied systems of surfactants-solubilizates are collected in Table 1.

Some studies have shown that solubilization might occur below a gemini surfactant's CMC [148, 163, 166], which is unusual and has not been observed for conventional surfactants. The solubilization efficiency increases with an increasing alkyl tail length in gemini surfactants with a constant spacer length [200], which is in accordance with the rule proposed by Rosen [213] that the solubilization power of surfactants increases with increasing tail length. The length of the spacer is also important; however, its relation to the solubilization efficiency is not clear. The solubilization depends on the nature of the solubilized compound and should be discussed in terms of the substance to be solubilized.

The first report on the solubilization properties of cationic *m-s-m* gemini surfactants was conducted in the early 1990s by Devinsky et al. [200].

As a solubilizate, the nearly insoluble *trans*-azobenzene, a substrate used to produce organic dyes, was examined. The authors noted solubilization behavior similar to that observed for conventional surfactants; the solubilizing efficiency increased linearly with *m* for a given *s*.

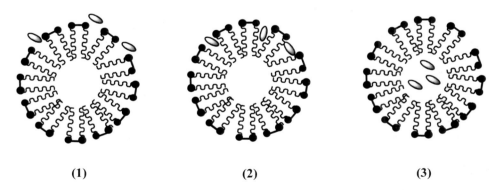

(1)   (2)   (3)

Figure 20. Possible solubilization sites of a hydrophobic compound within a gemini surfactant micelle.

Table 1. Studied systems of solubilization with gemini surfactants

Gemini surfactant	Solubilizate	Reference
Alkanediyl α,ω-bis[(dimethylalkyl ammonium)bromide]; (m-s-m, m = 8-16; s = 2-12)	$trans$-azobenzene	[200]
Alkanediyl α,ω-bis[(dimethylalkyl ammonium)bromide]; (m-s-m; m = 6, 10, 12; s = 2, 6, 10)	toluene, n-hexane	[201]
Alkanediyl α,ω-bis[(dimethylalkyl ammonium)bromide]; (m-s-m; m = 12, s = 2-12)	styrene	[202]
(Oligooxa) alkanediyl α,ω-bis[(dimethylalkyl ammonium)bromide]; (m-EO_x-m; m = 12, x = 2,3,4)	styrene	[81]
Alkanediyl α,ω-bis[(dimethylalkyl ammonium)bromide]; (m-s-m, m = 12; s = 3, 6)	1-(4-nitrophenylazo)-4-N,N-diethanolaminobenzene (NPDEAB); 1,4-diaminoanthraquinone(1,4-DAA) and p-aminobenzene (4-PAA)	[157]
[RN($C_3H_6NH_2$)]$_2C_2H_4$·n HO$_3$SCH$_3$	n-tetradecene	[159]
Didodecyl diphenyl ether disulfonate	toluene	[203]
Alkanediyl α,ω-bis[(dimethylalkyl ammonium)nitrate]; (m-s-m, m = 16, s = 3, 6, 12)	pyridine-2-azo-p-dimethylaniline, (PADA)	[141]
2-hydroxy-1,3-bis (octadecyldimethylammonium) propane dibromide, (18-3(OH)-18)	gold nanoparticles	[151]
Alkanediyl α,ω-bis[(dimethylalkyl ammonium)bromide]; (m-s-m; m = 12; s = 3, 4, 6)	pyrene	[165]
2-hydroxy-1,3-bis (octadecyldimethylammonium) propane dibromide, 18-3(OH)-18	silver nanoparticles	[204]
1,3-propane diaminium N,N-didodecyl-2-hydroxyl-$N,N,N'N'$-tetramethyl-dichloride	toluene, phenyl ethane, benzyl alcohol, 2-phenylethanol	[199]
Br[RRR$_1$N$^+$CH$_2$COO-(-CH$_2$CH$_2$O)$_n$COCH$_2$N$^+$RRR$_1$]Br; where R$_1$ = C$_{11}$H$_{23}$COOCH$_2$CH$_2$; C$_{15}$H$_{23}$COOCH$_2$CH$_2$; C$_{17}$H$_{23}$COOCH$_2$CH$_2$ (respectively: lauric, palmitic and stearic acid);	octanol, paraffin oil	[205]
Alkanediyl α,ω-bis[(dimethylalkyl ammonium)bromide]; (m-6-6; m = 12, 14, 16	dimyristoylphosphatidylcholine, DMPC	[134]
Alkanediyl α,ω-bis[(dimethylalkyl ammonium)bromide]; (m-s-m; m = 12, s = 6)	carbon nanotubes	[163]
Alkanediyl α,ω-bis[(dimethylalkyl ammonium)bromide]; (m-s-m; m = 16, s = 5)	pyrene, anthracene	[146]
Alkanediyl α,ω-bis[(dimethylalkyl ammonium)bromide]; (m-s-m, m = 10, 12, 14; s = 2, 3, 4)	methyl orange	[206]
Alkanediyl α,ω-bis[(dimethylalkyl ammonium)bromide]; (m-s-m; m = 10, s = 6)	titanium dioxide nanoparticles	[152]

Gemini surfactant	Solubilizate	Reference
Alkanediyl α,ω-bis[(dimethylalkyl ammonium)bromide]; 12-2-*m'*, where *m'* = 4, 8, 12, 16	pyrene, phenanthrene, naphthalene	[149]
1,2bis[*N,N*-dimethyl]-*N*-carbalkoxy methyl ammonio] ethane dichloride (*m*-2-*m, m* = 10-18)	sulforhodamine B	[148]
Alkanediyl α,ω-bis[(dimethylalkyl ammonium)bromide]; (*m-s-m; m* = 16, *s* = 5)	anthracene, pyrene	[142]
Alkanediyl α,ω-bis[(dimethylalkyl ammonium)bromide]; (*m-s-m; m* = 16, *s* =6)	naphthalene, anthracene, pyrene	[207]
Alkanediyl α,ω-bis[(dimethylalkyl ammonium)bromide]; *(m-s-m; m* = 12, *s* = 2)*	phenanthrene	[208]
Alkanediyl α,ω-bis[(dimethylalkyl ammonium)bromide]; Alkanediyl α,ω-bis[(dimethylalkyl ammonium)bromide] with ester bonds	Sudan I, Quinizarin	[164]
Sodium 2,2`-(6,6`-(ethane-1,2-diylbis(azanediyl)bis(4-(hexylamino)-1,3,5-triazine-6,2-diyl)bis(azanediyl)diethanesulfonate; Sodium 2,2`-(6,6`-(ethane-1,2-diylbis(azanediyl)bis(4-(octyloamino)-1,3,5-triazine-6,2-diyl)bis(azanediyl)diethanesulfonate; (*m-s-m, m* = 6, 8; *s* = 2)	liquid paraffin	[209]
N,N'-dialkyl-*N,N'*-dipyrrolidone ethylenediamine (Di-C$_n$P, where *n* = 6, 8, 10, 12)	cyclohexane	[58]
Cyclodextrine gemini agent [mono-6-O-3(bis{3-(N-dodecyl-*N,N*-dimethylamino)propylcarbamoyl}beta-ceclodextrin]$^{2+}$	curcumine analogues	[210]
Ethane-1,2-diyl bis(*N,N*-dimethyl-*N*-hexadecylammoniumacetoxy)dichloride; (*m-E2-m, m* = 16)	anthracene, pyrene	[143]
Alkanediyl α,ω-bis[(dimethylalkyl ammonium)bromide]; (*m-s-m; m* = 12, *s* = 2, 3, 4)	naphthalene, pyrene	[144]
Alkanediyl α,ω-bis[(dimethylalkyl ammonium)bromide]; (*m-s-m; m* =12, *s* = 2)	silver nanoparticles	[211]
Alkanediyl α,ω-bis[(dimethylalkyl ammonium)bromide]; (*m-s-m; m* = 16, *s* = 4)	gold nanoparticles	[212]

Devinsky's work initiated a series of studies on the solubilization of various organic dyes by gemini surfactants micelles. So far, in addition to dyes, the following hydrophobes have been tested: polycyclic aromatic hydrocarbons, simple hydrocarbons and other substances of special application, such as drugs and carbon nanotubes.

Most of the reported studies concern cationic surfactants of the *m-s-m* and *m-EO$_x$-m* structure and are performed with comparison to conventional, single-tail surfactant analogues. The research concerning solubilization conducted up until 2000 has been widely reviewed by Zana [77, 140].

Organic Dyes

One significant application of cationic surfactants, and a possible future application of gemini cationic surfactants, is as auxiliaries for textile dyeing by water-insoluble dyes. Most disperse dyes are azobenzene or anthraquinone derivatives. Choi et al. [157] investigated the solubilization capacity of two cationic gemini surfactants, propanediyl- (12-3-12) and hexanodiyl-α,ω-bis(dimethyldodecylammonium bromides) (12-6-12), towards three disperse dyes, NPDEAB, 1,4-DAA and 4-PAA. In comparison to their single-tail counterparts, the gemini surfactants demonstrated better solubilization power for two out of three dyes, NPDEAB and 1,4-DAA. The amount of the solubilized hydrophobes increased with the decreasing dimensions of the molecules: NPDEAB<1,4-DAA<4-PAA. The geminis with longer spacers (12-6-12) had better solubilization properties than the geminis with shorter spacers (12-3-12). The surfactant solubilization parameters Σ and S_e, strongly depended on the dye structure, which determined its location in the micelle. To determine the location of the dye within a micelle, visible absorbance measurements of the dye in an aqueous surfactant solution and different polar and non-polar solvents were conducted and compared. The spectra of the aqueous surfactant solution above the CMC were similar to those in ethanol. The authors suggested that the disperse dyes were solubilized in the outer hydrophilic part rather than in the hydrophobic area of the micelles.

Abdel-Salam and El-Said [148] investigated the solubilization of sulforodamine B in solutions of a series of homologues of 1,2-bis[N,N-dimethyl-N-carboxy methyl ammonio] ethane dichlorides (m-2-m, m = 10, 12, 16 and 18). The results showed that the solubilization of the sulforodamine B occurred even below surfactant CMC and increased with increasing alkyl tail length due to the enhancement of the hydrophobic interactions in the micelle.

The relationship between the structure and the solubilization efficiency of two different types of organic dyes, Quinizarine and Sudan I, were investigated by Tehrani-Bagha et al. [164]. They compared the dye solubilization by m-s-m geminis, corresponding surfactants with ester bonds and the single chain cationic surfactant DTAB (Figure 21). The ester geminis were less effective in the solubilization of the dyes than the compounds without ester bounds. The effectiveness of solubilization increased with the tail length of the gemini but was smaller for tails containing ester groups.

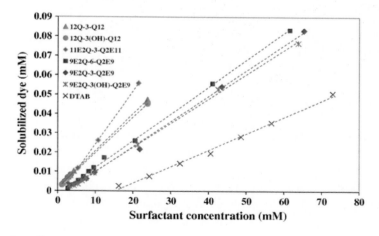

Figure 21. (Continued).

Reprinted from [164] Journal of Colloid and Interface Science, Vol. 376, Tehrani-Bagha et al., "Solubilization of two organic dyes by cationic ester containing gemini surfactants", p. 112-118, Copyright (2012) with permission from Elsevier.

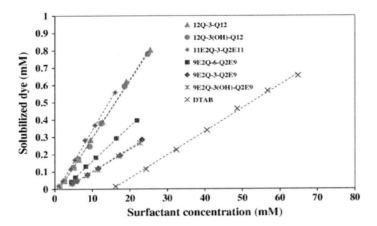

Figure 21. Solubility of Quinizarine (top) and Sudan I (bottom) as a function of the surfactant concentration, E – ester bond, Q – quaternary head group.

Reprinted from [164] Journal of Colloid and Interface Science, Vol. 376, Tehrani-Bagha et al., "Solubilization of two organic dyes by cationic ester containing gemini surfactants", p. 112-118, Copyright (2012) with permission from Elsevier.

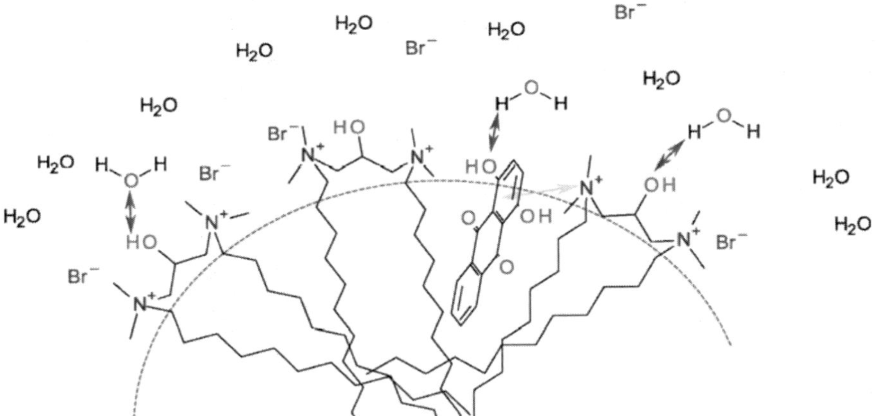

Figure 22. The location of the Quinizarine molecule within the micelle of gemini surfactant 12Q-3(OH)-Q12.

The geminis were all more effective than the single-tail DTAB. Spectroscopic measurements indicated that in the case of both dyes, their molecules were located in the polar head groups in the surfactant micelles (Figure 22).

Simple Alkanes and Aromatic Compounds

The first study on the solubilization of simple hydrophobic compounds, toluene and n-hexane, was performed by Dam et al. [201] for a series of bis(quaternary ammonium bromides) with different spacers and tail lengths. They exhibited significantly better solubilization properties than the corresponding single-chain alkylammonium bromides with comparable tail lengths. The solubility of both toluene and n-hexane increased with the increasing tail length.

Negm [205] investigated the effect of cationic gemini surfactants with hydrophilic polyoxyethylene spacers on the solubilization of paraffin oil and octanol. The surfactants studied were: $Br^-[RRR_1N^+CH_2COO-(CH_2CH_2O)_nCOCH_2N^+RRR_1]Br$; where $R_1 = C_{11}H_{23}COO$ CH_2CH_2; $C_{15}H_{23}COOCH_2CH_2$; $C_{17}H_{23}COOCH_2CH_2$ (respectively: lauric, palmitic and stearic acid); and n = 10, 15, and 25 ethylene oxide units. Based on turbidity changes, Negm divided the solubilization process in gemini surfactant micellar solutions into three stages: the adsorption of the solubilizate molecules at the micellar interface, the penetration of the adsorbed molecules into the micellar core and steady-state solubilization, when the hydrophobe is located in the micellar core. The location of some aromatic solutes within the micelles of 1,3-propane diaminium N,N-didodecyl-2-hydroxyl-N,N,N',N'-tetramethyl-dichloride was investigated by De-Wei et al. by ^1H NMR spectroscopy [199]. The results indicated that the more hydrophobic the solubilizates are, the deeper they penetrate into the micellar core.

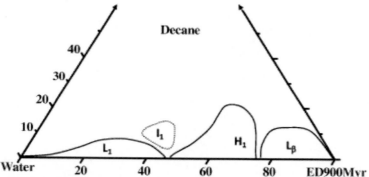

Reprinted from [214] Microporous and Mesoporous Materials, Vol. 169, May-Masnou et al., "Solubilization of decane into gemini surfactant with a modified Jeffamine backbone: Design of hierarchical porous silica", p. 235-241, Copyright (2013) with permission from Elsevier.

Figure 23. Phase diagram of the ED900Myr/decane/water system, wt %, 20 °C (L_1, I_1, H_1, L_β are the micellar phases).

May-Masnou et al. [214] studied the solubilization of n-decane by a gemini surfactant named ED900Myr as a derivative of commercial Jeffamine ED900 (Figure 23). The maximum amount of solubilized decane in the micellar structure of the studied surfactant did not exceed 8 % (region L_1 in Figure 23).

The ability of N,N'-didecyl-N,N'-di(ethyl-2-pyrrolidone)ethylenediamine to solubilize cyclohexane in the pH range from 2.0 to 12.0 has been examined [58]. The decrease of the light scattering intensity with the increasing pH of the surfactant aqueous solution-cyclohexane mixture (Figure 24) showed that cyclohexane was solubilized into the surfactant micelles at high pH.

After adding cyclohexane at pH=2.5 and pH=7, turbid macroemulsions were formed, whereas at pH=11, due to the formation of a microemulsion, the sample was clear. There are two pH-sensitive tertiary nitrogen atoms in the surfactant molecule that are protonated in acidic conditions, which determines the solubilization capacity at low pH.

Polycyclic Aromatic Hydrocarbons

Enhancement of the water-solubility of polycyclic aromatic hydrocarbons is especially important because of the environmental issues related to soil contamination.

A series of bis-quaternary ammonium bromides of different spacer lengths *(m-s-m*, s = 2-8) were examined as solubilizers of pyrene by Zhao and Zheng [165]. The solubilization increased with the increasing spacer length and was more effective compared to the single-tail cetyl trimethyl ammonium bromide, CTAB, solutions. The pyrene molecules were solubilized in the palisade layer of the gemini surfactant micelle.

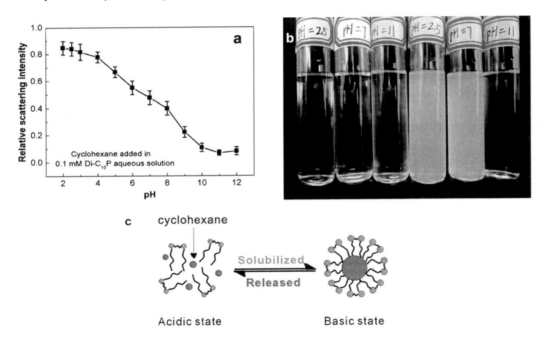

Reprinted with permission from [58] Copyright (2012) American Chemical Society.

Figure 24. (a) Variation of the scattered light intensity at θ =173° after cyclohexane added to 0.1 mM surfactant at 25 °C; (b) images of the samples before (in the left three tubes) and after adding cyclohexane (in the right three tubes) (c) solubilization of cyclohexane into surfactant micelles.

Sheikh et al. [142] studied the problem of the solubilization of the polycyclic aromatic hydrocarbons, pyrene and anthracene, by the cationic gemini surfactant pentadiyl-1,5-bis(dimethylcetylammonium bromide) $C_{16}H_{33}N^+(CH_3)_2$-$(CH_2)_5$-$N^+(CH_3)_2C_{16}H_{33}$,2Br$^-$ and its equimolar binary mixtures with nonionic polyoxyethylene 10 cetyl ether (Brij 56), anionic (sodium bis(2-ethylhexyl)sulfosuccinate, AOT) or cationic (cetylpyridinium chloride, CPC) surfactants.

For both polycyclic aromatic hydrocarbons, the enhancement of their solubility in water was observed. For the binary mixtures, the *MSR* values were higher than for pure surfactants due to the synergy effect related to mixed micellization.

The same group performed studies on the solubilization of pyrene and anthracene by the biodegradable gemini surfactant ethane-1,2-diyl bis(*N,N*-dimethyl-*N*-hexadecyl ammonium acetoxy) dichloride (16-E2-16) and its binary mixtures [143]. The geminis were better solubilizers for pyrene and worse for anthracene than the corresponding cetyltrimethylammonium chloride, CTAC. The authors suggested that this was because the anthracene is more easily accommodated in the palisade layer of the micelle than in the micellar core. In these studies, the solubilization efficiency was higher for binary mixtures and was the best in the gemini-anionic surfactant mixtures.

The solubilization of phenanthrene by a 12-2-12 gemini cationic surfactant alone and in binary mixtures with conventional surfactants, including the corresponding dodecyl trimethyl ammonium bromide, DTAB, was investigated by Wei et al. [208] The designated *MSR* values indicated that the 12-2-12 was the best solubilizer for phenanthrene compared to Brij 35, CPC, TX 100 and DTAB. The *MSR* was even higher for the pure 12-2-12 micellar solution than for their binary mixtures, which is atypical.

In other research conducted by Wei et al. [149], a series of dissymmetric gemini quaternary ammonium compounds with the same spacer and different alkyl chains lengths (12-2-*m*, where *m* = 4, 8, 12, and 16) and their binary equimolar mixtures, were used for the solubilization of naphthalene, phenanthrene and pyrene.

The water solubility enhancement for the examined PAHs in solutions of the individual geminis increased as follows: 12-2-4<12-2-8<12-2-12<12-2-16. These results agreed with the rule proposed by Rosen [213]. In the case of binary mixtures, the dissymmetric gemini surfactants with the longer tail (12-2-16) mixed with the symmetric 12-2-12 had a very good solubilization efficiency for pyrene. On the other hand, the dissymmetric geminis possessing shorter alkyl tails (12-2-4 and 12-2-8) in mixtures with 12-2-12 had comparable solubilization efficiencies for naphthalene. The PAH water solubility enhancement by multi-component gemini surfactant systems (binary and ternary) of alkanediyl-α,ω-bis(dodecyldimethyl-ammonium bromides), 12-*s*-12, *s* = 2, 3, and 4 were studied by Wei et al. [144]. The *MSR* values indicated that the solubilization efficiency of the binary systems increased with the spacer length.

Other Hydrophobic Compounds

Surfactants are important reagents in the solubilization of lipid vesicles. Fan et al. [134] investigated the solubilization of dimyristoylophosphatidylcholine (DMPC) vesicles in a micellar solution of cationic gemini surfactants (symmetric 12-6-12 and dissymmetric *m*-6-6, where *m* = 12,14, and 16) by the methods of isothermal titration calorimetry, turbidimetry and dynamic light scattering. The results showed that the gemini surfactants were more effective than DTAB, and that the dissymmetric surfactants series were more effective than the symmetric 12-6-12 in lipid solubilization.

Mirgorodskaya et al. [215] studied the solubilization of some *p*-nitrophenyl esters of carboxylic acids in solution of hydroxyethylated cationic gemini surfactants (hexanediyl-α,ω-bis((2-hydroxyethyl)methylhexadecylammonium) bromides, 16-6-16(OH). The results were compared with solubilization data for non-functional hexanediyl-α,ω-bis (hexadecylammonium bromides, (16-6-16, CTAB) and *N*-cetyl-*N*-(2-hydroxyethyl)-*N,N*-dimethylammonium bromide (CHAB). Except for the *p*-nitrophenyl acetate, the solubilization increased in the order: CTAB<CHAB<16-6-16<16-6-16(OH) (Figure 25).

Micellar Stabilization of Nanoparticles

The micellization of surfactants can be used for the preparation of stable dispersion of nanoparticles for special applications, for example, during the synthesis of metal nanoparticles. Some gemini surfactants have been used as gold, silver, carbon nanotube, or TiO_2 nanoparticle stabilizers.

To date, only cationic gemini surfactants have been examined.

Van der Waals attractive interactions between carbon nanotubes cause their undesirable aggregation into bundles in aqueous solutions. To improve the dispersibility of carbon nanoparticles, surfactants are commonly used.

Wang et al. [163] studied the effect of the hexyl-α,ω-bis(dodecyldimethylammonium bromide) (12-6-12) gemini surfactant structure on the stability of dispersions of multi-walled carbon nanotubes. Unlike the single-tail DTAB, the gemini was a good stabilizer, even below its *CMC*. The maximum amount of the suspended carbon nanotubes was approximately twice as much as in a DTAB solution.

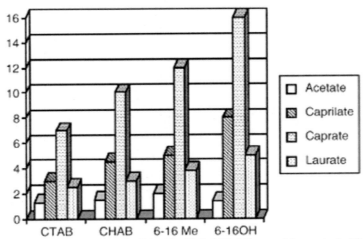

Reprinted from [215] Journal of Molecular Liquids, Vol. 169, Mirgorodskaya et al., "Solubilization and catalytic behavior of micellar system based on gemini surfactant with hydroxyalkylated head group", p. 106-109, Copyright (2012) with permission from Elsevier.

Figure 25. Solubility of the *p*-nitrophenyl esters of carboxylic acids in micellar solutions of cationic surfactants 6-16 Me – 16-6-16, 6-16OH and 16-6-16(OH).

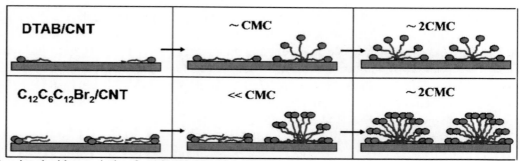

Figure 26. Schematic representation of the proposed mechanism by which conventional and gemini surfactants help to disperse carbon nanotubes in aqueous micellar solutions.

Fontana [166] and co-workers prepared stable single-walled carbon nanotube aqueous dispersions with two cationic geminis, 2,5-bis(n-dodecyloxy)-1,4-bis(N,N,N-trimethylammoniomethyl)phenyl bromide ([pXDo(TA)$_2$Br]) and 2,5-dimetoxy-1,4-bis[N-(n-dodecyl)-N,N-dimethylammoniomethyl)phenyl bromide ([pXMo(DDA)2Br]) and, for comparison, one conventional surfactant, N-[p-(-n-dodecyloxybenzyl)]-N,N,N-trimethylammonium bromide (pDOTABr). The authors investigated the effect of the surfactant structure on the stability of the dispersions and the adsorption capacity onto the carbon nanotube sidewalls. Figure 27 shows the aqueous dispersions of nanotubes obtained in the presence and in the absence of surfactant.

Figure 27. Aqueous dispersions of carbon nanotubes (0.2 mg/mL) obtained by sonication (5 h) with 1 mM aqueous solutions of A – pDOTABr, B – pXDo(TA)$_2$Br, C – pXMo(DDA)$_2$Br, D – in the absence of surfactant.

All of the surfactants appeared to be good dispersants for carbon nanotubes. The investigated gemini surfactants allowed stable dispersions below their *CMC*. The dispersing ability decreased in the order: pDOTABr > pXMo(DDA)$_2$Br > pXDo(TA)$_2$Br. The aqueous dispersions demonstrated a good stability after three months of monitoring.

CONCLUSION

The presented survey of research on gemini surfactants, based mainly upon data published after 2000, indicates that a considerable amount of work has been concentrated on these materials. This interest is driven by actual or envisaged industrial applications and is also motivated by legal regulations and ecological demands (lowering the amounts of surfactants used to lessen the environmental burden).

Gemini surfactants exhibit, in most cases, much lower critical micelle concentrations than their single chain counterparts. The *CMC* depends upon the structure of geminis: the structure of the charged head, the spacer and the tail. Many studies try to approach the problem in a systematic way, varying the structure of these elements, their hydrophilicity and thus, their expected interactions with water and the conformational freedom of the spacer and the tail. Attention is primarily focused on ionic gemini surfactants. In some cases, considerable progress was achieved in understanding these relations; however, general conclusions cannot yet be drawn. Self-organization remains the main problem. Not only is the critical micelle concentration of geminis lower than that of single chain surfactants, but the structure of the micelles is different. These structures depend upon the structure of single gemini macromolecules in a complex way, and not all relations are well understood.

Considerable progress has been made due to the development of modern characterization methods, especially scattering methods and visualization techniques, such as cryo-TEM.

The issues of gemini surfactants remain a vivid area of research and call for well-founded experimental data and deeper generalizations.

ACKNOWLEDGMENTS

This work was partially financed by the Polish National Science Centre, grant NN 209446939. Julia Hawranke is a recipient of a PhD scholarship under a project funded by the European Social Fund.

Reviewed by: Krzysztof Szczubialka, Faculty of Chemistry, Jagiellonian University, Cracow

REFERENCES

[1]   Takamatsu, Y., Iwata, N., Tsubone, K., Torigoe, K., Endo, T., Sakai, K., Sakai, H., Abe, M. *J. Colloid Interface Sci.* 2009, 338, 229-235

[2]   Menger, F. M., Keiper, J. S., *Angew Chem. Int. Ed.* 2000, 39, 1906-1920

[3]   Bunton, C. A., Robinson, L., Schaak, J., Stam, M. F. *J. Org. Chem.* 1971, 36, 2346-2350

[4]   Devinsky, F., Masarova, L., Lacko, I., *J. Colloid Interface Sci.* 1985, 105, 235-239

[5]   Devinsky, F., Lacko, I., Bitterova, F., Tomeckova, L. *J. Colloid. Interface Sci.* 1986, 114, 314-322

[6]   Okahara, M., Masuyama, A., Sumida, Y., Zhu, Y. P. *J. Jpn. Oil Chem. Soc.* 1988, 37, 746-748

[7]   Zana, R., Levy, H., *Colloid Surfaces* A 1997, 127, 229-232

[8]   Zana, R. *J. Colloid Interface Sci.* 2002, 246, 182-190

[9]   Zana, R., Benrraou, M., Rueff, R., *Langmuir* 1991, 7, 1072-1075

[10] Dreja, M., Gramberg, S., Tieke, B., *Chem. Commun.* 1998, 13, 1371-1372

[11] Wettig, S. D., Li, X., Verrall, R. E., *Langmuir* 2003, 19, 3666-3670

[12] Zheng, O., Zhao, J.-X., Yan, H., Gao, S. K., *J. Colloid Interface Sci.* 2007, 310, 331-336

[13] Bendjeriou, A., Derrien, G., Hartmann, P., Charnay, C., *Thermochim. Acta* 2005, 434, 165-170

[14] Wettig, S. D., Nowak, P., Verrall, R. E., *Langmuir* 2002, 18, 5354-5359

[15] Huang, X., Han, Y., Wang, Y., Cao, M., Wang, Y., Cao, M., Wang, Y. *Colloid Surfaces* A 2008, 325, 26-32

[16] Lim, J., Park, J., Jo Park, C., Min Lee, B., *Colloid Polym. Sci.* 2013, 291, 855-866

[17] Silva, S. G., Fernandes, R. F., Marques, E. F., do Vale, M. L. C. *Eur. J. Org. Chem.* 2012, 345-352

[18] Perez, L., Torres, J. L., Manresa, A., Solans, C., Infante, M. R. *Langmuir* 1996, 12, 5296-5301

[19] Tan, H., Xiao, H. *Tetrahedron Lett.* 2008, 49, 1759-1761

[20] Moran, M. C., Pinozo, A., Perez, L., Clapes, P., Angelet, M., Garcia, M. T., Vinardell, M. P., Infante, M. R. *Green Chem.*, 2004, 6, 233-240

[21] Menger, F. M., Mbadugha, B. N. A. *J. Am. Chem. Soc.* 2001, 123, 875-885

[22] Johnsson, M., Engberts, J. B. F. N. *J. Phys. Org. Chem.* 2004, 17, 934-944

[23] Negm, N. A., Mohamed, A. S. *J. Surfact. Deterg.* 2008, 11, 215-221

[24] Tatsumi, T., Zhang, W., Kida, T., Nakatsuji, Y., Ono, D., Takeda, T., Ikeda, I. *J. Surfact. Deterg.* 2001, 4, 279-285

[25] Wegrzynska, J., Chlebicki, J., Maliszewska, I. *J. Surfact. Deterg.* 2007, 10, 109-116

[26] Tehrani-Bagha, A. R., Holmberg, K. *Langmuir* 2010, 26, 9276-9282

[27] Tehrani-Bagha, A. R., Oskarsson, H., Van Ginkel, C. G., Holmberg, K. *J. Colloid Interface Sci.* 2007, 312, 444-452

[28] Pupak, M., Karlovska, J., *Acta Fac. Pharm. Univ. Comenianae* 2007, 54, 215-218

[29] Chen, M., Luo, L., Hu, X., Yang, J. *J. Surfact. Deterg.* 2013, 16, 327-332

[30] Menger, F. M., Migulin, V. A. *J. Org. Chem.* 1999, 64, 8916-8921

[31] Wu, C., Hou, Y., Deng, M., Huang, X., Yu, D., Xiang, J., Liu, Y., Li, Z., Wang, Y. *Langmuir* 2010, 26, 7922-7927

[32] Zhang, J., Zheng, Y., Yu, P., He, L., Wang, H., Wang, R. *J. Surfact. Deterg.* 2010, 13, 155-158

[33] Laschewsky, A., Wattebled, L., Arotcarena, M., Habib-Jiwan, J-L., Rakotoaly, R. H. *Langmuir* 2005, 21, 7170-7179

[34] Sikiric, M., Primozic, I., Talmon, Y. N. Filipovic-Vincekovic, *J. Colloid Interface Sci.* 2005, 281, 473-481

[35] Azz-Eddine Jouani, M., Szonyi, S., Yande Dieng, S., Cambon, A., Geribaldi, S. *New J. Chem.* 1999, 23, 557-652

[36] Massi, L., Guittard, F., Levy, R., Duccini, Y., Geribaldi, S., *Eur. J. Med. Chem.* 2003, 38, 519-523

[37] Asakawa, T., Ozawa, T., Ohta, A. *J. Oleo. Sci.* 2013, 62, 17-20

[38] Cerichelli, G., Luchetti, L., Mancini, G., Savelli, G. *Langmuir* 1999, 15, 2631-2634

[39] Camilleri, P., Kremer, A., Edwards, A. J., Jennings, K. H., Jenkins, O., Marshall, I., McGregor, C., Neville, W., Rice, S. Q., Smith, R. J., Wilkinson, M. J., Kirby, A. J. *Chem. Commun.* 2000, 14, 1253-1254

[40] Ronsin, G., Perrin, C., Guedat, P., Kremer, A., Camilleri, P., Kirby, A. J. *Chem. Commun.* 2002, 19, 2234-2235

[41] Shukla, D., Tyagi, V. K. *J. Oleo. Sci.* 2006, 55, 215-226

[42] Tyagi, P., Tyagi, R. *Eur. J. Lipid Sci. Technol.* 2011, 113, 848-855

[43] Jaeger, D. A., Wang, Y., Pennington, R. L. *Langmuir* 2002, 18, 9259-9266

[44] Adewuyi, A., Gopfert, A., Wolff, T. *Cent. Eur. J. Chem.* 2013, 11, 1368-1380

[45] Du, X., Lu, Y., Li, L., Wang, J., Yang, Z. *Colloid Surface* A 2006, 290, 132-137

[46] Hujun, X., Qicheng, L., Dandan, C., Xiaoya, L. *J. Surfact. Deterg.* 2012, 15, 703-707

[47] Hujun, X., Hui, G., Peng, K., Dandan, C. *J. Surfact. Deterg.* 2013, 16, 57-61

[48] Liu, X-P., Feng, J., Zhang, L., Gong, Q-T., Zhao, S., Yu, J-Y. *Colloid Surface* A 2010, 362, 39-46

[49] Ge, Y-S., Tai, S-X., Xu, Z-Q., Lai, L., Tian, F-F., Li, D-W., Jiang, F-L., Liu, Y., Gao, Z-N. *Langmuir* 2012, 28, 5913-5920

[50] Zaijun, L., Rui, Y., Zhongyun, L., Fushan, Y. *J. Surfact. Deterg.* 2005, 8, 337-340

[51] Li, X., Hu, Z., Zhu, H., Zhao, S., Cao, D. *J. Surfact. Deterg.* 2010, 13, 353-359

[52] Tai, S., Gao, Z., Liu, X., Zhang, Q. *Eur. J. Lipid Sci. Technol.* 2012, 114, 1062-1069

[53] Yoshimura, T., Esumi, K. *J. Colloid Interface Sci.* 2004, 276, 231-238

[54] Song, B., Hu, Y., Song, Y., Zhao, J. *J. Colloid Interface Sci.* 2010, 341, 94-100

[55] Acharya, D. P., Gutierrez, J. M., Aramaki, K., Aratani, K., Kunieda, H. *J. Colloid Interface Sci.* 2005, 291, 236-243

[56] Bong, M., Matsuoke, K., Honda, C., Endo, K. *J. Colloid Interface Sci.* 2009, 339, 230-235

[57] Krishnan, R. S. G., Thennarasu, S., Mandal, A. B. *J. Phys. Chem.* B 2004, 108, 8806-8816

[58] Jiang, Z., Li, X., Yang, G., Cheng, L., Cai, B., Yang, Y., Dong, J. *Langmuir* 2012, 28, 7174-7181

[59] Paddon-Jones, G., Rwgismond, S., Kwetkat, K., Zana, R. *J. Colloid Interface Sci.* 2001, 243, 496-502

[60] Zhou, T., Yang, H., Xu, X., Wang, X., Wang, J., Dong, G. *Colloid Surface* A 2008, 317, 339-343

[61] Alami, E., Holmberg, K., Eastoe, J. *J. Colloid Interface Sci.* 2002, 247, 447-455

[62] Altenbach, H-J., Ihizane, R., Jakob, B., Lange, K., Schneider, M., Yilmaz, Z., Nandi, S. *J. Surfact. Deterg.* 2010, 13, 399-407

[63] Mariano, J. L., Fernandez Cirellia, A., Kovensky, J. *J. Surfact. Deterg.* 2006, 9, 279-286

[64] Laska, U., Wilk, K. A., Maliszewska, I., Syper, L. *J. Surfact. Deterg.* 2006, 9, 115-124

[65] Warwel, S., Bruse, F., Schier, H. *J. Surfact. Deterg.* 2004, 7, 181-186

[66] Warwel, S., Bruse, F. *J. Surfact. Deterg.* 2004, 7, 187-193

[67] Han, F., Zhang, G. *Colloid Surface* A, 2004, 237, 79-85

[68] Kumar, A., Alami, E., Holmberg, K., Seredyuk, V., Menger, F. M. *Colloid Surface* A 2003, 228, 197-207

[69] Seredyuk, V., Holmberg, K. J. *J. Colloid Interface Sci.* 2001, 241, 524-526
[70] Seredyuk, V., Alami, E., Nyden, M., Holmberg, K., Peresypkin, A. V., Menger, F. M. *Colloid Surface* A 2002, 203, 245-258
[71] Alami, E., Holmberg, K. J. *J. Colloid Interface Sci.* 2001, 239, 230-240
[72] Nich, M-P., Kumar, S. K., Fernando, R. H., Colby, R. H., Katsaras, J. *Langmuir* 2004, 20, 9061-9068
[73] Xie, Z., Feng, Y. *J. Surfact Deterg.* 2010, 13, 51-57
[74] Geng, X. F., Hu, X. Q., Xia, J. J., Jia, X. C. *Appl. Surf. Sci.* 2013, 271, 284-290
[75] Yoshimura, T., Ichinokawa, T., Kaji, M., Esumi, K. *Colloid Surface A*, 2006, 273, 208-212
[76] Bordi, F., Cerichelli, G., Berardinis, N., Diociaiuti, M., Giansanti, L., Mancini, G., Sennato, S. *Langmuir* 2010, 26, 6177-6183
[77] Zana, R., *Adv. Colloid Interface Sci.* 2002, 97, 205-253
[78] Rodriguez, A., Mar Graciarni, M., Munoz, M., Robina, I., Moya, M. L. *Langmuir* 2006, 22, 9519-9525
[79] Li, Z. X., Dong, C. C., Thomas, R. K. *Langmuir* 1999, 15, 4392-4396
[80] Alami, E., Beinert, G., Marie, P., Zana, R. *Langmuir*, 1993, 9, 1465-1467
[81] Dreja, M., Pyckhout-Hintzen, W., Mays, H., Tieke, B. *Langmuir* 1999, 15, 391-399
[82] Diamant, H., Andelman, D. *Langmuir* 1994, 10, 2910-2916
[83] Cooke, D., Lu, J., Thomas, R. K., Pitt, A., Simister, E., Penford, J. *J. Phys. Chem. B* 1996, 100, 10298
[84] Li, P. X., Dong, C. C., Thomas, R. K. *Langmuir* 2011, 27, 1844-1852.
[85] Gao, T., Rosen, M. J., *J. Am. Oil Chem. Soc.* 1994, 71, 771-776
[86] Eastoe, J., Dalton, J. S., Rogueda, P. G., Crooks, E. C., Pitt, A. R., Simister, E. A. *J. Colloid Interface Sci.* 1997, 188, 423-430
[87] Pinoza, A., Infante, M. R., Chang, C. H., Franses, E. I. *Colloid Surface* A 1994, 87, 117-123
[88] Wegrzynska, J., Para, G., Chlebicki, J., Warszynski, P., Wilk, K. A. *Langmuir* 2008, 24, 3171-3180
[89] Para, G., Jarek, E., Warszynski, P., Adamczyk, Z., *Colloid Surface* A 2003, 222, 213-222
[90] Para, G., Jarek, E., Warszynski, P., *Colloid Surface* A 2005, 261, 65-73
[91] Li, P. X., Dong, C. C., Thomas, R. K., Penfold, J., Wang, Y. *Langmuir* 2011, 27, 2575-2586
[92] Frindi, M., Michels, B., Levy, H., Zana, R. *Langmuir* 1994, 10, 1140-1145
[93] Geng, Y., Romsted, L. S., Menger, F. *J. Am. Chem. Soc.* 2006, 128, 492-501
[94] Menger, F. M., Littau, C. A. *J. Am. Chem. Soc.* 1993, 115, 10083-10090
[95] Song, L. D., Rosen, M. J., *Langmuir* 1996, 12, 1149-1153
[96] Hadgiivanova, R., Diamant, H. *J. Phys. Chem. B*, 2007, 111, 8854-8859
[97] Hadgiivanova, R., Diamant, H. *J. Chem. Phys.* 2009, 130, 114901-114905
[98] Tiwari, A. K., Sowmiya, S. M., Saha, S. K. *J. Photoch. Photobiol. A* 2011, 223, 6-13
[99] Hirata, H., Hattori, N., Ishida, M., Okabayashi, H., Furusaka, M., Zana, R. *J. Phys. Chem.* 1995, 99, 17778-17784
[100] Hattori, N., Hirata, H., Okabayashi, H., Furusaka, M., O'Connor, C. J., Zana, R. *Colloid Polym. Sci.* 1999, 277, 95-100
[101] Danino, D., Talmon, Y., Zana, R. *Langmuir* 1995, 11, 1448-1456

[102] Bernheim-Groswasser, A., Zana, R., Talmon, Y. *J. Phys. Chem. B* 2000, 104, 4005-4009

[103] Lu, T., Lan, Y., Liu, C., Huang, J., Wang, Y. *J. Colloid Interface Sci.* 2012, 377, 222-230

[104] In, M., Bendjeriou, B., Noirez, L., Grillo, I. *Langmuir* 2010, 26, 10411-10414

[105] Zhu, S., Cheng, F., Wang, J., Yu, J. *Colloid Surface* A 2006, 281, 35-39

[106] Cao, X., Li, Z., Song, X., Cui, X., Wei, Y., Cheng, F., Wang, J. *J. Surfact. Deterg.* 2009, 12, 165-172

[107] Nyuta, K., Yashimura, T., Tsuchiya, K., Sakai, H., Abe, M., Iwase, H. *J. Colloid Interface Sci.* 2012, 370, 80-85

[108] Oh, S. G., Shah, D. O. *J. Am. Oil Chem. Soc.* 1993, 70, 673-678

[109] Patist, A., Jha, B. K., Oh, S. G., Shah, D. O. *J. Surfact. Deterg.* 1999, 2, 317-324

[110] Oh, S. G., Shah, D. O. *Langmuir* 1991, 7, 1316-1318

[111] Oelschlaeger, C., Watson, G., Candau, S. J., Cates, M. E. *Langmuir* 2002, 18, 7265-7272.

[112] Ulbricht, W., Zana, R. *Colloid Surface* A 2001, 183-185, 487-494.

[113] Kern, F., Lequeux, F., Zana, R., Candau, S. J. *Langmuir* 1994, 10, 1714-1723

[114] Zana, R. *J. Colloid Interface Sci.* 2002, 248, 203-220

[115] Groth, C., Nyden, M., Holmber, K., Kanicky, J. R., Shah, D. O. *J. Surf. Deterg.* 2004, 7, 247-255

[116] Yang, Q. Q., Hong, Q., Somasundaran, P. *J. Mol. Liq.* 2009, 146, 105-111

[117] Zana, R. *Langmuir* 1996, 12, 1208-1211

[118] Zana, R. *J. Colloid. Interface Sci.*, 1980, 78, 330-337

[119] Sugihara, G., Nakamura, A., Nakashima, T., Araki, Y., Fujiwara, M. *Colloid Polym. Sci.* 1997, 275, 790-796

[120] Li, H., Yu, C., Chen, R., Li, J., Li, J. *Colloid Surface* A, 2012, 395, 116-124

[121] Boot, C., Attwood, D. *Macromol. Rapid Commun.* 2000, 21, 501-527

[122] Grosmaire, L., Chorro, M., Chorro, C., Partyka, S., Zana, R. *J. Colloid Intrface Sci.* 2002, 246, 175-181

[123] Liu, G., Gu, D., Liu, H., Ding, W., Luan, H., Lou, Y. *J. Colloid interface Sci.* 2012, 375, 148-153

[124] Han, Y., Wang, Y. *Phys. Chem. Chem. Phys.* 2011, 13, 1939-1956

[125] Camesano, T. A., Nagarajan, R. *Colloid Surface* A 2000, 167, 165-177

[126] Borse, M., Sharma, V., Aswal, V. K., Goyal, P. S., Devi, S. *J. Colloid Interface Sci.* 2005, 284, 282-288

[127] Borse, M. S., Devi, S. *Adv. Colloid Interface Sci.* 2006, 123-126, 387-399

[128] Bergstrom, L. M., Garamus, V. M. *Langmuir* 2012, 28, 9311-9321

[129] Pisarcik, M., Rosen, M. J., Polakovicova, M., Devinsky, F., Lacko, I. *J. Colloid Interface Sci.* 2005, 289, 560-565

[130] Pei, X., Zhao, J., Ye, Y., Wei, X. *Soft Matter* 2011, 7, 2953-2960

[131] Zhang, Z., Zheng, P., Guo, Y., Yang, Y., Chen, Z., Wang, X., An, X., Shen, W. *J. Colloid Interface Sci.* 2012, 379, 64-71

[132] Wang, X., Wang, J., Wang, Y., Yan, H., Li, P., Thomas, R. K. *Langmuir* 2004, 20, 53-56

[133] Li, Y., Li, P., Wang, J., Wang, Y., Yan, H., Thomas, R. K. *Langmuir* 2005, 21, 6703-6706

[134] Fan, Y., Li, Y., Cao, M., Wang, J., Wang, Y., Thomas, R. K. *Langmuir* 2007, 23, 11458-11464

[135] Oda, R., Huc, I., Danino, D., Talmon, Y. *Langmuir*, 2000, 16, 9759-9769

[136] FitzGerald, P. A., Davey, T. W., Warr, G. G. *Langmuir*, 2005, 21, 7121-7128

[137] Seredyuk, V., Alami, E., Nyden, M., Holmberg, K., Peresypkin, A. V., Menger, F. M. *Langmuir* 2001, 17, 5160-5165

[138] Menger, F. M., Peresypkin, A. V. *J. Am. Chem. Soc.* 2003, 125, 5340-5345

[139] Jiang, N., Li, P., Wang, Y., Wang, J., Yan, H., Thomas, R. K. *J. Phys. Chem. B 2004*, 108, 15385-15391

[140] Zana, R. In *Gemini Surfactants, Synthesis, Interfacial and Solution-Phase Behavior, and Application, Surfactant Science Series*; Zana, R.; Xia, J.; Ed.; Marcel Dekker, Inc.: New York, NY, 2004, Vol. 117, pp 141-184

[141] Turco Liveri, M. L., Lombardo, R., Sbriziolo, C., Viscardi, G., Quagliotto, P. *New J. Chem.* 2004, 28, 793-799

[142] Sheikh, M. S., Kabir-ud-Din, Dar, A. A. *Colloid Surface* A 378, 2011, 60-66

[143] Ansari, W. H., Fatma, N., Panda, M., Kabir-ud-Din, *Soft Matter* 2013, 9, 1478-1487

[144] Wei, J., Huang, G., Wang, S., Fao, Y. *Colloid Surface* A 2013, 423, 50-57

[145] Gao, B., Sharma, M. M. *J. Colloid Interface Sci.* 2012, 404, 80-84

[146] Kabir-ud-Din; Shafi, M., Bhat, P. A., Dar, A. A. *J. Hazard. Mater.* 2009, 167, 575-581

[147] Xe, J., Liu, T., Liu, Y. *J. Dispersion Sci. Technol.* 2012, 33, 599-604

[148] Abdel-Salam, F. H., El-Said, A. *J. Surfact. Deterg.* 2011, 14, 371-379

[149] Wei, J., Huang, G., An, C., Yu, H. *J. Hazard. Mater.* 2011, 190, 840-847

[150] Zhang, Q., Gao, Z., Xu, F., Tai, S., Liu, X., Mo, S., Niu, F. *Langmuir* 2013, 28, 11979-11987

[151] Xu, J., Han, X., Liu, H., Hu, L. *J. Dispersion Sci. Technol.* 2005, 26, 473-476

[152] Veronovski, N., Andreozzi, P., La Mesa, C., Sfiligoj-Smole, M., Ribitisch, V. *Colloid Polym. Sci.* 2010, 288, 387-394

[153] Kuliszewska, E., Pozniak, B. P., Hordyjewicz-Baran, Z., *Przem. Chem.* 2013, 93, 331-335

[154] Van de Hulst, H. C. *Light Scattering By Small Particles*, Dover Publications, Inc: New York, NY, 1981

[155] Schartl, W. *Light Scattering from Polymer Solutions and Nanoparticle Dispersions*, Springer-Verlag: Berlin, 2007

[156] Minkeberg, C. B., Homan B., Boekhoven, J., Norder, B., Koper, G. J. M., Eelkema, R., van Esch, J. H. *Langmuir* 2012, 28, 13570-13576

[157] Choi, T.-S., Shimizu, Y., Shirai, H., Hamada, K. *Dyes Pigments* 2000, 45, 145-152

[158] Zana, R., Levy, H. *Langmuir* 1997, 13, 402-408

[159] Sokolowski, A., Wilk, K. A., Komorek, U., Rutkowski, B., Syper, L. *Physicochem. Probl. Miner. Process* 2002, 36, 51-64

[160] Pisarcik, M., Devinsky, F., Lacko, I. *Acta Facult. Pharm. Univ. Comenianae* 2006, 53, 184-192

[161] Mathias, J. H., Rosen, M., Davenport, L. *Langmuir* 2001, 17, 6148-6154

[162] Lakowicz, J. R. *Principles of Fluorescence Spectroscopy*, 3rd edition, Springer Sciences+Buisness Media LLC: New York, NY, 2006

[163] Wang, Q., Han, Y., Wang, Y., Qin, Y., Guo, Z. *J. Phys. Chem. B* 2008, 112, 7227-7233

[164] Tehrani-Bagha, A. R., Singh, R. G., Holmberg, K. *J. Colloid Interface Sci.* 2012, 376, 112-118

[165] Zheng, O., Zhao, J. X. *J. Colloid Interface Sci.* 2006, 300, 749-754

[166] Crescenzo, A. D., Germani, R., Del Canto, E., Giordani, S., Savelli, G., Fontana, A. *Eur. J. Org. Chem.* 2011, 5641-5648

[167] Danino D., Talmon Y. In *Molecular Gels, Materials with Self-Assembled Fibrillar Networks,* Weiss R. G.; Terech P.; Ed.; Springer: Dordrecht, 2005, pp 253-274

[168] *Handbook of Cryo-Preparation Methods For Electron Microscopy;* Cavalier, A.; Spehner, D.; Humbel, B. M.; Ed.; CRC Press: Boca Raton, 2008

[169] Guoyong, W., Wenshan, Q., Zhiping, D., Wanxu, W., Qiuxiao, L. *J. Phys. Chem. B* 2013, 117, 3154-3160

[170] Tadros, T. F. *Applied Surfactants: Principles and Applications*; WileyVCH: Weinheim, 2005

[171] Myers, D. *Surfactants Science and Technology*, 3rd ed.; Wiley-Interscience: Hoboken, NJ, 2006

[172] Knock, M. M., Bain, C. D. *Langmuir* 2000, 16, 2857-2865

[173] Subramanian, V., Ducker, W. A. *Langmuir* 2000, 16, 4447-4454

[174] Hugerth, A., Sundeloꞕf, L.-O. *Langmuir* 2000, 16, 4940-4945

[175] Lin, H.-P., Kao, C.-P., Mou, C.-Y., Liu, S.-B. *J. Phys. Chem. B* 2000,104, 7885-7894

[176] Kunz, W., Henle, J., Ninham, B. W. *Curr. Opin. In Colloid Interface Sci.* 2004, 9, 19-37

[177] Hofmeister, F. *Arch. Exp. Pathol. Pharmakol.* 1888, 24, 247-260

[178] Romsted, L. S. *Langmuir* 2007, 23, 414-424

[179] Mu, J.-H., Li, G.-Z., Jia, X.-L., Wang, H.-X., Zhang, G.-Y. *J. Phys. Chem. B* 2002, 106, 11685-11693

[180] Wattebled, L., Laschewsky, A. *Langmuir* 2007, 23, 10044-10052

[181] Manet, S., Karpichev, Y., Bassani, D., Kiagus-Ahmad, R., Oda, R. *Langmuir* 2010, 26, 10645-10656

[182] Lu, T., Huang, J., Li, Z., Jia, S., Fu, H. *J. Phys. Chem. B* 2008, 112, 2909-2914

[183] Siddiqui, U. S., Khan, F., Khan, I. A., Dar, A. A., Kabir-ud-Din, *J. Colloid Interface Sci.* 2011, 355, 131–139

[184] Khan, F., Siddiqui, U. S., Khan, I. A., Kabir-ud-Din, *Colloid Surface,* A 2012, 394, 46–56

[185] Yu, D., Huang, X., Deng, M., Lin, Y., Jiang, L., Huang, J., Wang, Y. *J. Phys. Chem. B* 2010, 114, 14955–14964

[186] Ryhanen, S. J., Saily, V. M. J., Parry, M. J., Luciani, P., Mancini, G., Alakoskela, J. M. I., Kinnunen, P. K. J. *J. Am. Chem. Soc.* 2006, 128, 8659–8663.

[187] Oda, R., Huc, I., Schmutz, M., Candau, S. J., MacKintosh, F. C. *Nature* 1999, 399, 566-569

[188] Berthier, D., Buffeteau, T., Le´ger, J.-M., Oda, R., Huc, I. *J. Am. Chem. Soc.* 2002, 124, 13486-13494

[189] Brizard, A., Aime´, C., Labrot, T., Huc, I., Berthier, D., Artzner, F., Desbat, B., Oda, R. *J. Am. Chem. Soc.* 2007, 129, 3754-3762

[190] Siddiqui, U. S., Ghosh, G., Kabir-ud-Din, *Langmuir* 2006, 22, 9874-9878

[191] Siddiqui, U. S., Khan, F., Khan, I. A., Kabir-ud-Din, *J. Solution Chem.* 2012, 41, 1133–1143

[192] Ansari, W. H., Aslam, J., Siddiqui, U. S., Kabir-ud-Din, *J. Mol. Liq*. 2012, 174, 5–10
[193] Graciani, M. M., Rodríguez, A., Martín, V. I., Moyá, M. L. *J. Colloid Interface Sci*. 2010, 342, 382–391
[194] Chavda, S., Singh, K., Perry, M. G., Marangoni, D. G., Aswal, V. K., Bahadur, P. *Colloids Surf.*, A 2011, 378, 79–86
[195] Chavda, S., Bahadur, P., *J. Mol. Liq*. 2011, 161, 72–77
[196] Kumar, B., Tikariha, D., Ghosh, K. K., Quagliotto, P. *J. Mol. Liq*. 2012, 172, 81–87
[197] Rangel-Yagui, C. O., Pessoa-Jr, A., Tavares, L. C. *J. Pharm. Pharmaceut. Sci.* 2005, 147-163
[198] Chaiko, M. A., Nagarajan, R., Ruckenstein, E. *J. Colloid Interface Sci.* 1984, 99, 168-182
[199] Wei, X.-L., Yin, B.-L., Liu, J., Sun, D.-Z., Li, G.-Z. *J. Dispersion Sci. Technol.* 2007, 28, 291-295
[200] Devinsky, F., Lacko, I., Imam, T., *J. Colloid Interface Sci.* 1991, 143, 2, 336-342
[201] Dam, Th., Engberts, J. B. F. N., Karthauser, J., Karaborni, S., van Os, N. M. *Colloid Surfaces* A 1996 118, 41-49
[202] Dreja, M., Tieke, B. *Langmuir* 1998, 14, 800-807
[203] Moshe, M. B., Magdassi, S., Cohen, Y., Avram, L. *J. Colloid Interface Sci.* 2004, 276, 221-226
[204] Xu, J., Han, X., Liu, H., Hu, Y. *Colloid Surface A* 2006, 273, 179-183
[205] Negm, N. A. *J. Surfact. Deterg.* 2007, 10, 71-80
[206] Alehyen, S., Bensejjay, F., El Achouri, M., Perez, L., Infante, M. R. *J. Surfact. Deterg.* 2010, 13, 225-231
[207] Panda, M., Kabir-ud-Din *J. Mol. Liq*. 2011,63, 93-98
[208] Wei, J., Huang, G., Yu, H., An, C. *Chem. Eng. J.* 2011, 168, 201-207
[209] Xue, J., Liu, T., Liu, Y. *J. Disper. Sci. Technol.* 2012, 33, 599-604
[210] Michel, D., Chitanda, J. M., Balogh, R., Yang, P., Singh, P., Das, U., El-Aneed, A., Dimmock, J., Verall, R., Badea, I. *Eur. J. Pharm. Biopharm*. 2012, 81, 548-556
[211] He, S., Chen, H., Guo, Z., Wang, B., Tang, C., Feng, Y. *Colloid Surfaces* A 2013, 429, 98-105
[212] Li, D., Fang, W., Wang, H., Gao, C., Zhang, R., Cai, K. *Ind. Eng. Chem. Res*. 2013, 52, 8109-8113
[213] Rosen, M. J. . *Surfactants and Interfacial Phenomena,* Second edition, John Wiley and Sons, New York, 1989
[214] May-Masnou, A., Pasc, A., Stebe, M. J., Gutierrez, J. M., Porras, M., Blin, J. L., *Micropor. Mesopor. Mat*. 2013, 169, 235-241
[215] Mirgorodskaya, A. B., Yackevich, E. I., Lukashenko, S. S., Zakharova, L. Ya., Konovalov, A. I. *J. Mol. Liq*. 2012, 169, 106-109

In: Micelles
Editors: Danielle Bradburn and Tom Bittinger

ISBN: 978-1-62948-444-0
© 2014 Nova Science Publishers, Inc.

Chapter 5

MICELLES FROM LIPOAMINO ACIDS

Célia Faustino[1], António Calado[1] and Luis Garcia-Rio[2]*

[1]iMed.UL – Research Institute for Medicines and Pharmaceutical Sciences,
Faculty of Pharmacy, University of Lisbon, Lisbon, Portugal
[2]Department of Physical Chemistry, Faculty of Chemistry,
University of Santiago de Compostela, Santiago de Compostela, Spain

ABSTRACT

Surfactants are used in a large scale in the petrochemical, agrochemical, food, cosmetic, pharmaceutical, textile, paint and coating industries due to their detergent, emulsifying, solubilising, wetting and foaming properties. The demand for more efficient and environmentally friendly surfactants leads to the growing need for new surfactants with improved performances and lower toxicity. Lipoamino acids (LAA), i.e. amino acids bearing a long hydrocarbon chain, are an important class of bio-based, eco-friendly surfactants that can be produced either by chemical synthesis or biotechnological procedures.

Our group is interested in the development of new biocompatible and biodegradable surfactants with improved performances for technological and biomedical applications. In that sense LAA become very attractive regarding their multifunctionality, low toxicity and renewable sources of raw materials and their potential use as antimicrobial, drug delivery and transfection agents.

LAA, with the exception of glycine derivatives, are chiral compounds, and stereochemistry variation may account for changes in surface active properties and self-assembly behaviour. Although the aggregation process of LAA in aqueous solution is analogous to conventional surfactants, their optical properties and the ability for hydrogen bond formation, especially in the case of the amide derivatives, confers them peculiar characteristics. LAA may form not only micelles but also other supramolecular aggregates in aqueous media, such as helical or cylindrical fibres, bilayers, vesicles and lyotropic liquid crystalline phases.

---

* Corresponding author; E-mail: cfaustino@ff.ul.pt.

This review summarizes research on synthetic LAA obtained from the common proteinogenic amino acids, with an emphasis on micelle formation. LAA production is briefly addressed, and their surface active and biological properties, namely antimicrobial activity, are described. Self-assembly behaviour of their aqueous solutions is analysed in terms of LAA architecture, including the length of the hydrophobic chain, nature of the amino acid residue and type of counter-ion, and external conditions such as ionic strength of the solution, pH and temperature are also considered. Structure-property relationships offer valuable information for modulation of the LAA properties in order to meet specific applications.

Technological and biomedical applications of LAA will be briefly summarized that account for the emergence of LAA as a promising and reliable alternative to speciality surfactants aiming at production of biocompatible compounds with low environmental impact from renewable natural sources.

Keywords: Amino acids; lipoamino acids; micelles; critical micelle concentration (CMC)

1. INTRODUCTION

Surface active agents (surfactants) are widely used in the pharmaceutical, cosmetic, textile, paint, coating, petrochemical, agrochemical and food industries [1, 2]. Surfactants are characterized by the presence of two distinct regions in their molecular structure, namely a hydrophilic, polar region, which can be ionic or non-ionic, and a hydrophobic region, usually a long hydrocarbon chain. Due to the geometric form adopted by surfactant molecules, the polar group is called the head group while the hydrocarbon chain is known as the tail.

The amphiphilic nature of surfactant molecules is responsible for their unique properties, such as adsorption at interfaces, lowering of interfacial or surface tension, and self-assembly in solution, at concentrations above a certain critical value [1, 2]. Micelles are supramolecular assemblies formed when surfactant concentration in solution exceeds a critical concentration, called critical micelle concentration (CMC). Micelle formation is involved in several important biological processes, such as interaction with cell membranes, lytic action and solubilisation of hydrophobic molecules [3, 4]. At increasing surfactant concentrations, micelles change in shape from spherical to elongate or cylindrical aggregates and at higher concentrations, well above the CMC, lyotropic liquid crystalline phases are formed [1–4].

The dual (polar-apolar) nature of surfactants and in particular the balance between the hydrophilic and hydrophobic regions of the molecules determines the technological application of surfactants, such as detergents, solubilisers, emulsifying, wetting, and (anti)foaming agents, dispersants and suspension stabilizers, among other functions that they are able to perform [1, 2]. Much attention has been focused on the potential use of surfactants as drug delivery agents, templates for nanoparticles, biomembrane models, reaction media and transfection agents in gene therapy, as an alternative to viral vectors [1–5].

The high global demand for surfactants – their annual global consumption at the beginning of the millennium exceeded 17 kt [6] and currently the estimated annual global production is over 12 Mt [7] – has a high environmental impact and represents added risks for public health associated with the relative toxicity of these chemicals and/or their production processes [6, 7]. The demand for more efficient and environmentally friendly surfactants leads to the growing need for new surfactants with improved performances and lower toxicity, preferentially derived from naturally occurring renewable sources. In this sense lipoamino acids (LAA) play a prominent role as biocompatible and biodegradable surfactants, often with intrinsic antimicrobial activity that meets the requirement of physiological and ecological compatibility [8–13]. They offer the additional advantage of being amenable to production by biotechnological procedures, as an alternative to chemical synthesis, either by fermentation or enzymatic catalysis [7, 14–17], or from protein hydrolisates from bioindustrial waste [8, 18], thus allowing the conversion of low-cost by-products into high value-added compounds.

2. LIPOAMINO ACIDS

2.1. Structure and Classification

Lipids conjugated with an amino acid residue are known as lipoamino acids (LAA). Naturally occurring LAA are condensation products of amino acids with fatty acids or fatty acid derivatives [8, 11, 13]. LAA are found in the inner and outer bacterial membranes, but plants and animals can also produce these compounds, which have attracted much attention due to their biological role as chemical messengers and their potent antimicrobial activity [8, 9, 12]. Synthetic LAA obtained from natural amino acids are usually biodegradable and biocompatible compounds with remarkable surface active properties, often with intrinsic biological activity [8–13]. A wide diversity in LAA structure and properties are possible, according to the type of amino acid residue.

Amino acids are the building blocks of proteins. There are about 20 proteinogenic amino acids, with the general formula $H_2NCHRCOOH$, where R is a side chain specific of each amino acid [19]. All are α-amino acids (i.e., the amine moiety and the carboxyl function are attached at the same carbon atom, called the α-carbon) and all are chiral, with the exception of glycine, occurring as L-enantiomers [19]. At physiological pH, deprotonation of the acidic carboxyl group and protonation of the basic amino group occur, therefore L-α-amino acids exist in the form of dipolar ions or zwitterions. The pH at which the extent of protonation equals that of deprotonation is called the isoelectric point, p*I*, which is characteristic of the amino acid [19].

Amino acids are usually classified according to the nature of their side chain, in terms of polarity and acid-base properties (nonpolar or hydrophobic, polar nonionic, anionic or acidic and cationic or basic) or structure composition (aliphatic, cyclic, aromatic, hydroxyl, sulphur-containing, amide-containing, acidic and basic). The names and structures of the 20 proteinogenic amino acids, along with the three- and one-letter code abbreviations [19], are listed in Table 1.

This review summarizes research on synthetic micelle-forming lipoamino acids, obtained from the proteinogenic amino acids listed in Table 1, during the last two decades (1993-2013).

Table 1. The common proteinogenic amino acids, H₂NCHRCOOH. R is the amino acid side chain

–R	Name	Abbreviation
Nonpolar side chains		
–H	Glycine	Gly (G)
–CH₃	Alanine	Ala (A)
–CH(CH₃)₂	Valine	Val (V)
–CH₂CH(CH₃)₂	Leucine	Leu (L)
–CH(CH₃)CH₂CH₃	Isoleucine	Ile (I)
–(CH₂)₂SCH₃	Methionine	Met (M)
–(CH₂)₃–	Proline	Pro (P)
–CH₂Ph	Phenylalanine	Phe (F)
–CH₂(3-indolyl)	Tryptophan	Trp (W)
Polar, nonionic side chains		
–CH₂OH	Serine	Ser (S)
–CH(CH₃)OH	Threonine	Thr (T)
–CH₂(4-hydroxyphenyl)	Tyrosine	Tyr (Y)
–CH₂SH	Cysteine	Cys (C)
–CH₂CONH₂	Asparagine	Asn (N)
–(CH₂)₂CONH₂	Glutamine	Gln (Q)
Acidic side chains		
–CH₂CO₂H	Aspartic acid	Asp (D)
–(CH₂)₂CO₂H	Glutamic acid	Glu (E)
Basic side chains		
–CH₂(4-imidazolyl)	Histidine	His (H)
–(CH₂)₄NH₂	Lysine	Lys (K)
–(CH₂)₃NHC(=NH)NH₂	Arginine	Arg (R)

2.2. (Bio)synthesis

2.2.1. Chemical Synthesis

The variety of natural amino acids, differing in structure and polarity, allows the preparation of a wide structural diversity of lipoamino acids with distinct properties. They can be anionic, cationic, non-ionic or amphoteric, depending on the free functional groups of the amino acid residue. The hydrophobic chain can be introduced by reaction of the amine group of the amino acid (**I**, Fig. 1) with a fatty acid (chloride) or an alkyl halide, to give the corresponding *N*-acyl (**II**, Fig. 1) and *N*-alkyl (**III**, Fig. 1) derivatives. Alternatively, the carboxyl group of the amino acid **I** can be condensed with alkylamines or long chain alcohols, to give alkylamide (**IV**, Fig. 1) and fatty esters (**V**, Fig. 1), respectively [8–12].

Chemical synthesis of LAA usually requires protection of the α-amine function and/or activation of the α-carboxyl group of the amino acid residue, followed by amine deprotection after reaction completion [8–12]. Typical amino acid protection and activating groups used in amino acid and peptide synthesis are generally employed [20]. Thus, the α-amine moiety can be protected by conversion to alkoxycarbonylamino derivatives (carbamates), usually benzyloxycarbonyl (Z), *t*-butoxycarbonyl (Boc), and 9-fluorenylmehoxycarbonyl (Fmoc) derivatives. The Z protecting group is neither affected by mildly basic or acidic conditions, nor by nucleophilic reagents. Classic cleavage conditions are acid hydrolysis with HBr in acetic acid or in alternative, catalytic hydrogenolysis. On the contrary, the Boc protecting group is stable to catalytic hydrogenolysis and reducing reagents in general but is very labile to acids, being therefore orthogonal to the Z group [20]. Basic and nucleophilic reagents do not affect the Boc group, which is removed under mild acidic conditions with trifluoroacetic acid (TFA). On the other hand, the Fmoc group is stable to acidic conditions, being rapidly cleaved in basic media, usually by a solution of piperidine in dimethyl formamide (DMF) [20].

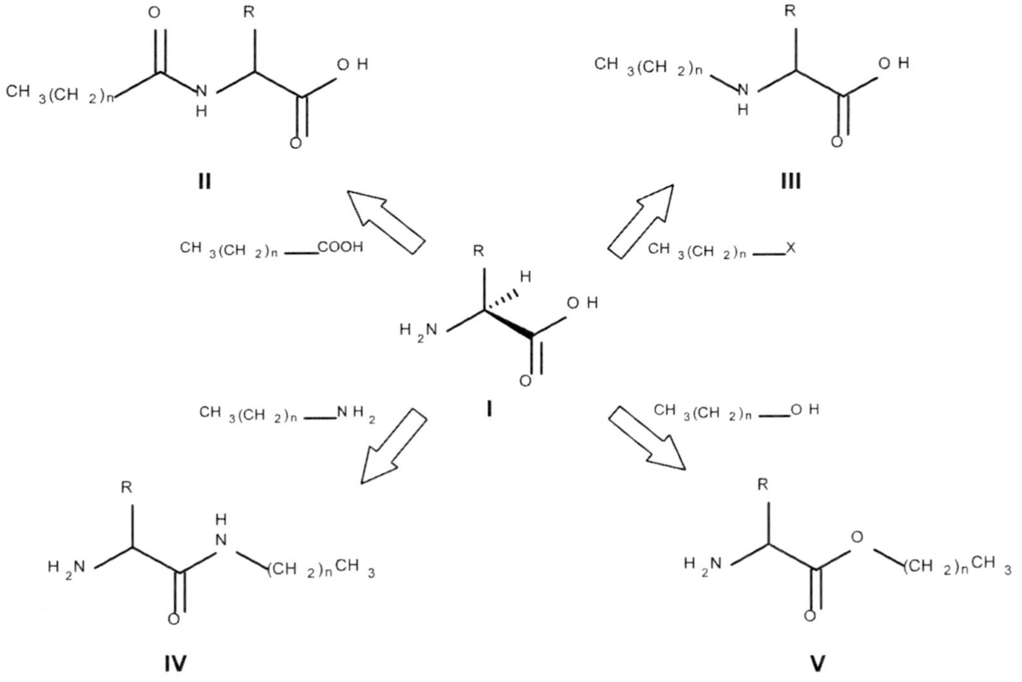

Figure 1. Synthetic pathways from proteinogenic amino acids (**I**) to lipoamino acids: *N*-acyl (**II**), *N*-alkyl (**III**), alkylamide (**IV**) and alkylester (**V**) derivatives. R is the amino acid side chain.

The usual procedure for α-carboxyl protection is esterification, usually as methy, ethyl, *t*-butyl, benzyl or phenyl esters [20]. These esters are compatible with standard coupling procedures and amine deprotective reactions. The stability and lability of the *t*-butyl and benzyl esters parallel the properties of the Boc and Z protecting groups, respectively. Deprotection requires saponification, which can cause racemisation and hydantoin formation, so hydrazinolysis is an alternative, while for phenyl esters removal of the protecting group can be achieved in smooth conditions by hydrogen peroxide in aqueous DMF [20].

Chemical activation of the carboxyl group, i.e., the attachment of a leaving group to the acyl carbon of the carboxyl component to enable nucleophilic attack, is necessary as carboxylic acids form salts with basic nucleophiles. Activation can be achieved by conversion of the carboxyl group to the correspondent acyl chloride, acyl azide, anhydride or to an active ester [20]. One of the most used coupling reagents is dicyclohexylcarbodiimide (DCC), which reacts with the acyl carbon of the carboxyl group to give the potent acylating agent *O*-acylisourea. Alternatively, phosphonium and uronium salts, such as *O*-(benzotriazol-1-yl)-*N*,*N*,*N'*,*N'*-tetramethyluronium tetrafluoroborate (TBTU), which react readily with carboxylate anions giving reactive electrophilic acyloxyphosphonium or acyloxyuronium species (activated ester intermediates), have been developed as coupling reagents. Although named as an uronium salt, TBTU is now believed to be a guanidinium derivative [20].

LAA prepared from amino acid residues with reactive side chains may require selective protection of the side chain functionalities. The reader is referred to specific literature on amino acid and peptide synthesis for more detailed information [21, 22].

2.2.2. Enzymatic Synthesis

Hydrolytic enzymes such as lipases and proteases can be made to catalyse amide bond formation instead of hydrolysis by appropriate choice of reaction conditions [23]. Thermodynamic controlled conditions can be adapted so as to shift the equilibrium towards LAA formation, instead of hydrolysis. Protecting groups for the amino acid substrate that ensure precipitation of the product can be employed for the purpose, as well as biphasic systems with passage of the LAA from the aqueous phase into an organic solvent as soon as it is formed, or by using water-miscible organic solvents able to displace the equilibrium in the desired direction [15–17, 24, 25]. A second alternative involves kinetic control conditions, where competition of the amine nucleophile with water for the acyl-enzyme intermediate occurs [15, 16]. Among the hydrolytic enzymes, lipases from *Candida antarctica* and *Rhizomucor miehei* (both free and immobilized), papain from *Carica papaya* latex and *Bacillus subtilis* protease have been extensively used [15–17, 24, 26].

Several reaction variables must be considered for optimization of the enzymatic process and product yield, namely aqueous buffer content, pH, temperature, enzyme concentration, biocatalyst configuration (free or immobilized) and synthetic approaches (thermodynamic or kinetic controlled biosynthesis) [24, 27]. However, enzyme catalysis, as a green chemistry-based approach to eco-friendly LAA, offers several advantages, namely mild reaction conditions, selectivity, absence of racemisation, circumvents cumbersome protection strategies of the amino acid residue, and allows for the use of immobilized enzymes with easy removal and recovery of the biocatalyst, with the possibility for industrial scale-up [24, 26, 27].

2.3. Physicochemical Properties and Self-Assembly Behaviour

2.3.1. Lipoamino Acids with Hydrophobic Residues

The nature of the amino acid residue strongly influences the self-assembly behaviour of lipoamino acids. *N*-Acyl lipoamino acids show a wide range of biological activities, namely antibacterial, antifungal, antiviral and antitumor and have therefore been exhaustively studied [8, 12, 28–34]. The compounds, as water-soluble salts, are easily prepared by acylation of the amine group of the amino acid residue, usually with a long chain acyl chloride, under Shötten-Baumann conditions. The ability of the amide bond of the *N*-acyl chain to participate in intra- and intermolecular hydrogen bonding strongly influences the LAA surface properties and even the morphology of the supramolecular aggregates that can be formed [28–34].

Both the length of the hydrophobic *N*-acyl chain and the hydrophobicity of the amino acid residue, i.e., the length and chemical structure of its side chain, have a profound effect on the surface and micelar properties of *N*-acyl LAA [8, 28–34]. From the huge amount of literature available on the theme it was possible to establish some correlations between *N*-acyl LAA structure and surfactant properties of their sodium salts. Thus, increasing the *N*-acyl chain length leads to a decrease in the CMC and to an increase in the aggregation number, as with conventional surfactants [8, 12, 30–32]. Increasing the hydrophobicity of the amino acid residue increases the area occupied per molecule at the air/water interface, which is accompanied by a decrease in surface activity due to a lower ability to pack tightly at the water surface [8, 12, 28–34]. The CMC usually decreases with the increase in the amino acid hydrophobicity, however specific intra- and/or intermolecular interactions between the amino acid residues may alter this trend [28, 29, 33, 34]. Table 2 summarizes the CMC values found in the literature for the sodium salts of *N*-acyl LAA bearing amino acid residues with apolar (hydrophobic) side chains [28–30, 32–34].

Table 2. Variation of critical micelle concentration (CMC) with acyl chain length for the sodium salts of some *N*-acyl lipoamino acids, in water at 25.0 °C, unless otherwise stated

Amino acid	10^3 CMC / mol dm^{-3}				
	C_{10}	C_{12}	C_{14}	C_{16}	C_{18}
Gly		0.83[a], 2.8[b]		0.176[c]	
Ala	48.0[d]	2.8[b],12.3[d]	3.00[d]	0.087[c],0.81[d]	
Val		1.1[b]		0.076[c],0.019[e]	
Leu	2.01[a]	0.92[a],0.54[b]	0.20[a]	0.08[a],0.015[e] 0.028[f]	0.02[a]
Ile				0.013[e]	
Met				0.041[f]	
Pro		0.74[a]		0.084[c],0.095[f]	
Phe		0.70[a],0.27[b]		0.017[c],0.077[f]	
Trp		0.55[a]			

[a]at 28 °C, Ref. [32]; [b]values in mmol kg^{-1}, Ref. [28]; [c]in 50 mmol dm^{-3} Tris buffer pH 9.3, Ref. [33]; [d]at 45.0 °C, Ref. [30]; [e]Ref. [29]; [f]at 20.0 °C, Ref. [34].

According to Table 2, for the *N*-acyl leucinates studied by Mhaskar *et al.* [32], CMC decreases with the increase in acyl chain length, due to increased hydrophobicity. The CMC of *N*-oleoyl leucinate was 0.21 mmol dm^{-3}, higher than the CMC of the saturated homologue, *N*-stearoyl leucinate, however the former was a better wetting agent than the latter, showing the favourable effect of unsaturation on wetting ability. Miyagishi *et al.* [30] also found a decrease of the CMC with increasing acyl chain length for the *N*-acylalanine series (Table 2), from conductivity measurements performed at 45.0 °C, and verified a linear correlation between log CMC and the number of carbon atoms in the acyl chain [30].

The effect of the side chain of the amino acid residue on micelle formation has been studied by isothermal titration calorimetry (ITC) in the temperature range 298.15–318.15 K for the sodium salts of a series of *N*-dodecanoyl amino acids (Gly, Ala, Val, Leu, Phe) [28]. The CMC of the LAA decreased monotonously with increasing hydrophobicity of the amino acid residue, at constant temperature (Table 2). The enthalpies of micelle formation were positive at the lower temperature of 288.15 K, revealing the importance of surfactant dehydration in micelle formation (which tends to minimize molecular interactions between water and the hydrophobic surfactant tails) and decreased linearly with increasing temperature to become negative at 318.15 K, with interaction between surfactant molecules predominating over dehydration at higher temperatures [28]. The enthalpies of micellization increased with the size of the amino acid residue, suggesting that dehydration involves not only the hydrophobic acyl chain of the surfactant but also the side chain of the amino acid residue. Actually, a close correlation was found between the enthalpy of micelle formation and the hydrophobic index of the amino acid residues, with the exception of Phe [28]. The increase in hydrophobicity is accompanied by a strong increase in entropy by micellization in the case of the aliphatic residues, while for C_{12}-Phe intra-micelle association between the aromatic side chains of the amino acid residue lowers the enthalpy of micellization, and therefore dehydration around the benzyl group corresponds to a lesser gain in entropy [28]. Intermolecular interactions between the aromatic residues were also responsible for the high aggregation number of C_{12}-Phe micelles [28].

More recently, these findings were corroborated by tensiometric and steady state fluorescence studies on N-palmitoyl amino acids (Gly, Ala, Val, Phe, Pro) in aqueous buffered solutions [33]. The CMC (Table 2) and the Gibbs energy of micellization decreased with the increase in the hydrophobicity of the amino acid residue, the hydrophobic interaction being the driving force for LAA self-assembly. The lowest CMC value was obtained for C_{16}-Phe, due to intramicellar π-π attractive interactions between the aromatic side chains of the amino acid residues that contributed to micelle stabilization, while the highest CMC value was found for C_{16}-Pro, associated with van der Waals repulsions between side chains arising from the bulky substituent [33]. Proline, actually an imino acid with a unique and rigid five-member ring structure, is known to disrupt α-helix assemblies in proteins due to geometric constraints [19]. A high CMC value was also observed for the sodium salt of C_{16}-Pro in pure water [34], attributed to steric hindrance between the cyclic side chains of the amino acid residues, which does not favour micelle stability.

The group of S. Miyagishi and T. Asakawa have exhaustively studied the self-assembly behaviour of N-acyl LAA in aqueous solutions and the influence of external conditions on the process [30, 35–39]. The CMC values of sodium N-acyl-alaninates and N-lauroyl-valinates were determined in the temperature range between 25.0 and 45.0°C and in the presence of different sodium chloride concentrations [30]. The CMC of the N-dodecanoyl derivatives increased slightly with temperature in the temperature range covered. The influence of sodium chloride concentration on the CMC has been examined for the lauroyl derivatives at constant temperature and CMC values decrease with increasing salt concentration. The Corrin-Harkins plots (log-log plot of CMC *versus* counterion concentration) were linear and the absolute value of the slope, corresponding to the degree of counter-ion binding to micelle (β), was 0.44 and 0.46 for C_{12}-Ala and C_{12}-Val, respectively [30]. The degree of counterion binding to micelle was used to estimate the aggregation numbers based on the method of Evans [40], and small values (14 for alaninates and 13 for valinates) were obtained [30].

The CMC values for different salts of N-dodecanoyl alanine (lithium, sodium, potassium, cesium, ammonium and triethanolammonium), measured using a fluorescence probe method, were found to be dependent on counterion concentration, regardless of the type of counterion [35]. At low salt concentrations the CMC decreased linearly with increasing counterion concentration, however at high salt concentrations the plot deviated downward from the linear relationship, the deviation being associated with a micelle shape transition, from spherical to cylindrical (rod-like) micelles [35]. The threshold concentration of counterion corresponding to the transition point of micelle growth is dependent on the size of the counterion and also on the chain length of the N-acyl amino acid, as determined in similar studies with sodium and potassium salts of N-acyl-alaninates and -valinates [36–38]. Micellar aggregation number was smaller for the triethanolammonium salt, varying between 37 and 55 with increasing counterion concentration, compared with variations between 48 and 72 for the other salts of N-lauroyl-alanine [35]. The bulky organic counterion was not so effective in reducing electrostatic repulsions between the ionic head groups thus leading to smaller micelles [35].

The Kraft temperature (K_T) is an important surfactant parameter as micelles form in aqueous solution only above K_T. The Kraft temperature of a series of N-palmitoyl amino acid surfactants was determined from both solubility measurements and differential scanning calorimetry (DSC) and it was found to increase with decreasing size of the amino acid residue, in the order Ile < Leu < Val < Phe < Ala < Gly, phenylalanine being again an exception [29]. Increase in size of the hydrophobic amino acid residue loosens the packing of surfactant molecules leading to a decrease in the K_T. Packing of surfactant molecules also becomes looser when the branch point of the residue is located nearer to the main chain, as comparison of the K_T for C_{16}-Leu and C_{16}-Ile suggests. The bulky aromatic ring of phenylalanine, instead of causing steric hindrance, leads to a favourable interaction in the solid state that has been attributed to stabilization by π-π interactions between the aromatic rings, resulting in a relatively high K_T [29]. The Kraft temperature of C_{16}-Ala, C_{16}-Val and C_{14}-Phe with different counterions (Li^+, Na^+, K^+ and Cs^+) increased with decreasing size of the counterion, from the combined effects of an increase of the hydration of the counterion in the micelar state and tightening of molecular packing in the solid state [39].

2.3.2. LAA with Nonionic Polar Residues

The self-assembly behaviour of LAA bearing polar residues is influenced by the presence of the hydrophilic substituent in the amino acid side chain. With the exception of cysteine, the other amino acids of this class have hydroxyl (Ser, Thr, Tyr) or amide (Asn, Gln) groups on their side chains (Table 1). Hence, intermolecular hydrogen-bonding interactions between head groups often occur in these LAA systems [28, 30, 32, 34].

The decrease of CMC values with increasing hydrophobicity of the amino acid residue is a general trend for sodium salts of N-acyl derivatives of Ser, Thr, Tyr, Cys, Asn and Gln [28, 32, 34]. For the same alkyl chain length, cysteine derivatives usually show slightly lower CMC than their hydroxyl analogues derived from serine, due to the more lipophilic nature of the sulphur atom [32]. An extra stabilization of the micelles due to the presence of the hydroxyl group has also been claimed for the threonine derivatives [34]. The higher efficiency in the adsorption characteristics of the hydrochloride salt of tyrosine dodecyl ester is due to the influence of the phenolic OH group on the conformation of the molecule, which provides more compact structures at the interface, contributing to lower interfacial area relatively to the more hydrophobic phenylalanine derivative, as demonstrated from molecular modelling studies [41].

Recently, novel single-chain cationic N-alkyl LAA based on serine and tyrosine with enhanced interfacial properties have been prepared from the corresponding amino acid methyl esters by reductive amination of fatty aldehydes with even chain lengths between C_{12}–C_{18}, a synthetic strategy that allowed for monoalkylation of the amine group of the amino acid residue [42, 43]. A linear dependence of log CMC with alkyl chain length was observed for their trifluoracetate salts, all compounds showing CMC values lower than the ones obtained for conventional N-alkyltrimethylammonium bromides of the same alkyl chain length. With the exception of the C_{16}-Ser and C_{18}-Ser derivatives, the surfactants had Kraft temperatures below or near room temperature. For the N-octadecyl serine derivative the introduction of a chain unsaturation considerably decreased the Kraft temperature and increased the CMC, due to chain packing constraints in the micellar core resulting from the presence of a kink in the alkyl chain of the LAA, while counterion change from trifluoroacetate to iodide had little effect on the aforementioned parameters [43]. The side chain of cysteine (**VI**, R^1 = H, R^2 = OH, Fig.2) contains a nucleophilic thiol group prone to oxidation to form a dimmer, cystine (**VII**, R^1 = H, R^2 = OH, Fig. 2), where a disulfide bond links the two cysteine residues. Disulfide bond formation plays an important biological role in protein stability and folding, as covalent cross-linking among the cysteine residues of the protein backbone increases rigidity and confers proteolytic resistance to the protein [19]. Cystine is a potential building block for cysteine LAA, as the disulfide bond can be cleaved by mild reduction agents, such as dithiothreitol (DTT) or trialkylphosphines, regenerating the free sulfhydryl group [20]. Cystine also allows the preparation of LAA of the dimeric type (Fig. 2). Dimeric (gemini) surfactants are made of two hydrophobic hydrocarbon chains and two polar head groups connected by either a rigid or flexible spacer at the level of the head groups [44, 45]. Gemini surfactants have shown remarkable properties when compared with their monomeric counterparts, including much lower CMC, superior efficiency in surface tension reduction, and a polymorphic phase behaviour [44–47].

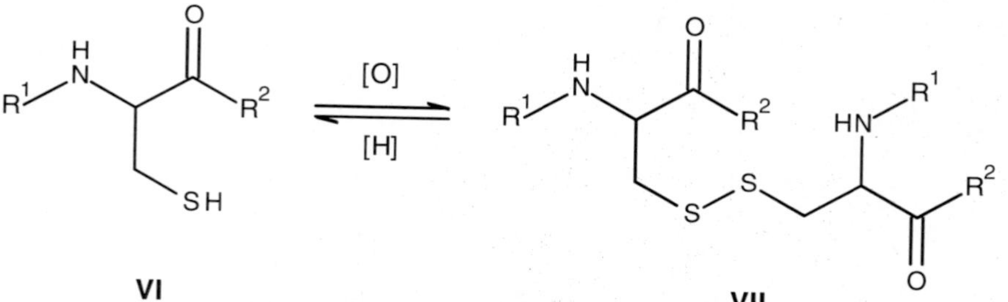

a) $R^1 = CH_3(CH_2)_n$, $R^2 = OH$
b) $R^1 = CH_3(CH_2)_nC=O$, $R^2 = OH$
c) $R^1 = CH_3(CH_2)_nNHC=O$, $R^2 = OH$
d) $R^1 = H$, $R^2 = CH_3(CH_2)_nO$

Figure 2. Monomeric (**VI**) and dimeric (**VII**) lipoamino acids based on the cysteine scaffold.

Yoshimura *et al.* [48] studied the sodium salts of N-alkylamine LAA derived from cysteine and cystine with octyl, decyl and dodecyl chains (**VI-VIIa**, n = 7, 9, 11). All the compounds formed micelles in aqueous solution, as proved by electron microscopy and neutron diffraction techniques, while for the dimeric LAA with dodecyl chains the coexistence of micelles and small unilamellar vesicles was also observed [48]. The gemini derivatives showed lower CMC (Table 3), higher efficacy in surface tension reduction and lower A_{min} when compared with their monomeric counterparts, an indication that geminis are packed more closely at the air/water interface due to stronger hydrophobic interactions resulting from the spacer, which brings the hydrocarbon chains close together [45–47]. Fan *et* *al.* [49] synthesized anionic gemini *N*-acyl LAA derived from cystine (**VIIb**, n = 8, 10) and made use of the ease of reduction of the disulfide bonds to control the surface properties and aggregation behaviour of these systems. The coexistence of micelles and spherical vesicles was also noted for disodium *N,N'*-didodecanoyl cystine [49].

Novel anionic *N*-carbamoyl LAA derived from cysteine and cystine (**VI-VIIc**, n = 7) were synthesized by our research group [50] and were found to interact with biological molecules, including membrane phospholipids [51], serum albumin proteins [52] and oligosaccharides [53]. The behaviour of their sodium salts in aqueous media had been characterized by conductivity, surface tension and fluorescence quenching methods, using pyrene as a fluorescent probe [50]. The new amphiphiles, with octyl chains, showed great efficiency in surface tension reduction, had CMC values (Table 3) close to other anionic surfactants of higher hydrocarbon chain length, such as sodium dodecanoate and sodium dodecyl sulphate (SDS), and were more likely to adsorb at the air/water interface rather than to form micelles. This behaviour can be attributed to the urea moiety and its ability to form hydrogen bonds, as it was also found in other urea surfactants derived from amino acids [54]. The gemini surfactant was less efficient in reducing surface tension than its monomeric counterpart, an unusual finding that may be the result of film formation by the hydrocarbon chains of the former at the air/water interface so that they can not adsorb effectively at the interface, a phenomenon already described for disodium *N,N'*-didodecyl cystine [48].

Table 3. Variation of critical micelle concentration (CMC) with the number of carbon atoms (n_C) in the hydrophobic chain, for monomeric and dimeric cysteine-based lipoamino acids in water at 25 °C, unless otherwise stated

Compound[a]	n_C	10^3 CMC / mol dm^{-3}	Ref.
VI a, n=7	8	6.52[b]	48
VI a, n=9	10	0.424[b]	48
VI a, n=11	12	0.180[b]	48
VI b, n=8	10	n.d.	
VI b, n=10	12	n.d.	
VI c, n =7	8	34.3	50
VI d, n=11	12	2.5	55
VII a, n=7	8	0.493[b]	48
VII a, n=9	10	0.139[b]	48
VII a, n=11	12	0.00135[b]	48
VII b, n=8	10	0.750[c]	49
VII b, n=10	12	0.0220[c]	49
VII c, n=7	8	8.22	50
VII d, n=7	8	0.0115[d]	56

[a]For chemical structures refer to Fig. 2; [b]at pH 13 (NaOH); [c]in 10 mmol dm^{-3} borax pH 9.2; [d]at 30 °C; n.d., not determined.

Cationic LAA derived from esterification of cysteine [55] and cystine [56] with fatty alcohols have also been obtained, with chloride as counterion. The cationic dodecyl ester of cysteine (**VId**, n = 11) formed micelles in aqueous solution and self-assembled on colloid gold nanoparticles [55]. TEM measurements revealed surfactant-coated gold NPs with a size of 55–111 nm [55]. The dioctyl ester of cystine (**VIId**, n = 7) had a remarkable surface activity, with a CMC value about one order of magnitude lower than that reported for other cystine surfactants with the same alkyl chain length (Table 3) [56]. Scanning electron microscopy (SEM) studies suggested formation of elongated micelles in aqueous solution [56]. The CMC values for the cysteine-based LAA discussed above are presented in Table 3.

2.3.3. Lipoamino Acids with an Acidic Residue

Dicarboxylic LAA, namely *N*-acyl derivatives of aspartic or glutamic acid, are an interesting class of surfactants with chelating properties due to the specific structure of the amino acid residue, with two carboxylate groups separated by only two (Asp) or three (Glu) methylene units from an adjacent amide bond [57, 58]. The disodium salts of *N*-dodecanoyl-aspartic and -glutamic acids had distinct calcium tolerance due to different chelating behaviour. *N*-dodecanoylaspartate forms an intramolecular chelate with the divalent calcium ion, leading to a seven-member ring structure, whereas *N*-dodecylglutamate forms preferentially an intermolecular complex [57, 58]. The latter is responsible for tight packing at the air/water interface, leading to very low surface tension values, below 30 mN m^{-1}, while the former favours adsorption on hydroxyapatite and other calcium-containing surfaces [57]. The CMC was also affected by the choice of the monovalent counterion, increasing in the order Li$^+$ < Na$^+$ < K$^+$, which is the opposite trend usually found for monovalent anionic surfactants in solution. This variation is expected to reflect the degree of binding of the counterion to the micelle (β) as the same trend was observed for micelle ionization degree (α). The effect can be explained by the hard carboxylate headgroup binding strongest to the harder lithium cation, according to the Hofmeister series [57, 58].

A micelar cubic phase, formed between the isotropic micelar solution phase and the anisotropic hexagonal liquid crystalline phase, has been reported from small-angle X-ray scattering (SAXS) and nuclear magnetic resonance (NMR) self-diffusion measurements of aqueous systems of potassium and triethanolamine salts of *N*-lauroyl glutamic acid at high surfactant concentrations [59]. The stability of the cubic phase was strongly enhanced by increasing the neutralization degree of the amino acid residue and its extension increased with the size of the counterion [59]. Formation of large micelar cubic phases is not uncommon for divalent surfactants regarding the high electric charge density of the micelar surface that results from the presence of two ionic head groups, which suppresses micelar growth when surfactant concentration increases, and a cubic phase can emerge [8, 59].

Tsubone *et al.* [60] first investigated anionic gemini LAA, namely sodium salts of *N*-acyl LAA derived from aspartic acid (**VIII**, n = 6, 8, 10, 12, 14; Fig. 3), which exhibited very low CMC values, in the micromolar range, between 0.786–123 μmol dm^{-3}. An inversion of the tendency of the CMC to decrease with the increase in acyl chain length was found for *N*-acyl chains longer than C$_{14}$, accompanied by a lower efficiency in surface tension reduction. This unusual behaviour was attributed to premicellar aggregation, the formation below the CMC of small size, soluble aggregates (dimmers) devoided of surface activity that decrease the concentration of free monomers and thus reduce surface activity [60].

Other peculiar aspects characterized the behaviour of these compounds in aqueous solution, namely a lack of steep conductivity variation with LAA concentration once the CMC is reached (responsible for the absence of a break in the conductivity *versus* LAA concentration plots) and an increase of the solution pH with LAA concentration in the CMC neighbourhood [60]. Also, CMC values from conductivity measurements were higher when compared to those obtained by the surface tension method. These findings suggest protonation of the carboxylate anion with simultaneous release of Na^+ during micellization. The consequent increase in hydroxyl ion concentration and the increasing conductivity with LAA concentration effect are in the origin of the anomalies observed for the conductivity *versus* LAA concentration plots [60]. Hydrogen bond formation between the carboxyl and the amide groups, which leads to an increase in size of the hydrophilic head group, is responsible for inhibition of the micellization process. The phenomenon results from a structural characteristic of anionic LAA whose molecules contain both *N*-dialkylamide and carboxylate groups and had previously been observed for monomeric LAA of the kind [61].

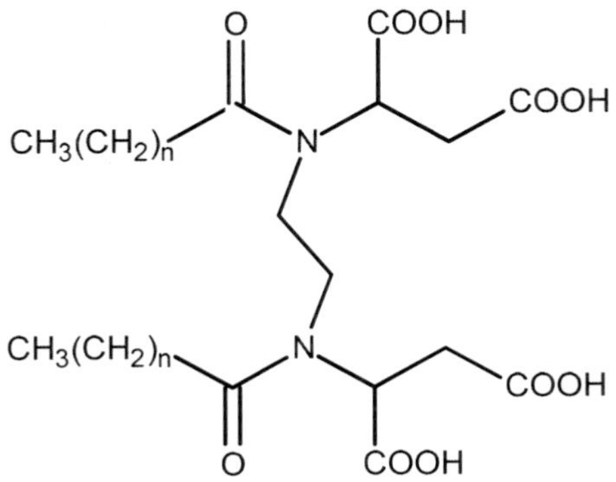

VIII

Figure 3. Gemini lipoamino acids from aspartic acid.

Nonionic LAA from Asp and Glu, with one polyoxyethylene methoxy-capped chain in the headgroup and two hydrophobic chains (**IX**, m = 5, 7, 9 and n = 2, 3; Fig. 4) have been synthesized as structural mimics of lecithins with improved chemical stability [62]. The hydrophobic and hydrophilic moieties are linked through amide bonds in the synthetic LAA, which are more resistant to hydrolysis than the corresponding ester bonds in natural lecithins. The hydrossolubility of the LAA at room temperature was poor, but at 60 °C an isotropic monophasic system was formed [62]. The same behaviour has been observed for short-chain diacyl lecithin analogues, at temperatures above 40 °C [62].

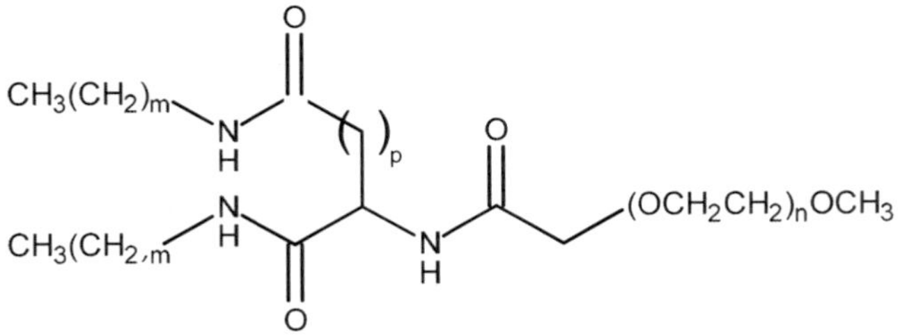

IX

Figure 4. Nonionic lipoamino acids from aspartic (p = 1) and glutamic (p = 2) acids.

Surface tension measurements in water at 60 °C yielded CMC and surface tension values at the CMC between 10^{-3}–10^{-5} mol dm^{-3} and 24–29 mN m^{-1}, respectively, within the range obtained for classical nonionic surfactants [61]. For the same hydrophilic group, these values decrease as the alkyl chain length increases, as usual [1–4]; for the same hydrophobic alky chain, both CMC and surface tension values increase with the number of oxyethylene units in the polyoxyethylene chain. The behaviour has been described for other nonionic surfactants, where increasing the size of the hydrophilic group inhibits micelle formation [1–4]. Substitution of Asp with Glu produced no significant changes on these systems [62].

Monosubstituted zwitterionic amides of glutamic acid showing surface activity have been obtained by coupling of the amino acid residue with fatty amines of even chain lengths between C_{10}–C_{18} [63]. The compounds were easily prepared from dehydration of the corresponding monoammonium salts of glutamic acid, since the large difference between the pK_a values of the two carboxyl groups of glutamic acid ($pK_\alpha = 2.19$ and $pK_\delta = 4.25$) allowed a good selectivity for the α-position during salt formation. Derivatives with alkyl chains longer than C_{16} were insoluble in water while for the remaining LAA the CMC in aqueous solution decreased with increasing chain length. Substitution at both the carboxyl groups of the amino acid residue leads to poorly water-soluble bicatenary cationic surfactants. A condensation strategy for the introduction of a polar sugar moiety into these molecules was devised in an attempt to reduce the high hydrophobicity of these LAA [63].

2.3.4. Lipoamino Acids with a Basic Residue

A wide variety of cationic LAA derived from arginine and lysine are known, due to their ease of synthesis and interesting biological properties, which include antimicrobial activity, high biodegradability, low aquatic toxicity and low cytotoxicity [8–12]. The group of M. R. Infante has been intensively involved in the synthesis and characterization of arginine- and lysine-based LAA, including the development of enzymatic methodologies as an alternative to, or in combination with, chemical synthesis [9–12, 15, 24–26].

Long-chain N^α-acylarginine methyl ester hydrochlorides (**X**, n = 8, 10, 12; Fig. 5) and dihydrochloride salts of long-chain arginine- N-alkyl amides (**XIa**, n = 9, 11, 13; Fig. 5) and O-alkyl esters (**XIb**, n = 7, 9, 11; Fig. 5), with two positively charged groups in the hydrophilic moiety, have been prepared on a multigram scale by enzymatic methodologies [24–26].

For all the LAA studied, the CMC decreases linearly with the increase in alkyl chain length as expected from the increase in the hydrophobicity of the LAA [64]. The number of positive charges on the head group also influenced the CMC, and for the same hydrocarbon chain length, CMC was lower for the dicationic derivatives [64]. The divalent compounds had higher A_{min} values than the corresponding monovalent LAA of the same alkyl chain length. The dicationic amphiphiles, owing to the size and nature of the hydrophilic moieties, are less tightly packed at the interface when compared to the monocationic species, due to an increase in the inter- and intramolecular electrostatic repulsion forces for the former [64]. The CMC values for the single chain arginine LAA were smaller than the ones for commercial quaternary ammonium surfactants with the same alkyl chain length. In quaternary ammonium salts the cationic charge on the headgroup is close to the α-carbon of the hydrophobic group, which increases the CMC, whereas in the arginine LAA, five methylene groups separate the guanidinium group, that bears the positive charge, from the α-carbon [9].

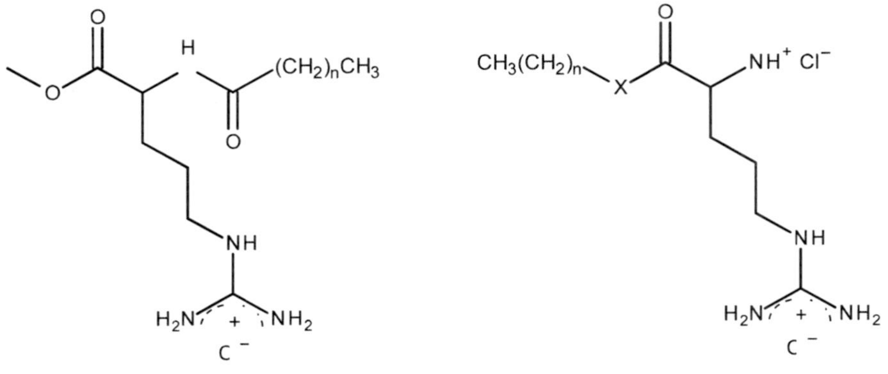

Figure 5. Single-chain cationic (**X**) and dicationic (**XI**) lipoamino acids derived from arginine.

Gemini cationic surfactants derived from arginine, N^α,N^ω-bis(N^α-acylarginine)-α,ω-alkylidenediamides (**XII**, n = 8, 10, 12; s = 2–10; Fig. 6), that consist of two symmetrical long-chain N^α-acyl-L-arginine residues linked by amide bonds to an α,ω-alkylenediamine spacer of variable chain length (s), have been prepared by appropriate dimerization of N^α-acylargine methyl esters using a chemoenzymatic approach [26, 65]. Unlike their monomeric counterparts, aqueous solutions of the geminis exhibited unconventional aggregation behaviour and two distinct CMC values were inferred from the different methodologies employed in the measurements. Very low CMC values, between 0.002 and 0.005 mmol dm^{-3} (CMC$_1$), were obtained primarily from surface tension measurements [65]. Conductivity and fluorescence data yielded a second CMC, in the concentration range 0.3–0.6 mmol dm^{-3} (CMC$_2$), comparable to the CMC values obtained from conductivity measurements for quaternary ammonium gemini surfactants [65]. Thus, the CMC$_2$ value is consistent with the formation of regular micelles, while CMC$_1$ has not been unequivocally determined, and alternative explanations based on highly charged small size aggregates or big noncharged entities have been proposed [9, 65].

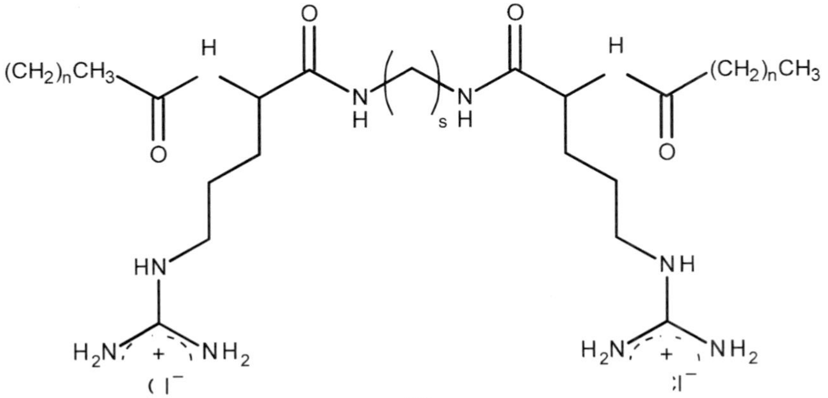

Figure 6. Cationic gemini lipoamino acids from arginine.

The arginine-based gemini LAA **XII** were more efficient surface active molecules than the corresponding single chain LAA **X**, with CMC values at least one order of magnitude lower and 10 times more efficient at reducing the surface tension of water [65–67]. Variations in the acyl chain length had a higher effect on the CMC and surface active properties of the geminis than variations in the spacer chain [66, 67]. For the same acyl chain length, the CMC values decreased when the number of methylene groups in the spacer chain increased, consistent with an increase in the hydrophobicity of the molecule [65–67].

Nonionic N^α,N^ε-diacyl lysine polyoxyethylene derivatives, bearing one or two polyoxyethylene methoxy-capped chains in the hydrophilic headgroup (**XIII**, Fig. 7) were prepared as structural mimics of lecithins [68]. The CMC and surface tension reduction for both series were similar to that of alcohol ethoxylates with the same hydrocarbon chain length and similar number of ethylene oxide units in the headgroup but larger than that for the corresponding lecithins. The CMC for the lysine derivatives **XIIIa**, with a single ethylene oxide chain per headgroup, was smaller than that of the derivatives **XIIIb**, with two ethylene oxide chains, which suggests that the aggregates formed by these LAA are dependent on the length of each chain and not on the total number of chains [68], in contrast to the zwitterionic lecithins and the LAA analogues bearing aspartate or glutamate residues (**IX**, Fig. 3) [62]. Since the amide functionality in the acyl chain of the lysine derivatives is in a reversed position relatively to the Asp and Glu analogues, the orientation of the amide groups in the hydrophobic chains is likely to influence the conformation of the molecules and subsequently their packing at interfaces, which affects their surface activity and ability to aggregate [62, 68].

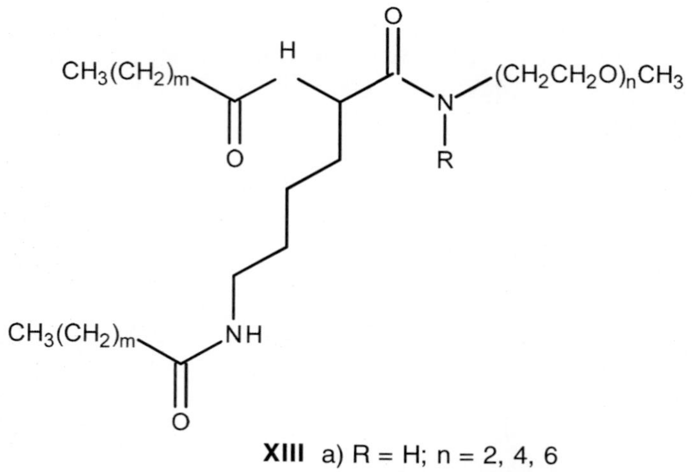

XIII a) R = H; n = 2, 4, 6
b) R = (CH₂CH₂O)ₙCH₃; n = 2, 3

Figure 7. Nonionic double-chain lipoamino acids derived from lysine.

The self-assembly behaviour in aqueous solution of anionic N^α,N^ε-dioctanoyl lysine surfactants with different inorganic and organic monovalent counterions (Li$^+$, Na$^+$, K$^+$, Lys$^+$, Tris$^+$) have been reported [69]. The CMC values, around 1.8–3 mmol dm^{-3}, are nearly independent of the counterion (Pinazo et al. 2008, 2011Rev) and the areas per molecule at the air/water interface (A_{min}) have very similar large values, around double that of a single-chain anionic surfactant, regardless of the counterion [69]. This anomaly has been attributed to a high degree of hydration favoured by the presence of multiple hydrogen bonding groups in the LAA head group and to the relatively short acyl chains [69](Pinazo et al. 2008).

Recently, cationic gemini surfactants derived from lysine intended for biomedical applications have been synthesized bearing *N*-dodecanoyl chains attached at either the α-amine or the side chain ε-amine groups of the lysine residue, linked by amide bonds to an 1,6-hexylenediamine spacer (**XIV**, Fig. 8) [70]. Their CMC values were similar to the ones obtained by conductivity measurements for cationic geminis from arginine with the same alkyl chain and spacer lengths [65], and about one order of magnitude lower than the ones for their similar cationic monomeric counterparts, the N^α- and N^ε-lauroyl-lysine methyl esters, respectively [70]. For both type of compounds, the position of the cationic charge, located either at the α-amine or at the side chain ε-amine group of the lysine residue, did not significantly affect the CMC [70].

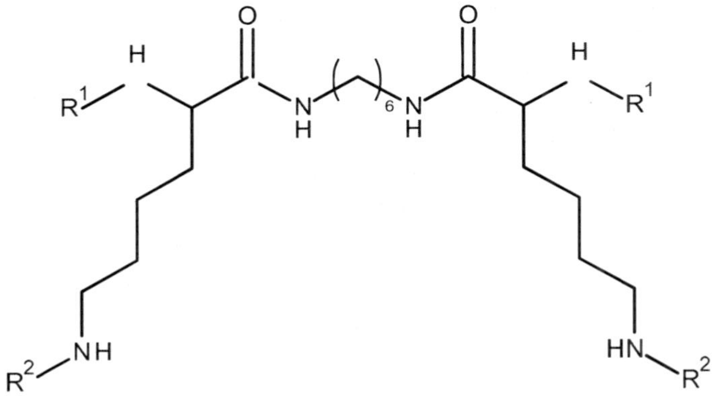

XIV a) $R^1 = CH_3(CH_2)_nC=O$, $R^2 = H$
b) $R^1 = H$, $R^2 = CH_3(CH_2)_nC=O$

Figure 8. Cationic gemini lipoamino acids derived from lysine.

3. BIOLOGICAL PROPERTIES AND APPLICATIONS

3.1. Chiral Discrimination

The chiral nature of LAA that allows them to interact selectively with enantiomers of a chiral solute has been successfully applied in the separation of racemic mixtures [71, 72], and nowadays chromatography columns packed with chiral *N*-acyl amino acids are commercially available. Other applications related to the chiral discrimination of LAA have been developed, including the use of LAA as enantiodiscriminating NMR solvents [73].

Chiral discrimination has been reported in the solid state, in Langmuir monolayers, and even for micelles [8, 11, 12]. Although LAA behaviour in water and in air/liquid interfaces has been exhaustively studied, there are still several unanswered questions about the influence of chirality on the physicochemical properties and self-assembly behaviour of LAA. Some studies on adsorption isotherms of LAA revealed significant chiral discrimination between enantiomeric pure films and their racemic mixtures, in function of variables such as amino acid structure, film pressure, temperature and nature of the surface [74]. For enantiomerically pure *N*-acylserine derivatives, the hydrogen bonds between amide groups of adjacent molecules formed a bidimensional network supported by strong hydrophobic interactions between the long *N*-acyl chains. The monolayer thus formed constitutes a chiral supramolecular surface of monomolecular width with important applications in micelar catalysis and on molecular recognition studies [75, 76].

Reports on the influence of chirality on micelle properties date back to 1974 when Takehara *et al.* [77] verified that the CMC of a racemic mixture of sodium salts of *N*-acyl glutamic acid was higher than the CMC of the corresponding pure enantiomers. Further thermodynamic studies on *N*-acylalanine and *N*-acylvaline salts yielded similar results and the phenomena was attributed to differences in the conformation of the amino acid residue at the micelar surface, where the establishment of intermolecular hydrogen interactions of different stability originated different micellization enthalpies [30, 31, 78]. Studies on serine-based LAA confirmed that the CMC of the micelles formed by racemic *N*-stearoylserine was slightly higher than the CMC of the micelles formed by the pure L or D enantiomers [79]. This effect was accompanied by strong variations of the circular dichroism spectra of the enantiomerically pure micelles and it was attributed to the formation of a repetitive array of the polar head groups at the surface of the micelles, stabilized by intermolecular hydrogen bonds between the amide groups [79].

The influence of stereochemistry in the self-assembly behaviour of sodium salts of gemini *N*-carbamoyl LAA derived from cysteine was studied by our research group [50, 52]. Chirality seemed to play a role in the surface active properties of the gemini LAA, but not on micelle formation, which shows the relevance of the stereochemistry effect on adsorption phenomena, such as monolayer formation and adsorption at the surface of macromolecules. Moreover, the association of the enantiomerically pure gemini LAA with the globular protein BSA was favoured when compared to the racemic mixture, with pure L-stereochemistry being favoured over D-stereochemistry [52].

On the other hand, no significant difference were observed between the CMC of the racemic mixture and the CMC of the enantiomerically pure surfactants for sodium salts of *N*-palmitoyl LAA with apolar residues [29, 34] and potassium salts of *N*-dodecanoylalanine [80] neither for cationic surfactants derived from *N*-lauroylarginine [12]. The influence of the chirality of the LAA on its micellar properties seems to be dependent on the structure of the amino acid residue. The preference for homochiral (L-L or D-D) over heterochiral (D-L) interaction depends on the stability of the hydrogen bond formed between the amino acid residues in combination with stereochemical effects [29, 39]. Supramolecular chirality is highly specific of monomer chirality and comprehension of chirality at the molecular level is thus essential, since the functionality of these biomimetic systems is interrelated with their structural morphology. Theoretical models have been developed for determination of the molecular origin of chirality in aggregates of chiral surfactants which suggest that chirality of the supramolecular aggregates depends essentially on the effective diameter of the groups around the chiral centre and on stereochemical hindrance [76, 81, 82]. Supramolecular chirality has been exploited in enantioselective micelar reactions with very promising results [83].

3.2. Detergents and Foaming Agents

The solubilising power of micelles, which are capable of dissolving low water-soluble molecules by incorporating them in the hydrophobic micellar core [1–4], is on the basis of the use of surfactants as one of the most important components in laundry and household cleaning products. Anionic surfactants are the most used for the purpose because of their highly effective detergency, ease of synthesis and relatively lower cost [8]. Several of these compounds are not biologically degradable, therefore posing a threat to the environment. LAA, as bio-based amphiphiles, represent a class of environmentally friendly surfactants with improved biocompatibility and biodegradability [10–12].

Sodium salts of *N*-acyl LAA have better water solubility than the corresponding carboxylate salts of conventional soaps, due to the presence of the hydrophilic amide bond. They also show good biocompatibility and antimicrobial properties, therefore being applied as mild preservatives in cosmetics, foods and dermopharmaceutical formulations [8].

Long-chain *N*-acyl glutamates are biodegradable and mild surfactants used for their detergency and foaming power in cosmetic and toiletry products such as shower gels and hair shampoos. Used in high concentrations (approx. 50% wt) *N*-dodecyl glutamate shows a higher transparency compared to other transparent soaps made from fatty acid salts [59].

Anionic gemini LAA derived from aspartic acid are less irritant to the skin than comparable conventional single-chain surfactants, which can in part be attributed to their lower CMC values, in the micromolar range [60]. Application of these molecules in industrial processes can lead to a dramatic reduction in the concentration of surface active material needed to attain the same level of performance.

3.3. Toxicity and Biodegradability

The massive use of surfactants in detergents and cosmetic formulations and their subsequent disposal in the aquatic environment demands for biodegradable surfactants with a low toxicity profile. The ability of surfactants to adsorb at interfaces and interact with biological membranes is responsible for most of the observed biological effects of surfactants, such as antimicrobial activity and haemolysis [1, 3, 4], therefore raising concerns regarding their environmental impact.

Surfactants can adsorb at the surface of biological membranes and bind through hydrophobic interactions to proteins, solubilising membrane components by mixed-micelle formation with membrane lipids and protein complexation, leading to disruption of membrane integrity and function [1, 3, 4]. The process, depending on surfactant concentration, can be reversed by simple dilution, with membrane reconstitution, and surfactants are commonly used as denaturing agents in the extraction and purification of membrane proteins and in protein characterization, a well-known example being the SDS-polyacrylamide gel electrophoresis routinely used for molecular weight determination of proteins [19].

Many studies have been performed on the biodegradability and toxicity of surfactants, which have been found to be basically correlated with surfactant hydrophobicity and not with surfactant-specific parameters [1, 3, 11, 12]. Surfactants with longer alkyl chains are less biodegradable and usually more toxic than surfactants with the same head group and shorter chain lengths [1, 3]. Biodegradation, i.e., the removal of organic compounds from the environment by microbial conversion into inorganic products, such as CO_2, water and assimilated biomass, is usually measured as dissolved organic carbon (DOC). According to the Organisation for Economic Cooperation and Development (OECD) guidelines, a surfactant can be considered readily degradable if the biodegradation level exceeds 60% (of DOC removal) within 28 days [1, 3, 6, 7].

The single-chain arginine LAA **X** and **XI** (Fig. 5) can be regarded as readily biodegradable and a relationship between the biodegradability rate and chemical structure was observed. While all the ester derivatives **X** and **XIb** were rapidly biodegraded within 7 days, the rate of biodegradation for amide derivatives **XIa** depended on the alkyl chain length. The ester bond is more labile to hydrolysis – either chemical or enzymatic – than the amide bond, hence the biodegradation enhancement in the case of the ester derivatives [10, 64]. Dimerization of the N^α-acylarginine methyl esters **X** yielded less biodegradable LAA **XII** (Fig. 6), due to increased hydrophobicity. The biodegradation rate for geminis **XII** decreased when both the spacer chain and the acyl chain lengths increased, i.e., with increased hydrophobicity of the LAA [10, 84].

Acute toxicity tests are usually performed on freshwater crustacean *Daphnia magna*, a very sensitive invertebrate, as well as on bioluminescent marine bacteria *Photobacterium phosphoreum*, in order to access aquatic toxicity of chemicals [1, 3, 84]. Concentration values causing immobilization in 50% of the *Daphnia* population after 24 h exposure, IC_{50}, and 50% reduction in the light emitted by bacteria after 30 min exposure, EC_{50}, are determined in each test, respectively.

Cationic surfactants of the quaternary ammonium type derived from *N*-dodecyl serine and –tyrosine [43] have IC_{50} values of 11 and 4.1 μmol dm^{-3}, respectively, lower than IC_{50} for dodecyltrimethylammonium bromide (DTAB), which is 1.4 μmol dm^{-3} [85]. For the single-chain arginine LAA, either of the ester (**X**; **XIb**; Fig. 5) or the amide (**XIa**; Fig. 5) type, in each series acute toxicity grew, i.e., IC_{50} and EC_{50} values decreased, with increasing hydrophobicity of the molecule, in agreement with the decrease in their CMC values [64]. Lower CMC values correspond to a higher tendency to aggregate in aqueous solutions resulting in surfactant accumulation at interfaces eliciting a toxic effect. The same trend was observed among the cationic geminis **XII** (Fig. 6), with IC_{50} and EC_{50} values between 1–3 ppm, whereas for the corresponding cationic geminis from quaternary ammonium salts these values are lower than 1 ppm [67].

The potential toxicity of surfactants to human cells can be evaluated by their haemolytic activity, HC_{50}, the surfactant concentration that causes 50% of haemolysis of red blood cells (RBC) from healthy human donors. [1, 3] Evaluation of haemolysis is of fundamental and practical importance, since erythrocytes lack internal organelles, are extremely fragile and can be used as a measure for cytotoxicity and as a model for mammalian cells [1, 3]. Erythrocyte lyses is accompanied by haemoglobin release that is susceptible to denaturation in the presence of surfactant, and the lyses/denaturation ratio, L/D, is used to predict the potential ocular irritation of the surfactant. The L/D ratio is obtained by dividing the HC_{50} by the denaturation index, DI, determined by comparing denaturation of haemoglobin induced by the test surfactant and by a positive control, SDS. Surfactants with L/D > 100 are classified as non-irritating, in comparison with the irritating effect of SDS (L/D = 0.44) [1, 3, 85].

The single-chain arginine methyl esters **X** can be regarded as non-haemolysing (HC_{50} > 1000 mg/L) and non-eye irritating (L/D > 100) agents [64, 84], especially when compared with commercial cationic surfactants of the quaternary ammonium type, which have HC_{50} values between 4–15 mg L^{-1} [11]. However, their dimeric derivatives have a higher haemolytic activity, as a result of higher hydrophobicity and lower CMC values, the haemolytic power being higher for the compounds with more hydrophobic character, i.e. with longer spacer and alkyl chain lengths [84]. The gemini structure is known to enhance hydrophobic interactions, giving rise to surfactants that can aggregate at very low concentrations, thus promoting the haemolytic effect due to increased hydrophobic interactions with the erythrocyte membrane [70]. For the lysine-based gemini LAA **XIV** (Fig. 8) the position of the cationic charge plays an important role in the haemolytic activity of the compounds, with N^{α}-acyl- (**XIVa**) and N^{ε}-acyl (**XIVb**) derivatives showing HC_{50} values of 199×10^{-6} and 391×10^{-6} mol dm^{-3}, respectively [70]. Thus, acylation of the α-amino group of the lysine residue leads to a more potent derivative in causing erythrocyte lyses than acylation of the side-chain ε-amino group.

The nature of the counterion for $N^{\alpha},N^{\varepsilon}$-dioctanoyl-lysine salts strongly influences the haemolytic activity, with HC_{50} values increasing in the order $Tris^{+} < Lys^{+} < Na^{+} < K^{+} < Li^{+}$ [86], while CMC values remain almost unaffected [86–88]. All HC_{50} values were below the CMC of the surfactants, suggesting that monomers, and not micelles, were responsible for the haemolytic activity. The compounds showed concentration dependent and pH-sensitive haemolytic activity and improved kinetics at the endosomal pH range [86] with potential application as endosomal disrupting agents for enhanced intracellular drug delivery. Surfactants with organic counterions were less cytotoxic than those with inorganic counterions [89].

3.4. Antimicrobial Activity

Drug resistance has become a major public health threat worldwide as a result of the use (and misuse) of antibiotics over the past decades and the high increase in the emergence and spread of drug-resistant pathogens that cannot be treated with currently available antibiotics. The antimicrobial activity of cationic surfactants has long been recognized and many have been in clinical use as antiseptics and disinfectants for several decades, a well-known example being the quaternary ammonium salts, such as benzalkonium chloride, a mixture of long-chain alkylbenzyldimethylammonium chlorides with alkyl chain lengths C_8–C_{18} [1–4]. Although their mode of action is not yet fully understood, it has been suggested that cationic surfactants, due to their amphiphilic nature, are able to associate with the negatively charged microbial cell membrane by a combination of hydrophobic adsorption and attractive electrostatic interactions at the membrane/water interface, resulting in depolarization, lyses and cell death through disruption of the membrane topology, some being also capable of translocation into the cell, where they can interfere with cellular processes [1–4]. In general, LAA antibacterial activity is more pronounced over Gram-positive than Gram-negative bacteria, due to the external layer of the outer membrane of the latter, which is rich in lipopolysaccharides and proteins that restrict the entrance of amphiphilic compounds [70]. Minimum inhibitory concentration (MIC) values – the lowest surfactant concentration that inhibits visible growth after 24 h of incubation at 37 °C – usually occur at concentrations well below the CMC, suggesting that surfactant monomers, and not supramolecular aggregates, are the biologically active species.

Arginine-based LAA are antimicrobial agents with a broad-spectrum of antimicrobial activity combined with high biodegradability and low toxicity profiles [84] that turns them into promising alternatives to commercial quaternary ammonium salts, the latter being associated with toxicological risks to the aquatic environment due to their high chemical stability and poor biodegradation rates. Antimicrobial activity is directly associated with the protonated guanidinium group of the arginine residue that enhances interaction with the cell membrane of bacteria [64]. Cationic amphiphiles bearing guanidinium groups have been reported as potent bactericides, a striking example being the chlorohexidine-based formulations for common antiseptics and disinfectants currently available in the market.

Dihydrochloride salts of long-chain arginine amides **XIa** and esters **XIb** (Fig. 5) exhibit a broad spectrum of activity with MIC values in the range 4–64 µg/mL, lower than MIC values for the hydrochloride salts of acylarginine methyl esters **X**, as the presence of two cationic charges enhances attractive electrostatic interactions with the polyanionic components of the microbial cell surface [64]. Moreover, the amide derivatives showed enhanced antimicrobial activity with respect to the corresponding esters, suggesting that the ester linkage could be hydrolyzed more easily by the pathogenic microorganism than the amide bond, leading to loss of antimicrobial activity [64].

The antimicrobial efficiency of the single-chain arginine LAA was affected by their alkyl chain length showing bell-shaped curves with a maximum at C_{12}. For surfactants with the same head group, optimum biological effects have been reported to occur at a specific alkyl chain length, usually in the range C_{12}–C_{14} [90]. This can be attributed to the combination of several physicochemical properties, such as surface activity, hydrophobicity, adsorption, CMC, aqueous solubility and transport in the test medium [90]. Moreover, the arginine N-lauroylamide (**XIa**, n = 11) was more active than the lauroylester (**XIb**, n = 11) which may be due to the higher chemical stability of the amide bond compared to the ester linkage. The loss of activity for the homologues with the highest chain length is most probably due to the decrease of their water solubility [64].

Gemini arginine-based LAA **XII** are structural analogues of bis(quaternary ammonium halide) surfactants, where the quaternary ammonium head group has been replaced by an arginine residue, that combine the biocompatibility of LAA and the antimicrobial efficiency of cationic gemini surfactants. The adsorption of the geminis, with two positively charged head groups, onto the negatively charged bacterial cell surface, through electrostatic interactions, is expected to take place to a greater extent than for the univalent monomers because of the higher charge density of the former. The geminis **XII** showed the expected enhanced antimicrobial activity, with MIC values between 4–128 µg/mL [84], when compared with their single-chain counterparts **X**. For the same alkyl chain length, activity decreases with the increase in spacer chain length, for $n \geq 9$, whereas when the spacer chain length is kept constant, at $n = 3$, the variation of antimicrobial activity with the alkyl chain length shows a maximum for the homologues with decyl chains [84].

Antimicrobial activity and MIC values for some cationic gemini and single-chain arginine LAA are indicated in Table 4.

Table 4. Minimum inhibitory concentration (MIC) values for some arginine-based cationic lipoamino acids against selected representative pathogens

Microorganism	MIC / μg mL^{-1}					
	X[a] n=8	X[a] n=10	XIa[b] n=11	XIb[b] n=11	XII[a] n=8,s=3	XII[a] n=10,s=3
Escherichia coli ATCC 27325	> 256	128	R	R	64	> 128
Streptococcus faecalis ATCC 1054	128	8	R	R	32	8
Pseudomonas aeruginosa ATCC 9721	>256	128	64	128	64	> 128
Klebsiella pneumoniae ATCC 13882	256	32	16	R	16	8
Bacillus cereus var. *mycoides* ATCC 11778	128	64	32	64	16	32
Bacillus subtilis ATCC 6633	32	128	-	-	64	4
Staphylococcus aureus ATCC 25178	32	4	16	32	8	64
Staphylococcus epidermidis ATCC 155-1	128	128	16	64	8	> 128
Candida albicans ATCC 10231	128	32	16	64	16	16

[a]Ref. [84]; [b]Ref. [64]. For chemical structures of compounds refer to Figs. 5 and 6.

The antibacterial activity of the lysine LAA, e.g. compounds **XIVa** and **XIVb** (Fig. 8), is in general lower than that of the arginine derivatives with similar chemical structures [70]. These variations can be attributed to differences between the pK_a values of the amino acid residues [70]. For the lysine LAA, MIC values decreased with the increase in pK_a of the amino group at which the cationic charge is located, although the CMC values were not significantly affected by the position of the cationic charge. The head group charge of these surfactants is modulated by the proportion of dissociation of the protonated amino group, which depends on the specific molecular structure [70]. Lysine derivatives of the N^α-acyl type (**XIVa**) have the ε-amino group protonated and the pK_a of these molecules is around 10–12, however LAA of the N^ϵ-acyl type (**XIVb**) have the α-amino group protonated with a pK_a around 8, so at physiological pH of 7.4 a percentage of molecules will be in their neutral form and thereby attractive electrostatic interactions with the anionic membrane of bacteria are prevented [70, 91].

Although usually less active than their cationic counterparts, anionic LAA also show antimicrobial activity. *N*-acyl leucines of biologically active uncommon fatty acids were synthesized and found to be more active in acid form than in the methyl ester form, and against Gram-positive bacteria than Gram-negative [92]. The presence of a cyclopropane ring, a hydroxyl group or unsaturation in the acyl chain increased antibacterial activity, which was also dependent on the position of these groups. For example, shifting the hydroxyl group toward the amide linkage resulted in diminished antibacterial activity [92].

Xia *et al.* (1995) studied sodium salts of *N*-acylserine and found highest antimicrobial activity for the *N*-miristoyl derivatives [93]. For the same alkyl chain length, alkylation of the hydroxyl group of the serine side chain with methyl or ethyl groups improved antimicrobial activity dramatically and decreased CMC values in the order of increasing hydrophobicity of the alkoxy chain. Changes in the hydrophobic acyl chain length, however, had a more pronounced influence on the LAA surface properties than changes in the alkyl chain of the alkoxy group, CMC values decreasing with increasing acyl chain length. The much lower antimicrobial activity of the serine derivative when compared to the methoxy and ethoxy analogues has been attributed to the possibility of the free hydroxyl group being involved in intramolecular hydrogen bonding with the carbonyl oxygen of the carboxyl group thus decreasing water solubility and hindering binding interactions with the microbial surface [93].

Although a correlation was found between CMC and MIC values for the serine LAA, the antimicrobial effect took place at concentrations below the CMC, again suggesting that antimicrobial activity is inherent to the monomers and not the micellar aggregates [93].

N^{α}-Acyl LAA are also promising anti-influenza agents, some serine and cysteine derivatives being selective noncompetitive inhibitors of the viral neuramidinase [94]. Several N^{α}-palmitoyl amino acids are effective inhibitors of Sendai virus (parainfluenza type 1) fusion [95]. The tryptophan derivative was the most potent virus fusion inhibitor and was also active at pH 5.0, an indication that ionisation of the carboxyl group of the amino acid residue is not required for antiviral activity [95]. Finally, a remark must be made when trying to establish general relationships between the surface properties of LAA and their biological properties that concerns the experimental conditions involved in the measuring of surface and biological parameters and those of the living cell systems.

3.5. Drug Delivery

A wide range of hydrophobic drugs can be solubilised in the lipophilic micellar core or within the lipidic bilayers of vesicles. The latter structures, formed by double-chain surfactants, usually with long alkyl chains, are also able to entrap water-soluble drugs by intercalation in the aqueous layer, thus enhancing transportation across biological membranes [1–4]. Encapsulation of the drug within the supramolecular aggregate offers several advantages, besides improving water solubility and/or absorption through biological membranes, such as prolonging drug circulation in the blood stream, protection from chemical or enzymatic degradation, decrease drug toxicity, and controlled release, thus improving the drug bioavailability and its pharmacokinetic profile [1–4].

A successful therapeutic delivery system must have optimal size and surface characteristics, high loading capacity efficiency, have physical and chemical stability and must be biodegradable and biocompatible. Thus, LAA represent an attractive class of surfactants with potential use as drug delivery agents. Vesicles of long-chain N^{α}-acyl LAA showed encapsulation efficiencies for solutes comparable to that of conventional liposomes of lecithin [9–12] and may be useful carriers for therapeutic peptides and proteins, preventing their hydrolysis in the physiological media and promoting absorption through biological membranes while simultaneously reducing their immunogenicity. N,N'-Didodecanoylcystine vesicles have already been employed for molecular entrapment, in their neutral form, and dissociated to their dianionic form by the decrease in the pH of the medium, with increase in the vesicular permeability and release of the entrapped molecules [96]. The phenomenon has potential application in the controlled release of antitumor drugs as the pH of tumour cells is considerably more acidic than normal tissues.

Recently, N^{ε}-acyl-bis(N^{α}-carboxymethyl)lysine derivatives differing in the length and saturation degree of the acyl chains (**XVa-d**, Fig. 9) were synthesized to improve solubilisation of a water-insoluble anticancer drug [97]. The surfactants showed CMC values in the range [2.2–78] $\times$ 10^{-5} mol L^{-1}. The derivatives with nonadecanoyl, pentacosanoyl and pentacosadiynoyl chains increased drug solubility from a value lower than 0.15 µg/mL up to 7 mg/mL, with 41–46% (w/w) drug loading, being more efficient than the control surfactant polysorbate 80. This is due to the high flexibility and linear conformation of their hydrophobic moieties that favours interaction with the hydrophobic drug, as evidenced by molecular modelling [97]. Acyl chain length and unsaturations have a pronounced influence on toxicity. Saturated surfactants, along with the diacetylenic derivative, had similar haemolytic activity, according to their low CMC values and linear configuration of the acyl chain. On the contrary, the arachidonoyl derivative (**XVb**) had the highest HC_{50} value, since the steric hindrance of the hydrophobic tail prevents its insertion into the erythrocyte membranes [97].

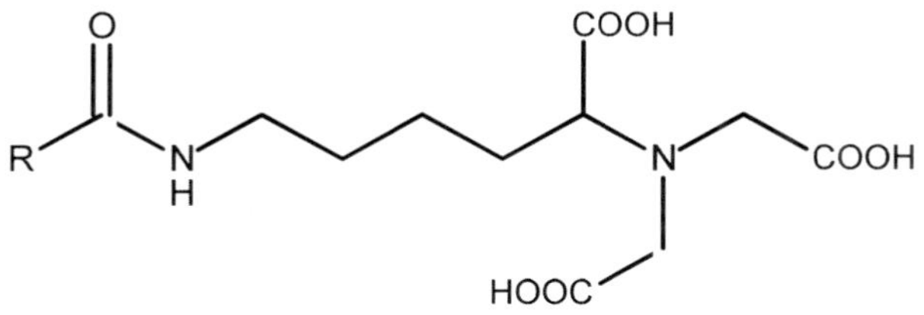

XV a) R = $CH_3(CH_2)_{17}$
b) R = $CH_3(CH_2)_4(CH{=}CHCH_2)_4(CH_2)_2$
c) R = $CH_3(CH_2)_{23}$
d) R = $CH_3(CH_2)_{11}C{\equiv}CC{\equiv}C(CH_2)_8$

Figure 9. Lysine-based lipoamino acids used for drug delivery.

LAA have also been proposed as useful promoieties able to impart a membrane-like character to drug molecules, enhancing their interaction with cell membranes and increasing biological uptake. Depending on the stability of the drug-LAA linkage, drug conjugation of LAA can result in either bioreversible prodrugs or stable derivatives, displaying an intrinsic biological activity.

Conjugation of tranylcypromine (TCP), a classical monoamino oxidase (MAO) inhibitor, with C^{α}-alkyl LAA derived from glycine, varying in the length of the alkyl side chain, resulted in increased interaction with phospholipid membrane models [98, 99]. The affinity for the blood brain barrier (BBB) was evaluated as the partition coefficient of the drug between the blood and brain (log BB) estimated from computational measurements [99]. Conjugates where the amino acid residue had alkyl side chains between C_{10}–C_{14} exhibited c log BB values between +0.4 and +0.7, superior to the value for the non-conjugated drug (c log BB = +0.2021), thus being expected to cross the BBB with efficacy [99]. Calorimetric and computational studies suggest that LAA with decyl, or longer, side chains, can be useful fragments to improve the biopharmaceutical profile and overall bioavailability of small drug molecules and therapeutic peptides, hence improving the effectiveness of CNS therapies for the treatment of neurodegenerative disorders, such as Alzheimer's and Parkinson's diseases [98, 99].

The hydrophobic ion pairing approach is another chemical strategy devised to reversibly modify the properties of drug molecules by reducing their hydrophilic character. For drug molecules containing ionisable functional groups, polar counter ions are stoichiometrically replaced with more hydrophobic ones. The resulting ion pairs, being more hydrophobic than the parent compounds, can improve drug permeability and transport through biological membranes thus enhancing drug uptake by cells. The strategy has been successfully applied to the aminoglycoside antibiotic tobramycin (TOB), a bactericidal agent with a broad-spectrum activity, effective against Gram-negative microorganisms, and used for the treatment of septicaemia, complicated and recurrent urinary tract infections and infections of the lower respiratory tract, among others [100]. Reduced cellular permeability can result in subtherapeutic concentrations of the antibiotic in the bacterial cells, with bacteria showing a natural resistance to tobramycin.

A series of organic amphiphilic ion pairs of tobramycin with C^α-alkyl LAA derived from glycine, with even chain lengths between C_{10}–C_{14}, were prepared by reduced pressure evaporation of an aqueous-ethanol co-solution of TOB, as a free base, and LAA [100]. A different degree of substitution of the TOB amine groups was obtained by using increased drug to LAA molar fractions (1:1 to 1:5). The antibacterial activity against Gram-negative pathogens was enhanced when at least three or all the five amine groups of TOB were salifyed with LAA residues, most probably due to a more efficacious and rapid penetration of the drug inside the bacterial cells. No evident relationship could be established between the *in vitro* antibacterial activity and the length of the alkyl side chain of the LAA residue [100].

3.6. Gene Therapy

Gene therapy has emerged as a promising approach for the treatment or prevention of both genetic and acquired diseases, such as severe combined immunodeficiency, cystic fibrosis and Parkinson's disease, as well as an alternative method to traditional chemotherapy in cancer treatment [5]. Successful gene therapy depends crucially on the development of effective vectors, especially for the safe introduction of the selected gene into living cells. Gene transfer vectors in common use are mostly based on viruses, which are immunogenic, have limited gene-carrying capacity and present a danger of residual infectivity. Synthetic vectors, although less efficient than their viral counterparts, have clear advantages, such as ease of preparation, lack of immune response and unlimited DNA-carrying capacity [101].

Cationic gemini LAA show particular promise as potential vehicles for enhanced gene delivery, due their ability to bind and condense the negatively charged DNA into nanosized complexes (lipoplexes), combined with good biodegradability, biocompatibility and low cytotoxicity. Lipoplexes enter mammalian cells primarily through endocytosis, and non-specific electrostatic interactions between cationic lipoplexes and anionic cell-surface proteoglycans enhance cellular uptake.

The ability to compact DNA, protect it against enzymatic degradation and release it after reaching the desired compartment in the target cell are crucial requirements for the design of effective vectors for gene delivery [101–104]. The characteristics of the cationic head groups, such as size and charge density, are generally more important for transfection efficiency than those of the hydrophobic tails [102]. Among the most common types of hydrophobic chains are hydrocarbon chains between C_8–C_{18}, varying in length and degree of unsaturation, with the mono-unsaturated ones being associated with higher transfection efficiency, probably due to their influence on enhancing membrane fluidity [102, 103].

Singh et al. [105, 106] developed cationic gemini surfactants from dodecyldimethylammonium salts bearing an amino acid residue (**XVI**, R = Gly, Lys; Fig. 10) in the spacer chain. The amino acid derivatives showed increased transfection efficiency, assessed in epithelial cells for topical cutaneous and mucosal applications [106], when compared with the parent nonsubsituted compound (**XVI**, R = H). The superior performance was attributed to their better biocompatibility and flexibility of the gemini LAA [105].

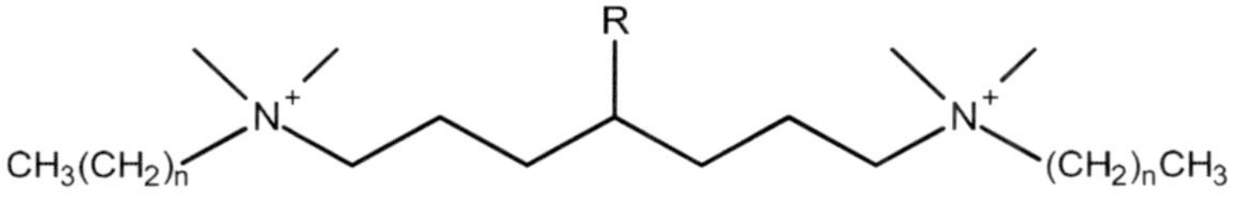

XVI

Figure 10. Cationic gemini lipoamino acids used as transfection agents. R is an amino acid residue.

Dauty et al. [107, 108] prepared a series of oxidizable cationic cysteinyl surfactants with a hydrophobic chain of length C_{12}–C_{16} attached to the carboxyl group of the amino acid residue through and amide bond. Different polyamine moieties (ornithine or spermine) were introduced into the head group by *N*-acylation of cysteine. Plasmid DNA was compacted by the cationic thiol detergents into nanoparticles, with diameters around 30 nm (regardless of the length of the alkyl tail) that were stabilized by dimerization, via disulfide bond formation, upon exposure to air oxygen [108]. The oxidized gemini structures were capable of effective cell transfection, and higher transfection efficiency was obtained for the derivatives with the longer alkyl chain [107].

A different approach, starting from the reducible cationic gemini surfactant, was also attempted [109, 110]. The idea was to modulate DNA release from the complexes through cleavage of the disulfide bond between the cysteine residues of the gemini, making use of reductive milieu of the intracellular environment. SAXS studies of the DNA-gemini complexes suggested the formation of a hexagonal structure that resulted in high levels of transfection [110]. Hence, the use of reduction-sensitive groups appears as a promising strategy for gene delivery.

The encapsulation of DNA by catanionic vesicle systems derived from LAA has also been investigated [111, 112]. Catanionic vesicles form spontaneously upon mixing cationic and anionic amphiphiles, presenting the advantage of ease of preparation combined with long term stability and a high degree of DNA encapsulation, where further DNA uptake is enabled by the release of the anionic surfactant from the amphiphile bilayer [111]. Vesicles composed of a single chain dicationic LAA, arginine *N*-lauroyl amide **XIa**, in excess, and an anionic alkyl sulphate of variable alkyl chain length (octyl or cetyl sulphate) were prepared. Adding DNA to solutions of the catanionic vesicles resulted in strong associative phase separation with precipitate formation, the driving force for the process being counter-ion release. SAXS and cryo-TEM studies revealed a self-assembly of the DNA-catanionic vesicle complexes into distinct lamellar nanostructures, with encapsulation of DNA within the lamellar stacks, the spacing between the lamellas increasing from 4.7 to 5.8 nm with the increase in the alkyl chain length of the anionic amphiphile [111, 112]. Manipulation of the internal structure, morphology and size of the complexes was achieved by changing the charge ratio between DNA and the catanionic vesicles.

CONCLUSION AND FUTURE PERSPECTIVES

In summary, LAA constitute a class of bio-based surfactants with excellent surface properties, broad antimicrobial activity and low toxicity combined with improved biocompatibility and biodegradability. Moreover, they can be efficiently prepared by clean biotechnology processes, such as enzymatic catalysis, or by a combination of chemoenzymatic methodologies, turning them into cost-effectiveness, environmentally friendly surfactants. All these features make LAA an outstanding alternative to conventional speciality surfactants.

The diversity of naturally-occurring amino acids, combined with their multifunctionality and chiral properties, leads to a wide variety of surfactant architectures with distinct physicochemical and biological properties, allowing for the production of tailor-made LAA to meet almost any specific application. Hence this new generation of surfactants may contribute to sustainable development and quality of life improvement, answering the increasing demand of the food, pharmaceutical and cosmetic industries for renewable raw-materials based on natural product scaffolds.

REFERENCES

[1]   Attwood, D.; Florence, A. T. *Surfactant systems: Their chemistry, pharmacy and biology*. Chapman and Hall: London, 1983.

[2]   Holmberg, K.; Jonsson, B.; Kronberg, B.; Lindman, B. *Surfactants and Polymers in Aqueous Solution*, 2nd ed.; John Wiley & Sons: Chichester, 2002.

[3]   Fendler, J. H. *Membrane Mimetic Chemistry: Characterizations and Applications of Micelles, Microemulsions, Monolayer, Bilayers, Vesicles, Host-guest Systems, and Polyions*; John Wiley & Sons: New York, 1982.

[4]   Tanford, C. *The Hydrophobic Effect: Formation of Micelles and Biological Membranes*, 2nd ed.; Wiley: New York, 1980.

[5]   Kumar, M.; Misra, A. Applications of Gene Therapy. In *Challenges in Delivery of Therapeutic Genomics and Proteomics*; Misra, A., Ed.; Elsevier, 2011, pp 271–323.

[6]   Deleu, M.; Paquot, M. From renewable vegetable resources to microorganisms: new trends in surfactants. *C. R. Chim.* 2004, *7*, 641–646.

[7]   Foley, P.; Kermanshahi, A.; Beach, E. S.; Zimmerman, J. B. Derivation and synthesis of renewable surfactants. *Chem. Soc. Rev.* 2012, *41*, 1499–1518.

[8]   Xia, J.; Nnanna, I. A.; Sakamoto, K. Amino Acid Surfactants: Chemistry, Synthesis and Properties. In *Protein-Based Surfactants. Synthesis, Physicochemical Properties and Application*; Nnanna, I. A.; Xia, J., Eds.; Surfactant Science Series 101; Marcel Dekker: New York, 2001.

[9]   Pinazo, A.; Pons, R.; Pérez, L.; Infante, M. R. Amino acids as raw material for biocompatible surfactants. *Ind. Eng. Chem. Res.* 2011, *50*, 4805–4817.

[10]   Morán, M. C.; Pinazo, A.; Pérez, L.; Clapés, P.; Angelet, M.; Garcia, M. T.; Vinardell, M. P.; Infante, M. R. "Green" amino acid-based surfactants. *Green Chem.* 2004, *6*, 233–240.

[11] Infante, M. R.; Pérez, L.; Pinazo, A.; Clapés, P.; Morán, M. C.; Angelet, M.; Garcia, M. T.; Vinardell, M. P. Amino acid-based surfactants. *C. R. Chim.* 2004, *7*, 583–592.

[12] Infante, M. R.; Pinazo, A.; Seguer, J. Non-conventional surfactants from amino acid and glycolipids: structure, preparation and properties. *Colloids Surf., A* 1997, *123-124*, 49–70.

[13] Holmberg, K. Natural surfactants. *Curr. Opin. Colloid Interface Sci.* 2001, *6*, 148–159.

[14] Reznik, G. O.; Vishwanath, P.; Pynn, M. A.; Sitnik, J. M.; Todd, J. J.; Wu, J.; Jiang, Y.; Keenan, B. G.; Castle, A. B.; Haskell, R. F.; Smith, T. F.; Somasundaran, P.; Jarrell, K. A. Use of sustainable chemistry to produce an acyl amino acid surfactant. *Appl. Microbiol. Biotechnol.* 2010, *86*, 1387–1397.

[15] Clapés, P.; Infante, M. R. Amino acid-based surfactants: enzymatic synthesis, properties and potential applications. *Biocatal. Biotransform.* 2002, *20*, 215–233.

[16] Valivety, R.; Gill, I. S.; Vulfson, E. N. Application of enzymes to the synthesis of amino acid-based bola and gemini surfactants. *J. Am. Oil Chem. Soc.* 1998, *1*, 177–185.

[17] Sarney, D. B.; Vulfson, E. N. Application of enzymes to the synthesis of surfactants. *Trends Biotechnol.* 1995, *13*, 164–172.

[18] Xia, J.; Qian, J.; Nnanna, I. A. Synthesis and surface properties of amino acid surfactants from industrial waste proteins. *J. Agric. Food Chem.* 1996, *44*, 975–979.

[19] Harvey, R. A.; Ferrier, D. R. *Biochemistry*, 5th ed.; Lippincott Williams & Wilkins, 2011.

[20] Montalbetti, C. A. G. N.; Falque, V. Amide bond formation and peptide coupling. *Tetrahedron* 2005, *61*, 10827–10852.

[21] Howl, J. *Peptide Synthesis and Applications*. Methods of Molecular Biology Series 298, Humana Press: New Jersey, 2005.

[22] Bodanszky, M. *Principles of Peptide Synthesis*, 2nd ed.; Springer-Verlag: Berlin Heidelberg, 1993.

[23] Villeneuve, P. Lipases in lipophilization reactions. *Biotechnol. Adv.* 2007, *25*, 515–536.

[24] Clapés, P.; Morán, C.; Infante, M. R. Enzymatic synthesis of argine-based cationic surfactants. Biotechnol. Bioeng. 1999, *63*, 333–345.

[25] Pinazo, A.; Infante, M. R.; Izquierdo, P.; Solans, C. Synthesis of arginine-based surfactants in highly concentrated water-in-oil emulsions. *J. Chem. Soc., Perkin Trans. 2*, 2000, 1535–1539.

[26] Piera, E.; Infante, M. R.; Clapés, P. Chemo-enzymatic synthesis of arginine-based gemini surfactants. *Biotechnol. Bioeng.* 2000, *70*, 323–331.

[27] Soo, E. L.; Salleh, A. B.; Basri, M.; Rahman, R. N. Z. A.; Kamaruddin, K. Response surface methodological study on lipase-catalyzed synthesis of amino acid surfactants. *Process Biochem.* 2004, *39*, 1511–1518.

[28] Ohta, A.; Toda, K.; Morimoto, Y.; Asakawa, T.; Miyagishi, S. Effect of the side chain of N-acyl amino acid surfactants on micelle formation: An isothermal titration calorimetry study. *Colloids Surf., A* 2007, *317*, 316–322.

[29] Ohta, A.; Ozawa, N.; Nakashima, S.; Asakawa, T.; Miyagishi, S. (2003a). "Kraft temperature and enthalpy of solution of N-acyl amino acid surfactants and their racemic modifications: effect of the amino acid residue". Colloid Polym. Sci. 281, 363–369.

[30] Miyagishi, S.; Nishida, M. (1978). Influence of chirality on micelle formation of sodium N-acylalaninates and sodium N-lauroylvalinates. *J. Colloid Interface Sci.* 1978, *65*, 380–386.

[31] Takehara, M. Properties and applications of amino acid based surfactants. *Colloid Surf., A* 1989, *38*, 149–167.

[32] Mhaskar, S. Y.; Prasad, R. B. N.; Lakshminarayana, G. Synthesis of *N*-acyl amino acids and correlation of structure with surfactant properties of their sodium salts. *J. Am. Oil Chem. Soc.* 1990, *67*, 1015–1019.

[33] Haldar, S.; Maji, S. K. Role of non-covalent interactions in the molecular organization of *N*-n-hexadecanoyl amino acid amphiphiles with hydrophobic C_α-side chains in Tris buffer (pH 9.3). *Colloids Surf., A* 2013, *420*, 10–21.

[34] Gerova, M.; Rodrigues, F.; Lamère, J.-F.; Dobrev, A.; Fery-Forgues, S. Self-assembly properties of some chiral *N*-palmitoyl amino acid surfactants in aqueous solution. *J. Colloid Interface Sci.* 2008, *319*, 526–533.

[35] Miyagishi, S.; Takeuchi, N.; Asakawa, T.; Inoh, M. Micellar growth of *N*-dodecanoyl-alaninates with different counterions and its quantitative relation with some factors. *Colloids Surf., A* 2002, *197*, 125–132.

[36] Miyagishi, S.; Wataru, A.; Hashimoto, T.; Asakawa, T. Effect of NaCl on aggregation number, microviscosity, and cmc of *N*-dodecanoyl amino acid surfactant micelles. *J. Colloid Interface Sci.* 1996, *184*, 527–534.

[37] Miyagishi, S.; Suzuki, H.; Asakawa, T. Microviscosity and aggregation number of potassium N-acylalaninate micelles in potassium chloride solution. *Langmuir* 1996, *12*, 2900–2905.

[38] Miyagishi, S.; Kurimoto, H.; Asakawa, T. Microviscosity of sodium *N*-acylvalinate micelles in sodium chloride solution. *Langmuir* 1995, *11*, 2951–2956.

[39] Ohta, A.; Nakashima, S.; Matsuyanagi, H.; Asakawa, T.; Miyagishi, S. Kraft temperature and enthalpy of solution of *N*-acyl amino acid surfactants and their racemic modifications: effect of the counter ion. *Colloid Polym. Sci.* 2003, *282*, 162–169.

[40] Evans, H. C. Alkyl sulphates. Part I. Critical micelle concentrations of the sodium salts. *J. Chem. Soc.* 1956, 579–586.

[41] Vijay, R.; Angayarkanny, S.; Baskar, G. Amphiphilic dodecyl ester derivatives from aromatic amino acids: Significance of chemical architecture in interfacial adsorption characteristics. *Colloids Surf., A* 2008, *317*, 643–649.

[42] Silva, S. G.; Rodríguez-Borjes, J. E.; Marques, E. F.; do Vale, M. L. Towards novel efficient monomeric surfactants based on serine, tyrosine and 4-hydroxyproline: synthesis and micellization properties. *Tetrahedron* 2009, *65*, 4156–4164.

[43] Brito, R. O.; Silva, S. G.; Fernandes, R. M. F.; Marques, E. F.; Enrique-Borges, J.; do Vale, M. L. C. Enhanced interfacial properties of novel amino acid-derived surfactants: Effects of headgroup chemistry and of alkyl chain length and unsaturation. *Colloids Surf., B* 2011, *86*, 65–70.

[44] Menger, F. M.; Littau, C. A. Gemini surfactants: A new class of self-assembling molecules. *J. Am. Chem. Soc.* 1993, *115*, 10083–10090.

[45] Menger, F. M.; Keiper, J. S. Gemini surfactants. *Angew. Chem., Int. Ed.* 2000, *39*, 1906–1920.

[46] Zana, R. Dimeric and oligomeric surfactants. Behaviour at interfaces and in aqueous solution: A review. *Adv. Colloid Interface Sci.* 2002, *97*, 205–253.

[47] Zana, R. Dimeric (gemini) surfactants: effect of the spacer group on the association behaviour in aqueous solution. *J. Colloid Interface Sci.* 2002, *248*, 203–220.

[48] Yoshimura, T.; Sakato, A.; Tsuchiya, K.; Ohkubo, T.; Sakai, H.; Abe, M.; Esumi, K. Adsorption and aggregation properties of amino acid-based *N*-alkyl cysteine monomeric and *N,N'*-dialkyl cystine dimeric surfactants. *J. Colloid Interface Sci.* 2007, *308*, 466–473.

[49] Fan, H.; Han, F.; Liu, Z.; Qin, L.; Li, Z.; Liang, D.; Ke, F.; Huang, J.; Fu, H. Active control of surface properties and aggregation behaviour in amino acid-based gemini surfactant systems. *J. Colloid Interface Sci.* 2008, *321*, 227–234.

[50] Faustino, C. M. C.; Calado, A. R. T.; Garcia-Rio, L. Dimeric and monomeric surfactants derived from sulphur-containing amino acids. *J. Colloid Interface Sci.* 2010, *351*, 472–477.

[51] Faustino, C. M. C.; Calado, A. R. T.; Garcia-Rio, L. Mixed micelle formation between amino acid-based surfactants and phospholipids. *J. Colloid Interface Sci.* 2011, *359*, 493–498.

[52] Faustino, C. M. C.; Calado, A. R. T.; Garcia-Rio, L. Gemini surfactant–protein interactions: effect of pH, temperature and surfactant stereochemistry. *Biomacromolecules* 2009, *10*, 2508–2514.

[53] Faustino, C. M. C.; Calado, A. R. T.; Garcia-Rio, L. Interaction between β-cyclodextrin and an amino acid-based gemini surfactant derived from cysteine. *J. Colloid Interface Sci.* 2012, *367*, 286–292.

[54] Faustino, C. M. C.; Calado, A. R. T.; Garcia-Rio, L. New urea-based surfactants derived from α,ω-amino acids. *J. Phys. Chem. B* 2009, *113*, 977–982.

[55] Azzam, E. M. S.; Morsy, S. M. I. Enhancement of the antitumour activity for the synthesized dodecylcysteine surfactant using gold nanoparticles. *J. Surfactants Deterg.* 2008, *11*, 195–199.

[56] Angayarkanny, S.; Vijay, R.; Baskar, G.; Mandal, A. B. Self-organization at the interface and in aqueous solution of a cationic gemini surfactant from the dioctyl ester of cystine. *J. Colloid Interface Sci.* 2012, *367*, 319–326.

[57] Bordes, R.; Holmberg, K. Physical chemical characteristics of dicarboxylic amino acid-based surfactants. *J. Colloid Interface Sci.* 2011, *391*, 32–41.

[58] Bordes, R.; Tropsch, J.; Holmberg, K. Counterion specificity of surfactants based on dicarboxylic amino acids. *J. Colloid Interface Sci.* 2009, *338*, 529–536.

[59] Kaneko, D.; Olsson, U.; Sakamoto, K. Self-assembly in some *N*-lauroyl-L-glutamate/water systems. *Langmuir* 2002, *18*, 4699–4703.

[60] Tsubone, K.; Ogawa, T; Mimura, K. Surface and aqueous properties of anionic gemini surfactants having dialkyl amide, carboxyl, and carboxylate groups. *J. Surfactants Deterg.* 2003, *6*, 39–46.

[61] Tsubone, K.; Rosen, M. J. Structural effect on surface activities of anionic surfactants having *N*-acyl-*N*-methylamide and carboxylate groups. *J. Colloid Interface Sci.* 2001, *244*, 394–398.

[62] Allouch, M.; Infante, M. R.; Seguer, J.; Stebe, M.-J.; Selve, C. Nonionic amphiphilic compounds from aspartic and glutamic acids as structural mimics of lecithins. *J. Am. Oil Chem. Soc.* 1996, *73*, 87–95.

[63] Rodehüser, L.; Chaumette, H.; Meyers, A.; Rogalska, E.; Gérardin, Ch.; Selve, C. Derivatives of glutamic acid as new surfactants. *Amino Acids* 2000, *18*, 89–100.

[64] Morán, C.; Clapés, P.; Comelles, F.; García, T.; Pérez, L.; Vinardell, P.; Mitjans, M.; Infante, M. R. Chemical structure/property relationship in single-chain arginine surfactants. *Langmuir* 2001, *17*, 5071–5075.

[65] Pinazo, A.; Wen, X.; Pérez, L.; Infante, M. R.; Franses, E. I. Aggregation behaviour in water of monomeric and gemini cationic surfactants derived from arginine. *Langmuir* 1999, *15*, 3134–3142.

[66] Pérez, L.; Pinazo, A.; Rosen, M. J.; Infante, M. R. Surface activity properties at equilibrium of novel gemini cationic amphiphilic compounds from Arginine, Bis(Args). *Langmuir* 1998, *14*, 2307–2315.

[67] Pérez, L.; Pinazo, A.; Rosen, M. J.; Infante, M. R. Synthesis, aggregation and biological properties of a new class of gemini cationic amphiphilic compounds from arginine, bis(Args). *Langmuir* 1996, *12*, 5296–5301.

[68] Seguer, J.; Selve, C.; Allouch, M.; Infante, M. R. Nonionic amphiphilic compounds from lysine as molecular mimics of lecithins. *J. Am. Oil Chem. Soc.* 1996, *73*, 79–86.

[69] Pinazo, A.; Pérez, L.; Lozano, M.; Angelet, M.; Infante, M. R.; Vinardell, M. P.; Pons, R. Aggregation properties of diacyl lysine surfactant compounds: Hydrophobic chain length and counterion effect. *J. Phys. Chem. B* 2008, *112*, 8578–8585.

[70] Colomer, A.; Pinazo, A.; Manresa, M. A.; Vinardell, M. P.; Mitjans, M.; Infante, M. R.; Pérez, L. Cationic surfactants derived from lysine: Effects of their structure and charge type on antimicrobial and haemolytic activities. *J. Med. Chem.* 2011, *54*, 989–1002.

[71] Ding, W.; Fritz, J. S. Carbamate chiral surfactants for capillary electrophoresis. *J. Chromatogr., A* 1999, *831*, 311–320.

[72] Ohta, A.; Hata, Y.; Mizuno, Y.; Asakawa, T.; Miyagishi, S. Phase diagrams of mixtures of diastereomeric salts of *N*-acyl amino acid-type surfactants and separation of enantiomers. *J. Phys. Chem. B* 2004, *108*, 12204–12209.

[73] Baczko, K.; Larpent, C.; Lesot, P. New amino acid-based anionic surfactants and their use as enantiodiscriminating lyotropic liquid crystalline NMR solvents. *Tetrahedron: Asymmetry* 2004, *15*, 971–982.

[74] Heath, J. G.; Arnett, E. M. Chiral molecular recognition in monolayers of diastereomeric *N*-acylamino acid methyl esters at the air/water interface. *J. Am. Chem. Soc.* 1992, *114*, 4500–4514.

[75] Arnett, E. M.; Harvey, N. G.; Rose, P. L. Stereochemistry and molecular recognition in "two dimensions". *Acc. Chem. Res.* 1989, *22*, 131–138.

[76] Nandi, N.; Volhardt, D. Chiral discrimination effects in Langmuir monolayers: monolayers of palmitoyl aspartic acid, *N*-stearoyl serine methyl ester and *N*-tetradecyl-γ,δ-dihydroxypentanoic acid amide. *J. Phys. Chem. B* 2003, *107*, 3464–3475.

[77] Takehara, M.; Yoshimura, I.; Yoshida, R. Surface-active *N*-acyl glutamate. IV. Physicochemical properties of triethanolamine long chain *N*-acylglutamates. *J. Am. Oil Chem. Soc.* 1974, *51*, 419–423.

[78] Sakamoto, K.; Hatano, M. Formation of chiral aggregates of acylamino acids in solutions. *Bull. Chem. Soc. Jpn.* 1980, *53*, 339–343.

[79] Shinitzky, M.; Haimovitz, R. Chiral surfaces in micelles of enantiomeric *N*-palmitoyl- and *N*-stearoylserine. *J. Am. Chem. Soc.* 1993, *115*, 12545–12549.

[80] Desando, M. A.; McGarvey, B.; Reeves, L. W. NMR spectroscopy and the effects of enantiomerism on the micelle formation of potassium *N*-n-dodecanoylalaninate. *J. Colloid Interface Sci.* 1996, *181*, 331–336.

[81] Nandi, N.; Volhardt, D. Effect of molecular chirality on the morphology of biomimetic Langmuir monolayers. *Chem. Rev.* 2003, *103*, 4033–4075.

[82] Nandi, N.; Volhardt, D. Prediction of the handedness of the chiral domains of amphiphilic monolayers: monolayers of amino acid amphiphiles. *Colloids Surf., A* 2002, *198-200*, 207–221.

[83] Roy, S.; Das, D.; Dasgupta, A.; Mitra, R. N.; Das, P. K. Amino acid based cationic surfactants in aqueous solution: physicochemical study and application of supramolecular chirality in ketone reduction. *Langmuir* 2005, *21*, 10398–10404.

[84] Pérez, L.; García, M. T.; Ribosa, I.; Vinardell, M. P.; Manresa, A.; Infante, M. R. Biological properties of arginine-based gemini cationic surfactants. *Environ. Toxicol. Chem.* 2002, *21*, 1279–1285.

[85] Brito, R. O.; Marques, E. F.; Silva, S. G.; do Vale, M. L.; Gomes, P.; Araújo, M. J.; Rodriguez-Borges, J. E.; Infante, M. R.; Garcia, M. T.; Ribosa, I.; Vinardell, M. P.; Mitjans, M. Physicochemical and toxicological properties of novel amino acid-based amphiphiles and their spontaneously formed catanionic vesicles. *Colloids Surf., B* 2009, *72*, 80–87.

[86] Nogueira, D. R.; Mitjans, M.; Infante, M. R.; Vinardell, M. P. The role of counterions in the membrane-disruptive properties of pH-sensitive lysine-based surfactants. *Acta Biomater.* 2011, *7*, 2846–2856.

[87] Sánchez, L.; Mitjans, M.; Infante, M. R.; García, M. T.; Manresa, M. A.; Vinardell, M. P. The biological properties of lysine-derived surfactants. *Amino Acids* 2007, *32*, 133–136.

[88] Vives, M. A.; Infante, M. R.; Garcia, E.; Selve, C.; Maugras, M.; Vinardell, M. P. Erythrocyte haemolysis and shape changes induced by new lysine-derivative surfactants. *Chem. Biol. Interactions* 1999, *118*, 1–18.

[89] Nogueira, D. R.; Mitjans, M.; Infante, M. R.; Vinardell, M. P. Comparative sensitivity of tumor and non-tumor cell lines as a reliable approach for in vitro cytotoxicity screening of lysine-based surfactants with potential pharmaceutical applications. *Int. J. Pharm.* 2011, *420*, 51–58.

[90] Balgavy, P.; Devinsky, F. Cut-off effects in biological activities of surfactants. *Adv. Colloid Interface Sci.* 1996, *66*, 23–63.

[91] Colomer, A.; Pinazo, A.; García, M. T.; Mitjans, M.; Vinardell, M. P.; Infante, M. R.; Martínez, V.; Pérez, L. pH-Sensitive surfactants from lysine: assessment of their cytotoxicity and environmental behaviour. *Langmuir* 2012, *28*, 5900–5912.

[92] Mhaskar, S.; Lakshminarayana, G.; Saisree, L. *N*-Acyl leucines of biologically active uncommon fatty acids: synthesis and antibacterial activity. *J. Am. Oil Chem. Soc.* 1993, *70*, 23–27.

[93] Xia, J.; Xia, Y.; Nnanna, I. A. Structure-function relationship of acyl amino acid surfactants: surface activity and antimicrobial properties. *J. Agric. Food Chem.* 1995, *43*, 867–871.

[94] Kondoh, M.; Furutani, T.; Azuma, M.; Ooshima, H.; Kato, J. Acyl amino acid derivatives as novel inhibitors of influenza neuramidinase. *Biosci., Biotechnol., Biochem.* 1997, *61*, 870–874.

[95] Epand, R. F.; Infante, M. R.; Flanagan, T. D.; Epand, R. M. Properties of lipoamino acids incorporated into membrane bilayers. *Biochem. Biophys. Acta* 1998, *1373*, 67–75.

[96] Okahata, Y.; Seki, T. pH-Sensitive capsule membranes. Reversible permeability control from the dissociative bilayer-coated capsule membrane by an ambient pH change. *J. Am. Chem. Soc.* 1984, *106*, 8065–8070.

[97] Ménard, N.; Tsapis, N.; Poirier, C.; Arnauld, T.; Moine, L.; Lefoulon, F.; Péan, J.-M.; Fattal, E. Drug solubilisation and in vitro toxicity evaluation of lipoamino acid surfactants. *Int. J. Pharm.* 2012, *423*, 312–320.

[98] Pignatello, R.; Puleo, A.; Guccione, S.; Raciti, G.; Acquaviva, R.; Campisi, A.; Ventura, C. A.; Puglisi, G. Enhancement of drug affinity for cell membranes by conjugation with lipoamino acids. I. Synthesis and biological evaluation of lipophilic conjugates of tranylcypromine. *Eur. J. Med. Chem.* 2005, *40*, 1074–1079.

[99] Pignatello, R.; Guccione, S.; Castelli, F.; Sarpietro, M. G.; Giurato, L.; Lombardo, M.; Puglisi, G.; Toth, I. Enhancement of drug affinity for cell membranes by conjugation with lipoamino acids. II. Experimental and computational evidence using biomembrane models. *Int. J. Pharm.* 2006, *310*, 53–63.

[100] Pignatello, R.; Mangiafico, A.; Basile, L.; Ruozi, B.; Furneri, P. M. Amphiphilic ion pairs of tobramycin with lipoamino acids. *Eur. J. Med. Chem.* 2011, *46*, 1665–1671.

[101] Mintzer, M. A.; Simanek, E. E. Nonviral vectors for gene delivery. *Chem. Rev.* 2009, *109*, 259–302.

[102] Ilarduya, C. T.; Sun, Y.; Duzgunes, N. Gene delivery by lipoplexes and polyplexes. *Eur. J. Pharm. Sci.* 2010, *40*, 159–170.

[103] Kirby, A. J.; Camilleri, P.; Engberts, J. B. F. N.; Feiters, M. C.; Nolte, R. J. M.; Söderman, O.; Bergsma, M.; Bell, P. C.; Fielden, M. L.; Rodríguez, C. L. G.; Guédat, P.; Kremer, A.; McGregor, C.; Perrin, C.; Ronsin, G.; van Eijk, M. C. P. Gemini surfactants: new synthetic vectors for gene transfection. *Angew. Chem., Int. Ed.* 2003, *42*, 1448–1457.

[104] Wettig, S. D.; Verrall, R. E.; Foldvari, M. Gemini surfactants: A new family of building blocks for non-viral gene delivery systems. *Curr. Gene Ther.* 2008, *8*, 9–23.

[105] Singh, J.; Yang, P.; Michel, D.; Verrall, R. E.; Foldvari, M.; Badea, I. Amino acid-substituted gemini surfactant-based nanoparticles as safe and versatile gene delivery agents. *Curr. Drug Delivery* 2011, *8*, 299–306.

[106] Yang, P.; Singh, J.; Wettig, S.; Foldvari, M.; Verral, R. E.; Badea, I. Enhanced gene expression in epithelial cells transfected with amino acid-substituted gemini nanoparticles. *Eur. J. Pharm. Biopharm.* 2010, *75*, 311–320.

[107] Dauty, E.; Remy, J. S,; Blessing, T.; Behr, J. P. Dimerizable cationic detergents with a low cmc condense plasmid DNA into nanometric particles and transfect cells in culture. *J. Am. Chem. Soc.* 2001, *123*, 9227–9234.

[108] Dauty, E.; Behr, J. P.; Remy, J. S. Development of plasmid and oligonucleotide nanometric particles. *Gene Ther.* 2002, *9*, 743–748.

[109] Byk, G.; Wetzer, B.; Frederic, M.; Dubertret, C.; Scherman, D. Reduction-sensitive lipopolyamines s a novel nonviral gene delivery system for modulated release of DNA with improved transgene expression. *J. Med. Chem.* 2000, *43*, 4377–4378.

[110] Wetzer, B.; Byk, G.; Frederic, M.; Auriau, M.; Blanche, F.; Pitard, B.; Scherman, D. Reducible cationic lipids for gene transfer. *Biochem. J.* 2001, *356*, 747–756.

[111] Rosa, M.; Miguel, M. G.; Lindman, B. DNA encapsulation by biocompatible catanionic vesicles. *J. Colloid Interface Sci.* 2007, *312*, 87–97.

[112] Rosa, M.; Móran, M. C.; Miguel, M. G.; Lindman, B. The association of DNA and stable catanionic amino acid-based vesicles. *Colloids Surf., A* 2007, *301*, 361–375.

In: Micelles
Editors: Danielle Bradburn and Tom Bittinger

ISBN: 978-1-62948-444-0
© 2014 Nova Science Publishers, Inc.

Chapter 6

CONSTRUCTION OF BLOCK COPOLYMER MICELLES AND SINGLE-CHAIN NANOPARTICLES IN NON-SELECTIVE SOLVENTS

José A. Pomposo[1,2,3]

[1]Centro de Fisica de Materiales (CSIC, UPV/EHU)-Materials Physics Center,
San Sebastian, Spain
[2]Departamento de Fisica de Materiales, Universidad del Pais Vasco (UPV/EHU),
San Sebastian, Spain
[3]IKERBASQUE-Basque Foundation for Science, Bilbao, Spain

ABSTRACT

Block copolymer micelles and single-chain nanoparticles are artificial soft nano-objects of small size which have gained prominence in nanoscience and nanotechnology due to their exceptional and sometimes unique properties. Micelles and single-chain nanoparticles are very useful nano-objects for many applications such as cosmetics, drug delivery, electronics, pollution control, heterogeneous catalysis or separation technologies. This chapter focuses on the current state of the investigations in synthetic techniques for highly-efficient block copolymer micelle and single-chain nanoparticle construction in non-selective, good solvents. A comprehensive description of several approaches employed for micelle formation (hydrogen bonding, quaternization / complexation, salt-induced hidrophobicity change, metalation, radical coupling, etc.) in non-selective solvents is reviewed. Significant emphasis is placed on efficient techniques available for reversible, multi-responsive (pH, temperature, oxidant/reductant, etc.) micelle preparation in non-selective solvents. Additionally, the recent and complementary topic of single-chain nanoparticle construction in good solvents through covalent and non-covalent interactions is reviewed. Recent progress achieved for the use of these complex nano-objects in some promising fields, such as nanomedicine and catalysis, is highlighted.

Keywords: Micelles; single-chain nanoparticles; non-selective solvents; covalent and non-covalent interactions

1. INTRODUCTION

Micelle construction starting from diblock copolymers of incompatible blocks (A, B) in a selective solvent for one of the blocks (e.g. A) is a well-known process both in academia and industry (see Figure 1A) [1]. The driving force behind micelle formation under such conditions is the aggregation of the *insoluble* blocks (B) into a micellar core that has *soluble* A-block branches forming a shell around it. In this way, the free energy of the resulting nano-assembly, ΔF, is minimized even if unfavorable stretching of the B block chains often takes place. Above the critical micelle concentration, the equilibrium between unimers (individual copolymer chains) and micelles is sifted towards nano-assembly formation. Theories describing micelle formation starting from diblock copolymers of incompatible blocks in a selective solvent [2-9] account for several contributions to ΔF, that must be negative for micelle formation: i) a free energy contribution arising from dilution, ii) a contribution from the mixing of A and B blocks in the corona, iii) an interfacial core-corona free energy term, and iv) a free energy contribution accounting for the reduction in configurational surface of the micellar core. Such theories allow one to predict the critical micelle concentration, the micelle size distribution, the average aggregation number, as well as the core radius and the shell thickness of the micelle as a function of solvent quality, compatibility degree between blocks, block length and interfacial energy. Depending on the composition of the starting block copolymer, two limiting structures can be drawn: 'star-like' micelles with a small core compared to the corona, and 'crew-cut' micelles with a large core and highly-stretched coronal chains.

More interesting but least investigated, however, is the case of micelle construction starting from diblock copolymers of incompatible blocks (A, B) in a non-selective solvent (i.e. a good solvent for both blocks) which is sometimes referred as induced micellization. In this case, micelle formation requires the presence of an *inductor* which sometimes is simply a variation of an external stimulus like pressure, temperature, pH, etc. but more often is a bifunctional small molecule which is reactive towards the functional groups of one of the blocks. A schematic illustration of micelle formation in non-selective solvents is illustrated in Figure 1B. In opposite to the case of micelle formation from diblock copolymers of incompatible blocks in a non-selective solvent, only one theoretical work is available which provides support for the experimental findings about micelle formation under good solvent conditions [10]. Related to the case of block copolymer micelle construction in a good solvent is the recent and complementary topic of single-chain nanoparticle construction in good solvents through *covalent* and *non-covalent interactions* (see Figure 1C) [11, 12]. Recently, coarse-grained molecular dynamics (MD) simulations have become a powerful tool for investigating the structure of single-chain nanoparticles in solution and to determine the effect of chain length, number of reactive groups, solvent quality, etc. on nanoparticle morphology [13].

In next sections, 2 and 3, a description of the main methods reported for highly-efficient block copolymer micelle and single-chain nanoparticle construction in non-selective, good solvents is provided. Both micelles and single-chain nanoparticles are interesting for several potential applications including the development of versatile and efficient probes for biological diagnosis, imaging and chemical detection (bio- or chemosensors), high-quality drug-delivery vehicles, development of improved catalysts, sacrificial elements for nanotemplating, etc. Section 4 will be devoted to the recent progress achieved for the use of these complex nano-objects in some promising fields, such as nanomedicine and catalysis.

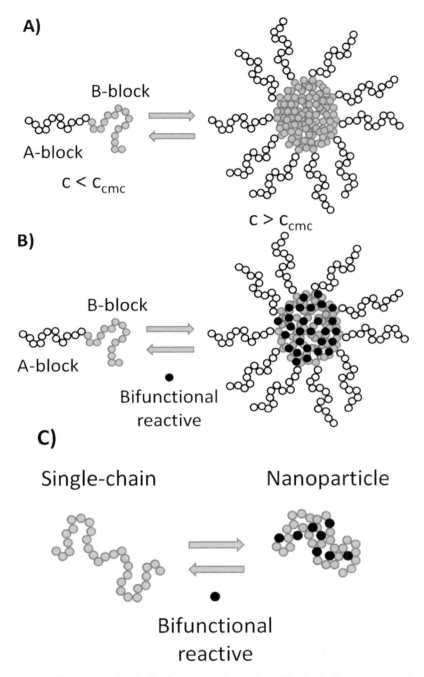

Figure 1. Schematic illustration of micelle formation above the critical micellar concentration (c_{cmc}) in: A) a selective solvent for the A-block of AB block copolymers, as a consequence of the insolubility of the B blocks and (B) a common solvent for A and B blocks of AB block copolymers, using external bifunctional reactive molecules for the cross-linking of the B blocks. C) Reversible single-chain polymer nanoparticle formation under good solvent conditions assisted by bifunctional molecules.

Table 1. Different block copolymers, micellization techniques and inductors employed for the construction of block copolymer micelles in non-selective solvents

Block Copolymer Type	Micellization Technique	Inductors	References
Block copolymers containing poly(N-isopropyl acrylamide)	Temperature induced micellization	Temperature	14, 15
Block copolymers containing poly(vinyl pyridine)	pH induced micellization	pH	16
Poly(2-(dimethylamino)ethyl methacrylate) containing block copolymers	Temperature and pH induced micellizations	Temperature, pH	17-21
Block copolymers containing poly(vinyl pyridine)	pH and salt induced micellizations	pH, Metal salts	22-24
Poly(vinyl triphenylphosphine) containing block copolymers	Salt induced micellization	Metal salts	25
Block copolymers containing poly(vinyl phenol)	Hydrogen bonding induced micellization	α,ω-diamine	26, 27
Poly(vinyl pyridine) containing block copolymers	Quaternization induced micellization	α,ω-dibromobutane	28, 29
Block copolymers containing poly(vinyl pyridine)	Acid-Base induced micellization	Formic acid	30
Poly(vinyl pyridine) containing block copolymers	Hydrophobic interaction induced micellization	Perfluorooctanoic acid	31
Block copolymers containing poly(acrylic acid)	Ionic complexation induced micellization	1-(3-Dimethylaminopropyl)-3-ethylcarbodiimide methiodide	32
Poly(vinyl pyridine) containing block copolymers	Ionic complexation induced micellization	Potassium persulfate	33
Block copolymers containing poly(vinyl pyridine) or poly(vinyl phenol)	Hydrogen bonding induced micellization	Bisphenol A or Bis-pyridyl ethane	34
Poly(vinyl pyridine) containing block copolymers	Polymerization induced micellization	Propargyl bromide	35
Block copolymers containing poly[4-(2-aminoethyl amino)styrene]	Salt induced micellization	$CuCl_2$	36
Poly(ethylene oxide) containing block copolymers	Salt induced micellization	NaCl	37
Block copolymers containing poly(4-vinylbenzyloxy-TEMPO)	Oxidation induced micellization	Cl_2	38

2. CONSTRUCTION OF BLOCK COPOLYMER MICELLES IN NON-SELECTIVE SOLVENTS

2.1. Micellization Techniques in Non-selective Solvents

Induced micellization of block copolymers has received considerable attention in recent years from the point of view of the potential reversible control over the self-assembly process. The micellization can be induced by variations in the surroundings of the solubilized block copolymers, such as: i) temperature, ii) pressure, iii) pH, iv) redox potential, v) metal salt formation, vi) hydrogen bonding formation, vii) covalent bond cross-linking, viii) non-covalent bond formation, etc. Due to these stimuli, the block copolymers are converted in situ from the nonamphiphilic copolymers molecularly dissolved in the solvent (unimers) to amphiphilic copolymers undergoing the subsequent micellization process. The most common micellization techniques reported in the literature are summarized in Table 1. We can distinguish between *physically-induced micellization* (*e.g.*, temperature, pressure) and *chemically-induced micellization* (*e.g.*, addition of salt, bifunctional chemical reagents, redox active species).

2.1.1. Physically-induced Micellization

Physically-induced micellization covers the change in a physical variable such as temperature, pressure, volume, etc. as the driving force for block copolymer micellization. By their own nature, physically induced micellization leads to reversible micellar nano-entities.

First reports about physically-induced micellization relied on the use of thermosensitive block copolymers containing poly(N-isopropyl acrylamide) (PNIPAM). This polymer is highly soluble in aqueous solutions below its cloud point (lower critical solution temperature, LCST ≈ 32°C) but precipitates above the LCST. In this sense, it was shown by Neradovic et al. [14] that block copolymers of PNIPAM with poly(ethylene glycol) (PEG) exhibit thermoresponsive solubility in aqueous solutions. Above the LCST, the thermosensitive PNIPAM block precipitates, and the diblock copolymers organize in polymeric micelles, which consist of a PNIPAM core and hydrophilic shell of PEG. Double hydrophilic block copolymers containing PNIPAM showing both LCST and upper critical solution temperature (UCST) behavior were first reported by Laschewsky and co-workers [15]. In this pioneering work, colloidal aggregates which switch reversible in water their "inside" to the "outside" as a function of temperature ("schizophrenic" block copolymers) were demonstrated based on block copolymers of PNIPAM and poly(3[N-(3-methacrylamidopropyl-N,N-dimethyl]ammoniopropionate sulfunate) (PSPP). In addition to PNIPAM, reversible temperature-induced micellization in aqueous media was also observed in poly(2-(dimethylamino)ethyl methacrylate)-*block*-poly(2-tetrahydropyranyl methacrylate) (PDMAEMA–*b*–PTHPMA) precursors upon complete removal of the 2-tetrahydropyranyl protecting groups leading to PDMAEMA–polymethacrylic acid zwitterionic block copolymers that form micelles at temperatures above 50 °C [20]. A further example of thermoresponsive "schizophrenic" block copolymers involved poly(sulfobetaine methacrylate)-*block*-poly(morpholinoethyl methacrylate)-based block copolymers (PSBMA–*b*–PMEMA) showing UCST and LCST behaviors at 20 and 50 °C, respectively. Hence, molecular dissolution occurred in dilute aqueous solution at 30–40 °C, whereas polydisperse, hydrated SBMA core micelles were formed below 20 °C and near-monodisperse, relatively dehydrated MEMA-core micelles were formed above 50 °C [17].

2.1.2. Chemically-induced Micellization

Depending on the reversibility of the chemical reaction used to induce the micellization (*i.e.*, covalent or non-covalent bonds) the resulting micelles will be permanent or reversible nano-assemblies. A detailed description of reversible micelles showing multi-responsive behavior is given in next section.

Chemically-induced micellization by changes in pH was reported as early as 1996 by Munk and co-workers [16] for poly(2-vinyl pyridine)-*block*-poly(ethylene oxide) (P2VP–*b*–

PEO) block copolymers and poly(2-vinyl pyridine) (P2VP) / P2VP–b–PEO mixtures. Hence, spontaneous micelle formation was observed in aqueous solutions of P2VP–b–PEO and P2VP / P2VP–b–PEO mixtures when increasing the pH from acidic to neutral or basic conditions. The micellization process was found to be completely reversible when pH was cycled above and below a critical pH (*ca.* pH 5). The unique features of these systems were: i) control of micellization by pH, and ii) formation of well-behaved micelles of variable size by titration of different ratios and different total polymer concentrations of PVP/PVP–b–PEO. Subsequently, Armes and co-workers [17-21] developed a series of novel pH-sensitive block copolymers which form micelles having coronae with various electrostatic properties: poly(2-(dimethylamino)ethyl   methacrylate)-*block*-poly(2-(diethylamino)   ethyl   methacrylate) (PDMAEMA–b–PDEAEMA),   poly(ethylene   oxide)-*block*-poly(2-(diethylamino)ethyl methacrylate) (PEO–b–PDEAEMA), and PDMAEMA–b–PDEAEMA with the DMAEMA block selectively quaternized with benzyl chloride (Q-PDMAEMA–b–PDEAEMA). Under acidic conditions, the amine groups on the PDEAEMA side chains were protonated, causing the copolymers to become hydrophilic and to remain as individual unimers in solution. The subsequent addition of base deprotonated the side chains, causing the PDEAEMA block to became hydrophobic. Above a critical pH the copolymers aggregated to form micelles. The PDEAEMA block formed the micelle core while the hydrophilic PDMAEMA, PEO, or Q-PDMAEMA block extended into the solvent and formed the micelle corona. The primary difference between the three copolymers was in the electrostatic properties of the hydrophilic block forming the micelle corona, displaying electrostatically neutral, weakly charged, and strongly   charged   hydrophilic   blocks   from   PEO,   PDMAEMA,   and   Q-PDMAEMA, respectively. An interesting aspect of these micelles is that the fractional charge on the PDMAEMA block can be varied by adjusting the solution pH, such that the degree of charge in the micelle corona can be varied.

Salt induced micellization was explored as early as 1999 by Antonietti and co-workers [22] using PEO–b–P2VP block copolymers. To examine how metal anions interact with fully protonated, nonmicellar PEO–b–P2VP, Na_2PtCl_6 was added to a water solution of PEO–b–P2VP at pH = 1.97. Addition of Na_2PtCl_6 to the clear solution of protonated block copolymer was found to induce micelle formation leading after 2 days to micellar nano-entities with a size of 75 nm. Additionally, Douglas and co-workers [23] reported that upon addition of cadmium ions into a solution of PS–b–P2VP block copolymer in tetrahydrofuran (THF), a good solvent for both of the blocks, micelles formed due to complexation of divalent Cd^{2+} ions with the 2-vinylpyridine (2VP) units. Hence, the micelle core was composed of $2VP/Cd^{2+}$ complexes, whereas the shell was composed of polystyrene blocks. Interestingly, aqueous micelles consisting of a PS core, a pH sensitive P2VP shell, and a PEO corona were prepared by Schubert and co-workers [24] from a metallo-supramolecular ABC triblock copolymer   (PS–b–P2VP-[Ru]-PEO)   containing   a   bis(2,2':6,2''-terpyridine)-ruthenium(II) complex as a supramolecular connection between the constituting poly(styrene)-*block*-poly(2-vinylpyridine) diblock and poly(ethylene oxide) block, respectively. Also, micelle formation in THF via complexation of triphenylphosphine groups from poly(styrene)-*block*-poly(-m-vinyltriphenylphosphine) (PS–b–PPH) block copolymers with palladium compounds has been reported by Chernyshov et al. [25].

The first attempt to form micelles from a diblock copolymer consisting entirely of solvent-philic polymer blocks using a bifunctional reagent was carried out by Yoshida and Kunugi [26] in 2002 by using poly(styrene)-*block*-poly(4-vinylphenol) (PS–b–P4VPh) block copolymers and α,ω-diamines in 1,4-dioxane, a good solvent for both blocks (see Figure 1B). The fact that the copolymer produced no micelles in the presence of a monoamine supported the fact that the micellization was induced by hydrogen bond cross-linking of the bifunctional reagent. The critical micelle concentration during the micellization was determined by several factors: one was by the concentration of the diamine at a constant copolymer concentration and the other was by the copolymer concentration at a constant diamine concentration. The block length of PS–b–P4VPh and mixed ratios of the copolymers also manipulated the critical micelle concentration (CMC) and the micellar size (30 to 70 nm). Furthermore, temperature was another factor controlling the dissociation-reconstruction of PS–b–P4VPh micelles. The driving force for micellization was hydrogen-bond cross-linking assisted by diamines. Interestingly, the dissociation process releases the diamine from the micelles, while the reconstruction takes it into the micellar cores [27].

A further extension of this method was carried out by Chen et al. [28] in 2003, using poly(styrene)-block-poly(4-vinylpyridine) (PS–b–P4VPy) block copolymers and 1,4-dibromobutane (DBB) as cross-linker. In this case, the driving force for micellization was quaternization of 4-vinylpyridine units induced by DBB leading to core-cross-linked nanoparticles with sizes between 70 and 190 nm at high solid contents (up to 200 mg/ml). Working at such high solid contents was possible due the relatively slow quaternization process allowing the PS chains to change their conformation much faster than the P4VPy chains aggregate. Hence, the PS blocks were able to extend themselves so as to form shells around the P4VPy aggregates. The kinetics of the micellization process was followed via H^1, C^{13}, and 2-D heteronuclear single quantum correlation (HSQC) NMR experiments by Pomposo and co-workers [39] showing a value of the apparent kinetic constant of the relatively slow core-shell nanoparticle formation process of 1.5×10^{-5} s^{-1}.

Interestingly, such a method was also implemented Chen et al. [29] in 2008 for the efficient synthesis of unimolecular polymeric Janus nanoparticles by using poly(styrene)-block-poly(2-vinyl pyridine)-block-poly(ethylene oxide) (PS-b-P2VP-b-PEO) triblock copolymers by efficient intramolecular cross-linking of the middle P2VP block using DBB in a common solvent, N,N-dimethylformamide (DMF), due to effective steric shielding of hydrophobic PS and hydrophilic PEO end blocks. Size exclusion chromatography (SEC) results indicated that intramolecular cross-linking of the middle P2VP block was possible up to a relatively high polymer concentration (20 mg/mL) and/or high DBB-to-2VP molar ratio. Intriguingly, these amphiphilic unimolecular polymeric Janus nanoparticles exhibited concentration dependent self-assembly in DMF. Supermicelles with PS forming the core and PEO being the corona were observed after slow DMF evaporation at room temperature from samples at a concentration of 0.25 mg/ml. Eventually, DBB cross-linked P2VP located between the PS core and PEO corona.

More recently, Pomposo and co-workers [34] reported a new approach for the preparation of block copolymer micelles in non-selective solvents via phenol–pyridine hydrogen-bonding interactions using block copolymers and bifunctional low-molecular-weight hydrogen bonding cross-linkers. Micelle formation in the symmetrical poly(styrene-block-4-vinyl phenol) / bis-pyridyl ethane (PS–b–P4VPh/BPE) and poly(styrene-b-4-vinylpyridine) / bisphenol A (PS–b–P4VPy/BPA) systems due to phenol–pyridine hydrogen bonding interactions was thoroughly investigated. The influence of several factors such as temperature, concentration, solvent and pH in the reversible micellization–demicellization process was analyzed by Fourier transform infrared spectroscopy (FTIR), differential scanning calorimetry (DSC), dynamic light scattering (DLS) and atomic force microscopy (AFM). Moreover, stabilized core–shell nanoparticles of *ca.* 40 nm in size were obtained by phase inversion followed by simple extraction of the excess of cross-linker molecules in solution. Toluene was employed as non-solvent for PVPy, BPA, PVPh and BPE but selective solvent for PS.

In addition to the use of bifunctional reagents, also monofunctional reactives with appropriate functional moieties can be used for induced micellation. Hence, in a first example by Chen et al. [30], perfluorooctanoic acid (PFOA) was used having a long hydrophobic tail that induces the self-assembly of PS–*b*–P4VPy block copolymers in chloroform ($CHCl_3$) upon quaternization of the P4VPy block, leading to micelles at a PFOA/4VPy ratio of 2/1 and vesicles at PFOA/4VPy ratios of 1/1, 1/2 and 1/5. The micelles formed at a PFOA/4VPy ratio of 2/1 were found to encapsulate the unbounded PFOA inside their cores instead of being solubilized in $CHCl_3$. A second example by the same group [31] involved the micellization of PS–*b*–P4VPy block copolymers with formic acid (FA) at FA/4VPy ratios greater of equal to 1/5.The aggregation of the insoluble FA/4VPy units was found to be the driving force for micellation.

Concerning ionic complexation induced micellization, Chen et al. [32] reported in 2004 the preparation of short-life (1-3 weeks) core-shell structured nanoaggregates of around 100 nm in size formed by the self-assembly of block copolymers containing poly(acrylic acid) with 1-(3-dimethylaminopropyl)-3-ethylcarbodiimide methiodide. The same technique was used by this group [33] for the construction of multi-responsive PEO–*b*–P2VPyH$^+$-$S_2O_8^{2-}$ micelles in water, as described in more detail in next section. The construction of core-shell nano-entities in DMF as a non-selective solvent of PS–*b*–P4VPy block copolymers via quaternization of 4VPy units and further polymerization of the activated propargylic groups has been recently reported by Chen and co-workers [35]. More recently, salt induced micellization in good solvents has been described for polystyrene-*block*-poly[4-(2-aminoethyl amino)styrene] (PS–*b*–PDAES) [36] and PEO-*block*-poly(vinyl alcohol) (PEO–*b*–PVA) [37] block copolymers. Additionally, oxidation induced complexation allowed the facile micellation of diblock copolymers containing stable nitroxyl radicals to spherical micelles of 50 nm in size [38].

2.2. Multi-responsive Micelles

In this section we will review the most relevant multi-responsive micelles synthesized through induced micellization in non-selective solvents.

2.2.1. Temperature- and pH-responsive Micelles

A novel type of polymeric micelles was designed by Neradivic et al. [14] from poly(NIPAM-co-HPMAM-lactate)-*block*-PEG block copolymers containing a temperature-sensitive block, which upon hydrolysis of the lactate groups at pH > 8.5 was converted to a polymer having a cloud point above 37 °C. Hence, the critical micelle temperature of poly(NIPAM-co-HPMAM-lactate)-*block*-PEG block copolymers with 35% and 50% HPMAM-lactate was found to reach values above 37 °C during incubation. This means that these block copolymers form micelles at physiological temperatures, but destabilize once the cloud point temperature of this block passes 37 °C because of the hydrolysis of the side groups. This is an attractive feature for drug delivery and biotechnological purposes.

Using PEO–b–PDMA–b–PDEA triblock copolymers, simultaneous temperature- and pH-responsive micelles were obtained by Armes and co-workers [19] showing a three-layer "onion" structure, with the PDEA block occupying the micelle core and the PDMA and PEO blocks forming the inner shell and corona, respectively. Below pH 7, this triblock copolymer was molecularly dissolved, with a hydrodynamic diameter of approximately 6-7 nm and very low scattering intensity. On addition of NaOH, micellization occurred above pH 7.1, as indicated by the appearance of bluish color that is characteristic of micellar solutions. Between pH 7.1 and 7.3, micellization was not complete since dynamic light scattering (DLS) revealed two populations at 8 and 35 nm, corresponding to unimers and micelles, respectively. At pH 7.3 or higher, only one population corresponding to micelles was observed by DLS. PEO–b–PDMA–b–PDEA triblock copolymer micelles at 0.5% w/v and pH 8.5 in water showed *ca.* 30 nm in size at temperatures below 45 °C. Above 45 °C (the cloud point of the PDMA block) the scattering intensity was found to increase abruptly, accompanied by a dramatic increase in the aggregate size from 30 to about 400-500 nm diameter.

Micelles formed from metallo-supramolecular ABC triblock copolymers, PS–b–P2VP-[Ru]-PEO, were also found to display simultaneous temperature- and pH-responsive behavior [24]. For these micelles two regimes were clearly observed as a function of pH: i) the "acidic" one with micelles with a size of approximately 80 nm and protonated P2VP shell, and ii) the "neutral" one with a hydrophobic P2VP shell and a size of approximately 65 nm. A sharp transition between both regimes was noted at pH 5, in agreement with the pK_a of P2VP. By changing the temperature from 20 to 50°C in the acidic regime, a reduction in size from 80 nm to 50 nm was observed, whereas a reduction from 65 nm to 35 nm was found in the neutral regime. A reasonable explanation for this behavior is that the input of thermal energy allowed a relaxation of the stretched PEO segments and a progressive dehydration of PEO which translated in a reduction of the steric stabilization due to the PEO corona.

Simultaneous temperature- and pH-responsive micelles were obtained by Pomposo and co-workers [19] by using symmetrical poly(styrene-*block*-4-vinyl phenol) / bis-pyridyl ethane (PS–b–P4VPh/BPE) and poly(styrene-b-4-vinylpyridine) / bisphenol A (PS–b–P4VPy/BPA) systems in 2-butanone, as non-selective solvent, in which the driving force for micelle formation was phenol–pyridine hydrogen bonding interactions. Hence, PS–b–P4VPh/BPE micelles showed hydrodynamic sizes of 30, 22 and 20 nm at 20, 40 and 60 °C, respectively, whereas PS–b–P4VPy/BPA micelles showed hydrodynamic sizes of 38, 27 and 18 nm at 20, 40 and 60 °C. These micelles were found to go back to individual unimers of *ca.* 4 nm upon addition of acetic acid (AA) or 4-(dimethylamino)pyridine (DMAP) due to the competition between the AA or DMAP molecules and the bifunctional cross-linker molecules (BPA or BPE).

2.2.2. Temperature- and Redox-responsive Micelles

Micelles having upper critical solution temperature (UCST) behavior (undergo dissociation when the temperature increases to a critical temperature) and redox-responsive behavior have been reported by Chen and co-workers [33]. These intriguing micelles were formed when an aqueous solution of PEO–b–P2VPy at pH 1.3 at a concentration of 1 mg/ml was mixed with $K_2S_2O_8$ at the molar ratio of $K_2S_2O_8$ to pyridine units of 1:1, resulting in blue opalescence as a consequence of micelle formation. The average hydrodynamic radius of the aggregates was around 100 nm, as determined by DLS and TEM measurements. The driving force for micellization was attributed to ionic cross-linking of the protonated (P2VPyH$^+$) blocks by $S_2O_8^{2-}$ anions. Other divalent anions like CO_3^{2-}, PO_4^{2-} and SO_4^{2-} were too weak to drive the micellation under such conditions.

Multi-responsive micelles prepared from PEO$_{329}$–b–P2VPy$_{128}$ block copolymers (the subscripts are the average number of the repeat units) were found to disintegrate upon heating to 38-40 °C. Excellent reversibility was demonstrated by turbimetry measurements of the micelles during heating-cooling cycles (25 to 40 °C). Interestingly, the UCST temperature can be tuned by changing the block copolymer length and its composition. Hence, when a copolymer PEO$_{134}$–b–P2VPy$_{251}$ was mixed with $K_2S_2O_8$ under the same conditions, the critical dissociation temperature raised to 70 °C, while when PEO$_{59}$–b–P2VPy$_{14}$ was used, no micelles were formed. Besides their thermal response, the micelles were sensitive to reductant as well. Mixed with a small amount of reductant such as oxalic acid, the micelles were found to dissociate promptly as proved by DLS and turbidity measurements. It is known that the persulfate ions are reduced to sulfate ions by the reductant. As mentioned before, the interaction between SO_4^{2-} and the P2VPyH$^+$ block chains is too weak to drive the micellization. However, after the addition of $K_2S_2O_8$, the micelles formed again.

3. CONSTRUCTION OF SINGLE-CHAIN NANOPARTICLES IN NON-SELECTIVE SOLVENTS

Single-chain polymer nanoparticles are the smallest individual nanogels that can be prepared through intrachain cross-linking by starting from a linear polymer precursors (see Figure 1C). The most notable differences between unimolecular soft nanoparticles and micelles are that no stabilizing corona exists and aggregation number is exactly one in the former, which translates in a nanoparticle size similar to that of unimers (*i.e.* one order of magnitude lower than the typical micelle size) as well as a significantly larger surface-to-volume ratio. Consequently, synthesis is often performed under high dilution (10^{-5} M) and good solvent conditions to avoid particle-particle aggregation and to guarantee the unimolecular nature of the resulting nanoparticles [40]. Nevertheless, controlled addition techniques have been developed allowing synthesizing individual soft nanoparticles up to a concentration of 0.1 M without significant inter-particle aggregation [41, 42].

Up to now, three different techniques have been reported for single-chain polymer nanoparticle construction: i) *intrachain homocoupling* (Figure 2A), ii) *intrachain heterocoupling* (Figure 2B), and iii) *cross-linker induced collapse* (Figure 1C). Concerning the bonding interactions employed, single-chain nanoparticles can be formed through intrachain covalent bonds, intrachain non-covalent interactions and intrachain dynamic covalent bonds. Table 2 provides a summary of the different irreversible and reversible single-chain polymer nanoparticle systems reported in the literature. Concerning irreversible single-chain nanoparticles, conventional organic reactions and "click" chemistry reactions have been described for the efficient preparation of robust unimolecular soft nanoparticles [11, 12].

A)

Single-chain   Nanoparticle

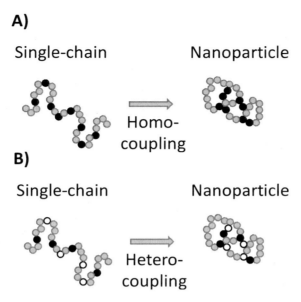

Homo-
coupling

B)

Single-chain   Nanoparticle

Hetero-
coupling

Figure 2. Illustration of the intrachain homocoupling (A) and intrachain heterocoupling (B) techniques for single-chain polymer nanoparticle construction.

3.1. Intrachain Homocoupling

The intrachain homocoupling technique is illustrated schematically in Figure 2A. Many functional groups can be used to promote the intrachain cross-linking of the single-chain polymeric precursor.

First reports about the synthesis of permanent single-chain nanoparticles by means of the intrachain homocoupling technique under high dilution conditions by Mecerreyes et al. relied in the use of poly(styrene)-, poly(alkyl methacrylate)- and poly(ε-caprolactone)-based precursor containing vinyl reactive functional groups [40]. Unsaturated functional groups were also used for synthesizing poly(4-N-Boc-aminostyrene)- and poly(carbonate)-based single-chain nanoparticles by Jiang et al. and Cherian *et. al.*, repectively [43, 44]. Poly(styrene)- and poly(alkyl methacrylate)-based unimolecular nanoparticles were synthesized in multigram quantities by Hawker and co-workers using benzocyclobutene-containing precursors via intramolecular Diels-Alder reactions at very high temperature (250 ℃) [42]. A special addition procedure was adopted in which the precursor polymers were added into the reaction medium slowly, to allow enough time for each individual chain to cross-link in isolation. Later, benzosulfone-decorated poly(styrene)- and poly(cyclohexyl acrylate)-based precursors were synthesized for the preparation of individual unimolecular nanoparticles via quinodimethane formation using this procedure by Harth and co-workers, although cross-linking reaction conditions were still harsh (250 ℃) [45, 46]. Poly(methyl methacrylate)-based single-chain nanoparticles have been obtained via intramolecular Bergman cyclization at relatively lower temperatures (150 ℃) by Zhu et al. [53, 54]. The synthesis of poly(styrene)- and poly(alkyl methacrylate)-based unimolecular nanoparticles via intramolecular cross-linking of sulfonyl azide-[55] and benzoxazine-[56] functionalized polymers still required very high temperatures (190–200 ℃). To solve the potential problems

of precursor and nanoparticle thermal degradation, a new route has been introduced by
Pomposo and co-workers in which naked, propargylic-decorated single-chain nanoparticle
precursors synthesized via redox-initiated RAFT polymerization were intrachain collapsed at
room temperature under normal air conditions by means of Glaser-Hay coupling (C-C "click"
chemistry) [57]. This technique has been further employed by this group for obtaining
poly(styrene)-based unimolecular soft nanoparticles of *ca.* 12 nm in size [58]. Very recently,
poly(styrene)-based unimolecular nanoparticles have been prepared by Dirlam et al. through
intrachain cross-linking via oxidative polymerization of 3,4-propylenedioxy-thiophene
functional groups at 50 ºC [60].

Table 2. Different routes to single-chain nanoparticles reported in the literature

Reactive Functional Groups	Reaction	Technique [a]	Bonding [b]	References
Vinyl	Radical coupling & Cross-Metathesis	A	CB	40, 43, 44
Benzocyclobutene	Diels-Alder	A	CB	42
Benzosulfone	Quinodimethane formation	A	CB	45, 46
Azide + Protected alkyne	Copper-catalyzed [3+2] cycloaddition	B, C	CB	47-50
Carboxilic acid	Amide formation	C	CB	51
Isocyanate	Urea formation	C	CB	52
Enediyne	Bergman & photo-Bergman cyclization	A	CB	53, 54
Sulfonyl azide	Nitrene-mediated cross-linking	A	CB	55
Benzoxazine	Ring opening polymerization	A	CB	56
Alkyne	Glaser-Hay coupling	A	CB	57, 58
β-Ketoester	Michael addition	C	CB	59
3,4-Propylenedioxy-thiophene	Oxidative coupling	A	CB	60
Benzamide	Benzamide hydrogen bonding	A	NCB	61
2-Ureido-Pyrimidone (UPy)	UPy dimerization	A	NCB	62
Coumarin	Coumarin photo-dimerization	A	NCB	63
Benzaldehyde	Acylhydrazone formation	C	DCB	64
β-Ketoester	Enamine formation	C	DCB	65
Methyl viologen + Naphtyl	Cucurbit[*n*]uril complexation	C	NCB	66
L-Phenylalanine (Phe)	Hydrophobic Phe-Phe interactions	A	NCB	67
Aminophenyl disulfide	Disulfide formation	A	DCB	68
Benzene-1,3,5-tricarboxamide (BTA)	Helical BTA stacking	A	NCB	69
Diene	Rhodium complexation	C	NCB	70

[a] A = Intrachain homocoupling. B = Intrachain heterocoupling. C = Crosslinker-induced collapse.
[b] CB = Covalent bonding. NCB = Non-covalent bonding. DCB = Dynamic covalent bonding.

Also, reversible/dynamic covalent bonded single-chain nanoparticles have been synthesized through intrachain homocoupling using a broad range of assembling/disassembling-enabling precursors, including benzamide- [61], 2-ureido-pyrimidone- [62], coumarin- [63], L-phenylalanine- [67], aminophenyl disulfide- [68] and benzene-1,3,5-tricarboxamide- [69] decorated polymer precursors (Table 2). Nanoparticle formation was performed in most cases at, or near, r.t.

3.2. Intrachain Heterocoupling

Complementary to the intrachain homocoupling technique is the intrachain heterocoupling technique, in which the coupling reaction takes place between groups of different chemical structure but not between groups of the same chemical identity, as illustrated schematically in Figure 2B.

A representative example of the use of the intrachain heterocoupling technique was the construction of single-chain nanoparticles through highly-efficient azide-alkyne "click" chemistry (i.e., copper-catalyzed [3+2] cycloaddition of alkynes and azides) (Table 2) [47]. By using this technique, biofunctionalized poly(methyl methacrylate) unimolecular nanoparticles were prepared at room temperature in high yield based on azide- and protected alkyne-decorated polymer precursors [47]. The technique was further simplified by Pomposo and co-workers starting with copolymers containing protected alkyne groups as well as chloromethyl groups, that were transformed rapid and quantitatively to azidomethyl groups by means of a simple substitution reaction using sodium azide [48]. More recently, the intrachain heterocoupling technique has been used to prepare thermoresponsive single-chain nanoparticles [50].

3.3. Cross-linker Induced Collapse

The difficulty to incorporate randomly along the precursor chain two complementary functional groups can be surpassed by using an alternative crosslinker-induced collapse technique (Figure 1C).

By extending the intramolecular "click" chemistry concept to the case of bifunctional crosslinker-induced collapse, a broad range of single-chain nanoparticles of different chemical nature and properties were synthesized by Pomposo and co-workers using azide-decorated polymers and dialkyne-based crosslinkers (Table 2) [49]. Hence, poly(t-butyl methacrylate)-based single-chain nanoparticles of 7 nm in size obtained by this technique were deprotected to give water-soluble poly(methacrylic acid) nanoparticles. By careful selection of the crosslinker molecules, these nanoparticles were found to be promising agents for nuclear magnetic image (MRI) applications. Water soluble poly(sodium 4-styrenesulfonate)-based unimolecular nanoparticles of 11 nm in size were also synthesized by "click" chemistry using bifunctional alkyne crosslinkers [49]. Moreover, thermoresponsive poly(N-isopropyl acrylamide)-based single-chain nanoparticles of 10 nm in size were easily obtained by this efficient technique. Interestingly, by tailoring the nature of the dialkyne crosslinker to maximize intramolecular triazole-mediated conjugation, fluorescent poly(styrene)-based unimolecular nanoparticles useful for biomedical applications were prepared by Pomposo and co-workers [48]. Water-soluble poly(γ-glutamic acid)-based single-chain nanoparticles have been fabricated through the crosslinker-induced collapse technique by using a biosynthetic poly(γ-glutamic acid) precursor and 2,2′-(ethylenedioxy) diethylamine as bifunctional crosslinker in the presence of carbodiimide [51]. The synthesis of poly(methyl methacrylate)- and poly(styrene)-based single-chain nanoparticles by intramolecular cross-linking of isocyanate functionalized copolymers with diamines (under severe anhydrous conditions) has been also reported by Hawker and co-workers [52]. Additionally, the Michael addition reaction has been introduced to synthesize poly(methyl methacrylate)-based single-chain nanoparticles mimicking transient-binding disordered proteins under mild reaction conditions (at room temperature and in the presence of oxygen) by Pomposo and co-workers [59].

Recently, dynamic covalent-bonded single-chain nanoparticles have been prepared by using benzaldehyde- [64] and β-ketoester- [65] decorated precursors through reversible acylhydrazone and enamine formation reactions, respectively. More recently, water-soluble poly(N-hydroxyethyl acrylamide)-based unimolecular nanoparticles have been fabricated trough host-guest interactions by using methyl viologen- and naphtyl-decorated precursors as well as cucurbit[n]uril as reversible complexation agent by Scherman and co-workers [66]. Direct access to organometallic single-chain nanoparticles via poly(cyclooctadiene) complexes of rhodium (I) has been also reported [70].

4. APPLICATIONS

Envisioned applications for stimuli-responsive micelles include their use in the emerging field of nanomedicine [14, 20], sensing [33, 35], synthesis [22, 23], catalysis [25] and other diverse applications. Concerning nanomedicine, applications include the development of novel formulations for drug delivery, encapsulation of both hydrophilic and hydrophobic functional compounds and adjustment of their release behaviors, development of smart nanocarriers for drug delivery systems and protein separation, among others. Sensing applications include the development of fluorescent chemo-sensors for divalent ions, whereas synthesis and catalysis applications cover the use of the stimuli-responsive micelles as nano-reactors to prepare inorganic, semiconductor and metal nanoparticles in water and as heterogeneous phase catalysis, respectively. Other diverse applications proposed cover from pigment dispersion agents to cosmetics ingredients and pollution control systems.

Potential applications of single-chain polymer nanoparticles include the fields of nanomedicine, catalysis and other diverse applications, as recently reviewed by Pomposo and co-workers [11]. For nanomedicine, unimolecular nanoparticles have been used for the delivery of peptidic molecules into cells [71], encapsulation of doxorubicin (Dox) as anticancer compound [72], selective L-phenylalanine anilide absorption [73], gene-silencing using siRNA [74], fluorescence [48] and image contrast agents [49, 75] as well as drug delivery nano-carriers [59]. For catalysis, enzyme-mimic nanoparticles have been developed based on three different approaches: i) the *imprinted particle* approach, allowing carbonate hydrolysis following Michaelis-Menten kinetics (like natural enzymes) but with a very low turnover frequency (TOF) value of 4.4×10^{-3} h^{-1} [76], ii) the *hydrophobic cavity* approach, for the reduction of cyclohexanone to cyclohexanol in 18 h by using only 0.5 wt% of ruthenium catalyst (TOF = 11 h^{-1}) [77] as well as the aldol reaction by using only 0.5 wt% of supported L-proline organocatalyst (TOF = 125 h^{-1}) [78], and iii) the *concurrent* approach, allowing the synthesis of single-chain polymer nanoparticles showing both reductase- (TOF = 5880 h^{-1}) and polymerase-like behavior allowing the synthesis of poly(tetrahydrofuran) of high molecular weight in a enzyme-like fashion [13]. Additional use of single-chain nanoparticles for different applications has been proposed, such as: i) rheology-improving agents for melts of thermoplastics [79], elastomeric polymers [48], nanocomposites [80] and paints [81], ii) polyelectrolytes with unconventional behavior [49], iii) compartmentalized sensors for metal ions [82], iv) templates for the preparation of photoluminiscent carbon nano-dots [83] and v) thermoresponsive hydrogels [84].

CONCLUSION

Even if a significant amount of work has been devoted in the last decades to the efficient construction of micelles and single-chain polymer nanoparticles in non-selective (good) solvents a detailed inspection to Tables 1 and 2 allows one to draw the conclusion that many other combinations of block copolymers / activators, as well as precursor polymers / intrachain cross-linking chemistries could be employed for multi-responsive micelle and functional single-chain nanoparticle preparation, respectively. These are in fact emerging research topics, for which different applications in the nanomedicine, catalysis and sensing fields are expected to be demonstrated in the near future for daily life applications.

REFERENCES

[1]   Du, J.; Lu, H. "Polymeric Micelles" in *Encyclopedia of Polymer Science and Technology* (Wiley).

[2]   Meier, D. J. *Polym. Sci., Part, C.*1969, *26*, 81.

[3]   Ruckenstein, E.; Nagarajan, R. *Phys. Chem.* 1975, *79*, 2622.

[4]   Leibler, L.; Orland, H.; Wheeler, J. C. *J. Chem. Phys.* 1983, *79*, 3550.

[5]   Noolandi, J.; Hong, K. M. *Macromolecules* 1983, *16*, 1443.

[6]   Halperin, A. *Macromolecules* 1987, *20*, 2943.

[7]   Bug, A. L. R.; Cates, M. E.; Safran, S. A.; Witten, T. A. *J. Chem. Phys.* 1987, *87*, 1824.

[8]   Marques, C. M.; Joanny, J.-F.; Leibler, L. *Macromolecules* 1988, *21*, 1051.

[9]   Nagarajan, R.; Ganesh, K. *J. Chem. Phys.* 1989, *90*, 5843.

[10]   Leermakers, F. A. M. *Macromol. Symp.* 2009, *278*, 57.

[11]   Sanchez-Sanchez, A.; Pérez-Baena, I.; Pomposo, J. A. *Molecules* 2013, *18*, 3339.

[12]   Altintas, O.; Barner-Kowollik, C. *Macromol. Rapid Commun.* 2012, *33*, 958.

[13]   Peraz-Baeana, I.; Barroso-Bujans, F.; Gasser, U.; Arbe, A.; Moreno, A. J.; Colmenero, J.; Pomposo, J. A. *ACS Macro Lett.* 2013, *2*, 775.

[14]   Neradovic, D.; Nostrum, C. F.; Hennink, W. E. *Macromolecules* 2001, *34*, 7589.

[15]   Arotcarena, M.; Heise, B.; Ishaya, S.; Laschewsky, A. *J. Am. Chem. Soc.* 2002, *124*, 3787.

[16] Martin, T. J.; Prochazka, K.; Munk, P.; Webber, S. E. *Macromolecules* 1996, *29*, 6071.

[17] Weaver, J. V. M.; Armes, S. P.; Butun, V. *Chem. Commun.* 2002, 2122.

[18] Lee, A. S.; Butun, V.; Vamvakaki, M.; Armes, S. P.; Pople, J. A.; Gast, A. P. *Macromolecules* 2002, *35*, 8540.

[19] Liu, S.; Weaver, J. V. M.; Tang, Y.; Billingham, N. C.; Armes, S. *Macromolecules* 2002, *35*,6121.

[20] Lowe, A. B.; Billingham, N. C.; Armes, S. P. *Chem. Commun.* 1997, 1035.

[21] Biitiin, V.; Billingham, N. C.; Armes, S. P. *Chem. Commun.* 1997, 671.

[22] Brontein, L. M.; Sidorov, S. N.; Valetsky, P. M. *Langmuir* 1999, *15*, 6256.

[23] Zhao, H.; Douglas, E. P.; Harrison, B. S.; Schanze, K. S. *Langmuir* 2001, *17*, 8428.

[24] Gohy, J.-F.; Lohmeijer, G. G.; Varshney, S. K.; Decamps, B.; Leroy, E.; Boileau, S.; Schubert , U. S. *Macromolecules* 2002, *35*, 9748.

[25] Chernyshov, D. M.; Bronstein, L. M.; Boerner, H.; Berton, B.; Antonietti, M. *Chem. Mater.* 2000, *12*, 114.

[26] Yoshida, E.; Kunugi, S. *J. Polym. Sci., A: Polym. Chem.* 2002, *40*, 3036.

[27] Yoshida, E.; Ohta, M.; Terada, Y. *Polym. Adv. Technol.* 2005, *16*, 183.

[28] Chen, D. Y.; Peng, H. S.; Jiang, M. *Macromolecules* 2003, *36*, 2576.

[29] Cheng, L.; Hou,G.; Miao, J.; Chen, D.; Jiang, M.; Zhu. L. *Macromolecules* 2008, *41*, 8159.

[30] Peng, H. S.; Chen, D. Y.; Jiang, M. *J. Phys. Chem. B* 2003, *107*, 12461.

[31] Yao, X. M.; Chen, D. Y.; Jiang, M. *J. Phys. Chem. B* 2004, *108*, 5225.

[32] Gu, C. F.; Chen, D. Y.; Jiang, M. *Macromolecules* 2004, *37*, 1666.

[33] Jia, X.; Chen, D.; Jiang, M. *Chem. Commun.* 2006, 1736.

[34] Ruiz de Luzuriaga, A.; Garcia, I.; Mecerreyes, D.; Etxeberria, A.; Pomposo, J. A. *Polymer* 2010, *51*, 1355.

[35] Huang, R.; Chen, D.; Jiang, M. *J. Mater. Chem.* 2010, *20*, 9988.

[36] Masunaga, H.; Nakano, A.; Yamamoto, K.; Uezu1, K.; Sakurai, K.; Akiba, I. *Journal of Physics: Conference Series* 2011, *272*, 012023.

[37] Zhou, J.; Ke, F.; Tong, Y.; Li, Z.; Liang, D. *Soft Matter* 2011, *7*, 9956.

[38] Yoshida, E.; Tanaka, T. *Colloid Polym. Sci.* 2006, *285*, 135.

[39] Ruiz de Luzuriaga, A.; Pomposo, J. A.; Grande, H.; Etxeberria, A. *Macromol. Rapid Commun.* 2009, *30*, 932.

[40] Mecerreyes, D.; Lee, V.; Hawker, C. J.; Hedrick, J. L.; Wursch, A.; Volksen, W.; Magbitang, T.; Huang, E.; Miller R. D. *Adv. Mater.* 2001, *13*, 204.

[41] Ryu, J.-H.; Chacko, R. T.; Jiwpanich, S.; Bickerton, S.; Babu, R. P.; Thayumanavan, S. *J. Am. Chem. Soc.* 2010, *132*, 17227.

[42] Hart, E; Van Horn, B.; Lee, V. Y.; Germack, D. S.; Gonzales, C. P.; Miller R. D.; Hawker, C. J. *J. Amer. Chem. Soc.* 2002, *124*, 8653.

[43] Jiang, J.; Thayumanavan. *Macromolecules* 2005, *38*, 5886.

[44] Cherian, A. E.; Sun, F. C.; Sheiko, S. S., Coates G. W. *J. Amer. Chem. Soc.* 2007, *129*, 11350.

[45] Croce, T. A.; Hamilton, S. K.; Chen, M. L.; Muchalski, H.; Harth, E. *Macromolecules* 2007, *40*, 6028.

[46] Adkins, C.; Muchalski, H.; Harth, E. *Macromolecules* 2009, *42*, 5786.

[47] Ruiz de Luzuriaga, A.; Ormategui, N.; Grande, H. J.; Odriozola, I.; Pomposo, J. A.; I. Loinaz. *Macromol. Rapid Commun.* 2008, *29*, 1156.

[48] Oria, L.; Aguado, R.; Pomposo, J. A.; Colmenero, J. *Adv. Mater.* 2010, *22*, 3038.

[49] Ruiz de Luzuriaga, A.; Perez-Baena, I.; Montes, S.; Loinaz, I.; Odriozola, I.; García, I.; Pomposo, J.A. *Macromol. Symp.* 2010, *296*, 303.

[50] Ormategui, N.; Garcia, I.; Padro, D.; Cabanero, G.; Grande, H. J.; Loinaz, I. *Soft Mater.* 2012, *8*, 734.

[51] Radu, J. E. F.; Novak, L.; Hartmann, J. F.; Beheshti, N.; Kjoniksen, A.-L.; Nyström, B.; Borbély, J. *Colloid. Polym. Sci.* 2008, *286*, 365.

[52] Beck, J. B., Killops, K. L.; Kang, T.; Sivanandan, K.; Bayles, A.; Mackay, M. E.; Wooley, K. L.; Hawker, C. J. *Macromolecules* 2009, *42*, 5629.

[53] Zhu, B.; Ma, J.; Li, Z.; Hou, J.; Cheng, X.; Qian, G.; Liu, P.; Hu, A. *J. Mater. Chem.* 2011, *21*, 2679.

[54] Zhu, B.; Qian, G.; Xiao, Y.; Deng, S.; Wang, M.; Hu, A. *J. Polym. Sci., Polym. Chem.* 2011, *49*, 5330.

[55] Jiang, X.; Pu, H.; Wang, P. *Polymer* 2011, *52*, 3597.

[56] Wang, P.; Pu, H.; Jin, M. *J. Polym. Sci., Polym. Chem.* 2011, *49*, 5133.

[57] Sanchez-Sanchez, A.; Asenjo-Sanz, I.; Buruaga, L.; Pomposo, J. A. *Macromol. Rapid Commun.* 2012, *33*, 1262.

[58] Khanjani, P.; Perez-Baena, I.; Buruaga, I.; Pomposo, J. A. *Macromol. Symp.* 2012, *321-322*, 145.

[59] Sanchez-Sanchez, A.; Akbari, S.; Etxeberria, A.; Arbe, A.; Gasser, U.; Moreno, A. J.; Colmenero, J.; Pomposo, J. A. *ACS Macro Lett.* 2013, *2*, 491.

[60] Dirlam, P. T.; Kim, H. J.; Arrington, K. J.; Chung, W. J.; Sahoo, R.; Hill, L. J.; Costanzo, P. J.; Theato, P.; Char, K.; Pyun, *J. Chem. Commun.* 2013, *4*, 3765.

[61] Seo, M.; Beck, B. J.; Paulusse, J. M. J.; Hawker, C. J.; Kim, S. Y. *Macromolecules* 2008, *41*, 6413

[62] Foster, E. J.; Berda, E. B.; Meijer, E. W. *J. Am. Chem. Soc.* 2009, *131*, 6964.

[63] He, J.; Tremblay, L.; Lacelle, S.; Zhao, Y. *Soft Matter.* 2011, *7*, 2380.

[64] Murray, B. S.; Fulton, D. A. *Macromolecules* 2011, *44*, 7242.

[65] Sanchez-Sanchez, A.; Pomposo, J. A. *Part. Part. Syst. Charact.* 2013 (in press).

[66] Appel, E. A.; Dyson, J.; del Barrio, J.; Walsh, Z.; Scherman, O. A. *Angew. Chem. Int. Ed.* 2012, *51*, 415.

[67] Akagi, T.; Piyapakorn, P.; Akashi, M. *Langmuir* 2012, *28*, 5249.

[68] Tuten, B. T.; Chao, D.; Lyon, C. K.; Berda, E. B. *Polym. Chem.* 2012, *3*, 3068.

[69] Mes, T.; van der Weegen, R.; Palmans, A. R. A.; Meijer, E. W. *Angew. Chem. Int. Ed.* 2011, *50*, 5085.

[70] Mavila, S.; Diesendruck, C. E.; Linde, S.; Amir, L.; Shikler, R.; Lemcoff, N. G. *Angew. Chem. Int. Ed.* 2013, *52*, 5767.

[71] Hamilton, S. K.; Harth, E. *ACS Nano* 2009, *3*, 402.

[72] Ryu, J.-H.; Chacko, R.T.; Jiwpanich, S.; Bickerton, S.; Babu, R. P.; Thayumanavan, S. *J. Am. Chem. Soc.* 2010, *132*, 17227.

[73] Njiang, G.; Liu, G.; Hong, L. *Langmuir* 2012, *27*, 7176.

[74] Tamura, A.; Oishi, M.; Nagaski, Y. *Biomacromolecules* 2009, *10*, 1818.

[75] Perez-Baena, I.; Loinaz, I.; Padro, D.; Garcia, I.; Grande, H. J.; Odriozola, I. *J. Mater. Res.* 2010, *20*, 6916.

[76] Wulff, G.; Chong, B.-O.; Kolb, U. *Angew. Chem. Int. Ed.* 2006, *45*, 2955.

[77] Terashima, T.; Mes, T.; De Greef, T. F. A.; Gillissen, M. A. J.; Besenius, P.; Palmans, A. R. A.; Meijer, E.W. *J. Am. Chem. Soc.* 2011, *133*, 4742.

[78] Huerta, E.; Stals, P. J. M.; Meijer, E. W.; Palmans, A. R. A. *Angew. Chem. Int. Ed.* 2013, *52*, 2906.

[79] Mackay, M. E.; Dao, T. T.; Tuteja, A.; Ho, D. L.; Horn, B. V.; Kim, H.-C.; Hawker, C. J. *Nature Mater.* 2003, *2*, 762.

[80] Tuteja, A.; Duxbury, P. M.; Mackay, M.E. *Macromolecules* 2007, *40*, 9427.

[81] Mistry, J. K.; Van de Mark, M. R. *J. Coat.. Technol. Res.* 2013, *10*, 453.

[82] Gillissen, M. A. J.; Voets, I. K.; Meijer, E. W.; Palmans, A. R. A. *Polym. Chem.* 2012, *3*, 3166.

[83] Zhu, B.; Sun, S.; Wang, Y.; Deng, S.; Qian, G.; Wang, M.; Hu, A. *J. Mater. Chem. C* 2013, *1*, 580.

[84] Whitaker, D.E.; Mahon, C.S.; Fulton, D.A. *Angew. Chem. Int. Ed.* 2013, *52*, 956.

In: Micelles
Editors: Danielle Bradburn and Tom Bittinger

ISBN: 978-1-62948-444-0
© 2014 Nova Science Publishers, Inc.

Chapter 7

BLOCK POLYELECTROLYTE MICELLES/PROTEIN MIXED NANOSTRUCTURES IN AQUEOUS MEDIA

Maria Karayianni and Stergios Pispas[*]

Theoretical and Physical Chemistry Institute, National Hellenic Research Foundation,
Athens, Greece

ABSTRACT

The interactions between a globular protein, hen egg white lysozyme (HEWL), and star-like block polyelectrolyte micelles formed by the self-assembly of a poly(tert-butylstyrene)-*b*-poly(sodium(sulfamate-carboxylate)isoprene) (PtBS-SCPI) amphiphilic diblock copolymer were studied in aqueous solutions. Due to the opposite charges present in HEWL (positive charges) and on the SCPI polyelectrolyte coronas of the block copolymer micelles (negative charges), nanostructured hierarchical complexes are formed at neutral pH and low ionic strength. Structure and properties of the complexes were investigated by means of dynamic, static and electrophoretic light scattering, as well as atomic force microscopy.

The solution behaviour, structure and effective charge of the formed nanoscale complexes proved to be dependent on the ratio of the two components. Presumably block polyelectrolyte micelles with a PtBS core and a SCPI corona decorated with HEWL molecules are initially formed. Moreover, the degree of charge neutralization caused by complexation determines the conformation and solubility of the complexes. Complexation of the macromolecular components at higher solution ionic strengths led to complexes of lower mass and nearly constant size. Such behavior may be correlated to the polyelectrolyte nature of the components. The structural investigation of the complexed protein by fluorescence and infrared spectroscopy revealed no signs of HEWL denaturation upon complexation.

Keywords: Polyelectrolyte block copolymer micelles, protein-polyelectrolyte complexation, macromolecular self-assembled nanostructures, light scattering

---

[*] Correspondence/Reprint request: Dr. Stergios Pispas, Theoretical and Physical Chemistry Institute, National Hellenic Research Foundation, 48 Vassileos Constantinou Avenue, 11635 Athens, Greece. E-mail: pispas@eie.gr.

1. INTRODUCTION

Polyelectrolyte block copolymers have attracted considerable scientific interest owing to their unique properties. Their most important asset is that they combine the structural characteristics of amphiphilic block copolymers, polyelectrolytes and surfactants. Therefore, they constitute an intriguing class of macromolecules and furthermore provide various possibilities for custom design. Due to their amphiphilic character polyelectrolyte block copolymers in aqueous solutions usually self-assemble into core-shell micelles with a hydrophobic core and a polyelectrolyte corona. This self-assembly process is affected by numerous parameters that concern both the primary chemical structure of the macromolecules, such as the degree of polymerization of each block and the dissociation of the charged groups of the polyelectrolyte block, as well as the solution parameters, namely the concentration, pH, temperature and ionic strength. The resulting polyelectrolyte block copolymer micelles can be regarded as stimuli-responsive nanoparticles, with potential use in various technological and pharmaceutical applications, since the polyelectrolyte nature of their corona renders them susceptible to the changes of the solution physicochemical parameters. Consequently, over the past decades polyelectrolyte block copolymers micelles have been the subject of systematic experimental and theoretical studies and the results have been extensively reviewed [1–5].

Furthermore, the polyelectrolyte corona of these micelles enables them to bind oppositely charged entities, such as ions, organic molecules, metal nanoparticles, surfactants or synthetic and biological macromolecules, through electrostatic interactions. Among the possible applications of such systems is the formulation of flocculants and stabilizers of colloidal dispersions, surface modifiers and biocompatible coatings, matrices for metal ions and metal nanoparticles, carriers of biologically active compounds and drugs, *etc* [6]. In this field of study numerous experimental investigations involve the interpolyelectrolyte complexation between polyelectrolyte block copolymer micelles and linear polyelectrolytes of opposite charge, which leads to the formation of different types of macromolecular self-assembled nanostructures, including soluble or insoluble complexes, multilayer nanoparticles, networks or even gels [7–12]. Equivalently, the interaction of polyelectrolyte micelles with double hydrophilic polyelectrolyte block copolymers can be used as a means of preparing three-layered core-shell-corona micellar complexes [13–15]. Of similar interest is the case of electrostatic interaction between synthetic or natural polyelectrolytes and proteins. Proteins are another category of natural polyelectrolytes with intriguing conformational properties and biological functions. Electrostatic interaction is employed in a vast variety of technological applications concerning protein encapsulation, immobilization, purification and separation, in the development of functional nanobiomaterials and bio-organic hybrids with potential use in nanobiotechnology, while its study provides valuable insight into the interactions between charged biomacromolecules that take place in several biological systems [16, 17]. Such studies have been successfully extended to the case of double hydrophilic block copolymer/protein systems in an effort to create sophisticated functional nanostructures [18–22]. However, a rather limited number of experimental investigations have been focused so far on the complexation of amphiphilic block copolymer micelles with a polyelectrolyte corona and proteins [23–26], although such systems may provide several new opportunities for nanostructure formation and advantageous properties.

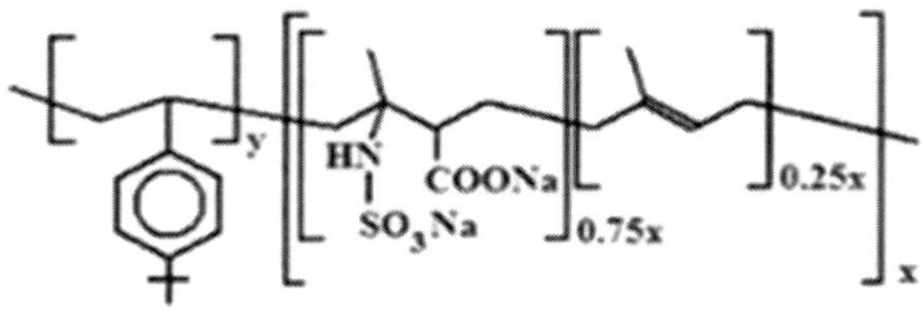

Scheme 1. Molecular structure of the PtBS-SCPI polyelectrolyte block copolymer. The degrees of polymerization are $x \approx 702$ and $y \approx 121$, while the degree of functionalization of the SCPI block is about 75%.

In a parallel manner, the interaction of proteins with spherical polyelectrolyte brushes is also interesting due to the structural analogies between the colloidal and micellar polymeric nanoparticles [27–29].

In this work we employ dynamic, static and electrophoretic light scattering (DLS, SLS and ELS), along with atomic force microscopy (AFM) in order to examine the complexation process, as well as the structure and solution behavior of the nanosized complexes formed between poly(tert-butylstyrene)-b-poly(sodium(sulfamate-carboxylate)isoprene) (PtBS-SCPI) (molecular structure shown in Scheme 1) polyelectrolyte block copolymer micelles and hen egg white lysozyme (HEWL) protein. Additional spectroscopic evaluation of the HEWL conformation after complexation was conducted, by means of fluorescence and infrared (IR) measurements. The central goal of this study is to create novel self-assembled and functional hybrid synthetic/biological macromolecular nanostructures and enrich basic understanding on behavioral motifs, as well as widen the application potential of nanostructured polymeric colloidal systems.

In aqueous solutions the PtBS-SCPI amphiphilic diblock copolymer self-assembles into micelles with a hydrophobic PtBS core and a polyelectrolyte SCPI corona. The SCPI block constitutes a novel strong polyelectrolyte, since each functionalized monomeric unit carries two negatively charged groups at neutral pH, while at the same time displays some intrinsic hydrophobic character due to the presence of unfunctionalized isoprene segments [30]. Moreover, HEWL is an extensively studied small globular protein with enzymatic activity and a pH-dependent net positive charge at pH values smaller than its isoelectric point pI ≈ 11 [31, 32]. Therefore, the complexation process and the structure and solution behavior of the formed complexes between the PtBS-SCPI micelles and HEWL have been studied at pH 7 as a function of the ratio of the two components (i.e. the concentration of the protein keeping the copolymer concentration constant) and the solution conditions with respect to the ionic strength. The structure of the complexed protein, which determines whether enzymatic activity can be preserved upon complexation, has been also investigated by means of fluorescence and infrared spectroscopy.

2. EXPERIMENTAL PART

2.1. Materials

Protein: HEWL (dialyzed, lyophilized powder) with a molecular weight of Mr = 14.7 kg/mol was purchased from Fluka and used without any further purification.

Synthesis of the PtBS-SCPI polyelectrolyte block copolymer: *The polyelectrolyte block copolymer sample was prepared by a post-polymerization functionalization reaction between chlorosulfonyl isocyanate (CSI, from Acros) and the isoprene segments of the polyisoprene (PI) block of the precursor PtBS-PI diblock copolymer prepared by anionic polymerization, as described in detail elsewhere [33]. The copolymer utilized in this study has a weight average molecular weight $M_w = 164.6$ kg/mol, and the weight fractions of PtBS and SCPI blocks are approximately 12% and 88%, which correspond to degrees of polymerization of about 121 and 702 monomeric units, respectively. Therefore, the particular PtBS-SCPI copolymer is considered an asymmetric amphiphilic diblock copolymer. The SCPI polyelectrolyte block is characterized by high charge density at neutral pH, since it combines strongly charged pH independent SO_3^- groups with weak acidic COO^- groups*, neutralized at pH < 4. Moreover, the extent of functionalization was found to be about 75 mole %, by means of potentiometric titrations, elemental analysis and ^{13}C-NMR. Thus, the polyelectrolyte block retains some hydrophobic character due to the presence of unfunctionalized PI segments. Finally, its structural resemblance to the natural polysaccharide heparin (as far as the functional polar groups are concerned) enables possible use in biomedical applications [34, 35].

Sample preparation: A pH 7 buffer solution was prepared, from NaOH and 5 mM sodium phosphate, with ionic strength $I = 0.01$ N. Stock solutions of the polyelectrolyte block copolymer and the protein were prepared by dissolving a weighed amount of the dialyzed sample in the appropriate volume of the buffer. Consequently, the PtBS-SCPI solutions were heated at 60°C overnight in order to achieve solubilization, while the HEWL solutions were left to stand at room temperature for the same period of time for better equilibration. The final concentrations of the PtBS-SCPI and HEWL solutions were 0.25 mg/ml and 0.5 mg/ml, respectively. The complexes were prepared by adding different amounts of the HEWL solutions to PtBS-SCPI solutions of the same volume and concentration, under stirring. Finally, appropriate volumes of buffer solutions were added, so as to achieve a constant final volume and ionic strength (equal to that of the buffer solution) for all solutions prepared. Thus, the concentration of PtBS-SCPI was kept constant throughout the series of solutions, while that of HEWL varied in order to control the required ratio of the two components (or equivalently the [−]/[+] charge ratio of the mixture). The solutions of the complexes developed bluish tint or turbidity upon mixing, indicating the formation of supramolecular complexes. Subsequently, the solutions of the complexes were left for equilibration overnight, which in some cases resulted in precipitation, depending on the HEWL concentration.

For the ionic strength dependent light scattering measurements, the ionic strength of the solution was increased by the addition of appropriate aliquots of a 1 N NaCl solution at pH 7, to 1 ml of the previously prepared solution of the complexes. After each addition the solution was rigorously stirred and left to equilibrate for 15 min before measurement. Changes in solutes concentrations due to NaCl solution addition were taken into consideration in the analysis of the light scattering data.

2.2. Techniques

Dynamic and Static Light Scattering (DLS and SLS): Light scattering measurements were performed on an ALV/CGS-3 compact goniometer system (ALVGmbH, Germany), equipped with an ALV-5000/EPP multi tau digital correlator, a He-Ne laser operating at the wavelength of 632.8 nm, and an avalanche photodiode detector. Buffer and sample solutions were filtered through 0.45 μm hydrophilic PTFE Millex syringe filters (Millipore) in order to remove any dust particles or large aggregates. The samples were loaded into standard 1 cm width Helma quartz dust-free cells and measurements were performed at a series of angles in the range 20-150°.

Dynamic light scattering (DLS) measurements were evaluated by fitting of the measured normalized time autocorrelation function of the scattered light intensity $g_2(t)$, related to the electric field time autocorrelation function $g_1(t)$ by the Siegert equation, $g_2(t) = 1 + \beta|g_1(t)|^2$, where β is the coherence factor, depending on the experimental conditions [36, 37].

The data were fitted either with the aid of the CONTIN analysis or the use of the second order cumulant expansion and the distribution of relaxation times τ or the mean relaxation rate $\Gamma = 1/\tau$, were obtained respectively. Furthermore, the cumulant analysis yields the size polydispersity index of the system $PDI = \mu_2/\Gamma^2$, where μ_2 is the second order coefficient of the expansion. Assuming that the observed fluctuations of the scattered intensity are caused by diffusive motions, the apparent diffusion coefficient D_{app} is related to the relaxation time τ as, $D_{app} = 1/\tau q^2$, where q is the scattering vector defined as with n_0, θ and λ_0 the solvent refractive index, the scattering angle and the wavelength of the laser in vacuum respectively.

From the apparent diffusion coefficient D_{app}, the hydrodynamic radius R_h can be obtained, using the Stokes-Einstein relationship

$$R_h = \frac{k_B T}{6\pi\eta_0 D_{app}}$$ (1)

where k_B is the Boltzmann constant, T is the temperature and η_0 is the viscosity of the solvent.

Static light scattering (SLS) measurements were treated by the Zimm method using the equation

$$\frac{Kc}{\Delta R_\theta} = \frac{1}{M_W}\left(1 + \frac{1}{3}R_g^2 q^2\right) + 2A_2 c$$ (2)

where M_W is the weight averaged molecular weight, R_g is the average radius of gyration, A_2 is the second osmotic virial coefficient, c is the polymer concentration, ΔR_θ is the corrected Rayleigh ratio, which depends on the polymer concentration c and the magnitude of the scattering vector q, and the constant factor K is given by the relationship

$$K = \frac{4\pi^2 n_0^2}{\lambda_0^4 N_A}\left(\frac{\partial n}{\partial c}\right)^2$$ (3)

where n_0, λ_0, N_A are the refractive index of the solvent, the laser wavelength in vacuum, the Avogadro's number respectively and is the refractive index increment of the sample solution with respect to the solvent.

Electrophoretic Light Scattering (ELS): ζ-potential measurements were performed with a ZetaPlus Analyzer (Brookhaven Instruments) equipped with a 35 mW solid state laser, operating at $\lambda = 660$ nm. ζ-potential values were determined using the Smolukowski equation relating the ionic mobilities with surface charge, and are reported as averages of ten repeated measurements.

Atomic Force Microscopy (AFM): AFM measurements were performed on a Quesant Q-Scope 250 atomic force microscope (Quesant Instrument Co., USA) in the tapping mode, under ambient conditions. The instrument was equipped with a NSC16 silicon (W_2C Si_3N_4) cantilever, available from Quesant instruments, USA, having a typical force constant of 40 N/m, a cone angle of less than 20° and radius curvature less than 10 nm. Imaging was carried out with a 40-μm Dual PZT scanner on different scanning areas, at a scanning rate of 3 Hz and with image resolution of 600x600 pixels in intermittent contact (broadband mode). The z axis calibration was performed by imaging a TGZ01 silicon grating with silicon oxide steps having height of 18.3 nm (Mikromasch Inc.). Samples for imaging were prepared by placing a drop of the aqueous solutions of the complexes onto fresh, dried silicon wafers, pre-cleaned with isopropanol. After keeping in contact for typically 5 to 10 min, excess water was bolted carefully by filter paper and samples were left to dry in air. In this way supramolecular structures were absorbed on the wafer surface from the same solutions investigated by light scattering for direct comparison.

Fluorescence spectroscopy: Steady-state fluorescence spectra of the tryptophan residues of the neat and complexed HEWL were recorded with a double-grating excitation and a single-grating emission spectrofluorometer (Fluorolog-3, model FL3-21, Jobin Yvon-Spex) at room temperature.

Excitation wavelength used was $\lambda = 290$ nm and emission spectra were recorded in the region 350-500 nm, with an increment of 1 nm, using an integration time of 0.5 s. Slit openings of 5 nm were used for both the excitation and the emitted beam. Under the employed experimental conditions fluorescence from the tryptophan residues of HEWL is observed and utilized to extract information on changes of the protein conformation. The neat PtBS-SCPI solution does not show any significant fluorescence.

Infrared spectroscopy (IR): Infrared spectra of the protein, polyelectrolyte block copolymer and complexes in thin film form were acquired at room temperature in the range 5000-550 cm^{-1}, using a Fourier transform instrument (Bruker Equinox 55), equipped with a single bounce attenuated total reflectance (ATR) diamond accessory from SENS-IR. A small aliquot of each solution was placed on the ATR element and dried under N_2 flow before measurement. For each sample the final spectrum is the average of three 100-scan measurements at 2 cm^{-1} resolution. The measurement of each sample was bracketed by two background spectra in order to allow for the elimination of H_2O vapor bands by interpolation.

3. RESULTS AND DISCUSSION

3.1. Characterization of the PtBS-SCPI Micelles

Dynamic and static light scattering (DLS and SLS) measurements were performed in order to characterize the PtBS-SCPI micelles.

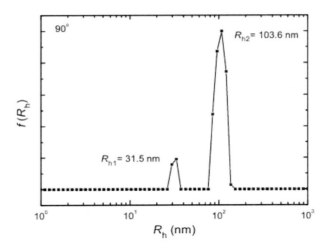

Figure 1. Hydrodynamic radius distributions from DLS measurements at 90° of a 0.083 mg/ml PtBS-SCPI solution at pH 7 and 0.01 N ionic strength.

Figure 1 shows the hydrodynamic radius (R_h) distributions obtained from the CONTIN analysis of DLS measurements at 90°, of a 0.083 mg/ml PtBS-SCPI solution at pH 7 and 0.01 N ionic strength. As it can be seen, the solution exhibits a main peak at high R_h values which apparently corresponds to the formed PtBS-SCPI micelles (R_{h2}) and a significantly smaller one at lower R_h values which most probably denotes the presence of a small number of free unimer diblock copolymer chains (R_{h1}) in the solution. The corresponding R_{h1} and R_{h2} values are 31.5 and 103.6 nm, respectively. Additionally, SLS measurements showed that the apparent weight average molecular weight of the micelles at pH 7 and 0.01 N ionic strength was $M_w \approx 1.6 \times 10^6$ g/mol, which denotes an aggregation number $N_{agg} \approx 10$, while the corresponding radius of gyration was $R_g \approx 107$ nm. It should be noted that the observed rather small N_{agg} of the micelles is a consequence of the highly asymmetric composition of the amphiphilic diblock copolymer chain, or in other words the high ratio of hydrophilic to hydrophobic monomeric units (~ 6) [38, 39].

3.2. Complexation of PtBS-SCPI Micelles and HEWL at pH 7 and 0.01 N Ionic Strength

Initially, the complexation process between the PtBS-SCPI polyelectrolyte micelles and HEWL at pH 7 and 0.01 N ionic strength was investigated by means of dynamic light scattering. At pH 7 the SCPI polyelectrolyte block carries two negatively charged groups per functionalized monomeric unit and HEWL has a net positive charge of +8, thus under these conditions electrostatically driven complexation is expected to readily occur. The obtained results from DLS measurements at 90° regarding the values of the light scattering intensity, I_{90}, the hydrodynamic radius, R_h, and the polydispersity index of the system, PDI, are shown in Figure 2, as a function of the protein concentration, C_{HEWL}, in the solutions of the complexes. The concentration of PtBS-SCPI copolymer is kept constant at 0.083 mg/ml throughout the series of solutions. In all cases, the point at zero protein concentration ($C_{HEWL} = 0$) denotes the corresponding value of the net PtBS-SCPI solution.

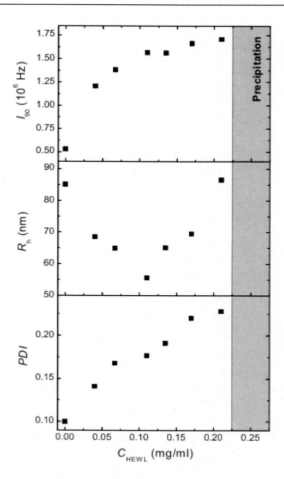

Figure 2. Light scattering intensity at 90°, I_{90}, hydrodynamic radius, R_h, and polydispersity index, *PDI*, as a function of C_{HEWL}, for the solutions of the PtBS-SCPI/HEWL system at pH 7 and 0.01 N ionic strength.

As observed, the value of the scattering intensity, I_{90}, which is proportional to the mass of the species in solution, increases abruptly upon the addition of the protein and continues to increase more gradually as a function of C_{HEWL}, providing proof of the occurring complexation. On the other hand, the hydrodynamic radius, R_h, of the complexes initially decreases up to C_{HEWL} = 0.11 mg/ml and subsequently increases. Moreover, the polydispersity index, *PDI*, shows increasing values as C_{HEWL} becomes higher. Finally, at high protein concentration precipitation of the solutions of the complexes takes place.

These changes suggest that upon the addition of HEWL to the PtBS-SCPI solution the protein molecules are complexed with the corona polyelectrolyte chains of the micelles. Complexation leads to neutralization of the charges on the SCPI polyelectrolyte block and thus to the weakening of the electrostatic repulsions. As a result the polyelectrolyte corona of the complexed micelles shrinks and their size decreases. As the protein concentration increases each polyelectrolyte chain interacts with an increasing number of protein molecules, which leads to a higher degree of charge neutralization and a further decrease of the size of the complexes. Nevertheless, the neutralization of the polyelectrolyte charges that takes place reduces the solubility of the formed complexes and causes their aggregation.

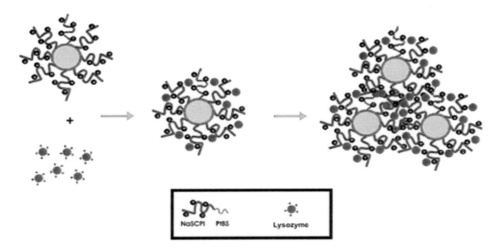

Figure 3. Schematic representation of the structure of the formed complexes as a function of C_{HEWL}, for the solutions of the PtBS-SCPI/HEWL at pH 7 and 0.01 N ionic strength.

The onset of the aggregation is marked by the transition to increasing R_h values. Actually, as the number of complexed protein molecules per polyelectrolyte chain becomes higher the aggregation is even more pronounced, *i.e.* each aggregate is comprised by a larger number of complexes. Eventually, the increase of the mass and size of the aggregates is so pronounced that they are no longer soluble and precipitation occurs. A schematic representation of the structure of the complexes is given in Figure 3.

As mentioned before in the PtBS-SCPI solution polyelectrolyte micelles and free unimer diblock copolymer chains were found to coexist. The effect of the protein addition on each population can be established from the hydrodynamic radius distributions of the complexes that are shown in Figure 4 for representative C_{HEWL} values. Obviously, in all cases two scattering populations are distinguished and the comparison with the distribution of the neat PtBS-SCPI solution, leads to the conclusion that these populations most probably correspond to the complexes formed by the protein molecules and the free unimer diblock copolymer chains or by protein and the polyelectrolyte micelles. Of course the latter species is the main population in all the solutions of the complexes. However, the size of both types of complexes changes in a similar manner and in accordance to the R_h values transition of Figure 1. An initial decrease is observed as a consequence of the shrinking of the polyelectrolyte chains caused by their complexation with the protein molecules, while further increase of the protein concentration provokes the aggregation of both types of complexes, which is expressed as an increase of their size. It should be noted that the R_h values in Figure 1 have been estimated using cumulants analysis, which yields a weighted average of all scattering species in solution and as a result are somewhat smaller than the corresponding values derived from the hydrodynamic radius distributions.

Multiangle light scattering measurements allowed for the determination of the ratio R_g/R_h for the complexes in all cases, where R_g is the radius of gyration of the nanostructures in solution. The ratio provides information on the shape of the particles formed by block polyelectrolyte micelles/protein complexation. Values of R_g/R_h were in the range $0.77 - 0.93$ indicating a spherical shape for the PtBS-SCPI/HEWL complexes at all compositions investigated.

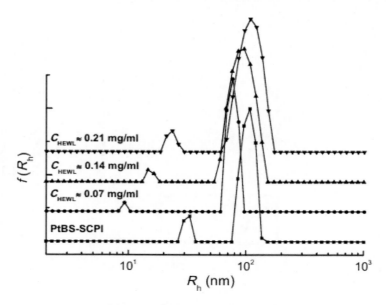

Figure 4. Hydrodynamic radius distributions at 90° for representative C_{HEWL} values, for the solutions of the PtBS-SCPI/HEWL system at pH 7 and 0.01 N ionic strength. The corresponding PtBS-SCPI distribution is included for comparison.

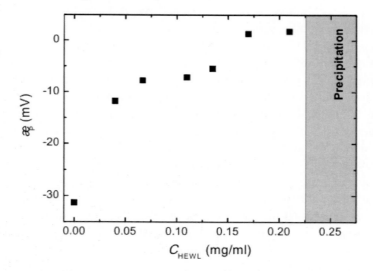

Figure 5. Zeta potential, ζ_P, as a function of C_{HEWL}, for the solutions of the PtBS-SCPI/HEWL system at pH 7 and 0.01 N ionic strength.

In order to obtain information regarding the effective charge of the complexes, electrophoretic light scattering (ELS) measurements were performed on the same series of solutions of the PtBS-SCPI/HEWL system at pH 7 and 0.01M ionic strength.

The measured values of the zeta potential, ζ_P, for the solutions of the complexes as a function of C_{HEWL} are presented in Figure 5.

As it can be seen, ζ_P decreases in absolute value as the concentration of the protein increases, or equivalently the effective negative charge of the complexes is reduced as a function of protein concentration.

This change is in agreement with the notion that as the number of protein molecules interacting with each polyelectrolyte chain of the corona of the micelles increases, the degree of neutralization of the SCPI block negative charges becomes higher and thus the effective charge of the complexes decreases.

Finally, atomic force microscopy (AFM) measurements provided additional information regarding the structure of the complexes. Figure 6 shows two AFM images with different resolution of the complexes formed at C_{HEWL} = 0.17 mg/ml of the PtBS-SCPI/HEWL system at pH 7 and 0.01 N ionic strength deposited on silicon wafers after evaporation of the solvent.

Although a direct comparison with the corresponding results from DLS measurements is not possible, due to the different state of the complexes (dry state in AFM measurements vs. solvated state in DLS measurements), some conclusions about their structure can be drawn. As it can be seen, assemblies of nearly spherical shape are discerned in both images with planar dimensions of about 100 – 200 nm, while their height ranges from 20 to 40 nm.

The observed spherical shape is in agreement with the results from light scattering measurements. The observed dimensions, in regard to the corresponding hydrodynamic size in solution, support the notion that the formed nanostructures adopt a more collapsed structure upon deposition.

Nevertheless, the assemblies seen in higher resolution (right image) seem to have a complicated internal structure, which probably stems from the fact that at this protein concentration supramicellar aggregates of individual polyelectrolyte micelles complexed with protein molecules are formed in the solution. It is the presence of several micelles within the same aggregate that results in the observed morphology and this should be attributed to the characteristics of the hard spherical cores of the micelles and the loose mixed polyelectrolyte/protein corona of the complexes.

Apparently, these supramicellar aggregates are characterized by a rather loose structure, able to deform to some extend upon surface deposition and after solvent evaporation. Nevertheless, complexation sites with protein molecules within the micellar coronas may act as crosslinks that allow the aggregates to retain their spherical overall shape (at least partially).

 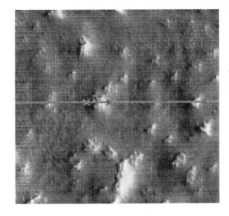

Figure 6. Atomic force microscopy images of complexes formed at C_{HEWL} = 0.17 mg/ml of the PtBS-SCPI/HEWL system at pH 7 and 0.01 N ionic strength on silicon wafers. Bars represent 1μm (left) and 200 nm (right) respectively.

3.3. Effect of Ionic Strength

The increase of the ionic strength in the solutions of the complexes is expected to influence greatly the solution behavior and structure of the preformed complexes since it induces charge screening and weakening of the electrostatic interactions. This effect was investigated by means of DLS measurements at 0.1 and 0.5 N ionic strength. The resulting I_{90}, R_h and PDI values (from measurements at 90°) for the solutions of the PtBS-SCPI/HEWL system at pH 7 are shown in Figure 7 as a function of C_{HEWL}. The corresponding values at 0.01 N ionic strength are also included for comparison.

Apparently, as the ionic strength of the solution increases the mass of the preformed complexes, which is proportional to I_{90}, decreases. At the same time their size is almost constant, except from the case of the complexes at higher C_{HEWL} values and 0.5 N ionic strength were an increase is observed. Finally, the polydispersity of the system seems to be unaffected from the initial increase of the ionic strength at 0.1 N, while further increase to 0.5 N results in higher PDI values.

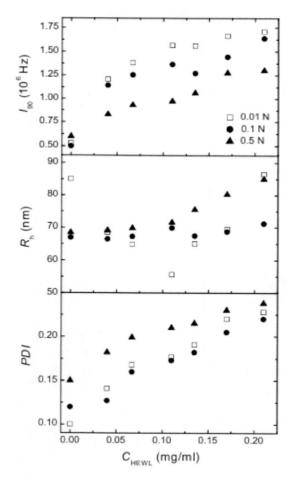

Figure 7. Light scattering intensity at 90°, I_{90}, hydrodynamic radius, R_h, and polydispersity index, PDI, as a function of C_{HEWL}, for the solutions of the PtBS-SCPI/HEWL system at pH 7 and 0.1 and 0.5 N ionic strength. The corresponding values at 0.01 N ionic strength are included for comparison.

From the observed changes it can be concluded that alterations in the ionic strength of the solution influences the structure of the preformed block polyelectrolyte/protein complexes at low ionic strength. Screening of ionic interactions results in complexes of lower mass as ionic strength increases. Hydrodynamic dimensions of the complexes depend on the ratio of the components as well as the actual ionic strength of the medium. Larger polydispersities are observed at 0.5 N probably due to some decomplexation of the initial aggregates as a result of the increased ionic strength that weakens appreciably ionic interactions. In summary, it can be concluded that the ratio of the two components and the ionic strength of the solution can be used as independent factor in order to fine tune and control the structure of the complexes.

3.4. Protein Structure within the Complexes

The preservation of enzymatic activity, which is directly correlated with the actual conformation of the protein in the complexes, is a key factor in most potential applications involving protein-polyelectrolyte complexes. Therefore, fluorescence and infrared spectroscopic measurements were conducted so as to investigate the structure of the complexed protein.

In the first place, three representative solutions at C_{HEWL} = 0.04, 0.11 and 0.17 mg/ml of the PtBS-SCPI/HEWL system at pH 7 and 0.01 N ionic strength were investigated by means of fluorescence spectroscopy. The measured spectra are shown in Figure 8, along with the corresponding spectrum of a neat HEWL solution at 0.5 mg/ml concentration for comparison. In spite of the observed intensity variation, which stems from the difference in the protein concentration, the general spectral characteristics of the neat protein are preserved and all spectra exhibit a maximum around 340 nm. Thus it can be concluded that no protein denaturation is observed upon complexation [40, 41], since that would result in a significant shift in λ_{max} and some broadening of the fluorescence peak of the protein.

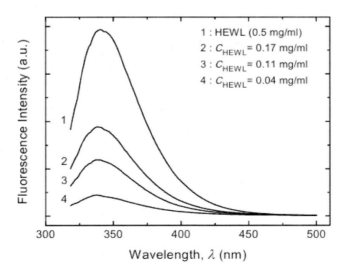

Figure 8. Fluorescence spectra of three representative solutions at C_{HEWL} = 0.04, 0.11 and 0.17 mg/ml of the PtBS-SCPI/HEWL system at pH 7 and 0.01 N ionic strength. The spectrum of neat HEWL at 0.5 mg/ml concentration is included for comparison.

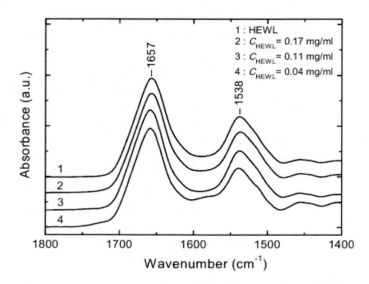

Figure 9. Infrared spectra in the Amide I and II region of three representative solutions at C_{HEWL} = 0.04, 0.11 and 0.17 mg/ml of the PtBS-SCPI/HEWL system at pH 7 and 0.01 N ionic strength. The corresponding spectrum of neat HEWL is included for comparison.

In addition, infrared spectroscopy measurements were performed and Figure 9 shows the IR spectra of the same representative solutions (C_{HEWL} = 0.04, 0.11 and 0.17 mg/ml) of the PtBS-SCPI/HEWL system at pH 7 and 0.01 N ionic strength in the Amide I and II region, including the corresponding spectrum of neat HEWL for comparison. The spectra have been normalized to the intensity of the Amide I band, after subtraction of the spectral contribution of the neat polyelectrolyte diblock copolymer. The constancy of the Amide I and II profiles, peaking at about 1657 and 1538 cm^{-1} respectively, indicates the absence of significant protein configuration changes, such as those observed upon denaturation [42, 43], even in the case of complexes in the solid state.

CONCLUSION

This study focuses on the electrostatic complexation process between the star-like polyelectrolyte micelles formed by the self-assembly of poly(tert-butylstyrene)-*b*-poly(sodium(sulfamate-carboxylate)isoprene) (PtBS-SCPI) amphiphilic diblock copolymer in water and the protein lysozyme (HEWL). It was shown that the structure and solution behavior of the formed complexes depend on the ratio of the two components. The interaction of the protein molecules with the polyelectrolyte chains of the corona of the micelles causes the neutralization of the opposite charges of the system, which in turn results in the shrinking of the polyelectrolyte corona and the reduction of the solubility of the micelles complexed with protein. These effects become more dominant as the number of interacting protein molecules per polyelectrolyte chain increases, leading to the aggregation of the complexed micelles and eventually the precipitation of the micelle/protein complexes. The increase of the ionic strength of the solution results in complexes of lower mass due to partial dissociation of the initial aggregates. Moreover, light scattering measurements together with atomic force microscopy imaging show that the complexes possess a nearly spherical shape. Finally, spectroscopic measurements revealed that the protein structure is preserved upon complexation. This investigation shows that it is possible to form hybrid synthetic/biological nanostructures in aqueous solutions via the electrostatic interaction of preformed block polyelectrolyte micelles and proteins (particularly enzymes). A number of parameters including block copolymer and micellar characteristics, as well as the ratio of the components and solution ionic strength can be utilized in order to control the characteristics of the particular chimeric nanostructures. Their utilization in a number of possible application oriented fields, including protein drug delivery, enzymatic nanocatalysis and functional surface modification remain to be investigated in the near future.

ACKNOWLEDGMENTS

Authors acknowledge financial support of the work by the NANOMACRO 1129 project which is implemented in the framework of the Operational Program "Education and Life-long Learning" (Action "ARISTEIA I") and it is co-funded by the European Union (European Social Fund) and by national funds.

REFERENCES

[1]   Moffitt, M.; Khougaz, K.; Eisenberg, A. *Acc. Chem. Res.* 1996, 29, 95-102.
[2]   Kötz, J.; Kosmella, S.; Beitz, T. *Prog. Polym. Sci.* 2001, 26, 1199-1232.
[3]   Förster, S.; Abetz, V.; Müller, A. H. E. *Adv. Polym. Sci.* 2004, 166, 173-210.
[4]   Cohen Stuart, M. A.; Hofs, B.; Voets, I. K.; de Keizer, A. *Curr. Opin. Colloid Interface Sci.* 2005, 10, 30-36.
[5]   Hales, K.; Pochan, D. J. *Curr. Opin. Colloid Interface Sci.* 2006, 11, 330-336.
[6]   Pergushov, D. V.; Borisov, O. V.; Zezin, A. B.; Müller, A. H. E. *Adv. Polym. Sci.* 2011, 241, 131-161.
[7]   Talingting, M. R.; Voigt, U.; Munk, P.; Webber, S. E. *Macromolecules* 2000, 33, 9612-9619.
[8]   Pergushov, D. V.; Remizova, E. V.; Feldthusen, J.; Zezin, A. B.; Müller, A. H. E.; Kabanov, V. A. *J. Phys. Chem. B* 2003, 107, 8093-8096.
[9]   Lysenko, E. A.; Chelushkin, P. S.; Bronich, T. K.; Eisenberg, A.; Kabanov, V. A.; Kabanov, A. V. *J. Phys. Chem. B* 2004,108, 12352-12359.
[10] Pergushov, D. V.; Remizova, E. V.; Gradzielski, M.; Lindner, P.; Feldthusen, J.; Zezin, A. B.; Müller, A. H. E.; Kabanov, V. A. *Polymer* 2004, 45, 367-378.
[11] Matějíček, P.; Uchman, M.; Lokajová, J.; Štěpánek, M.; Procházka, K.; Špírková, M. *J. Phys. Chem. B* 2007, 111, 8394-8401.
[12] Kulebyakina, A. I.; Lysenko, E. A.; Chelushkin, P. S.; Kabanov, A. V.; Zezin, A. B. *Polym. Sci., Ser. A* 2010, 52, 574-585.
[13] Zhang, W.; Shi, L.; Gao, L.; An, Y.; Wu, K. Macromol. Rapid Commun. 2005, 26, 1341-1345.

[14] Zhang, W.; Shi, L.; Miao, Z.-J.; Wu, K.; An, Y. *Macromol. Chem. Phys.* 2005, 206, 2354-2361.

[15] Masci, G.; De Santis, S.; Cametti, C. *J. Phys. Chem. B* 2011, 115, 2196-2204.

[16] Tribet, C. *Physical Chemistry of Polyelectrolytes*, ed. Radeva, T., Marcel & Dekker, New York, 2001, ch. 19, pp. 687-741.

[17] Cooper, C. L.; Dubin, P. L.; Kayitmazer, A. B.; Turksen, S. *Curr. Opin. Coll. Interface Sci.* 2005, 10, 52-78.

[18] Harada, A.; Kataoka, K. *Langmuir* 1999, 15, 4208-4212.

[19] Lindhoud, S.; de Vries, R.; Norde, W.; Cohen Stuart, M. A. *Biomacromolecules* 2007, 8, 2219-2227.

[20] Lindhoud, S.; Norde, W.; Cohen Stuart, M. A. *J. Phys. Chem. B* 2009, 113, 5431-5439.

[21] Pispas, S. J. *Polym. Sci., Part A: Polym. Chem.* 2007, 45, 509-520.

[22] Gao, G.; Yan, Y.; Pispas, S.; Yao, P. *Macromol. Biosci.* 2010, 10, 139-146.

[23] Schmidt, V.; Giacomelli, C.; Lecolley, F.; Lai-Kee-Him, J.; Brisson, A. R.; Borsali, R. *J. Am. Chem. Soc.* 2006, 128, 9010-9011.

[24] Schmidt, V.; Giacomelli, C.; Brisson, A. R.; Borsali, R. *Mater. Sci. Eng.*, C 2008, 28, 479-488.

[25] Schmidt, V.; Giacomelli, C.; Gounou, C.; Lai-Kee-Him, J.; Brisson, A. R.; Borsali, R. *Langmuir,* 2008, 24, 12189-12195.

[26] Karayianni, M.; Pispas, S. *Soft Matter,* 2012, 8, 8758-8769.

[27] Wittemann, A.; Haupt, B.; Ballauff, M. *Progr. Colloid Polym. Sci.* 2006, 133, 58-64.

[28] Henzler, K.; Wittemann, A.; Breininger, E.; Ballauff, M.; Rosenfeldt, S. *Biomacromolecules,* 2007, 8, 3674-3681.

[29] Henzler, K.; Haupt, B.; Rosenfeldt, S.; Harnau, L.; Narayanan, T.; Ballauff, M. *Phys. Chem. Chem. Phys.* 2011, 13, 17599-17605.

[30] Karayianni, M.; Mountrichas, G.; Pispas, S. *J. Phys. Chem. B* 2010, 114, 10748-10755.

[31] Tanford, C.; Roxby, R. *Biochemistry* 1972, 11, 2192-2198.

[32] Kuehner, D. E.; Engmann, J.; Fergg, F.; Wernick, M.; Blanch, H. W.; Prausnitz, J. M. *J. Phys. Chem. B* 1999, 103, 1368-1374.

[33] Pispas, S. J. Polym. Sci., Part A: Polym. Chem. 2006, 44, 606-613.

[34] Gebelein, C. G.; Murphy, D. *Advances in Biomedical Polymers*, ed. Gebelein, C. G., Plenum Press, New York, 1985, pp 277-284.

[35] van der Does, L.; Beugeling, T.; Froehling, P. E.; Bantjes, A. *J. Polym. Sci., Polym. Symp.* 1979, 66, 337-348.

[36] Huglin, M. B. *Light Scattering from Polymer Solutions*, Academic Press, New York, 1972.

[37] Chu, B. *Laser Light Scattering: Basic Principles and Practice*, Academic Press, New York, 1991.

[38] Förster, S.; Zisenis, M.; Wenz, E.; Antonietti, M. *J. Chem. Phys.* 1996, 104, 9956-9970.

[39] Qin, A.; Tian, M.; Ramireddy, C.; Webber, S. E.; Munk, P.; Tuzar, Z. *Macromolecules* 1994, 27, 120-126.

[40] Sato, T.; Mattison, K. W.; Dubin, P. L.; Kamachi, M.; Morishima, Y. *Langmuir* 1998, 14, 5430-5437.

[41] Nishimoto, E.; Yamashita, S.; Yamasaki, N.; Imoto, T. *Biosci. Biotechnol. Biochem.* 1999, 63, 329-336.

[42] Lad, M. D.; Ledger, V. M.; Briggs, B.; Green, R. J.; Frazier, R. A. *Langmuir* 2003, 19, 5098-5103.

[43] Smeller, L.; Meersman, F.; Heremans, K. *Biochim. Biophys. Acta* 2006, 1764, 497-505.

In: Micelles
Editors: Danielle Bradburn and Tom Bittinger

ISBN: 978-1-62948-444-0
© 2014 Nova Science Publishers, Inc.

Chapter 8

A Treatment Strategy for the Gastrointestinal Development of Extremely Premature Infants by Administration of Micelles Derived from Pulmonary Surfactants and the Vernix Caseosa in Pregnant Rabbits

Koji Nishijima, MD, PhD[*] *and Yoshio Yoshida, MD, PhD*

Department of Obstetrics and Gynecology, Faculty of Medical Sciences,
University of Fukui, Japan

Abstract

Introduction: Micelle particles have been derived from pulmonary surfactants in human amniotic fluid at term. Further, human pulmonary surfactant micelles are known to induce detachment of the vernix caseosa under *in vitro* conditions. Additionally, micellization is an important step in postnatal lipid absorption, with micelles being present in the amniotic fluid swallowed by the fetus and in human breast milk. Our study aimed to establish a treatment strategy to ensure the gastrointestinal development of extremely premature infants, by focusing on the presence of micelles in the environment of fetuses and neonates.

Methods: All procedures were performed in accordance with the University of Fukui Institutional Animal Care and Use Committee policy. The Institutional Review Board of the University of Fukui approved the study protocol. Because the direct assessment of the kinetics of human pulmonary surfactant and the vernix caseosa in amniotic fluid is difficult, we first prepared two types of fluorescently labeled liposomes with morphology similar to that of pulmonary surfactant and vernix caseosa complexes using the fluorescent membrane dye PKH26 and BODIPY®-labeled palmitic acid, and then

---

[*] Address for correspondence: Koji Nishijima, MD, PhD; Department of Obstetrics and Gynecology, Faculty of Medical Sciences, University of Fukui Eiheiji-cho, Yoshida-gun, Fukui 910-1193, Japan; Phone: +81-776-61-3111; Fax: +81-776-61-8117; E-mail: kojigyne@u-fukui.ac.jp.

continuously infused these liposomes into the amniotic fluid of pregnant rabbits. Fetal small intestines and livers were removed and examined histologically as stained frozen sections. In addition, we prepared bovine pulmonary surfactant (surfactant TA) and vernix caseosa complexes and introduced them into the amniotic fluid of pregnant rabbits. Fetal small intestines were removed and subjected to histologic and ultrastructural studies using light and transmission electron microscopy, respectively. The villous height was measured from the tip to the crypt-villous junction; at least 18 villi were measured in each hematoxylin and eosin sample. Ultrastructural examinations focused on the reduction in the number and length of the intestinal epithelial microvilli. Cesarean section was also performed for non-surgical interventional pregnant rabbits on gestational day 29 to confirm normal fetal intestinal morphology. Comparisons between groups were performed by using the paired Student t-test for continuous variables.

Results: (1) The intra-amniotically infused, fluorescently labeled liposomes were absorbed into the fetal intestinal epithelium, but were not transported to the livers of fetal rabbits. (2) The fetal intestinal villous heights were greater in the group receiving surfactant TA–vernix caseosa infusion than in the normal saline infusion group ($P < 0.05$). Moreover, ultrastructural examinations revealed reductions in the number and length of the intestinal microvilli on the epithelial surface in the control group. The non-surgical fetal villous heights of the intestines were significantly greater than those of the study and control group ($P < 0.05$).

Discussion: The continuous administration of micelles derived from pulmonary surfactants and the vernix caseosa influenced the intestinal morphology of the rabbit fetus, thus protecting the enterocytes from damage due to surgical intervention. We subsequently focused on a necrotizing enterocolitis (NEC) newborn rat model induced by loading enteral special formula feeding and exposure to hypoxia after cold stress and hyperoxygenation, which provide some common features with surgical intervention stresses. In our preliminary study, surfactant TA–vernix caseosa complexes reduced the severity of NEC by intervening in the apoptotic pathway. Amniotic fluid intake *in utero* is believed to prepare the gut for the dramatic shift from a highly controlled *in utero* environment to the heavily burdened environment encountered immediately after birth. The human gut is constantly exposed to micelles during the perinatal period. Although further studies are needed to confirm our findings, our results shed light on the physiological interactions among pulmonary, dermal-epidermal, and gastrointestinal developmental processes, and raise the intriguing possibility for the improved nutritional care of preterm infants immediately after birth.

I. INTRODUCTION

Turbidity of the amniotic fluid increases with gestational age during the third trimester [1–5]. Narendran et al. speculated that this turbidity is caused by a "roll-up" phenomenon: the detachment of the vernix caseosa from the fetal skin surface secondary to interaction with pulmonary surfactant [3]. We have previously reported the presence of micelle particles derived from pulmonary surfactant in human amniotic fluid at term [6] because the "roll-up" phenomenon is strictly controlled by the kinetics of micellization [7, 8] and, therefore, confirming pulmonary surfactant micelles are indispensable to proving the hypothesis of Narendran et al. We have also shown that human pulmonary surfactant micelles induce detachment of the vernix caseosa under *in vitro* conditions [6].

The vernix caseosa is a complex, proteolipid material synthesized in part by fetal sebaceous glands during the last trimester of pregnancy [9]. The strategic location of the vernix caseosa on the fetal skin surface suggests its participation in multiple overlapping functions required *at birth*, for example, as a lubricating oil to reduce friction in the birth canal, as a barrier to water loss, for temperature regulation, and for innate immunity [9]. This raises an important question. Since the vernix caseosa is a natural biofilm *at birth*, why do pulmonary surfactant micelles commence to detach the vernix from the fetal skin by at gestational week 34, i.e., well *before delivery* [1]? In an effort to explain this "paradox", we investigated the biological role of the human pulmonary surfactant and vernix caseosa in the amniotic fluid throughout the experimental studies using animals: pregnant rabbits and a newborn rat model of necrotizing enterocolitis.

II. POLICY FOR USE OF ANIMALS

All procedures were performed in accordance with the University of Fukui Institutional Animal Care and Use Committee policy. The Institutional Review Board of the University of Fukui approved the study protocol.

III. EXPERIMENTS USING TWO TYPES OF FLUORESCENTLY LABELED LIPOSOMES

The direct assessment of the kinetics of human pulmonary surfactant and the vernix caseosa in amniotic fluid is difficult. Therefore, we first prepared two types of fluorescently labeled liposomes with morphology similar to that of pulmonary surfactant and vernix caseosa complexes [6] and then continuously infused these liposomes into the amniotic fluid of pregnant rabbits [10]. Two types of fluorescently labeled liposomes were produced using the fluorescent membrane dye PKH26 (excitation wavelength, 551 nm; emission wavelength, 567 nm; Sigma-Aldrich Co., St. Louis, MO, USA) [11] and BODIPY®-labeled palmitic acid (excitation wavelength, 503 nm; emission wavelength, 512 nm) (BODIPY®-FL C_{16}; Life Technologies Corp., Carlsbad, CA, USA) [12, 13], and a dried empty cationic liposomal formulation (Coatsome® EL-01-C; NOF Corp., Tokyo, Japan) consisting of dipalmitoylphosphatidylcholine/cholesterol/stearyl amine (52/40/8) [13]. The PKH26-labeled liposomes were compared to pulmonary surfactant micelles (Figure 1). BODIPY®-FL C_{16} containing palmitic acid allowed adequate comparison to vernix caseosa, because palmitic acid (C16:0) is the main saturated fatty acid component of the vernix caseosa [14, 15] (Figure 1). We then introduced these complexes into the amniotic fluid of pregnant Japanese white rabbits on gestational day 25: right-ovarian-end fetuses received two fluorescently labeled liposomes (PKH26-labeled liposomes and liposomes containing BODIPY® FL C_{16}), while left-ovarian-end fetuses received hydrated Coatsome® EL-01-C alone as control (Figure 2). Fetal small intestines and livers were removed on gestational day 29 and examined histologically as stained frozen sections.

No differences were noted in the fetal somatic weights, liver weights, or small intestinal length between the group receiving fluorescent liposome infusion and the controls. The fetal small intestinal epithelia were stained with PKH26 and BODIPY®-FL C_{16} (Figure 3). However, none of the fluorescently labeled liposomes reached the fetal livers (Figure 3).

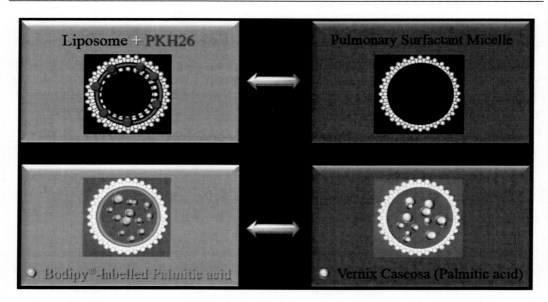

Figure 1. We prepared two types of fluorescently labeled liposomes displaying morphology similar to that of pulmonary surfactant and vernix caseosa complexes. The PKH26-labeled liposomes were compared to pulmonary surfactant micelles. The BODIPY®-FL C_{16} was compared to vernix caseosa, including abundant palmitic acid.

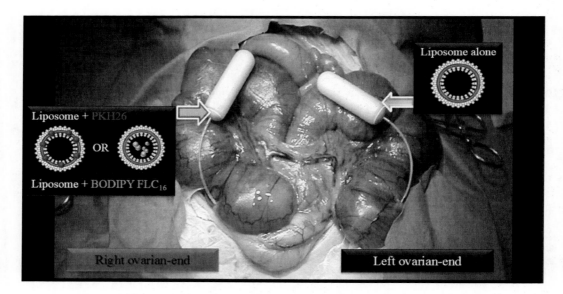

Figure 2. Right-ovarian-end fetuses received the fluorescently labeled liposomes; left-ovarian-end fetuses received hydrated empty liposomes for 4 days, starting on gestational day 25 by using mini-osmotic pumps (Alzet model 2ML1).

Our studies raise the possibility that human fetuses might also swallow pulmonary surfactant and vernix caseosa micelles present in the amniotic fluid, whereby they reach the fetal small intestines. Micelles in the swallowed amniotic fluid might locally influence fetal intestinal enterocytes.

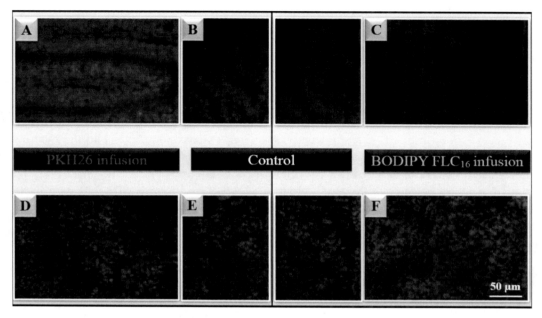

Figure 3. Fluorescence micrographs of fetal small intestines (top) and livers (bottom). The fetal small intestinal epithelia were strongly stained with PKH26 (A) and BODIPY®-FL C_{16}(C). The intra-amniotically infused fluorescently labeled liposomes were absorbed into the fetal intestinal epithelium. However, no fluorescently labeled liposomes reached the fetal livers (D-F). Calibration bar: 50 μm. (original magnification: ×400).

IV. EXPERIMENTS USING PULMONARY SURFACTANT AND VERNIX CASEOSA COMPLEXES

We prepared surfactant TA (Surfacten®; Mitsubishi Tanabe Pharma Corporation, Osaka, Japan)–vernix caseosa complexes according to the procedure described by Narendran et al., [3] and introduced them into the amniotic fluid of pregnant rabbits in order to determine the biological role of pulmonary surfactant and vernix caseosa in the amniotic fluid [10]. The composition of surfactant TA, which is isolated from bovine lung and used clinically [16], is similar to that of Survanta® (Ross Laboratories, OH, USA). Surfactant TA is composed of 83.5% phospholipids, 7.0% free fatty acids, 7.0% triglycerides, 1.0% hydrophobic surfactant-associated protein, and traces of other components [17]. Briefly, we applied 10 mg of vernix caseosa pooled from three full-term infants to the interior walls of 1.5-ml polypropylene microfuge tubes and spread it onto the wall using a glass pestle to form an even coating. Then, 1 ml of normal saline with 1180 μg phospholipid derived from surfactant TA was added to the tubes. The dose of surfactant TA was calculated from the amniotic fluid volume of pregnant rabbits at gestational day 30 (0.72 ml) [18], total lipid concentrations in human amniotic fluid at term (386 μg) [19], and the infusion volume of mini-osmotic pumps (240 μl/day). We then introduced these complexes into the amniotic fluid space of pregnant Japanese white rabbits on gestational day 23: right-ovarian-end fetuses received the surfactant TA-vernix caseosa complexes, while left-ovarian-end fetuses received normal saline as control. On gestational day 29, fetal small intestines were removed and subjected to histologic and ultrastructural studies using light (AX-80; Olympus Corporation, Tokyo) and transmission electron (H-7650; Hitachi, Tokyo) microscopy, respectively. The villous height was measured from the tip to the crypt-villous junction; at least 18 villi were measured in each hematoxylin and eosin sample by using a light microscope [20]. Ultrastructural examinations focused on the reduction in the number and length of the intestinal epithelial microvilli [21].

No differences were observed in the fetal somatic weights or small intestinal length between the group infused with surfactant TA–vernix caseosa complexes and the controls. The villous heights of the proximal intestine in the study and control groups were 285.8 ± 103.5 (mean ± SD) μm and 202.2 ± 82.4 μm, respectively ($P < 0.05$). The distal intestinal villous height was greater in the study group (257.4 ± 77.1 [mean ± SD] μm) than in the control (184.3 ± 87.3 μm) group ($P < 0.05$) (Figure 4). Moreover, ultrastructural examinations revealed reductions in the number and length of the intestinal microvilli on the epithelial surface and partial disintegrations of cellular junctions in the control group (Figure 4).

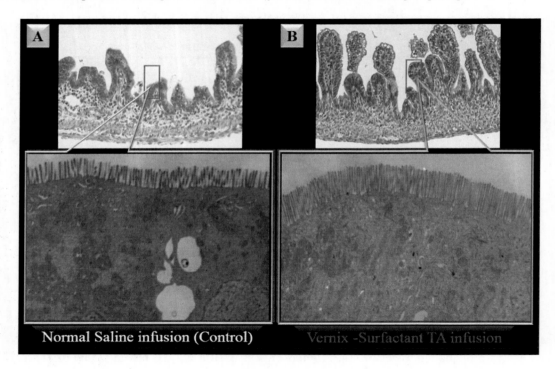

Figure 4. Histologic (top) and ultrastructural (bottom) micrographs of the distal intestines in the control (A) and study (B) groups. The distal intestinal villous height was greater in the study group than in the control group (top). Ultrastructural examinations revealed reduced numbers and length of the intestinal microvilli on the epithelial surface in the control group (bottom). Continuous administration of micelles derived from pulmonary surfactants and vernix caseosa protected the small intestine of the rabbit fetus from damage due to surgical intervention.

From another point of view, the non-surgical fetal villous heights of the proximal and distal intestines were 331.8 ± 76.7 (mean ± SD) μm and 292.4 ± 73.5 μm, respectively. These villous heights were significantly greater than those of the group receiving surfactant TA–vernix caseosa infusion and the normal saline infusion group ($P < 0.05$). Our surgical intervention interfered with villous growth and submucosal thickness of the small intestine in the rabbit fetus. Micelles derived from the pulmonary surfactant and vernix caseosa influenced the intestinal morphology of the rabbit fetus, thereby protecting enterocytes from damage due to surgical intervention [10]. We speculate that this phenomenon is the key to explaining the aforementioned "paradox".

V. THE HUMAN GUT IS CONSTANTLY EXPOSED TO MICELLES DURING THE PERINATAL PERIOD

Micellization is an important step in postnatal lipid absorption because fat is insoluble in the aqueous environment within the small intestine [2, 22]. Micelles exist in both the amniotic fluid swallowed by the fetus and human breast milk ingested by neonates [2, 3, 6]. Siggers et al. presented that amniotic fluid intake *in utero* acts as a mechanism to prepare the gut for the dramatic transition from the highly controlled *in utero* environment to the heavily burdened environment encountered immediately after birth [23]. Numerous studies have also shown that the maturation of the fetal gastrointestinal tract is partially enhanced by the swallowed amniotic fluid [2, 24]. Ran-Ressler et al. also suggested that the vernix caseosa is actively metabolized in the fetal gastrointestinal tract [25]. Although further studies are needed, micelles derived from pulmonary surfactant and vernix caseosa might be principal components of the enteral diet during the parenteral-to-enteral transition phase in preterm infants. Our findings shed light on the physiological interactions among pulmonary, dermal–epidermal, and gastrointestinal developmental processes [10].

VI. FUTURE STUDIES

The intra-amniotic administration of micelles derived from pulmonary surfactant and vernix caseosa protected enterocytes from damage due to surgical intervention. Surgical stresses include perioperative infection, hypothermia, instability of the respiratory control, including hypoventilation or hyperventilation, and change in the nutritional sources, including maternal fasting state. Guven et al. established an experimental model of necrotizing enterocolitis (NEC) in newborn rats by loading enteral special formula feeding and exposure to hypoxia after cold stress at 4°C and hyperoxygenation [26]. We focused on a NEC model created by Guven et al., which provided some common features with surgical stresses caused by our surgical intervention.

NEC is a fatal disease occurring in premature infants, afflicting 1–5% of all newborns and up to 7–14% of very low birth weight infants (500–1500 g) admitted to the neonatal intensive care unit [27]. Several factors appear to play either primary or secondary roles in its development: immature gut function, impaired intestinal barrier, disturbed gastrointestinal motility, imbalance in circulatory regulation, lack of some protective enzymes of cytokine-dependent injury, and undeveloped antioxidant capacity [28]. Intestinal ischemia, formula feeding, and bacterial infections are also believed to be risk factors for cellular injury in the premature intestine. Together, these factors result in an exaggerated inflammatory response, leading to extensive hemorrhagic inflammatory necrosis [23].

Siggers et al. recently showed that similar to colostrum, porcine amniotic fluid administered postnatally as minimal enteral nutrition to preterm neonates can increase body weight gain, alter the severity of bacterial colonization and NEC, and induce differential expression of mRNA coding for genes involved in gut inflammatory responses [23]. In our preliminary study, we tested the potential beneficial effect of surfactant TA–vernix caseosa complexes in an experimental model of NEC in newborn rats created according to the procedure described by Guven et al [26]. Surfactant TA–vernix caseosa complexes reduced the severity of NEC by intervening in the apoptotic pathway (data not shown). The multiple functions of the pulmonary surfactant have been reassessed in light of recent studies [29]. The fetal lung synthesizes and excretes pulmonary surfactant in amounts much greater than that needed for adaptation to breathing air after birth. Our results appear to raise the interesting possibility of improved nutritional care for preterm infants immediately after birth. Although further studies are warranted, our findings may facilitate the establishment of a treatment strategy for the gastrointestinal development of extremely premature infants, with special focus on the presence of micelles in the environment of fetuses and neonates.

ACKNOWLEDGMENTS

We thank Yuko Fujita, Midori Niwa, Hideyuki Maeda, Ichiro Mukougawa, Shintaro Nishijima, Sachiko Nishijima, and Hitoshi Takagi for the excellent technical assistance.

Grants: This work was supported in part by Grants-in-Aid for Scientific Research No. 15659392, 18791147, 20591909, and 2359297 from the Ministry of Education, Culture, Sports, Science, and Technology, Japan.

Disclosures: The authors have no conflicts of interest to declare.

REFERENCES

[1] Agorastos T, Lamberti G, Vlassis G, Zournatzi B, Papaloucas A. Methods of prenatal determination of fetal maturity based on differentiation of the fetal skin during the last weeks of pregnancy. *Eur. J. Obstet. Gynecol. Reprod. Biol.* 22:29–40, 1986.

[2] Avery GB, Fletcher MA, MacDonald MG. Neonatology: Pathophysiology and Management of the Newborn. 6th ed. Lippincott Williams & Wilkins Co., Philadelphia, 2005.

[3] Narendran V, Wickett RR, Pickens WL, Hoath SB. Interaction between pulmonary surfactant and vernix: a potential mechanism for induction of amniotic fluid turbidity. *Pediatr. Res.* 48:120–124, 2000.

[4] Notter RH. Lung Surfactants: Basic Science and Clinical Applications. Marcel Dekker, Inc., New York, 2000.

[5] Zabkar JH. Evaluation of fetal maturity by amnioscopy. *J. Perinat. Med.* 3:145–153, 1975.

[6] Nishijima K, Shukunami K, Tsukahara H, Orisaka M, Miura J, Kotsuji F. Micelles of pulmonary surfactant in human amniotic fluid at term. *Pediatr. Res.* 60:196–199, 2006.

[7]   Kabin JA, Tolstedt SL, Saez AE, Grant CS, Carbonell RG. Removal of organic films from rotating disks using aqueous solutions of nonionic surfactants: effect of surfactant molecular structure. *J. Colloid Interface Sci.* 206:102–111, 1998.

[8]   Lai KY, McCandlish EFK, Aszman H. Light duty liquid detergents. In: Lai K-Y (ed) Liquid Detergents (Surfactant Series/67) Marcel Dekker Inc., New York, p 207–259, 1996.

[9]   Visscher MO, Narendran V, Pickens WL, LaRuffa AA, Meinzen-Derr J, Allen K, Hoath SB. Vernix caseosa in neonatal adaptation. *J. Perinatol.* 25:440–446, 2005.

[10] Nishijima K, Shukunami K, Yoshinari H, Takahashi J, Maeda H, Takagi H, Kotsuji F. Interactions among pulmonary surfactant, vernix caseosa, and intestinal enterocytes: intra-amniotic administration of fluorescently liposomes to pregnant rabbits. *Am. J. Physiol. Lung Cell Mol. Physiol.* 303:L208–14, 2012.

[11] Inoki Y, Hakamata Y, Hamamoto T, Kinouchi T, Yamazaki S, Kagawa Y, Endo H. Proteoliposomes colocalized with endogenous mitochondria in mouse fertilized egg. *Biochem. Biophys. Res. Commun.* 278:183–191, 2000.

[12] Goedhart J, Hink MA, Visser AJ, Bisseling T, Gadella TW Jr. In vivo fluorescence correlation microscopy (FCM) reveals accumulation and immobilization of Nod factors in root hair cell walls. *Plant J.* 21:109–119, 2000.

[13] Hanato J, Kuriyama K, Mizumoto T, Debari K, Hatanaka J, Onoue S, Yamada S. Liposomal formulations of glucagon-like peptide-1: improved bioavailability and anti-diabetic effect. *Int. J. Pharm.* 382:111–116, 2009.

[14] Hauff S, Vetter W. Exploring the fatty acids of vernix caseosa in form of their methyl esters by off-line coupling of non-aqueous reversed phase high performance liquid chromatography and gas chromatography coupled to mass spectrometry. *J. Chromatogr. A* 1217:8270–8278, 2010.

[15] Rissmann R, Groenink HW, Weerheim AM, Hoath SB, Ponec M, Bouwstra JA. New insights into ultrastructure, lipid composition and organization of vernix caseosa. *J. Invest Dermatol.* 126:1823–1833, 2006.

[16] Fujiwara T, Maeta H, Chida S, Morita T, Watabe Y, Abe T. Artificial surfactant therapy in hyaline-membrane disease. *Lancet* 1:55–59, 1980.

[17] Tanaka Y, Takei T, Kanazawa Y, Seida K, Masuda K, Kiuchi A, Fujiwara T. Preparation of surfactant from minced bovine lung, chemical composition and surface properties. *J. Jpn Med. Soc. Biol. Interface* 13: 87–94, 1982.

[18] Karnak I, Müftüoğlu S, Cakar N, Tanyel FC. Organ growth and lung maturation in rabbit fetuses. *Res. Exp. Med.* (Berl) 198:277–287, 1999.

[19] Lentner C. Geigy Scientific Tables. Medical Education Division, Ciba-Geigy Corporation, New Jersey, p 201–203, 1981.

[20] Hampson DJ. Alterations in piglet small intestinal structure at weaning. *Res. Vet Sci.* 40:32–40, 1986.

[21] Baglaj SM, Czernik J, Kuryszko J, Kuropka P. Natural history of experimental intestinal atresia: morphologic and ultrastructural study. *J. Pediatr. Surg.* 36:1428–34, 2001.

[22] Murray RK, Rodwell VW, Bender D, Botham KM, Weil PA, Kennelly PJ. Harper's Illustrated Biochemistry, 28th ed. McGraw-Hill Medical, Columbus, OH, 2009.

[23] Siggers J, Ostergaard MV, Siggers RH, Skovgaard K, Mølbak L, Thymann T, Schmidt M, Møller HK, Purup S, Fink LN, Frøkiær H, Boye M, Sangild PT, Bering SB.

Postnatal amniotic fluid intake reduces gut inflammatory responses and necrotizing enterocolitis in preterm neonates. *Am. J. Physiol. Gastrointest Liver Physiol.* 304:G864-75, 2013.

[24] Ross MG, Nijland MJ. Development of ingestive behavior. *Am. J. Physiol.* 274: R879–R893, 1998.

[25] Ran-Ressler RR, Devapatla S, Lawrence P, Brenna JT. Branched chain fatty acids are constituents of the normal healthy newborn gastrointestinal tract. *Pediatr. Res.* 64:605–609, 2008.

[26] Guven A, Gundogdu G, Uysal B, Cermik H, Kul M, Demirbag S, Ozturk H, Oter S. Hyperbaric oxygen therapy reduces the severity of necrotizing enterocolitis in a neonatal rat model. *J. Pediatr. Surg.* 44:534–40, 2009.

[27] Schnabl KL, Van Aerde JE, Thomson AB, Clandinin MT. Necrotizing enterocolitis: a multifactorial disease with no cure. *World J. Gastroenterol.* 14:2142–61, 2008.

[28] Nanthakumar NN, Fusunyan RD, Sanderson I, Walker WA. Inflammation in the developing human intestine: A possible pathophysiologic contribution to necrotizing enterocolitis. *Proc. Natl. Acad. Sci. USA* 97:6043–8, 2000.

[29] Wright JR. Immunoregulatory functions of surfactant proteins. *Nat. Rev. Immunol.* 5:58–68, 2005.

INDEX

F

O

P

Q

R

T

V

W

Y

U

Z